Charles Richard

Southwestern Medical School

Dallas, Texas

HUMAN NEUROANATOMY

BY

OLIVER S. STRONG

Formerly Professor of Neurology and Neurohistology
College of Physicians and Surgeons
Columbia University

AND

ADOLPH ELWYN

Associate Professor of Neuroanatomy
College of Physicians and Surgeons
Columbia University

Second Edition

BALTIMORE
THE WILLIAMS & WILKINS COMPANY
1948

Published May, 1943
Reprinted December, 1943
Reprinted December, 1945
Reprinted December, 1946
Second Edition, 1948

COMPOSED AND PRINTED AT THE
WAVERLY PRESS, INC.
FOR
THE WILLIAMS & WILKINS COMPANY
BALTIMORE, MD., U. S. A

PREFACE TO SECOND EDITION

In the preparation of the second edition, the suggestions received from both students and practitioners were carefully considered, and as a result two main additions have been made to the text. One is the incorporation of a new chapter (Ch. X) on segmental and peripheral innervation, including a clinico-anatomical survey of the cervical, brachial and lumbosacral plexuses and of the main peripheral nerves. The second is an expansion of chapter XXI to give a more complete and fully illustrated account of the arterial supply and venous drainage of the brain. The remainder of the book, though generally revised, has been left substantially the same as in the first edition. Many of the recent advances, especially in the field of neurophysiology, could not be adequately included in a text of this scope, since the interpretation of the available data and their application to human clinical neurology are still in a controversial state. Reference to the newer work has been made wherever possible, and the more important publications have been listed in the enlarged bibliography.

Of the nineteen new illustrations, fifteen were selected from various sources which are duly acknowledged, and special thanks are due to the W. B. Saunders Company for permission to reproduce Figs. 105, 130 and 130A from Haymaker and Woodhall "Peripheral Nerve Injuries." The authors are deeply indebted to Frances H. Elwyn for her careful redrawing and relabeling of the new illustrations, and to the publishers for their unfailing courtesy and cooperation.

ADOLPH ELWYN.
OLIVER S. STRONG.

PREFACE

Neurology, more perhaps than any other branch of medicine, is dependent on an accurate knowledge of anatomy as a basis for the intelligent diagnosis and localization of neural disturbances. This book, the result of many years of neuroanatomical teaching, is intended to supply this basic anatomical need, to give the student and physician a thorough and clear presentation of the structural mechanisms of the human nervous system together with some understanding of their functional and clinical significance. It is an attempt to link structure and function into a dynamic pattern without sacrificing anatomical detail.

The book is a human neuroanatomy sufficiently rich in content to obviate the necessity of constantly consulting larger anatomical texts. It may be conveniently divided into two parts. The first part (Chapters I-VIII) is concerned with the general organization and meaning of the nervous system, its embryology and histological structure, and with some fundamental neurological problems as they apply to man. This is followed by a discussion of the organization and segmental distribution of the peripheral nerve elements, including an analysis of the functional components of the spinal nerves and of the various receptors and effectors. If these earlier chapters are perhaps more extensive than in most other texts, it is due to the conviction that the book should be complete in itself, and also that a knowledge of these preliminaries is essential for an understanding of the complex machinery of the spinal cord and brain.

The second and larger part (Chapter IX-XX) is devoted to the architectonics of the central nervous system and may be regarded as "applied neuroanatomy." Special features of this part are the many fine photographs, both gross and microscopic, of the human brain and spinal cord, the great wealth of anatomical detail, and the discussion of the structural mechanisms in the light of clinical experience. While the individual portions of the nervous system are treated separately, an attempt has been made to achieve organic structural continuity by judicious repetition and overlapping and by constant reference to related topics already familiar to the student from previous chapters. The plan of exposition is substantially the same for each topic. The gross structure and relationships are concisely but thoroughly reviewed with the aid of clear and graphic illustrations. The internal structure is then presented in detail, usually based on a carefully graded series of fine and clearly labeled microphotographs of human material. At each level the student is familiarized with the exact location, extent and relationships of the various structures seen in the section. Finally the anatomical features of each part are reviewed more comprehensively as three-dimensional structural mechanisms, with a full discussion of their connections and clinical significance. We believe that this treatment will make the complicated structural details alive and interesting to the student. The illustrations are not segregated in the back of the book in the form of an atlas but are scattered in the text, in proper relation to the levels studied.

Besides the many original illustrations, a number of others selected from various and duly acknowledged sources have been completely redrawn and relabeled for the sake of clarity and simplicity. All the illustrations, whether original or borrowed, have been executed by Frances H. Elwyn to whose skill and patience the authors are deeply indebted. We are also indebted to Dr. H. Alsop Riley for the use of several microphotographs; to Drs. R. C. Truex and Benjamin Salzer for the reading of several chapters; and especially to Dr. Otto Marburg for his many stimulating discussions and suggestions and for his critical reading of the chapters on the mesencephalon, diencephalon, and cerebral hemispheres. Thanks are also due to Rosette Spoerri for her competent help in preparing the manuscript and bibliography.

   The authors cannot express too strongly their obligation to the publishers for their continuous courtesy and coöperation in all matters, and for their infinite patience in waiting for a manuscript long overdue.

ADOLPH ELWYN.
OLIVER S. STRONG.

CONTENTS

CHAPTER I

CHAPTER XIX

CHAPTER XX

CHAPTER XXI

CHAPTER I

GENERAL ORGANIZATION AND SIGNIFICANCE OF THE NERVOUS SYSTEM

The biological significance of the nervous system, stated in the most general terms, is the coordination of bodily activities in response to both external and internal conditions. The complex vital activities of the human body may be regarded as a series of adjustments effecting harmonious action of the various parts and enabling the individual to respond properly to environmental changes. Many of these adjustments of a physicochemical nature are performed largely through the agency of the hemolymphatic vascular system. Others are brought about by changes passing from one part of the body to another along the conducting units or neurons which form the nervous system. Those adjustments or reactions of the organism to changes in its environment which are performed by the intervention of the nervous system are termed *neural reactions*. However, the vascular and neural mechanisms are by no means independent of each other but are in fact closely interrelated. Substances circulating in blood and lymph, such as metabolites, internal secretions and toxins; the amount, temperature and gaseous content of the blood itself, etc., change the physiological condition of the neural mechanisms and thereby alter neural reactions to various stimuli. In some cases they may even initiate neural reactions. Thus the accumulation of carbon dioxide in the blood directly stimulates the neural respiratory center, and similarly the centers for heat regulation are affected by the heightened temperature of the blood. On the other hand, vascular and glandular activities are in turn more or less definitely regulated by the nervous system.

The nervous mechanism of man, as of any other vertebrate, may be divided into the *central nervous system* consisting of brain and spinal cord, and the *peripheral nervous system* including the *cranial* and *spinal nerves* with their respective ganglia and the peripheral portions of the *autonomic nervous system*. The bundles of long nerve fibers which form the bulk of the peripheral nervous system connect the brain and the spinal cord with the various parts of the body, from which they transmit impulses to the central nervous system or to which they conduct impulses from the central nervous system for the initiation or modification of muscular or glandular activity. On the other hand, the central nervous system with its complicated interconnected neuron groups adjusts the incoming stimuli to the outgoing impulses, determining what parts of the body and to what extent shall be affected by the stimuli it receives. In other words, it is the adjusting or coordinating center of the neural mechanism.

The peripheral nerve fibers which conduct impulses to the central nervous system are called *afferent peripheral fibers* ("sensory" fibers) and the neurons of which these nerve fibers are a part are the *afferent peripheral neurons* ("sensory" neurons). Those peripheral fibers which conduct impulses from the brain and spinal cord constitute the *efferent peripheral fibers* and their neurons the *efferent peripheral neurons*. The various structures which first receive stimuli and which contain the distal endings of the afferent peripheral fibers are known as *receptors* (sensory endings, sense organs). Those structures in which changes or effects are produced by impulses transmitted to them by the efferent peripheral fibers and which contain the distal endings of the latter are termed *effectors*. In man these are principally muscles and glands. The changes brought about by neural impulses may be an initiation or increase of muscular or secretory activity (*excitation*) or a diminution or complete cessation of the same (*inhibition*), the neural impulses themselves being termed excitatory or inhibitory respectively. The vast numbers of neurons, which lie wholly in the central nervous system and have no direct contact with the periphery, constitute the *central, intermediate* or *associative neurons*. The various interactivities of these central neurons may likewise excite or inhibit each other.

It is evident from the above that a complete neural reaction will pursue the following circuit: receptor, afferent peripheral neurons, central neurons, efferent peripheral neurons, effector. Such a circuit may be termed a *neural* or *reflex arc*. While various neural reactions have to some extent their separate neural arcs and one of the purposes of this book is to trace the neural pathways of specific reactions, it must be emphasized that the various portions of the central nervous system are widely interconnected. The nervous system may be regarded as a highly differentiated nerve net in which are laid down the more permeable, more easily accessible pathways which form the neural arcs for specific reactions. But these arcs are never isolated, the excitation may spread from one to another, and the various reactions and their arcs mutually influence each other in many ways.

The general structure and organization of the nervous system is largely determined by two factors: (1) the presence, distribution and relative development of the receptor and effector organs, and (2) the nature and degree of development of the various central neural mechanisms which interrelate the afferent and efferent peripheral neurons. Certain important features of the nervous system showing the influence of these peripheral and central factors may be briefly discussed.

In a general way the body as a whole falls into two great divisions: (a) the outer body wall including the limbs and part of the head, and (b) the inner tube with its appendages comprising the alimentary, respiratory and reproductive tracts and other coelomic viscera. The former is derived embryologically from the somatopleure and, excepting its glands and blood vessels and other smooth muscles (pilomotor), may be termed *somatic*. The coelomic viscera together with the glands and smooth muscles (vascular and pilomotor) lying in the outer body wall may be termed *splanchnic* or *visceral*. Thus glandular epithelium and smooth muscle wherever found are to be regarded as splanchnic. The striped muscle of the heart is likewise splanchnic. The outer body wall is primarily concerned with reactions to changes in the external environment. Such reactions are initiated by external changes acting on the numerous superficial receptors, the *exteroceptors*, and effecting the rapidly contracting striped skeletal musculature, producing a movement of the whole or parts of the body. Most of our conscious volitional reactions and of the deep (kinetic) and superficial reflexes fall under this category and are performed by the somatic part of the nervous system. Reactions initiated by stimuli arising in the muscles and tendons of the body wall itself and effecting the skeletal musculature likewise belong to this type.

The inner tube and other viscera are mainly concerned with the nutritional, metabolic, secretory and vascular activities, the so called *vegetative* or *vital* functions. These reactions are for the most part initiated by internal changes acting upon visceral receptors (*visceroceptors*) and taking effect in the involuntary musculature and glands. Such reactions are under the control of the *visceral* portion of the nervous system, and are to a large extent unconscious and involuntary. Those which are conscious are usually of an instinctive or emotional character, dealing with fundamental imperative bodily needs. The visceral and somatic systems are, however, closely connected both in the central and peripheral nervous systems. While some reactions may be purely somatic or purely visceral, many are mixed. Thus external stimuli, as sight of food or cutaneous pain, may produce secretory or vasomotor effects, and visceral stimuli, as hunger or visceral pain, may produce energetic voluntary movements.

Peripherally, the *autonomic* nervous system innervating the viscera consists of several series of ganglia lying at varying distances from the brain and spinal cord. These are composed of neurons which send their fibers to the visceral effectors. They are connected with the central nervous system by fiber bundles known as *rami communicantes* (See Autonomic System). As will be seen more definitely later this system comprises two divisions: the sympathetic and parasympathetic, each of which innervates the same structures. As a result most of the viscera have a double innervation, the effect of the two being usually antagonistic to each other. For example, impulses from the parasympathetic slow up the activity of the heart, those from the sympathetic accelerate cardiac activity. Of these two, the parasympathetic has more to do with the self-regulation of the visceral organs, i.e. their regulation by stimuli from the organs themselves, while the sympathetic is concerned more with the adjustment of visceral mechanisms to external environmental conditions. In other words, the parasympathetic reactions are primarily viscero-visceral, while those mediated by the sympathetic are often somato-visceral. The external stimuli which produce the latter reactions are usually those which directly affect bodily welfare and are of a specially painful, disagreeable or agreeable character. Stimuli of this type together with visceral stimuli enter into combination with discriminative reactions of the cerebral cortex and form the basis of the emotional or affective side of many cortical actions.

Another important division of the nervous system relates to the neural mechanism involved in the self-regulation of *posture* and *movement*. Movements may be initiated by all kinds of stimuli, but their proper performance requires regulation by stimuli from the locomotor organs themselves, i.e. muscles and tendons, while the movement is being carried out. Similarly, a constant position or posture can only be steadily maintained by stimuli from the organs maintaining posture. The receptors thus stimulated by the tension states of the muscles, whether varying or constant, lie in or near the muscles or tendons themselves and are known as *proprioceptors*. The latter also include the vestibular sense organ of the ear (cristae and maculae) which is stimulated in like manner by the position and movement of the head. This whole self-regulating apparatus, to a large extent unconscious and involuntary, may be termed proprioceptive. The eye plays an important part in these reactions and there may be other neural factors. Naturally the mere physical properties of the locomotor system, such as the rigidity of bone, the respective contractile and tensile strength of muscle and tendon form a non-neural part of the proprioceptive mechanism.

The constant tension state of muscles concerned with maintaining a characteristic posture (primarily against gravity) is known as muscle *tonus* and the neural reactions involved in its maintenance are *tonic* or *static* reactions. "Reflex tonus is postural contraction." Reactions resulting in movement are *kinetic* or *phasic*. A movement may fix into a posture (kineto-static reaction) while steady maintenance of posture by postural stimuli may be termed stato-static or pure static. Any movement will obviously be affected by the tonus of the muscles involved, hence there is a static element in movement itself. "Tonus is the shadow of movement" (J. Ramsay Hunt)

While the most highly developed proprioceptive mechanisms are concerned with the somatic voluntary musclature and the above mainly applies to them, there are similar visceral mechanisms involved in maintaining the positions of the viscera and the adjustment of the walls of hollow organs to their contents, as for instance bladder pressure, etc. The same applies to the heart and blood vessels. All these are usually included in the visceral reactions and are carried out by the involuntary muscles of the organs involved.

Disturbances of the somatic proprioceptive mechanisms, both tonic and kinetic, are largely responsible for the breakdown of normal movement as expressed in the various hypotonias, hypertonias, ataxias, and at times abnormal involuntary movements. Many such phenomena are to be explained as a hyperactivity of certain neural mechanisms due to their being no longer correlated or opposed by influences from other neural mechanisms which have been injured or destroyed ("release phenomena").

The vertebrate is an elongated bilaterally symmetrical animal progressing in a definite direction, primitively perhaps by alternating contractions of a segmented lateral musculature. Corresponding to these characteristics is the bilateral character of the nervous system and its transverse segmentation, shown by its series of nerves, a pair to each muscle segment. The anterior end of the animal which during movement first encounters the new environment becomes highly differentiated. Here are located the mouth and respiratory apparatus. Here also are developed the complicated organs of special sense, such as the nose, eye, ear, lateral line organs and taste buds, which greatly increase the range of stimuli received by the animal and thereby render possible a greater range of responsive activities in obtaining and testing food, in protection and in reproduction. Corresponding to this specialization of the forward end or formation of the *head* (*cephalization*) the highest

development of the central nervous system also occurs in this region, leading to the formation of the *brain* or *encephalon*, a process which might be termed *encephalization*. A large part of the brain thus consists of the central coordinating neural mechanisms for the three great sense organs of the head: the nose, eye and ear. These centers are already indicated in early development by the three primary expansions of the brain: the forebrain expansion, from which the pallium or cerebral cortex is later formed, for the nose; the midbrain expansion for the eye; and the hind brain expansion known as the cerebellum for the primitive vestibular part of the ear. These three parts which become greatly enlarged and differentiated also receive stimuli from other parts of the head and from the body, and they constitute the highest coordinating portion of the nervous system. The manner in which they are lifted out of the lower segmental parts of the brain has led to their designation as the *suprasegmental* portions of the nervous system. The *segmental* part of the brain is in a general way that part more closely connected with the peripheral (segmental) nerves and containing the simpler and more fundamental coordinating mechanisms.

In the course of its development to the conditions seen in man, the vertebrate body has undergone many structural changes. Older parts have become modified or reduced; newer ones, often quite complicated, have arisen in response to environmental changes. The distinction between the older and newer parts of the human body is helpful to an understanding of many neural arrangements, since the two have to some extent separate, if interlocking, neural representations. Phylogenetically, the change from a water to a land habitat is expressed in profound structural alterations. The water breathing gills with their neural center in the brain (medulla) have been supplanted by air breathing lungs now directly controlled by the spinal cord, but the medullary centers are still necessary for respiration. There is a loss of certain sense organs receiving stimuli only through a watery medium, such as the lateral line organs and those taste buds lying outside of mouth and pharynx, and the acquisition of a new organ for the reception of aerial sound vibrations (the cochlea of the ear). Limbs adapted for locomotion displace the older locomotion by the axial musculature, with concomitant marked alterations and additions in the nervous system. In many parts of the latter, the neural mechanisms controlling the limbs are quite different from those of the older axial or trunk portions of the body. Later developments of the vertebrate body include the acquisition of separate head movements, of frontal and binocular vision, the development of the hand as an organ for finer sensory discrimination and as a highly differentiated motor apparatus, with its concomitant release from active locomotion. The latter entails locomotion with the lower extremity only and the acquisition of an erect posture introducing new problems of bodily equilibrium and posture maintenance. Other recent changes are the facial musculature of expression and the organization of lips, tongue and larynx into an apparatus of speech.

A most important development of the vertebrate brain, reaching its culmination in man, is the rise of a neural mechanism for the more complex correlation and discrimination of sensory impulses, and the greater utilization in various neural reactions of traces of former reactions. The principal function of this mechanism may be termed *associative memory* and such reactions *mnemonic* (memory) reactions. A reaction elicited by a certain stimulus associated with other stimuli may be subsequently elicited by one of these associated stimuli instead of the primary one. When a piece of meat is placed in the mouth of a newborn dog, salivation immediately occurs. This reaction is an inherited characteristic and has been termed by Pavlov an *unconditioned reflex*. Seeing the meat for the first time

will not cause salivation, but after eating a few times just the sight of food will start profuse salivary activity. The animal now *recognizes* the food before he has tasted it. Such reactions which depend on previous experiences Pavlov has called *acquired* or *conditioned* reflexes and these form the most important neural basis of the processes of educability.

The enormous importance of the mnemonic reactions in man is shown by the fact that their neural mechanisms constitute the greater part of the central nervous system. A primary factor in their development is the presence in the head of the receptors of the nose, eye and cochlea. These organs are *teloreceptors* or *teleceptors*, i.e. they receive stimuli from distant objects, permitting identification of such objects before actual contact with them is made. As a result of previous associations (experience), closer relations with distant objects are avoided or sought in accordance with their previously ascertained harmful or beneficial nature. The avoiding or seeking character thereby acquired by teleceptive mnemonic reactions constitutes their emotional or affective side. It is probable that the affective tone of neural activities has other sources than the above. The physiological states attendant upon neural activity, the influence upon neural structures of substances circulating in the hemolymphatic system, etc., all these probably contribute to the totality of feeling tone in affective consciousness.

Another important type of mnemonic reactions, usually termed proprioceptive, relates to the acquisition of skill which involves the increased motor ability to carry out the discriminative mnemonic reactions. Proprioceptive stimuli leave traces which regulate subsequent movement and posture, constantly modifying and perfecting them. This enables that partly unconscious reduction of unessential movements and the increase in speed and accuracy which characterizes the "learned" or skilled reactions. The basis of what is psychologically known as "voluntary" movement is probably the reception by the cerebral cortex of proprioceptive stimuli from the voluntary striped musculature and the resulting presence of proprioceptive traces or memories. On the other hand, the "involuntary" character of smooth muscle may be due in part to the absence of proprioceptive stimuli from them reaching the cortex and consequent absence of proprioceptive memories of their activities.

That part of the brain especially concerned in associative memory is the *pallium* or *cerebral cortex* which arises developmentally as a secondary subdivision of the forebrain expansion (*telencephalon*). In the lowest vertebrates it is small and devoted principally to the reception of olfactory stimuli. As phylogenetic differentiation progresses, stimuli from all parts of the body and from the organs of special sense project into this region forming a newer non-olfactory part, the *neopallium*, which becomes tremendously expanded in the higher vertebrates, reaching its greatest extent and differentiation in man. Coincident with this growth which might be termed *telencephalization*, there is a parallel development in other portions of the nervous system. The cerebellum, which is the highest proprioceptive center for the automatic regulation of movement and posture, the thalamus and other neural mechanisms likewise acquire new parts in immediate connections with the neopallium. These new acquisitions, i.e., the neopallium and other parts in immediate connection with it, are often collectively termed the *neencephalon* as distinguished from the older *palencephalon*. Newer motor mechanisms for the special execution of the most important mnemonic pallial reactions are seen in the development of the hand and speech organs as already mentioned.

The simpler neural reactions which, while influenced by other portions of the nervous system than those necessary for their performance, are not originated or essentially modified by past neural activities or experience of the individual are usually termed *reflexes*. They are thus not "acquired" and their performance in many cases at least does not involve the pallium, though their character may be altered by changes in the higher neural centers. How far, in general, the various fundamental neural mechanisms including reflexes have been altered by their being brought under the control of the pallial ones, is a problem which has not yet received full solution.

Reflexes may be kinetic when resulting in movement, static or tonic when resulting in setting or maintaining posture. In fact the greater part of tonic activities is of a reflex character. When posture is initiated by movement the reflex may be termed kinetostatic. Posture-setting and posture-maintaining impulses from the proprioceptors of muscles and tendons, from the vestibule of the ear and from the eye are correlated in various ways to bring about these adjustments. Some of the highest of these automatic kinetopostural mechanisms are those which bring the body as a whole from an abnormal into a normal position, the so called "righting reactions" ("Stellreflexe" of Magnus and de Kleijn).

Clinically, kinetic reflexes are usually divided into *deep* and *superficial*, according to the source of the stimulus. The deep reflexes are elicited by tapping the tendon of a muscle (tendon reflex) or the bone to which it is attached (periosteal reflex) thereby producing shortening of the muscle itself. Familiar examples of deep reflexes are the bicipital, tricipital, radial, ulnar, patellar (knee jerk), tibial and Achilles (ankle jerk). The superficial reflexes are elicited by stroking or otherwise stimulating the skin (cutaneous reflexes) or mucosal membranes (mucosal reflexes) and thus causing a contraction of the subjacent or other muscles. Examples are the corneal, abdominal and plantar cutaneous reflexes and the mucosal palatal and pharyngeal reflexes. Certain other reflexes obtained by stimulation of the organs of special sense, such as the important pupillary reaction to light, do not fall under the above categories. It is evident that the deep reflexes are proprioceptive kinetic reflexes and the superficial are exteroceptive reflexes. While the reflexes mentioned above are comparatively simple and segmental in character, many others, such as sneezing, coughing, vomiting, etc., and most of the postural reflex adjustments, are extremely complicated and involve large portions of the body.

Those reactions usually called *conscious* are difficult to define but appear in general to represent a heightened activity of various portions of the pallial mechanism of associative memory. The problem of distinguishing what is original or inherited and what is acquired by individual experience in neural reactions is one of great importance and equally great difficulty. The laws of growth and development apply to the brain as well as to other organs and there is every reason to suppose that the nervous system has its given neuronal structure which forms the basis for the acquisition and utilization of experience as well as the performance of reflex acts and thereby constitutes mental and emotional capacity for mnemonic reactions. However, the individual neural acquisitions are built upon previous acquisitions in such a complicated manner that the ascertainment of the non-acquired fundamental reactions upon which the acquired ones are built and of the given capacity for their acquisition still requires much investigation.

CHAPTER II

DEVELOPMENT OF THE NERVOUS SYSTEM

The entire nervous system except the olfactory epithelium and parts of certain ganglia, is derived ontogenetically from an elongated plate of thickened ectoderm, *the neural plate*, which extends longitudinally in the axis of the developing embryo. At first the thickened plate passes laterally without sharp demarcation into the thinner non-neural ectoderm. A more distinct boundary is formed in embryos of about 2 mm when the lateral edges of the plate curve dorsally to form the *neural folds*, enclosing now between them a median longitudinal groove, the *neural groove*. Already at this stage the cephalic portion of the plate is broader, the folds higher and the groove deeper, foreshadowing the future differentiation into brain and spinal cord (Figs. 1, 2, 3). The neural folds become more and more elevated, approaching the median line, and finally meet and fuse to form the *neural tube*. The fusion of the lips begins in the middle region of the plate at the boundary zone of spinal cord and brain and progresses both forward and backward (Fig. 3). The last portions to close are situated at the cephalic and caudal ends and the openings there are known as the anterior and posterior neuropore respectively. The former which marks the rostral wall of the neural tube (the future lamina terminalis) closes in embryos of about 18–20 somites. The posterior neuropore disappears somewhat later in embryos of 25–30 somites. When the latter occurs, the neural folds have become completely transformed into the closed neural tube detached from the overlying ectoderm which now covers it continuously. The tube thus formed shows an anterior enlarged portion, the *brain*, and posterior narrower portion, the *spinal cord*.

In the epithelial wall of the neural tube four plates or zones may be distinguished: a ventral median *floor plate*, a dorsal median *roof plate* where the fusion occurred, and two *lateral plates*. The roof and floor plates remain relatively thin, but the lateral plates become tremendously thickened and differentiated, expressive of the bilateral character of the neural tube. As the walls thicken, a longitudinal furrow, the *sulcus limitans*, appears on the internal surface of each lateral plate about midway between the roof and floor, dividing it into a dorsal and a ventral portion, the *alar* and *basal* plate respectively. In the course of further neural differentiation the motor cell groups develop in the basal plate, the receptive or sensory ones in the alar plate. The central autonomic cell groups related to visceral innervation are formed in the intermediate area, i.e. in the region of the sulcus limitans. Thus in the adult spinal cord and certain portions of the brain there is found a general territorial organization of functional significance, the dorsal half being primarily afferent or receptive in character, the ventral efferent or motor, each having its somatic and visceral divisions (Figs. 65, 9). The sulcus limitans is well marked in the hindbrain where it persists in the adult, but is difficult to distinguish in the midbrain even in developmental stages. There is evidence that the basal plate does not extend beyond the midbrain and that hence the whole forebrain wall corresponds in structure to the alar plate only (Kingsbury, 1922; Johnston, 1923).

While the neural plate is closing there occurs a differentiation of cells along each lateral edge, forming an intermediate zone between the neural plate and skin ectoderm. When the plate is converted into a tube, these zones are naturally brought together

8

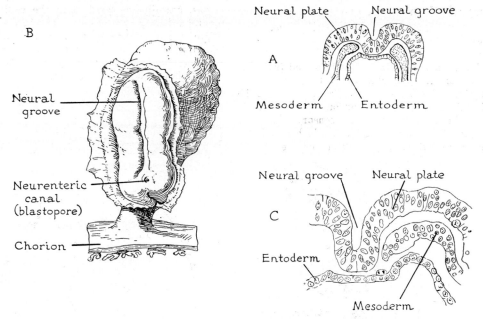

FIG. 1. *A*, transverse section through human embryo before appearance of somites. (After Keibel.) *B*, dorsal view, and *C*, transverse section of 2 mm. human embryo. (After Graf Spee.)

at the point of fusion of the neural folds, fuse likewise and become detached from the overlying ectoderm. They are not, however, included in the wall of the neural tube proper but form an unpaired ridge of smaller paler staining cells, the *neural* or *ganglionic* crest, lying along its dorsal surface wedged in between the fusing neural folds (Fig. 5). The beginnings of the crest are already visible in embryos of seven somites. Somewhat later, in embryos of about 3 mm, the crest detaches itself from the neural tube, splits longitudinally into a right and left half, and the cells of each half migrate from the dorsal to the lateral periphery of the tube. In this way two ridges are formed. Soon, as the result of unequal cellular proliferation, the originally unsegmented ridges break up into a series of cellular blocks or aggregations situated on either side of the neural tube, the aggregations corresponding to the metamerism of the primitive somites. These are the rudiments of the cerebrospinal ganglia which give rise to the afferent peripheral neurons, in part at least to efferent

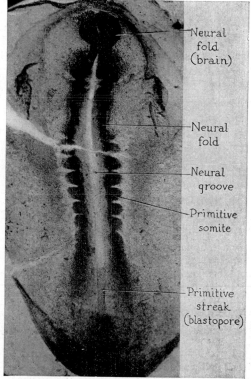

FIG. 2. Dorsal view of cat embryo with eight mesodermal somites. Microphotograph.

sympathetic neurons, and to certain other structures (capsule cells, sheath cells. See chapter on neuron).

All afferent neurons are not formed from the neural crest. The olfactory cells whose fibers constitute the olfactory nerve are derived from the epithelium of the nasal mucous membrane. It is certain also that some of the sensory cells in the ganglia of the seventh, eighth, ninth and tenth nerves are derived from thickened patches of skin

cones, are differentiated from the wall of the neural tube. As will be seen below, the retina represents a migrated portion of the brain and contains not only photoreceptors but several categories of neurons as well. Hence the "optic nerve" is in reality a fiber tract connecting two portions of the brain.

The neural crest is formed along the whole extent of the spinal cord and extends also into the region of the brain, thus furnishing

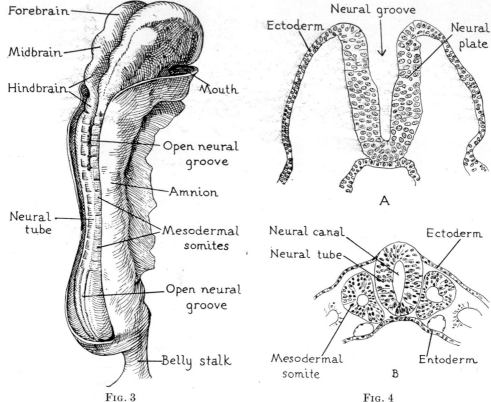

FIG. 3

FIG. 4

FIG. 3. Lateral view of human embryo about 2.2 mm. in length, showing partially closed neural tube. (After Kollmann.)

FIG. 4. Transverse sections through neural tube of 2.7 mm. human embryo. *A*, through brain; *B*, through upper portion of spinal cord. (After Kollmann.)

ectoderm, called *placodes*, which are in close contact with those ganglia during early development (Landacre, 1910). The formation of these placodes, like that of the neural tube itself, is the embryological expression of the tendency of highly specialized neural tissue to concentrate and withdraw from the surface. The neural tube itself is likewise derived from a plate of thickened ectoderm, the neural plate, which thus may be regarded as the oldest and most extensive placode.

The sensory cells of the retina, the rods and

a spinal and cerebral portion. The latter is well formed only in the region of the hindbrain where it detaches itself from the neural tube and forms typical ganglia. In front of the hindbrain a similar type of cell proliferation occurs at the line of fusion of the tube but apparently remains abortive and does not become detached. Traces of such crest formation are even visible in the still open fundament of the forebrain. Schulte and Tilney (1915) have suggested that the optic vesicles and mesencephalic nucleus of the trigeminal nerve (see p. 218) are derived from portions of the cerebral crest which have failed to separate from the neural tube.

Development of the brain. When closure of the tube is completed the wider cephalic portion or brain already shows three imperfectly separated expansions, the primary brain "vesicles", known as the *forebrain* (prosencephalon), *midbrain* (mesencephalon) and *hindbrain* (rhombencephalon).

at junction of hindbrain and spinal cord is less marked. The rhombencephalon shows an indistinct division into six or seven segments or "neuromeres" separated by shallow furrows. The ganglion of the trigeminal nerve (V) is already associated with the first neuromere, the acustico-facial ganglion (VII and VIII) with the third.

In embryos of about 5 mm (Fig. 7) the forebrain is more definitely marked off from the midbrain by the appearance ventrally of the mammillary protuberance. The optic pouches are moving laterally, their now con-

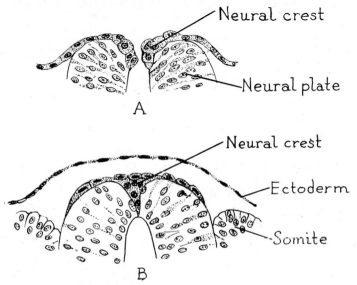

FIG. 5. Two stages in the closure of the neural tube and formation of the neural crest. From transverse sections of a 2.5 mm. human embryo. (After Lenhossék.)

These conditions are seen in Fig. 6. The forebrain and midbrain vesicles are still small and difficult to delimit and in the former are visible two large ventrolateral evaginations, the optic pouches. A more marked constriction separates the midbrain from the much larger rhombencephalon which passes without any definite demarcation into the spinal cord. The whole wall of the neural tube is still epithelial. The brain shows two ventrally directed flexures. The rostral of these, the *cephalic flexure*, is in the region of the midbrain and is bent almost at right angles. The *cervical flexure*

stricted attachments to the forebrain forming the optic stalks. In front and above the optic pouches a dorsal protrusion of the anterior brain wall marks the appearance of the future hemisphere. The primary forebrain vesicle now exhibits two as yet indistinctly separable regions. The anterior region represented by the hemispheric bulge and soon to reach massive proportions, is known as the *endbrain* or *telencephalon*, the rest of the forebrain is called *interbrain* or *diencephalon*. The midbrain is still simple and little changed, and is separated dorsally and caudally from the large rhombencephalon by a definite furrow. The constricted portion of the hindbrain where it joins the midbrain is known as the *isthmus rhombencephali.*

The primary hindbrain or rhombencephalon is different from the other brain regions with a pointed extremity in the region of the isthmus, it gradually widens to about the middle of the hindbrain (region of future lateral recesses) and then gradually narrows again to end in a caudal point. Corresponding to this the floor plate likewise

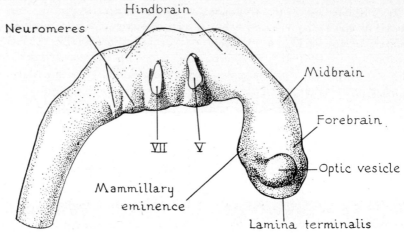

FIG. 6. Brain of 3.4 mm. human embryo, lateral view. *V*, trigeminal ganglion; *VII*, acustico-facial ganglion.   (After Hochstetter.)

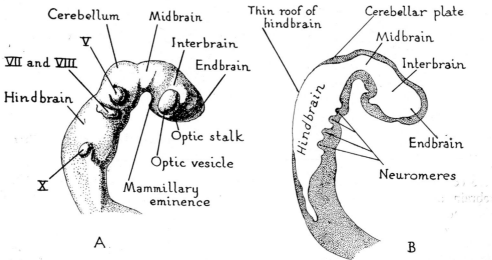

FIG. 7. *A*, brain of human embryo with 28 somites, lateral view. *B*, median sagittal section through brain of 5 mm. human embryo.   (After Fischel.)

in that its dorsal wall becomes thickened only in its most cephalic and most caudal portions (Figs. 7, 8). Throughout the largest extent the roof remains exceedingly thin, expands laterally and assumes a diamond-shaped appearance.   Beginning assumes a rhomboid shape.   When the thin roof is removed, the cavity of the hindbrain or fourth ventricle appears as a shallow diamond-shaped depression and hence is known as the *fossa rhomboidea*.   In early stages the rhomboid fossa can be seen externally shining through the ectoderm and thin epithelial roof of the hindbrain.

In the rhombencephalon two main regions may already be distinguished. In front, above the widest portion of the rhomboid fossa the roof plate becomes narrower and the dorsal parts of the lateral wall thicken to form the rudiments of the cerebellum. This part is known as the secondary hindbrain or *metencephalon* which later forms the

respective differentiation of the forebrain and hindbrain into two main regions, the midbrain alone remaining undivided. These from before backward are telencephalon, diencephalon, mesencephalon, metencephalon and myelencephalon.

The neuromeres of the hindbrain are still distinct, and associated with the last pair are the ganglionic rudiments of the *vagus* (X) and *glossopharyngeal* (IX) nerves.

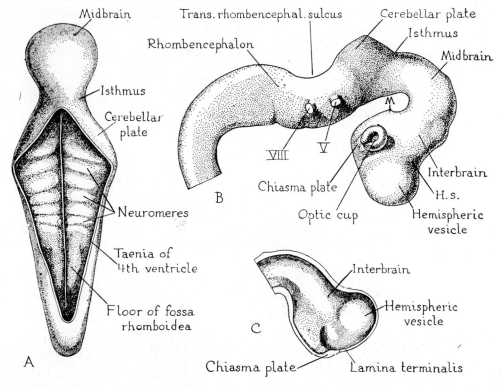

FIG. 8. Brain of 7.5 mm. human embryo. *A*, dorsal view; *B*, lateral view; *C*, median sagittal section showing ventricular surface. (After Hochstetter.) *H.S.*, hemispheric sulcus; *M*, mammillary eminence.

pons and cerebellum. The rest of the rhombic brain forms the *myelencephalon* or *medulla oblongata*. On the dorsal surface the boundary zone between metencephalon and myelencephalon is marked by a transverse groove, the *transverse rhombencephalic sulcus*.

Thus at this stage five secondary cerebral expansions or vesicles have been formed from the three primary ones, due to the

In a 7.5 mm embryo the five divisions of the brain are more easily distinguishable (Fig. 8). The telencephalon arising as a median structure has grown laterally to form a conspicuous bulge on each side, separated from the diencephalon by a shallow circular furrow, the *hemispheric sulcus*. The relatively large diencephalon has absorbed the terminal portions of the optic stalks, thus forming the chiasmatic plate. The optic vesicles have become invaginated into optic cups, due to the formation of the lens which as an ectodermal thickening presses against the lateral surface of the vesicle. The midbrain is practically unchanged. The cephalic and cervical flexures have deepened considerably and the ventral wall of the rhombencephalon has become convex indicating the beginning of another dorsally bending *pontine* flexure. This produces on the dorsal surface a transverse kink or fold in the thin roof in the region of the greatest width of the fourth ventricle. The transverse rhombencephalic sulcus thus formed,

develop the various telencephalic commissures (anterior, corpus callosum, commissure of fornix). A ridge corresponding externally to the hemispheric sulcus separates endbrain from interbrain.

From the five secondary vesicles all parts of the definitive brain are ultimately derived. The further development is characterized by the tremendous increase in size of the endbrain which soon overshadows in mass all the other portions. The various flexures become more and more marked for a while, but in later stages the reverse occurs. The cephalic flexure gradually flattens out

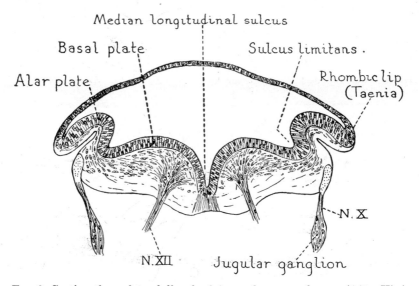

FIG. 9. Section through medulla of a 9.1 mm. human embryo. (After His.)

as already stated, constitutes the boundary between the more cranially placed metencephalon and the more caudal myelencephalon. The rhomboid fossa still shows indications of neuromeres, and the roof and dorsolateral walls of the metencephalon have thickened to form the cerebellar plate.

The ventricular surface of an embryo of the same age is seen in Fig. 8C. The anterior median wall of the brain is formed by a thin membrane, the *lamina terminalis*, which passes ventrally into the thickening of the chiasmatic plate. Dorsally the median wall thickens to form the so called *commissural plate* (Fig. 14) in which later

and is greatly reduced in the fully formed brain. The cervical and pontine flexures disappear altogether. The further development of the individual parts may be briefly summarized.

Rhombencephalon. As already stated, the rhombencephalon differentiates into an anterior metencephalic and a posterior myelencephalic portion, the boundary between the two being the transverse sulcus which marks the widest part of the fourth ventricle and is later continued into its lateral recesses. The rhombencephalon shows the following conditions (Fig. 8A). In its caudal portion it has the same form as the cervical spinal cord with which it is continuous. The lumen is small and completely surrounded by thickened walls. Proceeding forward, the dorsally placed thickened alar plates begin to diverge laterally, corresponding to the widening of the (Figs. 7, 9). The dorsal border of the alar plate to which the thin roof is attached forms a thickened ridge known as the *rhombic lip*. In the myelencephalon, caudal to the lateral recess, this develops into the taenia of the fourth ventricle. Above the lateral recess

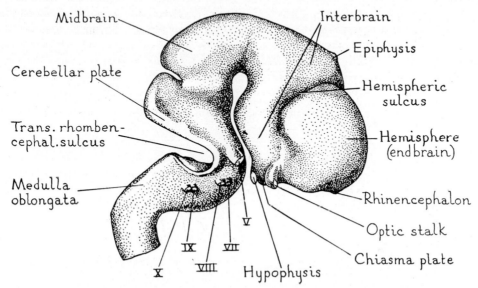

FIG. 10. Brain of 13.8 mm. human embryo, lateral view. (After Hochstetter.) Roman numbers indicate cranial nerves

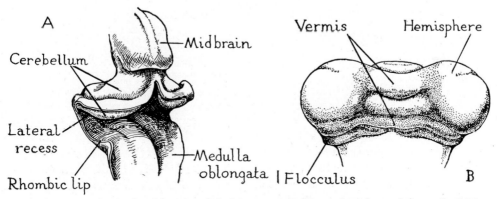

FIG. 11. Two stages in the development of the human cerebellum. *A*, embryo of six weeks (13.6 mm.); *B*, four months foetus (110 mm.). (*A*, after His; *B* after Prentiss and Arey.)

thin roof of the ventricle until in the widest portion the alar and basal plates come to lie more nearly in the same plane and form the ventral wall or floor of the fossa rhomboidea. The wide roof remains very thin, consisting of a single-layered epithelial membrane. the *lamina chorioidea epithelialis* the rhombic lip becomes considerably enlarged and contributes to the formation of the cerebellum. A median longitudinal sulcus appears in the floor of the fossa rhomboidea dividing it into two lateral halves, and another longitudinal furrow, the *sulcus limitans*, divides each half into a broader medial or basal plate and a narrower alar plate. All these sulci extend the whole length of the rhombencephalon. In the median portion are formed the motor cell groups or nuclei, comprising the somatic motor nuclei of the VIth and XIIth nerves and the general and special visceral motor nuclei of the Vth, VIIth, IXth, Xth and XIth nerves (Fig. 9). Of these, the VIth and XIIth nuclei are more mesially placed and correspond to ventral horn cells of the spinal cord. In the alar plates, lateral to the sulcus limitans, are formed the receptive areas for nerves V, VII, VIII, IX and X. The floor of the rhomboid fossa above the

approach each other until in the most anterior portion they are separated only by a narrower zone of the roof plate which is thicker in this region (Fig. 8). From this portion of the alar lamina the cerebellum is formed. The rhombic lip and adjacent region become considerably thickened to form the *cerebellar swellings* or *plates* which bulge into the ventricle (Figs. 10, 11). As the swellings increase in size, they approach each other, finally invade the roof and fuse to form a transverse structure above the fourth ventricle (Figs. 11, 13). In further growth the lateral ends of this structure expand to form the cerebellar hemispheres,

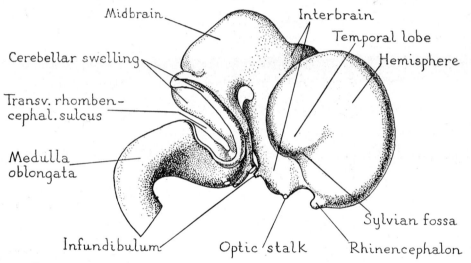

FIG. 12. Brain of 27 mm. human embryo, lateral view. (After Hochstetter)

lateral recess gives rise to the pons, the part below becomes the medulla oblongata.

The thin epithelial roof fuses with the investing pial connective tissue to form the *tela chorioidea*. In embryos of about 20 mm a fold of the tela dips into the ventricle, and by proliferation of the epithelium and richly vascular connective tissue is ultimately transformed into the chorioid plexus of the fourth ventricle (Fig. 14).

In front of the lateral recess, the thin roof of the fourth ventricle becomes progressively narrower and consequently the alar plates, situated laterally in the medulla, assume a more dorsal position and gradually

the narrower middle portion gives rise to the vermis. The first transverse furrows appear in the vermis at the end of the third month, somewhat later in the hemispheres. At the end of the seventh month all the main folia and sulci are already laid down.

The floor of the metencephalon is constituted by the upper portion of the fossa rhomboidea which thickens to form the *tegmentum* of the pons. As already mentioned, it contains the motor and sensory cell groups associated with the fifth, sixth, seventh and eighth nerves. Ventral to the tegmentum the *basilar* portion of the pons, or pons proper, is formed by massive cell groups and fiber tracts primarily related to the cerebellum (Fig. 14).

The uppermost narrowed portion of the hindbrain, lying in front of the cerebellum, is known as the *isthmus rhombencephali*. Its junction with the midbrain is marked by the emergence of the fourth nerve. Its thin roof, the *superior medullary velum*, is formed from the middle portion of the cerebellar plate.

Mesencephalon. The midbrain undergoes the least changes of any of the cerebral vesicles. Towards the end of the third month, the wall begins to thicken tremendously, gradually reducing the lumen to a

basis peduncli (crus cerebri). Tegmentum and basis together are often known as the cerebral peduncles or crura cerebri. It is usually stated that the quadrigeminal plate is derived from the "alar", the tegmentum from the "basal" lamina, but a real sulcus limitans is difficult to make out in the midbrain.

Diencephalon. Like the other portions of the brain, the embryonic diencephalon consists of a roof plate, a floor plate and two lateral walls. During growth the latter become greatly thickened, finally reducing the lumen to a vertical cleft-like space, the *third ventricle*. In most brains actual fusion

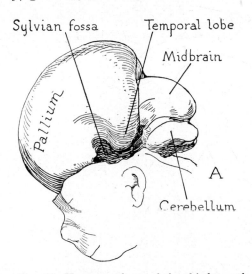

Sylvian fossa   Temporal lobe

Midbrain

Pallium

A

Cerebellum

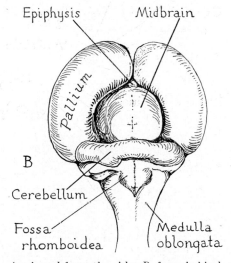

Epiphysis   Midbrain

Pallium

B

Cerebellum

Fossa rhomboidea

Medulla oblongata

FIG. 13. Human embryo of the third month. *A*, viewed from the side; *B*, from behind

narrow channel, the *iter* or *cerebral aqueduct* (Fig. 14). The roof or tectum forms the quadrigeminal plate, at first undivided but later differentiating into the paired nuclear masses of the superior and inferior colliculi. The ventral portion becomes the massive tegmentum. Some of the nerve cells group themselves on each side of the midline of the floor of the iter into the motor nuclei of the third and fourth nerves. Others by migration give rise to the nucleus ruber, substantia nigra and other tegmental nuclei. Ventral to the tegmentum are the massive fiber tracts descending mainly from the cerebral cortex which constitute the *pes* or

of the walls may occur at one place to form a narrow bridge of gray extending across the ventricle, the *massa intermedia*. The thickening of the walls is not uniform, being relatively less in a narrow longitudinal zone about the middle of the diencephalon. As a result, there is formed on the medial surface a shallow longitudinal groove, the *hypothalamic sulcus*, which demarcates a dorsal from a ventral plate in each lateral wall (Fig. 15 A). From the dorsal portion which becomes the most massive part of the diencephalon, are formed the large gray masses of the *thalamus* and *metathalamus*. According to some, this part also furnishes the globus pallidus of the lenticular nucleus (Spatz). The ventral portion together with the floor plate gives rise to the various structures of the *hypothalamus* including the subthalamus laterally, and the tuber cinereum, neurohypophysis and mammillary bodies in the floor of the third ventricle (Fig. 14). Immediately anterior to the tuber cinereum is the thickening of the optic chiasma containing an extension of the ventricular cavity, the *optic recess*. The chiasma marks the junction of the interbrain

ventricular foramen) to the optic recess may be considered the boundary zone between diencephalon and telencephalon.

The roof of the diencephalon remains thin. From the caudal end a median diverticulum gives rise to the *pineal body* or *epiphysis* which retains an extension of the fourth ventricle, the *pineal* recess. On either side of the pineal body along the line of attachment of the thin roof to the thalamus, a longitudinal thickening develops into the *habenula*, a ganglionic mass associated with

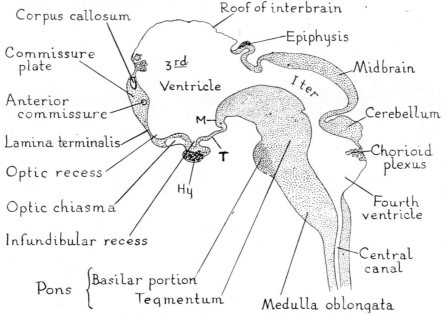

Fig. 14. Median longitudinal section through brain of 68 mm. human embryo. (After Hochstetter.) *Hy*, hypophysis; *M*, mammillary body; *T*, tuber cinereum.

and endbrain and is considered by many as the telencephalic portion of the hypothalamus. In front of the chiasma the medial anterior wall of the third ventricle turns upward and ascends as a thin membrane, the *lamina terminalis*, to the dorsal anterior margin of the thalamus. This membrane constitutes the cephalic median wall of the primary forebrain and belongs to the telencephalon, since the latter is formed by a secondary evagination from this portion of the brain. A line passing from the anterior margin of the thalamus (or from the inter-

olfactory pathways. As in the case of the hindbrain, the thin roof forms the epithelial chorioid lamina which together with the richly vascular connective tissue of the investing pia, constitutes the tela chorioidea. Two vertical longitudinal folds extend from the tela into the ventricle and develop into the chorioid plexus. At the rostral margin (region of the interventricular foramen) the tela becomes directly continuous with that of the lateral ventricles. Laterally the slightly thickened margin of attachment of the thin roof to the thalamus is known as the *taenia thalami.* Tela chorioidea, epiphysis and habenula collectively constitute the *epithalamus.*

Telencephalon. Arising as a hollow unpaired bud from the dorsal anterior wall of the primary forebrain, the telencephalon

which undergoes relatively little growth and is composed of the lamina terminalis and the most rostral portion of the third ventricle, known as the *cavum Monroi.* The lateral extension of the cavity into the hemispheric vesicles constitute the future lateral ven-

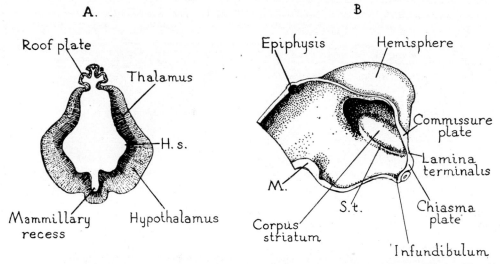

Fig. 15. *A*, section through diencephalon of a five weeks human embryo. (After His.) *Hs.*, hypothalamic sulcus. *B*, ventricular surface of brain of 13.8 mm. human embryo. (After Hochstetter.) *M*, mammillary swelling; *S.t.*, sulcus terminalis (semicircularis).

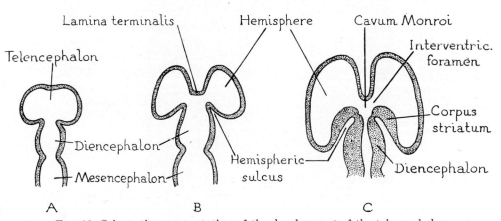

Fig. 16. Schematic representation of the development of the telencephalon

begins to bulge laterally and expands into the two *hemispheric vesicles* which begin to overlap the diencephalon and are separated from the latter by the hemispheric sulcus (Figs. 8, 10, 16). These vesicles are now connected to each other by the median portion of the endbrain (*telencephalon medium*)

tricles which at this stage communicate with the cavum Monroi by wide interventricular foramina (Figs. 16, 17).

The hemispheric vesicles rapidly expand in all directions. Their medial surfaces at first extend backward along the lateral surfaces of the diencephalon, producing a progressive deepening of the hemispheric sulcus whose fundus marks the place of attachment between endbrain and hindbrain (Figs. 8, 10, 16). Soon they expand dorsally to cover

tudinal or *interhemispheric* fissure. As expansion continues, the midbrain and ultimately the cerebellum become likewise covered by the cerebral hemispheres.

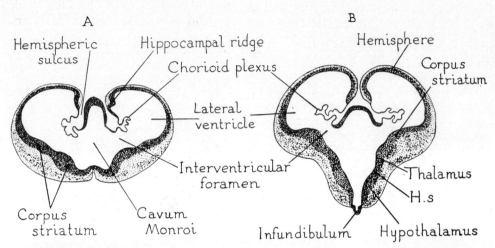

FIG. 17. Transverse sections through forebrain of human embryos. *A*, 17 mm.; *B*, 19.4 mm. (After Hochstetter.) *H.s.*, hypothalamic sulcus.

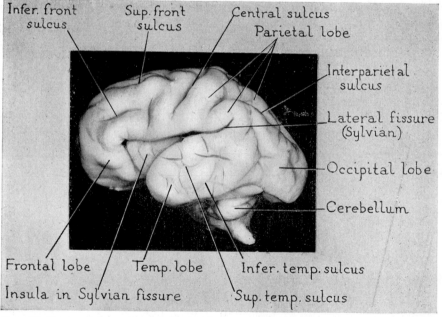

FIG. 18. Brain of six and one-half months human foetus, lateral view. Photograph

the roof of the diencephalon as well. In this manner the two hemispheric vesicles tower dorsally above the interbrain, their medial surfaces being separated from each other by a deep sagittal cleft, the *longi-*

From the hemispheric vesicles develop the three main structures of the endbrain—*olfactory lobe (rhinencephalon), corpus striatum* and *pallium.* The rhinencephalon arises as an evagination in the ventral wall of each hemisphere and is already visible in embryos of about 13 mm (Figs. 10, 12). That part of the ventromedial wall adjacent to the diencephalon, i.e. the fundus region of the hemispheric sulcus, becomes greatly thickened to form a ganglionic mass, the *corpus striatum*, projecting into the lateral ventricle (Fig. 15 B). The rest of the hemispheric wall, remaining relatively thin at first, develops into the *pallium* or cerebral cortex which becomes tremendously expanded in later development.

The chorioid plexus of the lateral ventricles is formed from the medial wall of the hemisphere, and the early stages are shown in Fig. 17. A little distance from the dorsal margin each hemispheric wall shows a longitudinal thickening, the hippocampal ridge, which is the forerunner of the future hippocampal formation. Below this the medial wall remains very thin and sends a longitudinal fold, the *plica chorioidea*, into the lateral ventricle. This fold, composed of the thin epithelial lamina and richly vascular connective tissue from the investing pia, is comparable to the tela chorioidea described in other portions of the brain, and by cellular proliferation gives rise to the chorioid plexus of the lateral ventricle. At the interventricular foramen this becomes continuous with the tela chorioidea of the third ventricle.

The hemispheres expand anteriorly to form the frontal lobe, posteriorly and ventrally to form the occipital and temporal lobes respectively. The middle portion in close relation to the diencephalon becomes the parietal lobe. During the second month, a shallow depression, the *lateral* or *Sylvian fossa*, appears in the region overlying the corpus striatum (Figs. 12, 13). The fossa is not produced by invagination but is due to the more rapid expansion and thickening of the adjacent portions of the wall, frontal, parietal and temporal. Gradually these portions overgrow the depression whose external opening becomes reduced to a deep cleft, the *lateral* or *Sylvian* fissure. The now hidden floor of the Sylvian fissure develops into the *insula* or *island of Reil* (Fig. 18).

In the fifth month, sulci begin to appear on the lateral surface of the hemisphere, though several have already been formed before on the medial surface. At the end of the seventh month, all the main sulci and convolutions are definitely indicated (Fig. 18). The lateral ventricles enlarge corresponding to the growth of the hemispheres, sending frontal, occipital and temporal extensions or horns into the respective parts of the brain. The relatively wide interventricular foramina become smaller and smaller and are finally reduced to slit-like openings communicating with the cavum Monroi which now forms the most rostral portion of the cleft-like third ventricle.

CHAPTER III

THE NEURON

The structural units of the nervous system concerned specifically with the nervous functions of conduction and integration are the highly excitable *nerve cells* or *neurons*, each composed of a cell body and one or more elongated processes. These neurons are set in a framework of a peculiar type of interstitial tissue, the *neuroglia* or *glia*, which like the neurons themselves is for the largest part derived from the ectoderm of the neural plate and ganglionic crest. Ordinary mesodermal connective tissue forms the envelopes (meninges) of the brain and spinal cord, the sheaths of the peripheral nerves and ganglia and in scanty amounts accompanies the numerous blood vessels of the central nervous system.

The most striking morphological feature of the neuron is the presence of protoplasmic extensions or processes, some of which, the *nerve fibers*, may become exceedingly elongated, thus permitting a rapid and uninterrupted conduction of nerve impulses over considerable distances. The relation of these long processes to the cell body was not understood at first, and nerve tissue was long described as consisting of two elements, nerve cells and nerve fibers. With the establishment of the continuity of nerve cell and nerve fiber, it became clear that the two together constituted a *single* structural unit, to which the name *neuron* is now given. A neuron may thus be defined as a nerve cell with all its processes. However, the term "nerve cell" is still used somewhat loosely to designate the neuron body and its processes exclusive of the nerve fiber.

The neurons, though showing wide variations in form and size, may be grouped in two main classes: those which possess dendrites and those which do not. The dendritic neurons which constitute the majority of nerve cells in the central nervous system and sympathetic ganglia, are *multipolar* in shape, being composed of a cell body or *perikaryon* from which extend a number of processes. One of these processes and one only, is structurally different from the others and is known as the *axon (neurite, axis cylinder process)*. It is a slender process, often of considerable length, characterized by a fairly uniform diameter and a smooth contour, and arises from a conical elevation on the cell body or one of the larger dendrites, known as the *implantation cone* or *axon hillock*. During its course it generally gives off several branches or *collaterals* which extend at right angles to the main fiber. Such collaterals may arise from any part of the axon but most commonly they are given off a short distance from the cell body. Both axon and collaterals finally terminate in complicated end branchings known as telodendria.

The other processes of a multipolar cell are structurally similar to the protoplasm of the cell body and are known as *protoplasmic processes* or *dendrites*. They may be considered as simple protoplasmic extensions which enormously increase the receptive surface of the cell and perhaps also aid in its nutritive processes. They are wide at the base, taper rapidly, have an irregular and roughened contour and are often beset with fine spiny or knobby thickenings or *gemmules* (Fig. 20). They fork repeatedly at acute angles and generally terminate not far from the cell body.

Neurons without dendrites give off only one structural type of process which has the histological character of an axon. Some are *bipolar*, having two processes which arise one at each end of the cell body. Examples are the bipolar cells of the retina and the cells forming the spiral and the vestibular ganglion of the eighth nerve. The olfactory cells of the nose likewise belong in this group.

The great majority of the neurons in the cerebrospinal ganglia are *unipolar* cells possessing a single process which divides not

development these cells have a typical bipolar form but in later growth the two processes converge and fuse, forming the T or Y-shaped process characteristic of the adult cell (Figs. 22, 68).

Physiologically the terms "axon" and

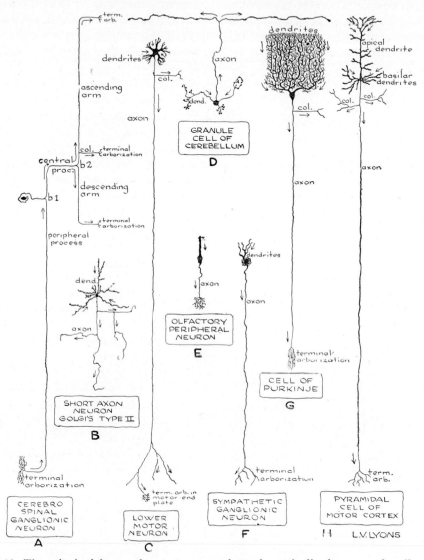

FIG. 19. The principal forms of neurons, somewhat schematically drawn.   col, collateral

far from the cell body into two branches, one proceeding to some peripheral sense organ, the other entering the brain or spinal cord. The single process as well as both of its arms have the structural features of an axon and may give off collateral branches. In early

"dendrite" are often used to denote the direction of conduction of nerve impulses. All processes conducting toward the cell body are considered dendrites, those conducting away from the cell body are axons. Regarded in this manner, the peripheral processes of the unipolar and bipolar neurons would be called dendrites though they have the histological features of an axon. This would obviously make difficult a structural definition of either dendrite or axon, since the direction of conduction can not be ascertained by microscopic study. Moreover, the peripheral branches of the unipolar sensory neurons actually do conduct distally, i.e., in a direction away from the cell

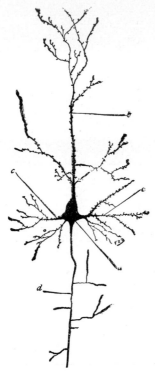

FIG. 20. Pyramidal cell from human cerebral cortex. Golgi method. *a*, cell body; *b*, main or apical dendrites showing gemnules; *c*, lateral dendrites with gemnules; *d*, portion of axon with collaterals.

body in the phenomenon of antidromic conduction. It is also known that axons by themselves, as in excised nerve, conduct nerve impulses in either direction. For these reasons, it seems advisable that the terms "axon" and "dendrite" should be used to denote processes possessing different structural characteristics.

The form of multipolar neurons shows innumerable variations. Some of the more

well marked types are the primary motor neurons of the spinal cord and brain stem, the pyramidal cells of the cerebral cortex, the Purkinje cells and granule cells of the cerebellum (Figs. 19, 20, 21). According to length of axon, Golgi has classified all nerve cells into long-axon (Type I) and short-axon (Type II) neurons. In the latter, the axon breaks up into an extensive terminal arborization in the immediate vicinity of the cell body.

The length of some nerve fibers is quite remarkable. Certain pyramidal cells of the cerebral cortex may send axons to the caudal tip of the spinal cord, i.e. from the top of the head to the lumbar region of the body. Axons of motor neurons in the spinal cord may extend the whole length of the lower extremity to terminate in muscle fibers of the toes. A sensory unipolar neuron situated in the first sacral ganglion may send a peripheral fiber to one of the toes, while its central fiber may ascend the whole length of the spinal cord and terminate in the medulla. The total length of such a neuron would be approximately from toe to nape of neck. In a full grown giraffe such a fiber would reach the astounding length of over fifteen feet.

The size of the neuron body likewise fluctuates within wide limits, from a diameter of 4 micra in the smallest granule cells of the cerebellum and cerebral cortex to well over 100 micra in the largest motor cells of the spinal cord. In general, the dimension of the cell body is proportional to the length, thickness, richness of branchings and terminal arborizations of its nerve fiber.

The cell body or perikaryon. The neuron body consists of a nucleus surrounded by a mass of cytoplasm whose surface layer forms a delicate plasma membrane. This membrane is of great physiological importance, especially in regulating the direction of transmission of nerve impulses from one cell to another.

The spherical nucleus, varying in size from 3–18 micra, is usually centrally placed, a striking exception being its eccentric position in the cells of Clarke's column in the spinal cord (Fig. 114).   In the larger and deeply staining nucleolus in which most of the chromatin is apparently concentrated (Fig. 25).   In certain small cells such as the

FIG. 21. Purkinje cell from cerebellum showing tremendous dendritic arborization.   Golgi method Photograph.

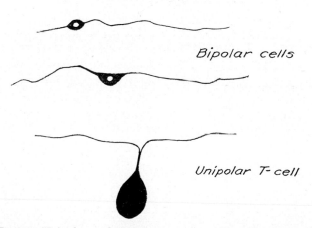

FIG. 22. Unipolar and bipolar neurons.   (After Moellendorf)

many of the smaller cells the nucleus has a characteristic vesicular appearance, composed of a definite nuclear membrane, a pale staining achromatic reticulum practically devoid of chromatin, and usually one large granule cells of the cerebellum and the substantia gelatinosa of the spinal cord, the small nucleus consists of a dense network of deeply staining chromatin without a nucleolus.   These nuclei are often difficult to distinguish from the nuclei of neuroglia cells. Binucleate nerve cells are rare, but occur in some sympathetic ganglia.

In the cytoplasm, with the use of various technical methods, are found the following structures: *neurofibrils, chromophil substance, Golgi reticular apparatus, mitochondria, central body*, and various *inclusions*, as pigment, fat and lipoids. The neurofibrils and chromophil substance are especially characteristic of nerve cells; most of the others are normal constituents of any tissue cell.

It may be stated here that the above named constituents are demonstrated only by the employment of many special tech-

cially in the axon which practically constitutes a cable of densely packed neurofibrils. They have been observed in the living nerve fibers of several invertebrates (de Renyi, Bozler) and more recently in the living ganglion cells of chick embryos (Weiss and Wang), and hence can not be regarded as artefacts. According to de Renyi, they are discrete threads of greater viscosity than the surrounding medium, which though interwoven do not branch or anastomose.

The neurofibrils lie imbedded in a substance collectively termed the *perifibrillar substance* or *neuroplasm* which obviously contains the other cytoplasmic constituents.

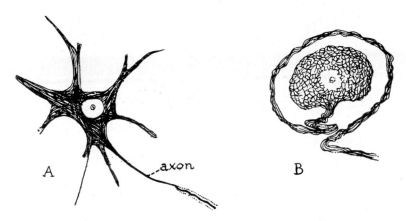

A   .-axon   B

FIG. 23. *A*, giant pyramidal cell from human motor cortex with fascicular arrangement of neurofibrils; *B*, spinal ganglion cell with neurofibrillar network. Bielschowsky silver stain. (After Bielchowsky.)

niques, each of which may selectively stain one or a few of them. A composite picture of nerve cell structure can only be obtained from a study of many preparations treated with different technical methods.

The *neurofibrils* are found in *all* nerve cells. As demonstrated by the reduced silver methods of Cajal, Bielschowsky and others, they are delicate, homogeneous threads which are continuous throughout the cell body and its processes (Figs. 23, 24). In the cell body they cross and interlace and in many preparations appear to anastomose into a true network (Cajal). In the processes they run straight and parallel to each other and are more closely grouped, espe-

The function of the neurofibrils is not fully understood. Their universal occurrence in all nerve cells and in all parts of nerve cells (dendrites, cell body, axon and terminal aborizations) and the fact that the chief conducting process consists practically of neurofibrils only, has led to the belief that they constitute the specific conductive substance of the neuron, a view which is still widely held. However, recent physiological evidence suggests that the propagation of nerve impulses is primarily a surface phenomenon and has little to do with the internal structures of the cell. There are some who have ascribed to the neurofibrils a purely mechanical supportive function.

In preparations stained with basic aniline dyes, the *chromophil substance* of *Nissl* appears in the form of deeply staining granules or clumps of granules known as *Nissl bodies* or *tigroid bodies*. They are found in the cell bodies and dendrites of all large and many of the smaller cells, but are invariably

which they are chemically related. They are believed to be of nuclear derivation similar to the "chromidial" substance found in certain gland cells.

According to the amount and distribution of their chromophil substance, nerve cells may be classified in two groups. The *caryo-*

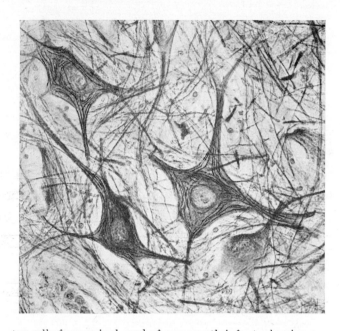

Fig. 24. Large motor cells from spinal cord of one month infant, showing neurofibrillar structure. Portions of dendrites and axons of other neurons fill the field. Cajal silver method. Photograph.

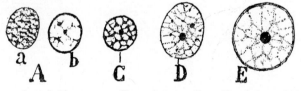

Fig. 25. Various types of nuclei in nerve cells and neuroglia cells of the rabbit. (Cajal.) *A*, *a* and *b*, neuroglia nuclei; *C*, nucleus of granule cell of cerebellum; *D*, nucleus of pyramidal cell of the cerebral cortex; *E*, nucleus of motor cell of the spinal cord.

absent in the axon and axon hillock from which that process arises. They are most abundant and sharply defined in the larger cells whose clear vesicular nucleus contains practically no chromatin (Figs. 26, 27). They are nucleoproteins containing phosphorus and iron and have the same staining affinities as the chromatin of the nucleus to

chrome cells are small, with deeply chromatic nuclei and scanty perinuclear cytoplasm in which no Nissl bodies can be demonstrated. The *somatochrome* cells with pale staining nuclei have a more abundant cytoplasm containing Nissl bodies. The latter may be *gryochrome* or *stichochrome* according to whether the Nissl bodies appear as granules or as larger bodies of linear or triangular shape. The Nissl bodies are larger in motor cells than in sensory, and attempts have been made to distinguish the many neuron types by the size, shape, distribution and staining capacity of the chromophil granules.

cell always presents the same appearance or "equivalent picture" in normal conditions. Such picture thus furnishes a norm for comparison with cells which show pathological changes and which have been subjected to the same technique.

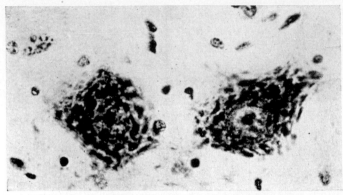

Fig. 26. Two motor cells from spinal cord of infant, showing Nissl bodies. Methylene blue. Photograph.

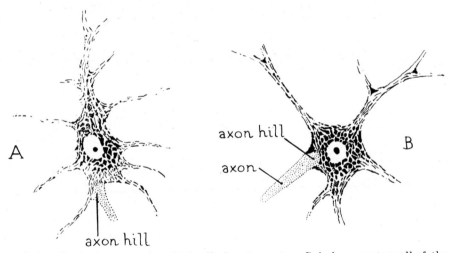

Fig. 27. Nissl bodies in A, giant pyramidal cell of motor cortex; B, in large motor cell of the human sacral cord. (After Bielschowsky.)

The structure of the Nissl bodies is readily changed in pathological conditions or even in altered physiological states as in fatigue. They lose their appearance as discrete bodies and seemingly become dissolved in the cytoplasm, a phenomenon termed *chromatolysis*. The significance of the Nissl stain from a pathological standpoint lies in the fact that with a given technique, each type of nerve

Nissl bodies cannot be seen in the living cell, and most investigators believe that the granules are precipitated in their characteristic form by the action of fixatives on a dissolved or suspended substance distributed uniformly through the cytoplasm. Some recent evidence, however, suggests that they may be present in the living protoplasm as definite bodies. In ganglion cells which

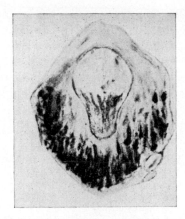

FIG. 28. Concentration of Nissl bodies at the centrifugal pole of a rat's spinal ganglion cell which had been centrifuged for half an hour at very great force. (Beams and King.)

ness (Beams and King, Fig. 28). Bensley and Gersh, using the freezing-drying technique which eliminates many of the artefacts caused by commonly used fixation methods, have obtained Nissl pictures quite similar to those found in the usual histological preparations. Beams and King conclude that "Nissl bodies react like definite masses of greater density imbedded in lighter substance."

The chromophil substance is probably of the nature of a nutritive element, possibly constituting reservoirs of easily oxidizable material rich in potential energy. The distribution of the Nissl granules would make possible their rapid oxidation through-

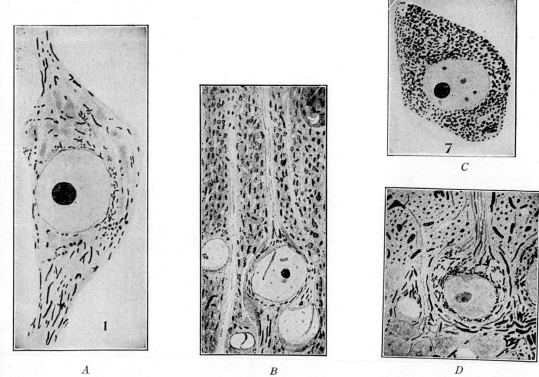

FIG. 29. Mitochondria in several types of nerve cells of the white mouse. (Nicholson.) A, large ventral horn cells; B, large pyramidal cell from the cortex; C, cell of Gasserian ganglion; D, Purkinje cell of cerebellar cortex.

have been centrifuged with tremendous force, the Nissl bodies become concentrated in the centrifugal pole of the cell without apparently losing their individual discrete-

out the cell body with consequent sudden release of the large amount of energy characteristic of neuronal activity.

Granular or filamentous *mitochondria* are

scattered throughout the entire cell body, dendrites and axon (Fig. 29). A modified *central body* or *microcentrum* has been demonstrated in most nerve cells (Del Rio-Hortega). It usually consists of one or two granules surrounded by a clear cytoplasmic area from which in some cases fine wavy fibrils radiate (Fig. 30). Occasionally a rod

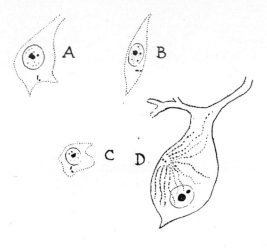

FIG. 30. Microcentra in several types of adult human nerve cells. (Redrawn from Del Rio-Hortega.) *A*, pyramidal cell; *B*, granule cell of dentate gyrus; *C*, stellate cell from cortex; *D*, Purkinje cell.

sist of disconnected granules or threads, and in some of the small cells it may be reduced to a single granule (Golgi body). The apparatus reflects altered physiological states and pathological conditions even more sensitively than the chromophil substance (Penfield). In the cell body of neurons whose axon has been cut, the substance of the apparatus becomes dispersed toward the periphery, with subsequent fragmentation and dissolution (Fig. 32). These phenomena have been termed "retispersion" and "retisolution" respectively (Penfield).

Most of the larger adult nerve cells contain a yellowish pigment known as *lipochrome* or *lipofuscin*. It appears in the form of granules which are usually aggregated in a dense mass in some part of the cell body (Fig. 33). Occasionally they may be dispersed throughout the cell. They are insoluble in the usual lipoid solvents, are blackened by osmic acid and stain with Scharlach R. The cells of the new born do not contain the pigment. It appears about the sixth year in the spinal ganglia, a few years later in the spinal cord, and after the twentieth year it is found in the cerebral cortex. It increases in amount with ad-

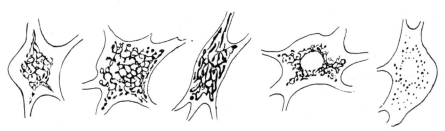

FIG. 31. Several forms of the Golgi apparatus in the motor neurons of the spinal cord of a 15 days old rabbit. (After Cajal.)

shaped body replaces one of the granules. The significance of the microcentrum is obscure, since adult neurons are incapable of cell division.

The *reticular apparatus* is most highly developed in the large nerve cells where it forms a complicated perinuclear reticulum which may extend a distance into the dendrites (Fig. 31). In other cells it may con-

vancing years and during senescence it may take up the largest part of the cytoplasm (Obersteiner).

Granules of a blackish pigment, known as *melanin*, are found in the substantia nigra, locus caeruleus and in certain pigmented cells scattered through the brain stem. It is also found in some cerebrospinal and sympathetic ganglion cells. Melanin appears at the end of the first year and increases in amount until puberty, after which it apparently remains constant until senescence. Little is known of the significance of either type of pigment.

The dendrites are simple protoplasmic extensions which have the same structure as the cytoplasm of the cell body.

up into more or less extensive terminal arborizations, the *telodendria* (Fig. 19).

In the central nervous system the axons may be naked, or *unmyelinated*, or possess a sheath of myelin for at least a portion of their course, when they are known as *myelinated* fibers. In the peripheral nervous system both myelinated and unmyelinated

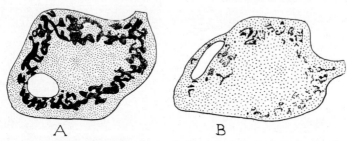

FIG. 32. *A*, retispersion in cell of Clarke's column in spinal cord of cat four days after cutting its axon. *B*, same as *A* but showing retisolution as well. (Redrawn from Penfield.)

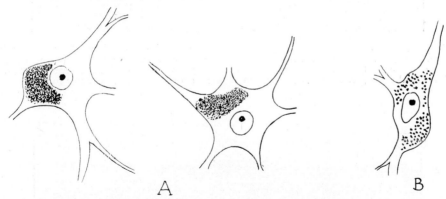

FIG. 33. *A*, lipochrome pigment in ventral horn cells of human spinal cord, blackened with osmic acid *B*, cell from substantia nigra with melanic pigment granules.

The nerve fiber (the axon and its sheaths). The axon is a slender, usually long process which arises from a conical mass of specialized protoplasm known as the implantation cone or axon hill. It is composed of closely packed parallel running neurofibrils continuous with those of the cell body, and imbedded in a scanty amount of perifibrillar substance in which rod-shaped mitochondria are scattered. It is distinguished from the cell body and dendrites by the complete absence of Nissl bodies which are also lacking in the axon hill. Distally each axon breaks

fibers have, in addition, an outer delicate nucleated membrane, the *neurilemma* or sheath of Schwann.

The *peripheral myelinated fiber* is structurally the most differentiated type, consisting of axon, myelin sheath and neurilemma. In the fresh condition, the axon is broad and is either homogeneous in appearance or shows faint longitudinal striations corresponding to the neurofibrils. In most fixatives, the axon usually shrinks down to a thin axial thread, hence its older name of axis-cylinder. In careful preparations its

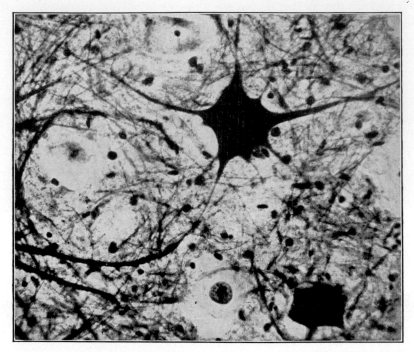

Fig. 34. Large motor cell from ventral gray horn of infant's spinal cord showing several dendrites and the origin of the axon. The latter arises from the lower side, tapers to a thin thread which runs for a short distance and then thickens at the point where the myelin sheath begins. Numerous small neuroglia nuclei, stained black, are shown. Modified Weigert's myelin stain. Photograph.

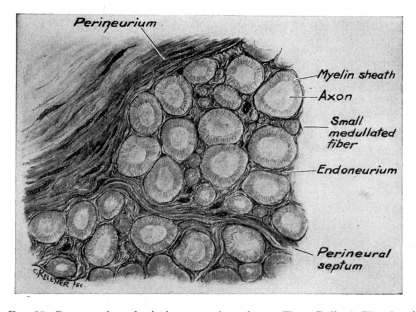

Fig. 35. Cross section of sciatic nerve of monkey. (From Bailey's Histology)

normal size may be more nearly approximated (Fig. 35).

The myelin sheath is acquired a short distance from the cell body, a short proximal portion of the axon being as a rule unmyelinated. It is a relatively thick sheath composed of a semi-fluid doubly refracting lipoid substance known as *myelin* which in the fresh state has a glistening white appearance. Chemically it is a complex substance containing lecithin, cerebrosides and cholesterin. The sheath is not continuous but is interrupted at intervals by constrictions known as the *nodes of Ranvier* (Figs. 36, 37, 38). The length of the internodal segments varies from about 80–600µ and is apparently proportional to the size of the fiber, the smaller fibers having the shorter internodes. In many fixed preparations, as with osmic acid, the myelin sheath of each internode is broken up into irregular segments by oblique clefts, the *incisures of Schmidt-Lantermann*, which extend from neurilemma to axon (Fig. 37). In other preparations, the myelin sheath may contain a delicate trabecular reticulum, the *neurokeratin network* (Figs. 38, 39). The view that this network and the incisures constitute a cytoplasmic reticulum derived from the neurilemma cells and enmeshing the myelin droplets is disputed by many. The neurokeratin network is not demonstrable in the living fiber (de Renyi). The myelin sheath ends at or near the point where the terminal aborizations are given off, the latter always being unmyelinated.

The neurilemma or sheath of Schwann is a delicate structureless membrane enclosing the myelin, which at the nodes of Ranvier dips inward and comes in contact with the axon. In this membrane, about half way between two nodes, is found a flattened oval nucleus surrounded by an area of granular cytoplasm from which several cytoplasmic bands extend along the length of the internode, branching and anastomosing to form a flat cytoplasmic network (Fig. 40). Nu-

cleus and cytoplasm constitute a sheath cell or neurilemma cell, one for each internode.

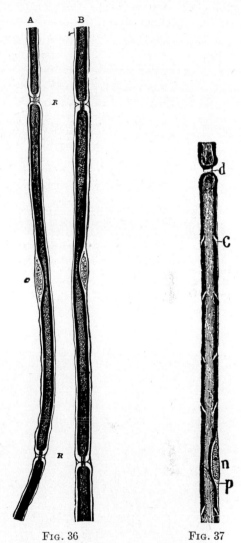

Fig. 36   Fig. 37

Fig. 36. Longitudinal section of portions of two myelinated fibers stained with osmic acid. Semidiagrammatic. (J. E. Neale in Quain's Anatomy.) *R, R,* nodes of Ranvier with axis cylinder passing through; *c,* nucleus surrounded by protoplasm, lying between neurilemma and myelin sheath.

Fig. 37. Longitudinal section of small portion of a myelinated nerve fiber. Osmic acid. (Cajal.) *c,* cleft of Schmidt-Lantermann; *d,* node; *n,* nucleus; and *p,* cytoplasm of neurilemma cell.

In the adult fiber the myelin seems to be more intimately related to the axon than to the neurilemma. In living fibers the myelin resists detachment from the axon, while the neurilemma is easily separated from the myelin as a continuous membrane (de Renyi). In fibers cut off from the cell body the axon and myelin disintegrate and com-

quently come into relation with sheath cells which arrange themselves at intervals along the surface of the fibers. These sheath cells are probably derived from the neural crest. Myelin formation occurs first in the vicinity

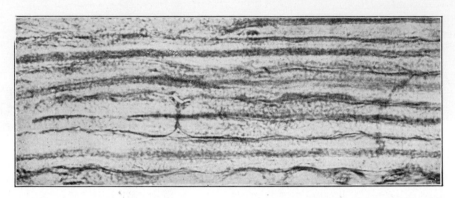

FIG. 38. Longitudinal section of several myelinated nerve fibers. The somewhat shrunken axis-cylinder is seen as a dark band surrounded by the unstained myelin in which the neurokeratin network is faintly seen. The thin lines between adjacent fibers are the neurilemma sheaths together with a small amount of connective tissue. A node of Ranvier is shown in one of the fibers. Photograph.

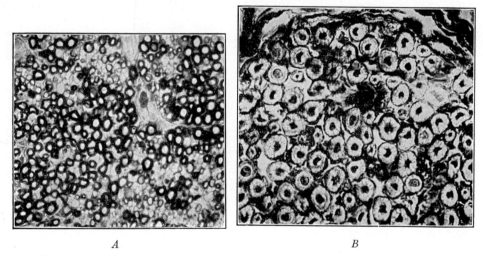

A   B

FIG. 39. Transverse sections through portions of a nerve trunk, each containing a number of myelinated fibers. In A, the myelin sheaths appear as black rings enclosing the unstained axis-cylinders. In B, the somewhat shrunken axis-cylinders appear black. The pale myelin sheath is covered externally by the dark staining neurilemma and displays a delicate neurokeratin reticulum. Photographs.

pletely disappear, the sheath cells alone show no degenerative changes but actually multiply and increase in size. Yet the formation of myelin is definitely dependent on the presence of neurilemma cells. The axons of growing fibers are at first naked but subse-

of the nucleus and continues in either direction until an entire myelin segment is established between two nodes. Whether the myelin is formed by the sheath cell or by the axon under the influence of the sheath cell, is still an unsettled question though the latter is considered more probable. It must be emphasized that sheath cells are also applied to peripheral fibers which do not become myelinated.

The *unmyelinated peripheral nerve fibers* or *fibers of Remak*, have a slender axon enveloped by a delicate nucleated sheath which is considered the equivalent of a neurilemma

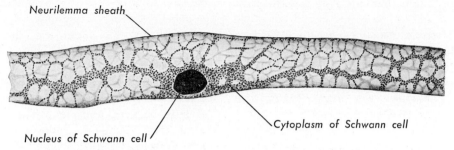

FIG. 40. Sheath of Schwann cell in nerve fiber from cauda equina of cat. (Bailey's Histology, after Nemiloff.)

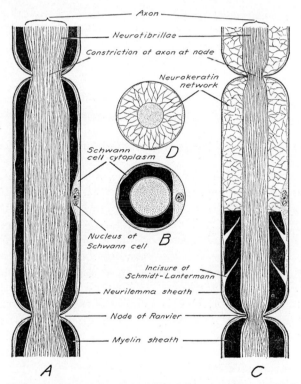

FIG. 41. Schematic drawings of peripheral myelinated nerve fibers. (Bailey's Histology.) In *A* and *B* the relative diameters of axon and myelin sheaths are based on de Renyi's studies of living nerve fibers. *C* and *D* show them as seen in many fixed preparations.

In addition to the above described sheaths, most medullated peripheral fibers are surrounded by a nucleated sheath of delicate connective tissue, the *endoneurium* or *sheath of Henle*, which, however, does not form part of the nerve fiber proper.

sheath (Fig. 42). The axons of most sympathetic ganglion cells and of many small cerebrospinal ganglion cells are unmyelinated.

The nerve fibers in the central nervous system do not possess a neurilemma sheath but are surrounded by neuroglia tissues (see neuroglia). In the myelinated fibers the nodes of Ranvier are less definite and more closely spaced (Cajal). The unmyelinated fibers, of which there are many in the gray substance of the brain and spinal cord, are naked axons of small caliber imbedded in neuroglia.

Myelinated fibers vary greatly in size. The fine fibers have a diameter from 2–4μ, those of medium size from 4–10μ, the largest from 10–20μ.

Collaterals or branches are given off by most fibers of the central nervous system. They are usually of finer caliber than the parent stem, extend at right angles and often arise from the proximal unmyelinated part of the axon. In the myelinated portion they are given off at the nodes of Ranvier, and become myelinated themselves. In the

than ummyelinated, the speed being greater in the larger fibers than in the smaller ones. The myelin sheath has been regarded by some as an insulator, by others as having a nutritive relation to the enclosed axon. The phenomena seen in secondary degeneration indicate a close metabolic relationship between myelin and axon, which may secure the rapid recuperation of the latter, thus accounting for the rapid conduction and non-fatigability of the myelinated fiber.

Relationship of neurons. The synapse. The simplest segmental reflexes require a chain of at least two neurons. A wave of excitation, the nerve impulse, is set up in a peripheral sensory nerve ending and passes along the peripheral and central process of a ganglion cell into the spinal cord. There it activates a motor neuron whose impulse travels along the motor fiber and

FIG. 42. Three unmyelinated fibers (fibers of Remak) with neurilemma nuclei. (After Cajal)

peripheral nervous system the fibers of somatic motor neurons which supply striped muscle, branch repeatedly at acute angles before reaching the muscle, and within the latter the branching may be very extensive, so that a single nerve fiber may furnish motor terminals for many muscle fibers (Sherrington, Clark). A motor neuron, and the muscle fibers innervated by it, constitutes a "motor unit" (Sherrington). In the small muscles, such as eye and finger muscles, the ratio of nerve fiber to muscle fibers is low, but in the larger ones more than a hundred muscle fibers may be supplied by a single nerve fiber. Many sensory fibers probably branch in a similar manner since their terminal arborizations extend over a considerable area. According to Weddell a single myelinated fiber may supply sensory endings to more than 300 hair follicle groups. The term "sensory unit" has been suggested for a sensory fiber including all its terminals.

Myelinated fibers conduct more rapidly

causes a muscular contraction (Fig. 149). Even such simple reactions have as a rule a third or *central* neuron interposed between the afferent and efferent cell (Fig. 149), while in the more complicated neural circuits the number of such intercalated central neurons may be tremendously multiplied. All neural pathways therefore consist of chains of neurons so related to each other as to make possible the physiological continuity of nerve impulse conduction over the complete circuit. The place of junction of neurons, i.e., where the axonal end arborizations of one neuron come in contact with the cell body or dendrites of another, is known as the *synapse*. It is generally accepted that the processes of one neuron do not fuse or become structurally continuous with those of others, and that the relationship at the synapse is one of contact only, the axonal branchings being everywhere separated from the cell body and dendrites by a delicate surface membrane.

Such a membrane would form a site for the occurrence of various surface phenomena, thus offering increased resistance and other-

Synaptic junctions show many structural variations.   Most commonly the axon terminals end in small bulb-like expansions

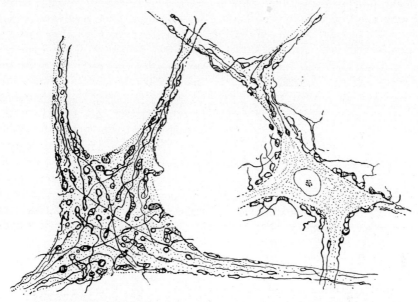

FIG. 43. Neuropodia (end feet) on body and dendrites of large cells in the reticular formation of the medulla.   Adult rabbit.   (Redrawn from Cajal.)

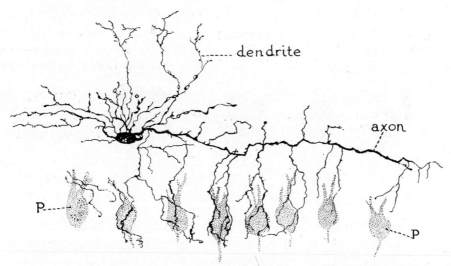

FIG. 44. Basket cell of human cerebellum with dendrites and axon.   (After Jakob.)   The collaterals of the axon end in terminal (synaptic) arborizations on the bodies of a number of Purkinje cells (P).

wise modifying the transmission of impulses across the synapse; or may perhaps furnish a mechanism for the setting up of new nerve impulses.   This view is supported by impressive histological as well as physiological evidence.

or *neuropodia* (*end feet, boutons terminaux*) applied to the cell body or dendrites.   Each neuropodium consists of a neurofibrillar loop imbedded in perifibrillar substance, sometimes there are simply small neurofibrillar rings (Fig. 43).   A large motor cell in the spinal cord may receive several hundred of such endings. In another type of synapse the axon terminals are delicate fibers which do not form end feet but come in lengthwise apposition with the dendrites or cell body,

conversely a single neuron may receive impulses from the axons of many neurons.

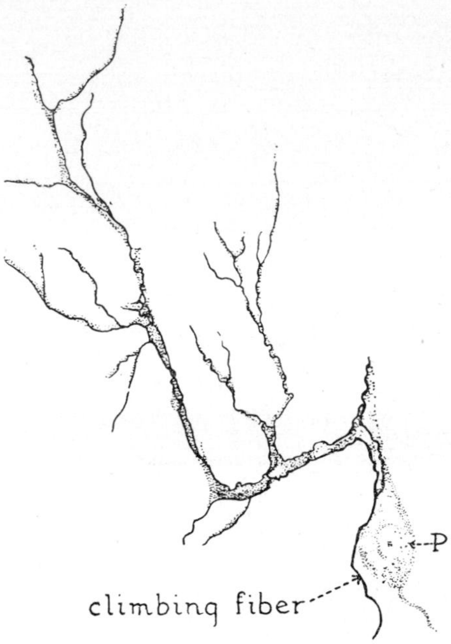

Many physiological peculiarities are associated with the synapse. While an activated nerve fiber conducts equally well in either direction, impulses are transmitted over the reflex arc, i.e. across the synapse in one direction only, from the axon of one neuron to the cell body and dendrites of another, a phenomenon known as *dynamic polarization*. Some of the other ways in which conduction across the synapse differs from that in a nerve fiber may be briefly mentioned (Sherrington). Over a reflex arc, (1) conduction is slower; (2) there may be persistence of response after cessation of the stimulus (after-discharge); (3) there is less close correspondence between the rhythm of stimulus and rhythm of response; (4) repetition of a given stimulus may produce a response where a single one will not (summation); (5) greater variability in the threshold value of a stimulus, i.e., the ease with which responses can be elicited; (6) much greater fatigability; (7) greater dependence on oxygen supply and greater susceptibility to anesthetics and other drugs; (8) greater refractory period; and (9) re-

FIG. 45. Parallel axo-dendritic synapses formed by the terminal arborization of a climbing fiber with the dendrites of a Purkinje cell (*P*). Human cerebellum. (Redrawn from Jakob.)

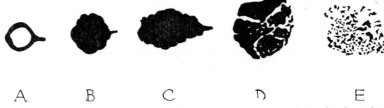

A   B   C   D   E

FIG. 46. Diagrams showing several stages in the degeneration of end feet in the spinal cord of a cat, following section of a dorsal root. (After W. C. Gibson.) *A*, normal end foot. *B, C, D, E*, after section of root. *B*, 2 days; *C*, 4 days; *D, E*, 5 days.

often for considerable distances. (Figs. 44, 45). The most striking examples are the climbing fibers of the cerebellum. In some cases, unmyelinated axons run at right angles to the dendrites and apparently come in contact with the spiny excrescences or *gemmules* with which the dendrites are beset. It is obvious that one axon may carry impulses to a number of neurons and that

enforcement and inhibition of one reflex by another.

Degeneration and regeneration of nerve fibers. The cell body is the trophic center of the neuron and any process detached from it disintegrates and completely disappears. When an axon is divided, degenerative changes of a traumatic character first affect the cut edges. In the proximal portion of the fiber which is attached to the cell body, the degenerative changes extend only a short distance, though sometimes as much as two or three centimeters, and are soon succeeded by reparative processes leading to the formation of new axonal sprouts from the central stump. The distal portion, however, completely disintegrates, degeneration occurring throughout the whole length of the fiber and including its terminal arborization, a process known as *secondary* or *Wallerian degeneration*. The changes, as a rule, appear simultaneously along the whole length of the nerve fiber.

simpler intermediate substances which react to the Marchi stain, and ultimately into neutral fat.

While these changes occur, the nuclei of the neurilemma cells proliferate by mitotic division, and their cytoplasm increases in amount but does not divide, the sheath cells of each fiber now forming a syncytial protoplasmic tube or band (*band fiber*) containing the debris of the degenerating axon and myelin sheath (Fig. 48c). The neurilemma cells are apparently concerned with the digestion and absorption of the axon and myelin, and the granules in their cytoplasm

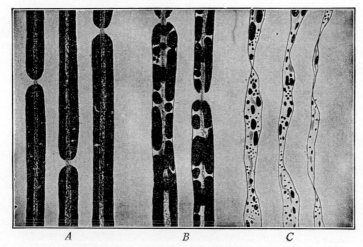

A   B   C

Fig. 47. *A*, normal nerve fibers from sciatic nerve of rabbit; *B*, two fibers from distal part of rabbit's sciatic nerve 5 days after cutting the nerve, showing segmentation of myelin; *C*, three fibers from distal part of rabbit's sciatic nerve 3 weeks after cutting nerve. Most of the myelin has been absorbed. Osmic acid.

The terminal arborization and axon are affected first. The neurofibrils change their staining reaction, become irregular in shape and by the end of the fifth day have become broken up into granules (Fig. 46). The axon as a whole swells, fragments and finally disappears. In the myelin sheath the changes observed are fragmentation of the myelin into irregular segments, subsequent break-up of the segments into granules or droplets, and finally complete absorption (Figs. 47, 48). Coincident with the physical changes, the myelin also undergoes chemical changes, breaking down into

are probably formed from the absorbed material. In the central nervous system the neuroglia cells which surround the fibers play a similar role, but no band fibers are formed since a continuous neurilemma is lacking.

The neuron body whose axon is injured likewise shows marked degenerative changes (Fig. 49). The cell body swells and becomes turgescent, the nucleus is displaced toward the periphery, and the Nissl bodies undergo dissolution, the chromatolysis beginning in the center of the cell and spreading outward (central chromatolysis). The extent and rapidity of these changes depend on the

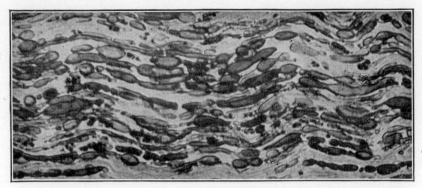

A

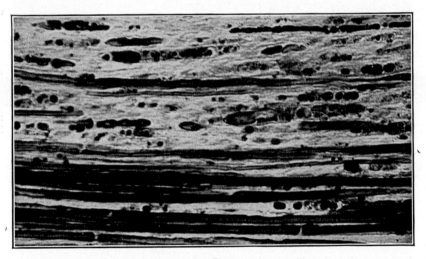

B

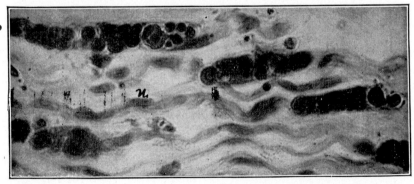

C

Fig. 48. *A*, distal stump of a nerve cut 3 to 5 days previously. Osmic acid. *B*, distal stump of a nerve partly cut 12 to 15 days previously. Osmic acid. Normal fibers and two nodes of Ranvier are shown at the bottom. *C*, distal stump of a nerve cut 12 to 15 days previously. Osmic and iron hematoxylin. In addition to the degenerating myelin, several band fibers and their nuclei (*n*) are shown. Photographs.

type of neuron involved, the nature of the injury and especially on the location of the distantly placed. In other words, the effect depends upon the percentage of the neuron

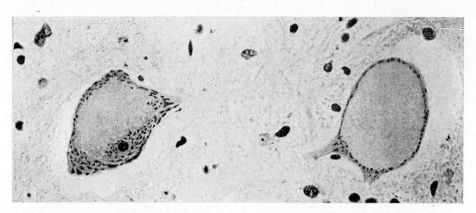

Fig. 49. Two motor cells from adult lumbar cord, showing "central chromatolysis", nuclear eccentricity and swelling of cell body. Photograph. The lumbosacral nerve roots had some time previously been crushed in an accident.

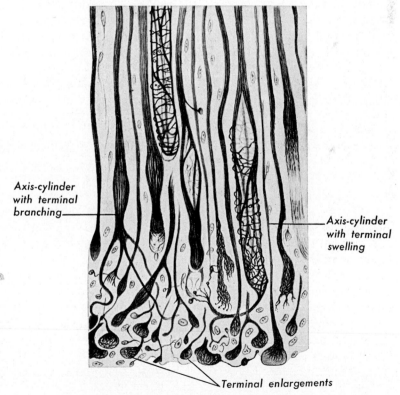

Axis-cylinder with terminal branching

Axis-cylinder with terminal swelling

Terminal enlargements

Fig. 50. Regenerating axons in the central stump of a cat's sciatic nerve $2\frac{1}{2}$ days after section of the nerve. (After Cajal, from Bailey's Histology.)

injury, a lesion near the cell body producing a greater central effect than one more cut off. If the lesion is very near the cell body, the latter may ultimately die with consequent degeneration of the proximal portion of the nerve fiber which remains attached to it.

If the neuron body survives the injury, *regeneration* takes place. The Nissl bodies reappear, the nucleus returns to its normal position and the turgescence gradually subsides. While this is going on, axonal sprouts arise from the central stump, traverse the scar tissue formed at the site of the injury, and reach the protoplasmic fiber bands formed by neurilemma cells (Fig. 50). Along or within these bands the regenerating axons find their way for long distances to their proper destinations. The regenerating axons are at first unmyelinated, but subsequently myelin segments are added as already described (p. 34), and the fibers ultimately assume their normal appearance. In the regenerated fibers the internodes are, as a rule, shorter and more numerous.

In the central nervous system where no band fibers are formed, regeneration does not occur, there being at most an abortive attempt. Apparently the band fibers are essential for the proper guiding of the regenerating axons.

A knowledge of the mode of nerve regeneration by outgrowths is important as a basis for intelligent surgical treatment. Thus in human trauma it is desirable to approximate the severed ends of the nerve or, if some time has elapsed since the injury, to remove the scar tissue which forms an obstacle to the passage of the growing axons to the band fibers and thence to their destination. Further details concerning the regenerative processes following injury of peripheral nerves are given on page 127.

The importance of secondary degeneration from the standpoint of anatomy lies in the fact that by using appropriate methods one is enabled to trace the connections between cells and nerve fibers throughout the nervous system. The Weigert method and osmic acid, which stain normal myelin, will bring out the fragmentation of the myelin sheath.

On the other hand the Marchi method, osmic staining after treatment with bichromate, will bring out the intermediate products of myelin disintegration and leave the normal myelin practically unstained. By this method, if used at the proper stage of degeneration (about one to three weeks after injury), even scattered degenerating nerve fibers can be traced throughout their whole length as black granules easily distinguished from the normal fibers (Fig. 141). In later stages when the myelin has completely disappeared, the Weigert method for normal myelin is again helpful. This, of course, only gives a negative picture, the degenerated fibers being indicated by unstained areas (Fig. 138). Only bundles of fibers, not isolated ones, can be thus distinguished. By means of certain silver stains, the fragmentation and disintegration of the axis-cylinder may in some cases be demonstrated. Finally, to ascertain the cell bodies to which the cut fibers belong, the Nissl method is usually employed and the abnormal cells distinguished by the characteristic changes described above.

The neuron doctrine. The various facts regarding the individuality of the neuron were formulated by Waldeyer in 1891 into the *neuron doctrine*. Briefly summarized, this states that the neuron is the *genetic* and *anatomical* unit of the nervous system. The neuron including all its processes constitutes an anatomical entity related to other neurons by contact only, each derived from a single embryonic cell.

The neuron is likewise the *trophic* unit. The nucleus is the regenerative center of the cell and processes cut off from the cell body completely degenerate. Regeneration may occur by new outgrowth from the nucleated portion.

Finally, the neuron is the *"functional"* unit of the nervous system and is the only element which conducts nerve impulses. All the neural circuits are composed of chains of such units.

CHAPTER IV

NEUROGLIA, THE INTERSTITIAL TISSUE OF THE NERVOUS SYSTEM

As already stated, the interstitial supportive framework of the brain and spinal cord is formed by a special tissue, the *neuroglia* or *glia*, composed of cells, fibers and a homogeneous intercellular substance. The structural features of this tissue are difficult to demonstrate except by selective and often complicated staining methods, and

be added, for the peripheral nervous system, the *neurilemma cells* of the nerve fibers and at least the inner *capsule cells* surrounding the neuron bodies of the spinal and cranial ganglia. The neurilemma and capsule cells differentiate from cells which have migrated from the neural plate and hence represent a sort of peripheral neuroglia, although that

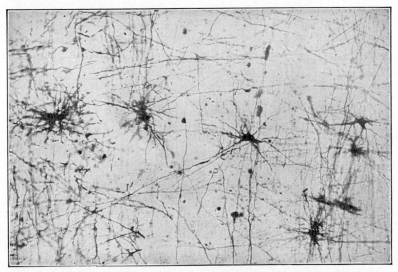

FIG. 51. Several fibrous astrocytes in the white matter of the spinal cord. The one to the left appears to be transitional to the protoplasmic form. A number of unbranched neuroglia fibers are seen coursing through the field. Golgi silver method. Photograph.

in ordinary preparations with basophil dyes as a rule only the nuclei are seen (Fig. 56). Our knowledge concerning the structure and function of neuroglia has been greatly increased by the investigations of Cajal, Achucarro, Del Rio-Hortega, Penfield and others.

Neuroglia in the broadest sense may be divided into the following types: (1) *astroglia* or *macroglia*, whose cells are known as *astrocytes;* (2) *oligodendroglia;* (3) *microglia* or *mesoglia;* (4) *ependyma.* To these should

term is usually not applied to them. According to Penfield, they most closely resemble the oligodendroglia of the central nervous system. With the exception of microglia, all of the above types are derived from the neural ectoderm.

(1) The **astrocytes** or neuroglia cells proper are branched stellate cells whose cytoplasm contains small rounded or ovoid granules, the *gliosomes* (Figs. 51, 52). The nucleus is irregularly ovoid and pale staining, with scanty chromatin and no nucleolus.

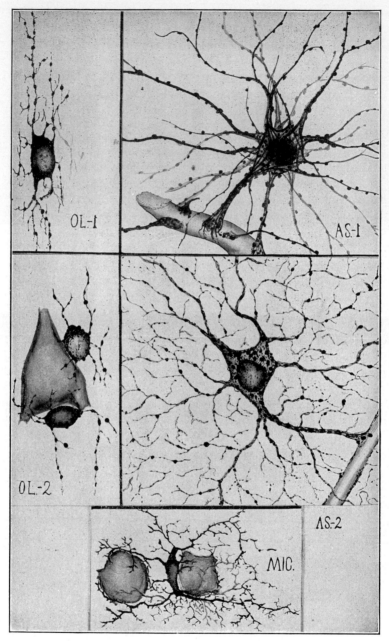

Fig. 52. Various types of neuroglia cells. (Penfield.) *AS-1*, fibrous astrocyte with one or two processes forming foot plates against a neighboring blood vessel; *AS-2*, protoplasmic astrocyte with foot plate, and containing gliosomes (dark granules) in its body and processes; *MIC*, microglia cell whose delicate spiny processes embrace the bodies of two neurons; *OL-1*, oligodendroglia cell in the white matter (interfascicular form); *OL-2*, two oligodendroglia cells lying against a nerve cell (perineuronal satellites).

Centrosome, reticular apparatus, and usually a small amount of lipochrome pigment are found in the granular cytoplasm. Two types of astrocytes may be distin- guished, *protoplasmic* and *fibrous*. The former, also known as mossy cells, have numerous freely branching processes and are destitute of fibers. They are found principally in the gray matter of the spinal cord and brain, where they often partly envelop the neuron bodies and thus constitute one of the varieties of perineuronal *satellite cells.*

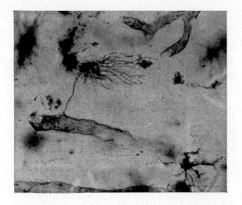

FIG. 53. Astrocyte with process adhering to wall of blood vessel. Golgi silver stain. Photograph.

the peripheral cytoplasm. Whether these fibers actually leave the cell and become intercellular structures, as is the case in connective tissue, is still a somewhat open question. There appears to be considerable evidence that normally the neuroglia fibers, no matter how long, are surrounded by a thin film of cytoplasm. Fibrous astrocytes are found mainly in the white matter.

Cajal and others have described a mixed type of astrocyte which contains both protoplasmic and fibrous processes.

In both the protoplasmic and fibrous astrocytes, one or more of the processes have peculiar terminal expansions, the *foot plates* or *perivascular feet,* which are anchored to the outer walls of the blood vessels lying within the central nervous system (Figs. 52, 53). According to some, these foot

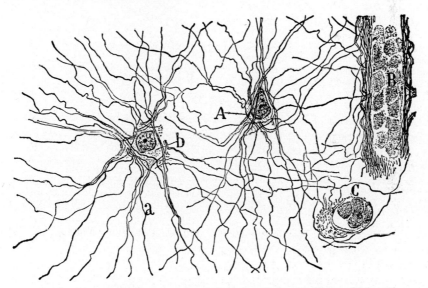

FIG. 54. Fibrous astrocytes from white matter of the human cerebellum. Weigert's neuroglia stain. (Cajal.) *A,* cell body; *B, C,* blood vessels; *a,* neuroglia fibers; *b,* cytoplasm of neuroglia cell.

The fibrous astrocytes or spider cells are characterized by thin unbranched fiber-like processes which radiate from the cell in all directions and extend for a considerable distance (Figs. 52, 54). With adequate staining it can be seen that these processes are composed of delicate fibers which extend through the cell body, coursing mainly in

plates form a continuous glial membrane around the blood vessels, the *perivascular limiting membrane.* Another glial membrane, the external glial limiting membrane, is found directly underneath the pia by a condensation of neuroglia, formed in part at least by foot plates of fibrous astrocytes anchored to the inner pial surface. These glial membranes are thus everywhere interposed between the true nervous tissue and the mesodermal coverings and blood vessels.

(2) **Oligodendroglia** consists of somewhat smaller cells with rather few and exceedingly slender processes which never form foot plates (Figs. 52, 57). The spherical nucleus is more darkly staining than that of an astrocyte, the cytoplasm contains gliosomes but no fibers. In the white matter, they are often seen lying in rows

cells of peripheral nerves. Similar to the latter, they also seem to be concerned with the breaking down of the axon and myelin and the elimination of debris in secondary degeneration of nerve fibers in the central nervous system. In the same way, the perineuronal satellites may be compared to the inner capsule cells of the spinal ganglia. It is probable that in certain pathological conditions these satellites play a part in the eroding and even complete removing of

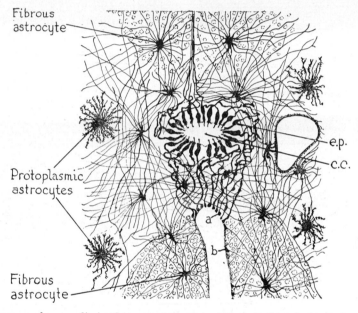

Fibrous astrocyte

Protoplasmic astrocytes

Fibrous astrocyte

e.p.

c.c.

a

b

FIG. 55. Ependyma and neuroglia in the central portion of the spinal cord of an infant eight days old. Golgi impregnation. (After Cajal.) *a*, terminal foot plate of ependyma cell; *b*, terminal foot plate of fibrous astrocyte; *c.c.*, central canal; *e.p.*, ependyma cell.

between the myelinated fibers (interfascicular glia), their delicate processes wrapping around the myelin sheath. In the gray matter, they may lie closely apposed to neuron bodies as *perineuronal satellite* cells, while in both gray and white matter some of them have their cell bodies closely applied to the walls of capillaries as *perivascular satellites*.

The function of oligodendroglia cells is probably metabolic rather than supportive. It has been suggested (Penfield) that they regulate the formation of myelin and hence correspond most closely to the neurilemma

weakened nerve cells, a process known as *neuronophagia*.

(3) The **microglia** cells, unlike the other types of neuroglia, are of mesodermal origin and appear to enter the nervous system not long before birth. They are apparently fibroblasts or histoblasts which have migrated from the pia and it is possible that some arise by detachment of similar cells from the adventitial connective tissue of the neural blood vessels. The cells are very small with scanty cytoplasm and several delicate tortuous processes which bear small spines (Figs. 52, 57). Occasionally only

two processes may be present. The deeply staining nucleus is irregularly elongated triangular or kidney-shaped, the cytoplasm devoid of gliosomes and fibers. Microglia cells are found in both gray and white matter. They have no foot plates but are often closely apposed to neuron bodies as perineuronal satellites or to the walls of blood vessels as perivascular satellites.

In normal conditions the function of logical conditions, microglia is considered by many as part of the reticulo-endothelial system. (See texts of histology).

(4) The **ependyma** lines the central canal of the spinal cord and the ventricles of the brain, and in ordinary preparations has the appearance of a simple columnar epithelium (Fig. 108). With adequate staining methods the cytoplasm is seen to contain neuroglia fibers which are continued into

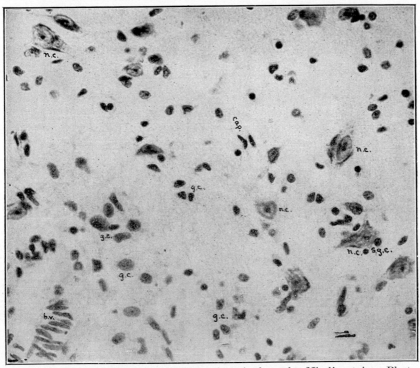

Fig. 56. Portion of intermediate gray of infant's spinal cord. Nissl's stain. Photograph. *bv,* blood vessel with nuclei of circular smooth muscle coat; *cap,* capillary with two endothelial nuclei; *gc,* nuclei of neuroglia cells. The larger pale nuclei belong to astrocytes, the darker smaller round nuclei to oligodendroglia, and the darkest smallest round or elongated nuclei to microglia. *nc,* small and medium sized nerve cells showing Nissl bodies.

microglia is obscure, but in trauma or other destructive lesions of the nervous system they undergo striking changes. The protoplasm swells and becomes granular and the small cells are transformed into large actively phagocytic scavenger cells which exhibit ameboid movement. In certain pathological conditions (glioma), they may devour the processes of the giant astrocytes present in such cases (Penfield). On account of its origin and behavior in patho-

the slender process projecting from the base of each cell (Fig. 58). In embryonic life these processes traverse the whole thickness of the neural wall to become attached to the pia by terminal expansions or end feet, and this condition is still seen in the adult in places where the neural wall is relatively thin, as in the ventral floor plate of the spinal cord (Fig. 55). In the thick-walled portions the ependymal fibers usually end within a short distance from the cell body.

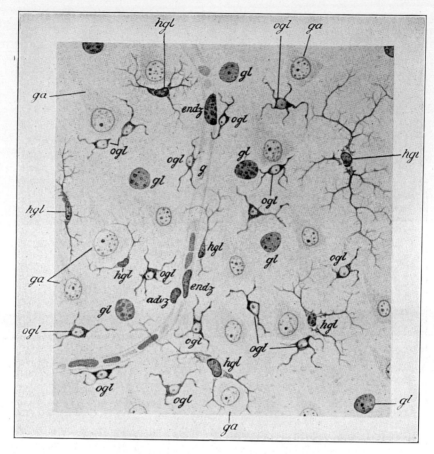

FIG. 57. Various types of neuroglia cells in human cerebral cortex. Hortega silver stain. (Jakob.) *advz*, adventitial cell; *endz*, endothelial cell; *g*, capillary; *ga*, nerve cell; *gl*, nuclei of protoplasmic astrocytes; *hgl*, microglia; *ogl*, oligodendroglia.

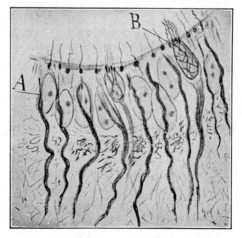

FIG. 58. Ependymal cells in spinal cord of a one and one-half months old cat. (Cajal.) *A*, uniflagellate ependyma cell; *B*, pluriflagellate ependyma cell.

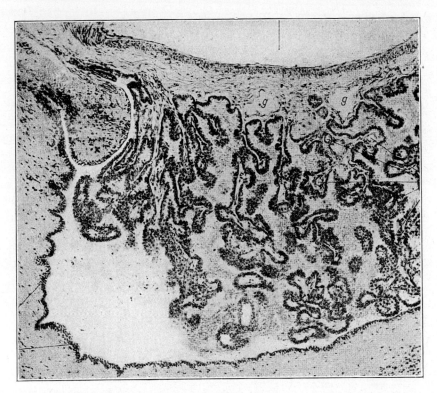

FIG. 59. Normal human chorioid plexus. Nissl stain. Photograph. (Jakob.) *g*, blood vessel.

In certain forms and in certain places at least, cilia or flagellae protrude from the free surface of the ependymal cells into the neural cavity (Fig. 58), and may perhaps assist in the circulation of the cerebrospinal fluid. In man such cilia are only observed in embryological stages and appear to be absent in the adult. Ependyma may be regarded as composed of neuroglia cells which have retained their embryonic shape and position.

In certain places the wall of the brain is exceedingly thin and is composed solely of a simple epithelial membrane of modified ependyma cells, the *epithelial chorioid lamina.* The cells are cubical in shape, contain cytoplasmic granules, and are believed to be concerned with the production of the cerebrospinal fluid, though the mode of such production is not entirely clear. This epithelial lamina is thrown into complicated folds and invested externally by highly vascularized pial connective tissue, the two together constituting the telae chorioideae and chorioid plexuses of the fourth, third and lateral ventricles (Fig. 59).

An analogous structure is the pars ciliaris retinae of the eye, where part of the neural wall is likewise composed of a single layer of cubical epithelial cells. Here too a similar function probably exists in the formation of the fluids filling the eye cavity.

CHAPTER V

HISTOGENESIS OF THE NEURAL ELEMENTS AND THEIR SEGMENTAL DISTRIBUTION

The neural plate originally consists of a simple layer of columnar epithelium. As the plate is closing, the epithelium thickens and assumes a stratiform appearance. The cell outlines become indistinct and disappear and the nuclei assume positions in varying depths of the wall, except for a narrow outer zone, the marginal layer, which contains no nuclei (Fig. 60). Near the central canal,

tion of the germinal cells, more and more nuclei become displaced toward the periphery, increasing the depth of the *nuclear* or *ependymal* layer which, however, is always separated from the external limiting membrane by the *marginal* non-nucleated zone (Fig. 60).

By means of the Golgi and other silver methods, two kinds of cells may be demon-

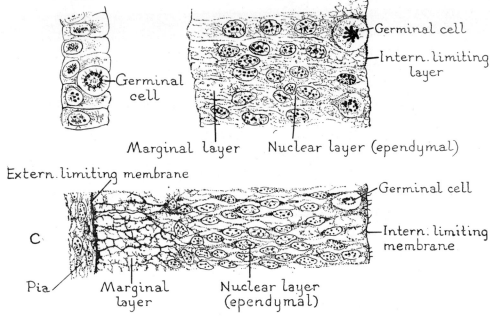

FIG. 60. Three stages in the histogenesis of the neural tube. *A*, from rabbit embryo before closure of tube. (After His.) *B*, from 5 mm., and *C*, from 10 mm. pig embryos. (After Hardesty.)

mitotic figures are present, the ovoid or rounded dividing cells being known as *germinal cells*. The protoplasm between the nuclei becomes alveolar, giving the appearance of a reticulum of anastomosing protoplasmic trabeculae. The trabeculae unite along the inner and outer surface of the wall to form the internal and external limiting membranes. By rapid prolifera-

strated in these early developmental stages: *spongioblasts* and *germinal cells*. The former are spindle-shaped bipolar cells which extend through the whole thickness of the wall, their nuclei placed close to the lumen, their processes attached to the internal and external limiting membranes (Figs. 61, 62). Many of these soon lose their connection with the central canal and withdraw to

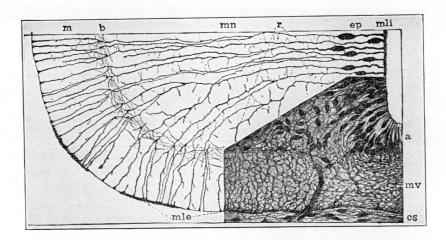

FIG. 61. Combination drawing from sections of 15 mm. pig embryo. (Hardesty.) Upper portion stained by Golgi method. *a, ep*, ependymal layer; *m, mv*, marginal layer; *cs*, embryonal pia mater; *mle, mli*, external and internal limiting membranes. The cells of the mantle layer (*mv*) are indicated in the lower right hand portion between the ependymal and marginal layers.

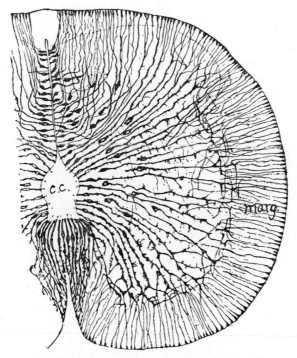

FIG. 62. Section of spinal cord of 44 mm. human embryo. (Cajal.) Golgi silver method. Migration and transformation of ependymal spongioblasts into the unipolar type. *c.c.*, central canal; *marg.* marginal layer.

deeper portions of the wall as unipolar spongioblasts which later develop numerous processes and are ultimately transformed into neuroglia cells, probably protoplasmic and fibrous astrocytes (Figs. 62, 70). Others retain their original position and become ependyma cells, their peripheral processes as a rule losing their connection with the external limiting membrane and extending only a short distance from the cell body. In the thin-walled portion of the fourth, third and lateral ventricles, the ependyma cells are modified into cubical

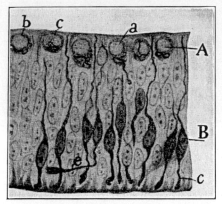

FIG. 63. Section through wall of forebrain vesicles of a three and one-half days chick embryo, showing differentiating neuroblasts. (Cajal.) *A*, apolar cells; *B*, bipolar cells.

appears in the cytoplasm on the side away from the central canal. This is the apolar stage of the neuroblast. The cell migrates away from the lumen to which it often remains attached by a process and at the same time sends out a neurofibrillar process, the axon, toward the periphery (Fig. 63). This bipolar stage lasts only a short time, the central process disappearing and the cell becoming a unipolar neuroblast. Somewhat later, dendritic processes grow out from the cytoplasm and the neuroblast assumes the multipolar shape characteristic of the adult neuron. While these changes occur, the differentiating neuroblasts become displaced peripherally and now form a more or less distinct layer, the *mantle layer*, between the nuclear and marginal layers (Fig. 64).

The mantle layer is not formed uniformly throughout the neural wall. The floor and

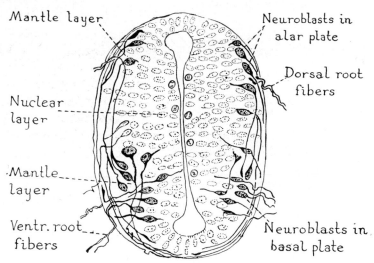

FIG. 64. Section through spinal cord of 56 hours chick embryo. (After Cajal)

granular cells, the chorioidal epithelial cells, which form the inner lining of the chorioid plexuses (Figs. 59, 70). The microglia alone is not formed from the medullary ectoderm but from connective tissue which later invades the neural tube.

Differentiation of neurons. Many of the germinal cells or medulloblasts begin to increase in size and a neurofibrillar zone

roof plates remain relatively thin and furnish only spongioblastic elements. But even in the lateral wall the neuroblasts are primarily concentrated in the most dorsal and the most ventral portion, corresponding to the alar and basal plate respectively (Figs. 64, 65). Between these regions the cells are few and scattered. The mantle layer constitutes the future gray of the spinal cord, the alar portion developing into the dorsal horn, the basal into the ventral horn.

The neuroblasts of the basal plates become the *efferent peripheral neurons.* Their axons penetrate the marginal layer and external limiting membrane and leave the cord as ventral root fibers which go directly to striped muscle or to autonomic ganglia for the innervation of visceral structures (Figs. 64, 67). The axons of cells from the alar plate all remain within the central nervous system. Some arch ventrally, cross through

progressively diminishes in size and is ultimately reduced to a single layer of columnar ependymal cells. In certain places, as in the ventral commissure of the spinal cord, some of the ependymal cells may retain their embryonal spongioblastic character and extend the whole thickness of the neural wall (Fig. 55).

The mantle layer, on the other hand, progressively increases in size and furnishes the gray matter of the spinal cord, surrounded by a constantly expanding marginal

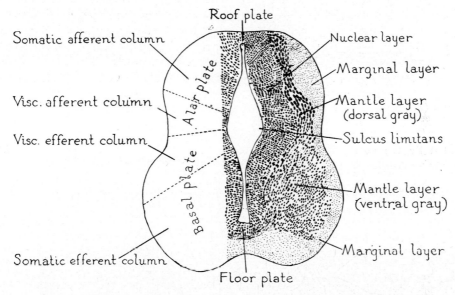

FIG. 65. Section through spinal cord of a 7 mm. human embryo.   (Modified from Fischel)

the basal plate to the opposite side and reach the marginal layer where they ascend or descend for variable distances. Other axons remain on the same side and likewise ascend or descend in the marginal layer. These cells whose processes are entirely confined to the central nervous system constitute the *central, intermediate* or *associative* cells. Those whose axons remain on the same side are known as *tautomeric* cells, those whose axons cross are *heteromeric* or *commissural.*

As development proceeds, the proliferations of the germinal cells gradually decreases and ultimately stops altogether. As more and more indifferent cells are transformed into neuroblasts, the nuclear layer

layer which contains the descending and ascending axons of the central cells. At a much later period, most of the axons become myelinated and the marginal layer assumes the whitish, glistening appearance characteristic of the white matter of the cord.

In the spinal ganglia, derived from the neural crest, a similar differentiation takes place. Many of the cells originally polygonal or rounded become spindle-shaped and bipolar by the development of two neurofibrillar processes, a central and a peripheral one (Figs. 67, 68). The central processes enter the spinal cord as dorsal root fibers and there bifurcate into ascending and descending arms which contribute to the

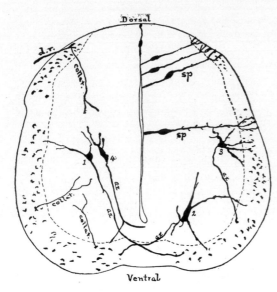

FIG. 66. Section through spinal cord of seven days chick embryo, showing tautomeric (3), heteromeric (1, 2) and hecateromeric (4) central or column cells. *ax*, axon; *collat.*, collateral; *d.r.*, dorsal root fiber; *sp*, spongioblast. The boundary between the mantle and marginal zones is indicated by the dotted line. Golgi silver impregnation.

various receptors of the body. These spinal (or cranial) ganglion cells constitute the *afferent peripheral neurons* (sensory neurons). At first bipolar, the majority of these cells become subsequently unipolar by the fusion of the two original processes, the single process thus formed now dividing into a central and a peripheral arm (Fig. 68).

Not all of the cells in the spinal ganglia differentiate into neuroblasts. Some develop into *capsule cells* or *amphicytes* which form a capsule around the bodies of the spinal ganglion cells. Others wander out along the course of the growing peripheral nerve fibers, envelop the latter and ultimately become neurilemma cells (*lemnocytes*). As already stated, these play some part in the formation of myelin and may be considered as a peripheral type of neuroglia, perhaps most closely related to oligodendroglia (Penfield).

Besides the spinal ganglia there are other peripheral aggregations of nerve cells known

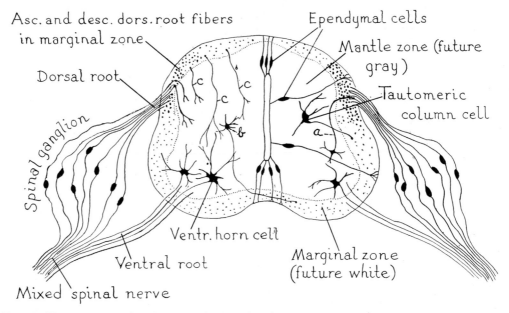

FIG. 67. Transverse section through spinal cord and spinal ganglia of an embryo chick. Silver impregnation. *a*, efferent fiber leaving by dorsal root; *b*, heteromeric column cell; *c*, collateral.

formation of the marginal layer (Figs. 69, 67). The peripheral processes continue as afferent or sensory fibers to terminate in

as *autonomic* or *sympathetic* ganglia. Arising in part probably from the neural crest, in part migrating from the ventral part of the cord along the ventral roots, these cells form two ganglionic chains on the ventro-lateral aspect of the vertebral column (verte-

probable that in mammals at least, both neural crest and cord contribute to such formation. It has been reasoned that inas-

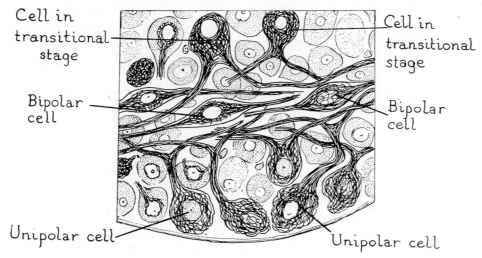

FIG. 68. Section through spinal ganglion of twelve days chick embryo. Reduced silver stain. (After Cajal.)

bral sympathetic ganglia). Others wander still further to form the ganglia of the mesenteric plexuses (collateral or preverte-bral ganglia), while still others actually invade the walls of the viscera or settle close to them as the terminal or peripheral sympathetic ganglia. Here too differentia-tion occurs along several directions. Some enlarge to form the multipolar sympathetic ganglion cells whose axons terminate in visceral effectors, smooth muscle, heart muscle and glandular epithelium. Others as in the case of the spinal ganglia, give rise to amphicytes which envelop the bodies of one or several ganglion cells. Finally, there are some which differentiate into the chro-maffin cells found in the adrenal medulla, carotid bodies and other portions of the body.

The origin of the autonomic ganglia is still in dispute. While some believe they are formed from the neural crest (Müller and Ingvar, Detwiler), others maintain that the largest part is derived from the ventral part of the spinal cord, the cells migrating by way of the ventral roots (Kuntz). It is

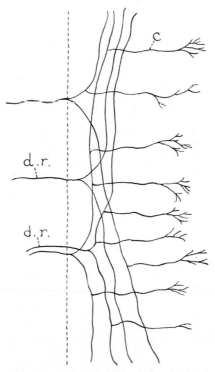

FIG. 69. Dorsal root fibers (d.r.) entering cord and bifurcating into ascending and descending arms. c, collateral terminating in gray of spinal cord. Eight days chick embryo. Silver impreg-nation.

much as the sympathetic cells are efferent in character their origin would most likely be from the efferent part of the spinal cord, i.e. the ventral horn. It must be remembered, however, that efferent fibers have been demonstrated in the dorsal roots of many animals, and that some afferent fibers

nerve elements. With the differentiation of the various types of nerve cells, there is established in early stages of development a neuronal mechanism adequate for complete if simple reflex arcs and consisting of afferent, intermediate and efferent neurons and their peripheral extensions. However, the

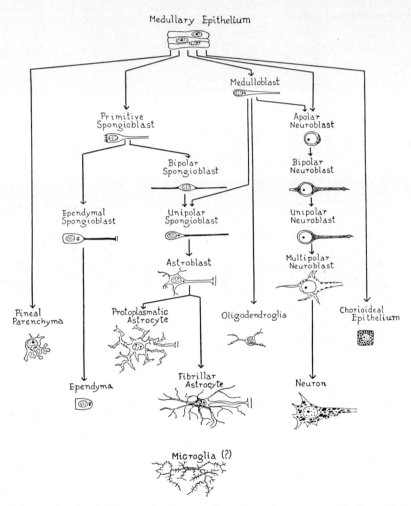

FIG. 70. Schema showing histogenesis of neuroglia cells and neurons. (Bailey and Cushing)

may enter the cord through the ventral roots (Foerster and Gagel).

In recent years some evidence has been presented that the enteric and perivascular sympathetic plexuses are not of ectodermal origin at all, but are derived from the splanchnopleuric mesoderm (Szantroch).

Segmental arrangement of the peripheral

synaptic junctions of these cells which would make such an arc functional are as yet unformed.

In embryos of about 10 mm, the various components of the peripheral nervous system are already laid down and may be recognized in a transverse section of any typical body segment (Fig. 71). The central processes of the spinal ganglion cells form the *dorsal roots,* the ventral root is composed of axons from cells in the ventral gray of the spinal cord (mantle layer). Distal to the ganglion, the ventral root unites with the peripheral processes of the ganglion cells to form the mixed *spinal nerve* which now contains

tinguished: somatic efferent, somatic afferent, visceral efferent and visceral afferent, all of these types being found in both dorsal and ventral rami. The somatic efferent or "motor" fibers arise from large cells in the ventral gray matter, pass out through the ventral roots and go directly to

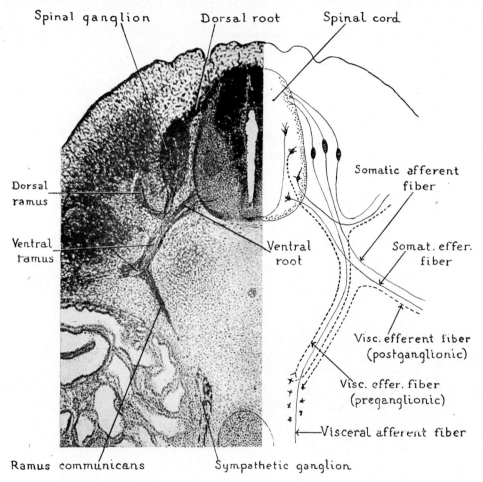

FIG. 71. Transverse section through 14 mm. pig embryo. Bielschowsky's silver stain. Photograph

afferent and efferent fibers. Each spinal nerve divides into a *dorsal* and a *ventral ramus,* and also sends a fiber bundle known as the *ramus communicans* to the vertebral sympathetic chain. The dorsal ramus supplies the muscles and skin of the back, the larger ventral one goes to the ventrolateral parts of the body wall. Four functional types of peripheral nerve fibers may be dis-

the striped voluntary muscles of the body wall. The somatic afferent or "sensory" fibers are the peripheral processes of spinal ganglion cells, which terminate as receptors in the skin and deeper portions of the body wall. The central processes enter the cord as dorsal root fibers.

The efferent innervation of visceral structures is somewhat different from that of the somatic muscles, for two neurons are always involved in the conduction of impulses from the central nervous system to the effector organs (Fig. 71). The *preganglionic visceral efferent* fibers are axons from cells of the spinal cord which pass through the ventral root and ramus communicans to terminate in a vertebral or prevertebral sympathetic ganglion. The axons of sympathetic cells then form the *postganglionic visceral efferent* fibers which course through the ramus communicans in the reverse direction, join the main branches of the spinal nerve and are distributed to the smooth muscle and glandular epithelium of the body wall. In the adult the ramus communicans is seen to consist of a white and a gray portion. The former contains the *myelinated* preganglionic fibers, the latter the *unmyelinated* postganglionic fibers.

Finally, there are the *visceral afferent* fibers which bring in impulses from the thoracic and abdominal viscera. Like the somatic afferent ones, they have their cell bodies in the spinal ganglia and enter the cord through the dorsal root.

CHAPTER VI

THE PERIPHERAL NERVES AND THEIR GANGLIA

The spinal cord is connected with the various parts of the body by 31 pairs of segmentally arranged spinal nerves: eight cervical, twelve thoracic, five lumbar, five sacral and usually one coccygeal. The first cervical nerve emerges between the occipital bone and the atlas, the eighth cervical between the seventh cervical and first thoracic vertebrae. Below this each spinal nerve emerges from the intervertebral foramen between its own and the next lower vertebra (Fig. 105).

Each spinal nerve arises from the cord by two roots, a dorsal afferent and a ventral efferent one. The two roots traverse the dural sac, penetrate the dura and reach the intervertebral foramen where the dorsal root swells into the spinal ganglion which contains the cells of origin of the afferent fibers (Figs. 72, 77). Distal to the ganglion, the dorsal and ventral roots unite and emerge from the intervertebral foramen as the *mixed spinal nerve* or *common nerve trunk*, which now contains both afferent and efferent fibers. The dorsal roots are, as a rule, stouter than the ventral ones and vary with the size of their respective ganglia. The only exception is the first cervical nerve whose dorsal root is greatly reduced and often missing altogether.

Each dorsal root is composed of myelinated and unmyelinated fibers which vary in caliber from 2–20 micra. The larger myelinated fibers, 10–20 micra in thickness, are sensory fibers from muscles and tendons and from tactile receptors, while the finer myelinated and the unmyelinated ones are believed to be mainly concerned with the conduction of temperature and pain. Though mainly afferent in character, there is evidence that some efferent fibers from cells of the spinal cord also pass through the dorsal roots (Fig. 67), and join the spinal nerves as vasodilators of the cutaneous blood vessels (Cajal, Kahr and Sheehan, Young and Zuckerman).

The ventral root is composed of large and small myelinated fibers originating from cells in the ventral and lateral horns of the spinal cord. The large ones are somatic motor fibers going to striped muscle. The smaller ones are preganglionic fibers from spinal cord to sympathetic ganglia (Fig. 73). These fibers are found only in the thoracic, upper lumbar and some sacral roots. In the cervical and lower lumbar nerves the ventral roots contain only the large somatic fibers. According to Foerster and Gagel (1933), some finely myelinated and unmyelinated *afferent* fibers enter the cord through the ventral roots. They are in part processes of spinal ganglion cells and may be concerned with the conduction of painful impulses.

The spinal nerve. After fusion of the dorsal and ventral roots, the common nerve trunk divides into four branches or rami: dorsal ramus, ventral ramus, meningeal ramus, and ramus communicans (Figs. 72, 71). The dorsal rami supply the muscles and skin of the back, the larger ventral ones innervate the ventrolateral portion of the body wall and all the extremities. The ramus communicans connects the common spinal trunk with the sympathetic ganglia and consists of a white and a gray portion. The former contains the myelinated preganglionic fibers from cord to sympathetic ganglion, the latter the unmyelinated postganglionic fibers which join the dorsal and ventral rami to be distributed to the body wall. In the white rami are also afferent fibers from the viscera whose cell bodies are situated in the spinal ganglia (Fig. 71).

The meningeal branch is a small nerve trunk which usually arises by several twigs from both the common trunk and the ramus

The dorsal and ventral rami divide into superficial (cutaneous) and deep (muscular) peripheral nerves. These nerve trunks

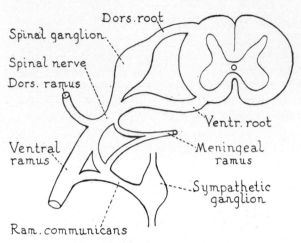

FIG. 72. Diagram of a spinal nerve.

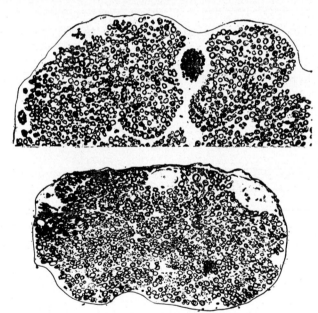

FIG. 73. Sections of lumbar (upper figure) and thoracic ventral rootlets. Weigert's myelin stain. Photograph. Same magnification for both sections. The lumbar root is composed almost entirely of coarse nerve fibers. In the thoracic root, the coarse fibers are somewhat smaller than in the lumbar root and there are in addition numerous fine myelinated preganglionic autonomic fibers. The greater caliber of the coarse fibers of the lumbar root is related to the greater length and larger cell bodies of the somatic motor neurons innervating the muscles of the lower extremity as compared with those innervating the muscles of the trunk.

communicans (Fig. 72). It reënters the intervertebral foramen to supply the meninges and vertebral column.

branch repeatedly and become progressively smaller as they extend toward the periphery, ultimately breaking up into individual nerve fibers which terminate in their respective receptors or effectors. The cutaneous nerves are composed mainly of sensory fibers of various size, but also contain efferent vasomotor, pilomotor and secretory fibers for the blood vessels, hair and glands of the skin. In the muscular nerves there is a greater mixture of sensory and motor fibers. There are somatic motor for the striped muscle fibers, vasomotor for the blood vessels, and numerous afferent fibers from the receptors in muscle, tendon and bone. Thus in each peripheral nerve there are fibers of various categories, myelinated and

the cervical and lumbosacral ventral rami branch and anastomose to form the cervical, brachial and lumbosacral plexuses. In these plexuses a regrouping of fibers occurs, and each of the peripheral nerves which arise from them now contains contributions from two or three or even four ventral rami. The peripheral nerves are therefore "mixed" in a double sense, consisting not only of afferent and efferent fibers, but also of fibers which come from several segments of the spinal cord.

Morphologically each peripheral nerve consists of parallel running nerve fibers in-

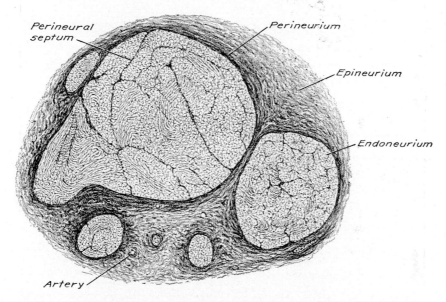

FIG. 74. Cross section of sciatic nerve of monkey. (Bailey's Histology)

unmyelinated, large and small, sensory and motor, which can not be morphologically distinguished from each other (Figs. 75, 76).

While each spinal nerve in a general way supplies its own body segment, there is considerable intermixture and "anastomosis" of adjacent nerve trunks. The dorsal rami remain relatively distinct, though even here interconnections between rami of adjacent segments are common in the cervical and sacral regions. The ventral rami, however, form more extensive connections. With the exception of the thoracic nerves which retain their segmental distribution,

vested by a thick sheath of rather loose connective tissue, the *epineurium* (Fig. 74). From this sheath septa extend into the interior and divide the fibers into bundles or *fascicles* of varying size, each of which is surrounded by a fairly distinct perifascicular sheath or *perineurium*. These fascicles do not run like isolated cables but may split at acute angles and connect with adjacent fascicles for an interchange of fibers. As a result, the fascicular arrangement varies in different portions of the nerve.

From the perineurium delicate strands invade the bundle as intrafascicular connective tissue or *endoneurium*. This separates the fibers into smaller and smaller bundles and ultimately invests each fiber as a delicate tubular membrane, the *sheath of Henle*. In the epineurial and perineurial connective tissue are blood vessels and spaces lined with endothelium which communicate with lymph channels within the fascicle.

On emerging from the spinal cord, the dorsal and ventral roots receive an investment of connective tissue as they pass

initiated by stimulation of the areas supplied by that root. Owing to the overlapping distribution of fibers of adjacent roots, the anesthesia may not be marked unless two or more contiguous roots are cut. The areflexia is not only a loss of the superficial and deep kinetic reflexes but also of the tonic proprioceptive ones, resulting in a diminution of tone (hypotonia) in the muscles affected. Also, failure of impulses from the muscles to reach the higher cerebellar and

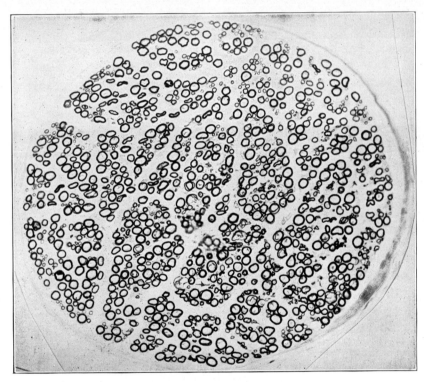

Fig. 75. Transverse section of a fasciculus from the sciatic nerve of a cat. Osmic acid. From a eparation of S. W. Ranson. Large and small myelinated fibers are shown.

through the pia. This is reinforced by additional connective tissue as they pass through the arachnoid and dura, the latter becoming continuous with the epineurium of the spinal nerve.

Functional considerations. Injury to the spinal nerves or their peripheral branches will naturally cause disturbances of sensation and movement. Section of a dorsal root produces a loss of all sensation (anesthesia) and loss of all reflexes (areflexia)

cortical centers results in irregularity or incoördination of movement usually termed *ataxia*.

The various activities of the central nervous system can only take effect by impulses passing through the efferent peripheral neurons, somatic and visceral, whose axons form the ventral roots. These neurons, also known as the *lower motor neurons*, constitute the *final common pathway* (Sherrington).

Destruction of the ventral roots produces a complete paralysis of reflex and voluntary movement with loss of tone (flaccidity) and degenerative atrophy of the striped muscle fibers affected. The muscle also shows certain changes in its reaction to electrical stimulation, these changes con-

the circuit, and normally it is the application of the negative pole or cathode which produces the strongest contraction on closing the current. In the complete reaction of degeneration which appears 10–14 days after the injury, the muscle no longer reacts to faradic or galvanic stimulation when

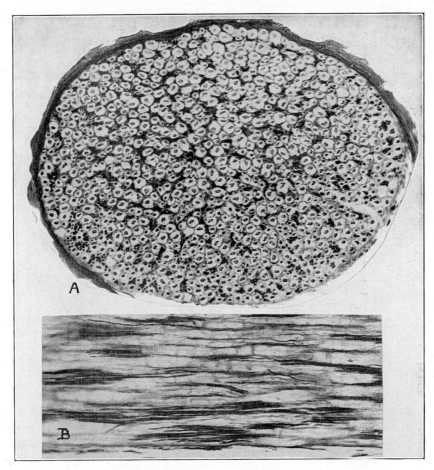

Fig. 76. Transverse (A) and longitudinal (B) sections of parts of the sciatic nerve of a sympathectomized cat. Ranson's silver pyridin stain. From a preparation by S. W. Ranson. The myelinated fibers appear as brown dots in A and bands in B surrounded by clear spaces (myelin sheaths). Besides, there are a great number of deeply stained fine unmyelinated fibers not seen in Fig. 75. As the sympathetic ganglia had previously been removed, these are not postganglionic fibers but are peripheral processes of small spinal ganglion cells.

stituting the *reaction of degeneration* (R D). Healthy muscle responds to stimulation by both the faradic (interrupted) and galvanic (continuous) current. In faradic stimulation the response lasts as long as the stimulus is applied. In galvanic stimulation the response occurs only on closing or opening

applied to its motor nerve. However, it still responds to direct stimulation with the galvanic current by sluggish wave-like contractions, but now it is the positive pole or anode which induces the strongest response on closing the current.

If preganglionic visceral fibers are also

involved, as in the case of the thoracic and upper lumbar roots, there will be vasomotor (and trophic) disturbances expressed by dryness and cyanosis of the skin.

Section of the mixed spinal nerve immediately after union of the dorsal and ventral roots will naturally cause combined symptoms of muscular paralysis and sensory loss in the affected area. In the case of the peripheral nerves a knowledge of the exact distribution of each nerve is essential for an understanding of the sensory and motor defects resulting from injury to such nerve.

autonomic ganglia. The structure of the latter is described in the chapter on the Autonomic Nervous System.

The *spinal ganglia* are aggregations of nerve cells appearing as spindle-shaped swellings on the dorsal roots (Figs. 77, 104). Each ganglion is surrounded by a connective tissue capsule continuous with the epineurium and perineurium of the spinal nerves. From this capsule trabeculae extend into the interior and form a connective tissue framework which contains the blood vessels and surrounds the nerve cells and their

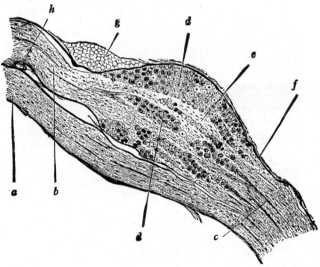

Fig. 77. Longitudinal section through spinal ganglion. (Stöhr.) *a*, ventral root; *b*, dorsal root; *c*, spinal nerve; *d*, groups of ganglion cells; *e*, nerve fibers; *f*, capsule; *g*, fat; *h*, blood vessel.

Since familiarity with the structure of the spinal cord will aid in understanding the formation and composition of the more complex spinal nerves, a full account of peripheral innervation is given in Ch. X.

THE SPINAL GANGLIA

The spinal and autonomic ganglia are part of the peripheral nervous system and contribute fibers to the peripheral nerves. The majority if not all of the afferent fibers, both somatic and visceral, have their cell bodies in the spinal ganglia, while all the efferent visceral fibers which go directly to visceral muscle and glandular epithelium wherever found, are axons of cells in the

processes. The nerve cells themselves are separated into irregular groups by bundles of nerve fibers which run through the long axis and constitute the central and peripheral processes of the ganglion cells.

The majority of the ganglion cells are unipolar cells of irregularly ovoid or spherical shape, which vary tremendously in size, from less than 20 micra for the smallest to over 100 micra for the largest. Each ganglion cell is surrounded by a capsule of flat, concentrically arranged cells, the inner ones of which are probably derived from the ectodermal cells of the neural crest and are known as amphicytes (Figs. 78, 81). This capsule extends over the emerging

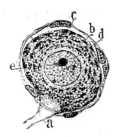

FIG. 78. Unipolar cell from spinal ganglion of rabbit with capsule and concentrically arranged Nissl bodies. (After Cajal.) *a*, axon; *b*, perinuclear zone free from Nissl bodies; *c*, capsule cell (amphicyte); *d*, nucleus; *e*, nucleolus.

of a glomerulus. Then the process straightens out, extends deeper into the ganglion and bifurcates into a central process which enters the cord through the dorsal root, and a peripheral one which becomes an afferent fiber of the peripheral nerve. The glomeruli are most complex and conspicuous in the axons of the large cells (Figs. 80, 81). In the unmyelinated axons of the small cells they are reduced or altogether lacking. It is evident from the above that the longitudinal fiber bundles of the

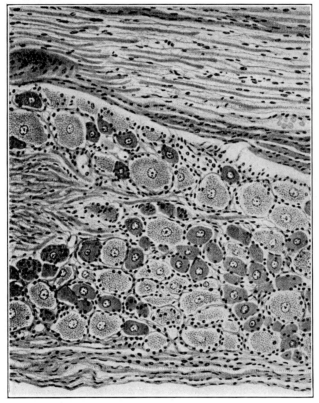

FIG. 79. Section of human spinal ganglion. Hematoxylin-eosin stain. The cells are of two types, a large clear type with well marked Nissl bodies and a smaller, more darkly staining type ("obscure cells"). The nuclei of the capsule cells are also seen. (Ph. Stoehr, Jr., from v. Moellendorff's Handbuch der mikroskopischen Anatomie des Menschen.)

process and becomes continuous with the neurilemma sheath of that fiber. The single process has always the structure of an axon and if myelinated acquires a medullary sheath soon after leaving the cell. It winds and coils about itself in an intricate manner near the cell body, resembling the structure

ganglion consist of myelinated and unmyelinated processes of spinal ganglion cells, which run centrally into the cord, and peripherally into the spinal nerve.

As a result of careful studies with methylene blue and reduced silver stains, many types of ganglion cells have been distinguished on the basis of size, shape, distribution of chromophilic bodies and types of processes (Dogiel, Hirt, Warrington, Ranson). Of these the large *clear cells* and the small *obscure cells* form the main which then unite again into a single process. Or a number of processes may arise from the cell, anastomose with one another and then give rise to a single process. In some of the cells the process may give off collaterals

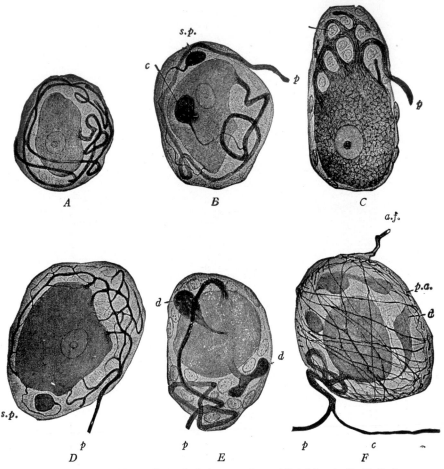

FIG. 80. Cerebrospinal ganglion cells and their capsules. (Cajal.) *A, B, E, F*, from man; *C*, from dog; *D*, from ass. *A*, cell with glomerulus; *B*, cell with main process giving off collaterals ending in bulbs; *C*, "fenestrated" cell with several processes uniting to form main process; *D*, more complicated form of same; *E, F*, cells with short bulbous dendrites. *F* is enveloped by pericellular arborization (*pa*) of fibers (*af*) terminating around cell. *c*, collateral; *d*, dendrite; *p*, main process. Cajal's silver stain.

types (Warrington). The former are light staining cells with vesicular nuclei and fine chromophilic bodies (Fig. 79). Usually considered as the typical spinal ganglion cells, they constitute less than 30 per cent of the total number. The axons of these cells form the glomeruli described above, but many variations occur (Fig. 80). The axon may split into a number of processes which terminate in the ganglion by end bulbs or other terminal arborizations. The axons of these larger cells are probably all myelinated.

The *obscure* cells are smaller, stain more deeply and diffusely and comprise about 50–75 per cent of the ganglion cells (Figs. 79, 81). The fibers of some of these also may give off collaterals which end in bulb-

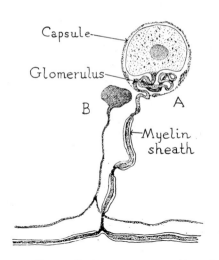

FIG. 81. Two cells from vagus ganglion of cat. Ehrlich's methylene blue. (After Cajal.) *A*, large clear cell; *B*, small "obscure" cell with deeply staining cytoplasm.

shaped terminations within the ganglion. The obscure cells supply in considerable part the fine unmyelinated fibers which are concerned with the transmission of impulses of a painful and possibly otherwise affective character. These fibers remain intact after the postganglionic efferent fibers, also unmyelinated, have been removed by destruction of the sympathetic ganglia from which they arise (Fig. 76).

Besides the cells described, there are others whose peripheral process does not join the spinal nerve but terminates by arborizations or end bulbs within the ganglion or its sheath or in the neighborhood of the dorsal roots, resembling certain peripheral sensory endings. Bipolar cells are occasionally observed, and also small multipolar cells whose significance is obscure.

CHAPTER VII

PERIPHERAL TERMINATIONS OF AFFERENT AND EFFERENT NERVE FIBERS

TERMINATION IN RECEPTORS

Those parts of the body which are excitable to stimuli and contain the terminations of the afferent peripheral nerve fibers are known as *receptors*. They have the general function of transforming various kinds of physical and chemical changes affecting them into nerve impulses and there is considerable evidence that each receptor is activated by only one particular kind of physical or chemical change. In other words, it lowers the threshold to one kind of stimulus and raises it to all others. The nature of the reaction naturally also depends on the central connections of the afferent fibers to which the receptors are related and on the effectors with which they are ultimately connected. However, the capacity of reacting differently to different kinds of stimuli depends primarily on the analytic capacity of the receptors.

The receptors and their associated modalities of sensation have been classified in several more or less overlapping ways. (1) Topographically, many kinds of receptors are found more or less profusely distributed over all parts of the body, and collectively represent *general somesthetic sensibility* (body sense). They include the receptors for touch, pressure, pain, temperature, sense of position and movement, and visceral sense. Others comprising smell, taste, sight, hearing, and head position and movements are found only in certain parts of the head and constitute the *organs of special sense*.

(2) Sherrington (1906) has classified all receptors into three main groups: *exteroceptors, proprioceptors* and *interoceptors*. The exteroceptors, situated on the external surface of the body, receive impressions from the outside which result in somatic movements. They include touch, light pressure, cutaneous pain and temperature, smell, sight and hearing. Some of these are *contact receptors*; others, such as smell, sight, hearing and part of temperature, are stimulated by distant objects and are known as *teloreceptors* or *teleceptors*. It is possible that deeply acting agencies as radium emanations, X-rays and diathermy which directly affect the tissues may be partly picked up by some of these receptors.

The proprioceptors receive stimuli from the deeper portions of the body wall, especially from the muscles, tendons and joints, and give rise to sensations of position and movement. Since they are primarily concerned with the regulation of movement in response to exteroceptive stimuli, the proprioceptors and exteroceptors may be grouped together as somatic receptors or *somatoceptors*. The deeper portion of the body wall also contains receptors for deep pain and pressure.

The interoceptors are the visceral sense organs receiving internal impressions and concerned with the visceral activities of digestion, excretion, circulation, etc., which are primarily under control of the autonomic system. They give rise to sensations of taste, visceral pain and temperature and to the more obscure forms of visceral sensibility such as hunger, thirst, sexual feeling and to the general feelings of well-being or of *malaise*. Smell, though not interoceptive, has close visceral affiliations and may be in part at least considered as visceral.

(3) Sensibility may also be divided into *superficial* and *deep*. The former obviously coincides with exteroceptive sense, the

latter comprises both interoceptive and proprioceptive, including also deep pressure. A special form of sensation is the ability of recognizing the vibrations of a tuning fork applied to bone or of a faradic current to the skin. This is usually known as *vibratory sense*. The nature of its receptors is not known.

(4) An analysis of sensation, important from a clinical and comparative viewpoint, was introduced by Head (1905). He distinguishes two systems in sensibility, one *protopathic* or affective, the other *epicritic* or discriminative, and believes that the two have their separate receptors, at least for the cutaneous innervation. Protopathic sensation is of a marked affective character, agreeable or disagreeable, but gives little information of the nature or exact location of the stimulus. In epicritic sensibility, the discriminative element predominates. The stimulus is accurately localized, two points simultaneously applied are properly discriminated and variations in intensity of stimuli are appreciated. Affective sensations are primarily related to reactions which most directly involve bodily welfare and in which there is reason to suppose that the thalamus plays an important part. They are consequently often termed *vital* or *thalamic*. Discriminative sensibility forms the basis for the complex associative and cognitive reactions of the cerebral cortex, hence it is called *gnostic* or *cortical*. In a general way, pain, temperature, visceral sensibility and part of touch are predominantly affective, while part of touch and the proprioceptive and teleceptive sensibilities are predominantly discriminative. From neither category is one or the other element entirely absent.

Structurally the modes of termination of afferent fibers in receptors are extremely varied and often of a very complicated character. They may be classified into two main groups: (a) the *free* or *diffuse* endings, and (b) the *encapsulated* endings

which are enclosed in a connective tissue capsule.

The **free nerve endings** are the most widely distributed in the body. They are most numerous in the skin, but are also found in the mucous and serous membranes, in muscle and in the connective tissue of many visceral organs. The skin is supplied by many cutaneous nerve trunks composed of myelinated and unmyelinated fibers. Some of the myelinated fibers are large and are destined for the encapsulated organs described below, but the majority have a relatively small caliber. The fibers of these small nerve trunks separate as they approach the epidermis, lose their myelin

Fig. 82. Sensory nerve terminations in corneal epithelium. (Cajal.)

sheath, undergo branching and form extensive unmyelinated plexuses in the deeper portion of the dermis, and immediately beneath the epidermis (Fig. 83). From this sub-epithelial plexus, delicate fibers penetrate the epithelium, divide repeatedly and form an end arborization of delicate terminal fibrils which wind vertically through the epidermis and end in small knob-like thickenings, often within the cytoplasm of the epithelial cells (Figs. 82, 83). In the cornea, which has no horny layer, these intraepithelial endings may reach the surface, but in other portions of the skin they do not extend beyond the germinative layer. Intraepithelial endings are also found in mucous membranes which are lined by stratified epithelium, as the eosophagus and bladder, and probably in many simple columnar epithelia as well.

Other nerve fibers form unmyelinated arborizations or terminal nets in the connective tissue of the dermis. There is some evidence that the intraepithelial endings are derived from fine myelinated fibers, while the subepidermal arborizations and plexiform nets are in the main terminals of unmyelinated ones (Woollard). Diffuse

them "smooth muscle spindles" (Fig. 84). They are endings of medium sized or large myelinated fibers and may perhaps initiate proprioceptive bronchial reflexes.

An important type of diffuse cutaneous receptors is represented by the *peritrichial* endings of the hair follicles, which are activated by the movements of the hairs. They vary considerably in complexity and are best developed in the vibrissae of certain mammals. In the simpler forms several myelinated fibers approach the hair follicle

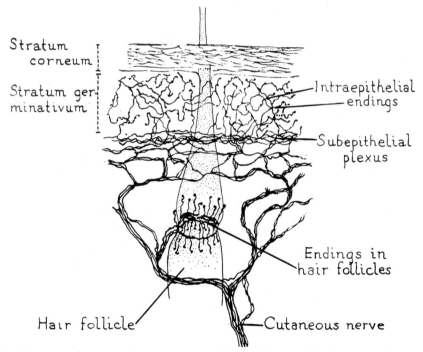

Stratum corneum

Stratum ger-minativum

Intraepithelial endings

Subepithelial plexus

Endings in hair follicles

Hair follicle

Cutaneous nerve

FIG. 83. Nerves and nerve endings in skin and hair follicles. (Modified from Retzius)

nerve endings in the form of nerve nets or arborizations of varying complexity are widely distributed through the visceral organs. They have been described in the serous membranes, heart, bronchial tree, alimentary canal and blood vessels (Fig. 84). They are also found in the chorioid plexuses of the brain and in striped muscle. They are for the larger part terminals of unmyelinated fibers. Complicated arborizations have been found in the smooth muscle of the bronchi by Larsell who terms

just below its sebaceous gland, lose their myelin sheath and divide in several branches which encircle the outer root-sheath (Fig. 83). From these spring numerous fine flattened fibers which run for a short distance upward and often also downward in the outer root-sheath and terminate in flattened or bulbous endings.

Besides the intraepithelial endings described above, which end among or within ordinary epithelial cells, there are found in the deeper portion of the germinative layer somewhat more specialized endings known as the *tactile discs* of Merkel (Fig. 85). Each consists of a concave neurofibrillar disc or meniscus closely applied to a single epithelial cell of modified structure. A single epidermal nerve fiber may by repeated

cells receiving sensory nerve endings is exemplified in various *neuroepithelial* cells which have special forms and show staining affinities similar to nerve cells. The specific cells of the taste buds (Fig. 86) and the hair cells in the sensory epithelia of the

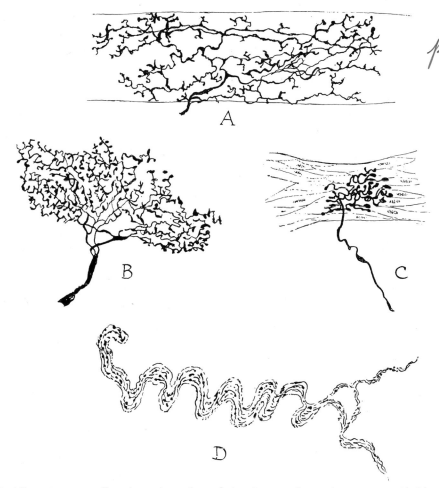

pain
non capsulated

FIG. 84. Afferent nerve endings in various visceral structures.   *A*, on a large pancreatic blood vessel. (After Castro.) *B*, in endocardium of dog. (After Smirnow.) *C*, in bronchial musculature of child. (After Larsell and Dow.) *D*, in longitudinal muscle coat of stomach of cat. (After Carpenter.)

branching give rise to a number of such discs. This type of termination is transitional to more specialized forms, such as the corpuscles of Grandry, found in the skin of birds. In these the flat tactile discs lie between two or more specialized epithelial cells.

The tendency to modification of epithelial

cochlear and vestibular apparatus are examples of such neuroepithelial cells.

Encapsulated endings.   These include the *tactile corpuscles of Meissner*, the *end bulbs*, the *Pacinian corpuscles*, the *corpuscles of Ruffini* and of *Golgi-Mazzoni*, the *neuromuscular spindles* and the *neurotendinous organs of Golgi*.

Touch

The *tactile corpuscles of Meissner* are elongated ovoid bodies, about 90–120 micra in length, which are found in the dermal papillae, close to the epidermis (Fig. 87). Each corpuscle is surrounded by a thin nucleated connective tissue sheath and the interior consists of many flattened epithelioid cells whose nuclei are placed transversely to the long axis of the corpuscle. From one to four myelinated nerve fibers

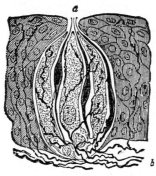

FIG. 85. Tactile discs in epithelium of pig's snout. (After Ranvier.)

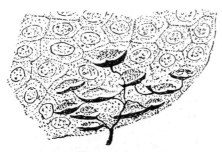

FIG. 86. Taste bud from circumvallate papilla of tongue. (Merkel-Henle.) *a*, taste pore; *b*, nerve fiber entering taste bud and ending upon neuroepithelial cells. On either side are some free intraepithelial endings.

supply each corpuscle. As each fiber enters, its connective tissue sheath becomes continuous with the fibrous capsule, the myelin sheath soon disappears and the naked axon winds spirally among the epithelioid cells, giving off numerous branches which likewise course spirally, show numerous varicosities and end in flattened neurofibrillar expansions. Besides the myelinated fibers, the corpuscles may also receive one or more fine unmyelinated fibers whose source is not

definitely known (Fig. 88). Meissner corpuscles occur mainly in the hairless portion of the skin and are most numerous on the volar surface of the fingers, toes, hands and feet. In lesser numbers they are also found

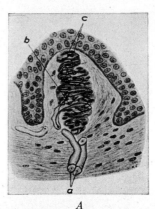

A

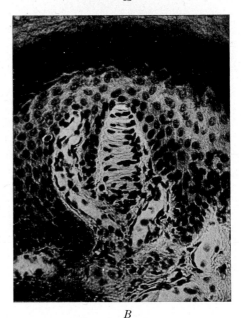

B

FIG. 87. *A*, Meissner's corpuscle from sole of human foot. (After Braus.) *a*, myelinated fibers; *b*, terminal arborization; *e*, end swellings. *B*, Meissner's corpuscle in dermal papilla of human finger tip. Photograph.

in the lips, eyelids, tip of tongue and volar surface of the forearm.

cold The *end bulbs* resemble the tactile corpuscles in structure and are spherical or ovoid bodies which vary greatly in dimension. The simplest and smallest ones are

Kraus's end bulbs cold.

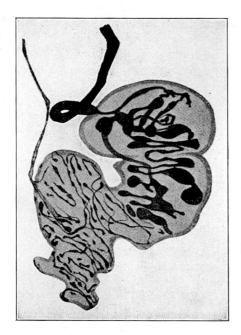

FIG. 88. Meissner's corpuscle showing termination of a large myelinated and a fine unmyelinated fiber. (Ruffini.)

nuclei may often be seen. One or more myelinated fibers lose their myelin on entering the capsule and give off numerous lateral branches which form a complicated terminal arborization. Some end bulbs may be compound. End bulbs of various form have a wide distribution, being found in the conjunctiva, mouth, tongue, epiglottis, nasal cavity, peritoneum and other serous membranes, lower end of rectum and external genitalia, especially the glans penis and clitoris. They are also found in tendons, ligaments and synovial membranes and in the connective tissue of nerve trunks.

The *Pacinian bodies* or *corpuscles of Vater-Pacini* are the largest and most widely distributed of the encapsulated receptors (Fig. 90). They are laminated, elliptical structures of whitish color, each supplied by a large myelinated fiber, and differ from the other encapsulated organs mainly in the greater development of their perineural

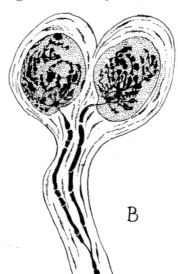

A

B

FIG. 89. *A*, end bulb of Krause from conjunctiva. (Dogiel.) *B*, compound corpuscle of Golgi-Mazzoni from the subcutaneous tissue of the finger tip. (Ruffini.)

found in the conjunctiva, the largest in the connective tissue of the external genitalia where they are also known as *genital corpuscles*. In its simplest form (Fig. 89 A) the end bulb consists of a nucleated capsule enclosing a soft gelatinous core in which

capsule. This capsule is formed by a large number of concentric lamellae, each lamella consisting of connective tissue fibers lined by a single layer of flattened cells. These lamellae, separated from each other by a clear semifluid substance, enclose a cylindrical core of protoplasm known as the inner bulb. As the nerve fiber reaches the corpuscle, its sheath of Henle becomes continuous with the capsule, the myelin sheath is lost and the naked axon extends through the length of the inner bulb, usually terminating in a knob-like perifibrillar expansion. Fine blood vessels accompany the nerve and branch within the lamellae but do not enter the inner bulb. According to Sokoloff, a fine unmyelinated fiber may also enter the corpuscle and arborize on the surface of the inner bulb.

The size of the Pacinian corpuscle varies within wide limits. The smallest may be

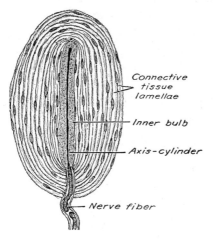

Connective
tissue
lamellae

Inner bulb

Axis-cylinder

Nerve fiber

FIG. 90. Human Pacinian corpuscle. (After Cajal, from Bailey's Histology.)

less than half a millimeter long, while the largest ones reach a length of 3 mm. and a diameter of 2 mm. The corpuscles are found in the subcutaneous tissue, especially of the hand and foot, in the peritoneum, pleura, mesenteries, penis, clitoris, urethra, nipple, mammary glands, pancreas and in the walls of many viscera. They are especially numerous in the periostium, ligaments and joint capsules, and also occur in the muscular septa and occasionally in the muscle itself.

Related to the Pacinian bodies are the lamellated *corpuscles of Golgi-Mazzoni*, found in the subcutaneous tissue of the fingers and on the surface of tendons (Fig. 89 B). They are ovoid bodies with lamellated capsules of varying thickness and a central core of granular protoplasm in which the single myelinated fiber which supplies the corpuscle forms a rich arborization with varicosities and terminal expansions. In the subcutaneous tissue of the finger tips are also found the *corpuscles of Ruffini*, elongated bodies of considerable size whose capsule encloses several bundles of connective tissue fibers. Several nerve fibers enter the corpuscle and ramify extensively, the branches lying between and partly encircling the small connective tissue bundles.

It is obvious that the different types of encapsulated receptors described above have a fundamentally similar structure, with numerous and often transitional variations as regards the size of the corpuscles and the complexity of the capsule and terminal ramification.

In the striped muscles there are found complicated nerve endings known as *neuro-muscular spindles* (Figs. 91, 92). Each spindle consists of a bundle of slender muscle fibers enclosed within a lamellated capsule and supplied with several nerve fibers which arborize in an exceedingly complicated manner (Fig. 92). The spindles may be simple or compound. The former are usually fusiform, thicker in the center and tapering toward the ends. The compound spindles show a number of dilations but also become pointed at the ends. Each spindle has its own blood and lymph supply.

The muscle fibers of the spindle, considerably thinner than ordinary muscle fibers, branch and anastomose like those of heart muscle. Each fiber shows a definite cross-striation except at one place, usually in the belly of the spindle, where the striations disappear and the fiber contains a closely packed mass of bubble-like structures. Each spindle is supplied with both sensory and motor endings which are spatially separated. Two or more myelinated fibers enter the spindle, their endoneurial sheaths becoming continuous with the fibrous capsule. The thicker sensory fibers divide dichotomously into secondary and tertiary branches. These then become closely applied to the muscle fibers, lose their myelin sheath and give rise to two types of endings. In one, the naked axons break up into a most extensive flower or ivy-like arborization consisting of varicosities connected by fine filaments. These

cross-striations are found. The perfect annulo-spiral endings described in the spindles of many mammals (Ruffini) are not characteristic for human muscle spindles, while the ivy-like endings are always present and show a truly remarkable complexity and extent.

The usually thinner motor fibers terminate in typical end plates situated at the poles of the spindles (p. 79). Each spindle contains also a number of fine unmyelinated fibers. Some are vasomotor fibers for the

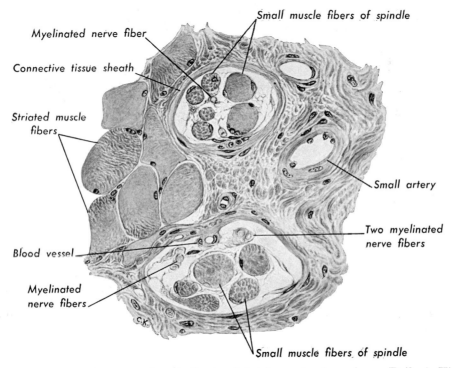

FIG. 91. Cross section of two muscle spindles in skeletal muscle of monkey. (Bailey's Histology)

"flower-sprays" (Ruffini) terminate on that portion of the muscle fiber which contains the bubble-like structures. In the other type of ending, the naked axons become flattened like ribbons and either wind spirally around the muscle fiber, terminating in free expansions, or the ribbon runs along one side of the muscle fiber and gives off band-like branches which like tendrils clasp the circumference of the muscle fibers. This "annulo-spiral" ending may terminate in portions of the spindle where normal

blood vessels of the spindle. The source and significance of the other fine fibers is not fully understood.

The recorded dimensions of human muscle spindles fluctuate enormously, the extremes for length being 0.05 to 13 mm. The more usual length is 2 to 4 mm. The spindles have been found in practically all muscles and are more numerous in the extremities than in the trunk. They are especially abundant in the small muscles of the eyes and distal portions of the extremities.

movement
position

The *neurotendinous organs of Golgi* are spindle-shaped structures most commonly found at the junction of muscle and tendon, but occasionally also in the muscular septa and sheaths (Fig. 93). They have been demonstrated in practically all muscles. The spindle consists of several tendon fascicles surrounded by a lamellated connective tissue capsule and, as a rule, supplied by one,

bundles, meanwhile giving off side branchlets which again repeatedly divide. All these terminal branches show numerous flat leaf-like expansions, the whole ramification appearing as a delicate net enveloping the tendon bundles. In man these spindles have a length of about 1.35 mm. and a thickness of about 200 micra.

Besides the neuromuscular and neurotendinous organs, muscle and tendon have a variety of other sensory structures: free nerve endings, end bulbs and Pacinian corpuscles. The latter are especially numerous in tendons.

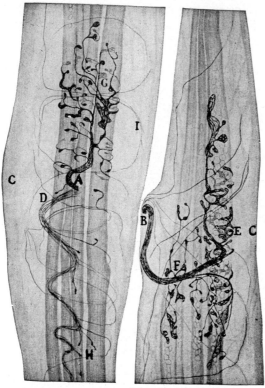

Fig. 92. Neuromuscular spindle in a human foetus of six months. (Tello.) *A*, coarse nerve fiber with arborescent (flower-spray) terminations at *G*; *B*, coarse fiber with spiral and annular terminations at *E* and *F*; *H*, motor fibers; *I*, fine unmyelinated fibers; *C*, connective tissue capsule.

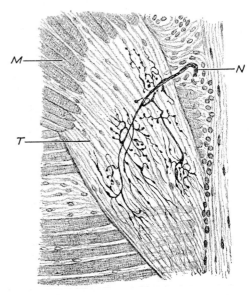

Fig. 93. Neurotendinous organ from six months human foetus. (After Tello.) *M*, muscle fibers; *N*, nerve fiber; *T*, tendon fibers.

occasionally two or three myelinated nerve fibers. On penetrating the spindle, the fiber loses its sheath of Henle which becomes continuous with the capsule, and divides into primary, secondary and tertiary branches which still retain their myelin sheath. The latter then split into numerous unmyelinated branches which wind between and around the primary tendon

Relation of receptors to sensory modalities.

It is generally maintained, though not proven conclusively, that each type of receptor is activated by only one kind of physical or chemical change and is hence associated with only one kind of sensory modality. The problem of relating the various receptors to their specific sensory modalities has been an exceedingly difficult one and many important details are still to be elucidated.

It seems probable that painful impulses

are received by the diffuse cutaneous end arborizations. Not only would their universal presence and unspecialized type indicate this but also their sole presence in places where stimuli give rise to pain only, such as the tympanic membrane of the ear, the cornea of the eye and the pulp of the teeth. Recent evidence suggests that the intraepithelial endings derived from fine myelinated fibers are related to sharply localized pain, while poorly localized pain is represented by the subepidermal terminations of unmyelinated fibers (Woollard). It is probable, however, that the intraepithelial fibers also mediate a low form of tactile sensibility (Waterston).

Touch is represented by the endings in hair follicles, Meissner's corpuscles and similar encapsulated organs, and probably also by the tactile discs and some other intraepithelial endings. The peritrichial endings stimulated by movements of the hair give rise to a sensibility quite delicate and discriminative yet having a marked affective tone. Shaving greatly reduces the sensibility to touch. On the hairless parts of the body tactile stimuli are received primarily by the corpuscles of Meissner which are probably the chief sense organs of discriminative touch.

The receptors for temperature are not known as well, but are probably end bulbs of various kinds and possibly also some diffuse endings. It is known that the margin of the cornea is sensitive only to cold and pain and is provided only with diffuse endings and end bulbs of Krause. Hence the latter and similar subcutaneous end bulbs are believed to be receptors for cold. In the same way, the corpuscles of Ruffini are considered as related to warmth. There is still much to be learned about the temperature receptors.

The different parts of the body surface vary considerably as to their capacity for affective and discriminative sensibility. The hands and fingers represent the highest development of the latter, being practically stalked sense organs for cortical sensibility. In other parts as the back, abdomen and especially the genitalia, affective sensibility predominates, to the partial exclusion of the other type.

The corpuscles of Pacini are both deep subcutaneous and visceral structures. Their form and position indicate that they are stimulated by deep or heavy pressure. This view is perhaps not negatived by their presence in the viscera where pressure produced by distension and spasm forms an important mode of visceral stimulation. It is probable that other lamellated corpuscles as those of Golgi-Mazzoni have a similar function.

The proprioceptive stimuli of position and movement, initiated by the constant or varying tension states of the voluntary muscles and their tendons and by the movements of the joints, are undoubtedly received by the muscle spindles and tendon organs and by the Pacinian corpuscles found in the joint capsules, ligaments and periosteum. The important proprioceptive kinetic and tonic reflexes and mnemonic reactions initiated by these stimuli have already been mentioned.

There is much that is still obscure about visceral sensibility. It is known that the viscera are insensitive to many mechanical and chemical stimuli, yet they may be the source of intense pain as well as of the organic sensations of hunger, thirst, etc. Visceral pain is mainly due to either distension or to abnormal contraction or spasm of the muscle coats. Hence the intramuscular diffuse nerve endings would appear to be the probable receptors for these stimuli. The blood vessels may also give rise to painful sensation, likewise due to muscular spasms in their walls and to the resulting stimulation of similar diffuse endings. The totality of stimuli which are constantly initiated by these diffuse visceral receptors during normal or abnormal organic functioning probably gives rise to the general affective sensibility of internal well-being or of *malaise*.

One peculiarity of visceral pain is that painful visceral stimuli are often "felt" in the corresponding segment or segments

which arise from cells of the various autonomic ganglia. These fibers supply the heart (cardiomotor), visceral muscle (visceromotor), blood vessels (vasomotor), hair (pilomotor) and glands (secretory). Pig-

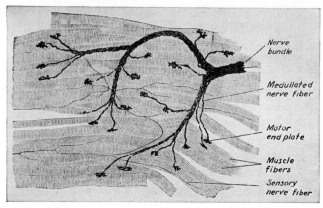

Fig. 94. Motor endings in intercostal muscle of rabbit. (After **v.** Moellendorf, from Bailey's Histology.)

of the external body wall, a phenomenon known as "referred pain". The most common explanation is that the unusual visceral stimuli are discharged into the same cord centers as the somatic ones. They then pass upward on the ascending pathways of the latter and thus produce the usual reactions to somatic stimuli from the segments involved. This passing over to a somatic path may, however, occur in the spinal ganglion by collaterals from visceral to somatic ganglion cells. If, as believed by some, there are afferent autonomic cells, the transfer may be effected by the fibers of such cells terminating around the somatic spinal ganglion cells.

TERMINATIONS IN EFFECTORS

The endings of the efferent peripheral fibers in the effector organs of the body fall into two groups: somatic efferent and visceral efferent. The somatic efferent are terminations of myelinated fibers whose cell bodies are situated in the ventral horn of the spinal cord and which go directly to the striped skeletal muscles. The visceral endings are terminals of unmyelinated fibers

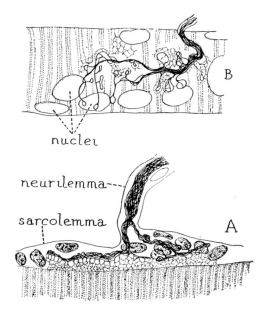

Fig. 95. *A*, motor end plate from superior oblique muscle of cat; *B*, motor end plate from tongue of bat. (After Boeke.)

ment cells and possibly the endothelium of capillaries may perhaps be also innervated by such autonomic fibers.

Somatic effectors. The somatic efferent fibers terminate in the striped muscle fibers in small flattened expansions of oval shape, known as the *motor end plates* (Fig. 94, 95).

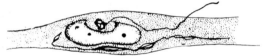

FIG. 96. Intraprotoplasmic ending of a nerve fiber in a smooth muscle fiber of the human ciliary muscle. (After Boeke.)

protoplasm, the *sole* of the plate, containing a number of light staining nuclei derived in part from the muscle, in part from the neurilemma.

Boeke and others have described small "accessory" motor end plates innervated by fine unmyelinated fibers. These may be placed within the sole of the larger end

FIG. 97. Motor nerve terminations in the smooth muscle bands of a bronchus. Rabbit. (Larsell). *tfi*, terminal fibrils.

They are 40–60 micra in length, about 40 micra in width and have a thickness of about 6–10 micra. The myelinated fibers in their course to the muscle repeatedly divide, and branch even more extensively within the muscle itself. In this manner a single nerve fiber may furnish end plates to a variable number of muscle fibers. Each of the terminal fibers on reaching the neurilemma suddenly loses its myelin sheath and the neurilemma becomes continuous with the sarcolemma. The naked axon enters the muscle fiber and immediately beneath the neurilemma forms a delicate localized arborization of flattened or club-shaped neurofibrillar terminals. This arborization is embedded in a mass of finely granular

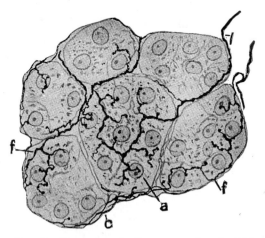

FIG. 98. Nerve terminations around and within acini of the pancreas of an adult mouse. (Castro). *c*, periacinous fibers; *f*, interepithelial and intraepithelial fibers.

plates or may be found as isolated structures underneath the sarcolemma. Their significance is not understood, but they are believed by some to be of autonomic origin.

As already stated, each nerve fiber may furnish motor plates for several or many muscle fibers. On the other hand, a single muscle fiber may be innervated by several nerve fibers, even by fibers from different segments of the spinal cord. These fibers may contribute to a single motor plate, or each may form its own separate ending.

Visceral effectors. The unmyelinated autonomic fibers which supply visceral muscle either end in simple arborizations, or first form extensive intramuscular plexuses from which the terminals arise. The terminal fibrils wind between the smooth muscle cells and end in small neurofibrillar thickenings or delicate loops on the surface or more probably within the protoplasm of the muscle fibers (Figs. 96, 97). Similar terminals arise from delicate plexuses which surround the tubules or acini of glands, pass between the cells and terminate in part at least within the cytoplasm of the glandular cells (Fig. 98).

CHAPTER VIII

THE MENINGES OF THE CENTRAL NERVOUS SYSTEM

The brain and spinal cord are enclosed by two connective tissue sheaths, the *dura mater* and *pia-arachnoid*, the latter being usually described as two separate membranes: the *pia mater* and *arachnoid* (Fig. 99). These membranes are collectively known as the meninges, the dura mater constituting the *pachymeninx* and the pia-arachnoid the *leptomeninx* or *leptomeninges*.

The **dura mater** is the outer sheath and consists of dense fibrous tissue. The *cerebral dura* serves both as an investing sheath for the brain and as periosteum for the inner surface of the cranium. It consists of two layers: (a) an inner layer of dense fibrous tissue lined on its brain surface with a single layer of flat cells; and (b) an outer layer much richer in blood vessels and nerves, which forms the periosteum. Between the two layers are situated the large venous sinuses of the brain. The *spinal dura* corresponds to the inner layer of the cerebral dura, the vertebrae having their own separate periosteum. Both inner and outer surface of the spinal dura are covered by a single layer of flat cells, and it is separated from the periosteum by the narrow *epidural space* in which are found anastomosing venous channels lying in areolar tissue rich in fat. It is maintained by some that the spinal dura contains lymphatics which open on both of its surfaces. Between the dura and the arachnoid is the capillary *subdural space* filled with fluid and believed to communicate by clefts with the tissue spaces in the sheaths of nerves and through them with the deep lymphatic vessels of the neck and groin. It has no direct communication with the subarachnoid space. The spinal dura is attached to the outer surface of the arachnoid by thread-like subdural trabeculae.

The nerve roots when penetrating the dura receive a dural investment which is continuous with the epineurium.

The spinal dura forms a closed sac which extends to the second or third sacral vertebra. Since the spinal cord ends at the caudal border of the first lumbar vertebra, the lower portion of the dural sac is occupied by the filum terminale and cauda equina (see p. 87). The caudal end of the dura fuses externally with the periosteum of the coccyx.

The cerebral dura gives off several reduplications or septa which tend to divide the cranial cavity into incomplete compartments (Fig. 103). The *falx cerebri* is a sickle-shaped median septum extending from the crista galli to the internal occipital protuberance and separating the two hemispheres. The *tentorium cerebelli* is a transverse, dorsally arched septum placed between the occipital lobes and the cerebellum. Its free anterior border forms the tentorial incisure through which the brain stem passes. From the midline of its under surface, a small sagittal septum, the *falx cerebelli*, incompletely separates the hemispheres of the cerebellum. The *diaphragma sellae* forms the fibrous roof of the pituitary fossa (sella turcica) and is perforated by the infundibulum (Fig. 103).

The **pia mater** closely invests the brain and spinal cord, extending in all the sulci and fissures, and protrudes into the ventricles in the chorioid plexuses where it is lined on its inner surface by a layer of neural chorioideal cells (see p. 47). It consists of fibrous connective tissue, rather rich in elastic fibers, which contains many fine nerve fibers, scattered pigment cells and numerous blood vessels which send perpendicular branches into the spinal cord and brain. These branches, in addition to their adventitial coats, may be accompanied for some distance by prolongations of pial tissue.

The spinal cord is anchored to the dura by two lateral septa which extend the whole length of the cord and are collectively known as the *ligamentum denticulatum* (Figs. 99,

where it fuses with its mate of the opposite side to continue as the covering of the *filum terminale* (see p. 87).

The **arachnoid** or outer portion of the pia-arachnoid is a delicate non-vascular membrane which passes over the sulci without dipping into them and extends for a short distance along the roots of the

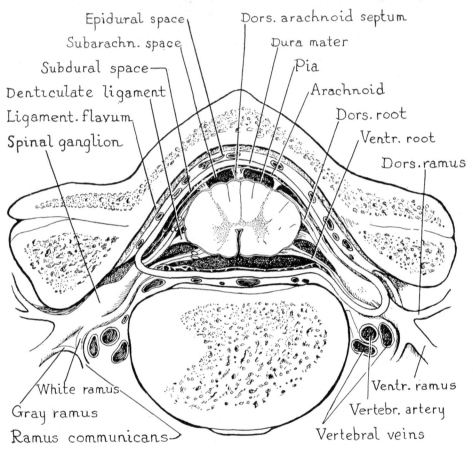

FIG. 99. Transverse section through first thoracic vertebra, showing spinal cord and its coverings. (After Rauber-Kopsch.)

104). Mesially each septum is continuously attached to the pia, but laterally it is broken up into 19–21 flat denticulate processes which are inserted in the dura (Fig. 104). The first process is given off above the first cervical nerve root, the last one just below the first lumbar. Below this each ligament continues as a narrow seam to the tip of the conus medullaris

cerebrospinal nerves and along the "optic nerve". It is partly separated from the pia by numerous spaces traversed by trabeculae which pass from pia to arachnoid. These are the *subarachnoid spaces* or *space* and may be regarded as dilations of pial spaces by which the embryologically single leptomeninx is transformed into the double incompletely separated pia-arachnoid.

They are thus intraleptomeningeal spaces. The subarachnoid spaces dip into the sulci of the brain and spinal cord. In the cerebral pia-arachnoid the subarachnoid spaces are traversed by numerous trabeculae and there is no clear distinction between pia and arachnoid (Fig. 101). In the spinal pia-arachnoid the trabeculae are few and usually concentrated into several subarachnoid septa, hence the subarachnoid space is a more continuous cavity and the arachnoid a more distinct membrane. The arachnoid, trabeculae and outer pial surface are all covered with a single layer of flattened cells with large pale oval nuclei.

along the interhemispheric fissure, in relation to the superior longitudinal sinus, but are also found along the other venous sinuses of the brain. Rudimentary arachnoid villi have been described in the spinal arachnoid, but their function is probably not the same (Hassin). In both the spinal and cerebral arachnoid, cell clusters are sometimes formed which become attached to the dura. These growths may become calcified or under abnormal conditions form the sites of neoplastic tumors. They are more frequent with advancing age.

The subarachnoid space is filled with cerebrospinal fluid and is in direct com-

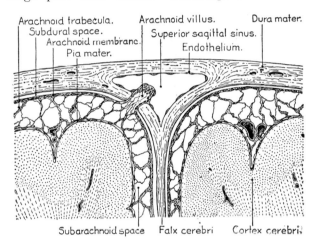

FIG. 100. Diagram of meninges surrounding cerebral cortex, showing relation of arachnoid villus to dural venous sinus. (Weed.)

When certain substances are injected in the subarachnoid space, these cells may swell and assume a phagocytic activity, ingesting particles of the foreign material. They may even become detached and form free macrophages.

In certain places the cerebral arachnoid sends prolongations into the dura, which protrude into a venous sinus or venous lacuna. These prolongations, into which extend the subarachnoid spaces and trabeculae, are likewise covered with an endothelial lining and form the *arachnoid villi* which when hypertrophied are known as *Pacchionian bodies* or *Pacchionian granulations* (Fig. 100). They are most numerous

munication with the fourth ventricle of the brain by means of three apertures, one median and two lateral ones. The median aperture or *foramen of Magendie* is placed in the caudal part of the thin roof, the lateral apertures or *foramina of Luschka* open into the lateral recesses of the ventricle (Fig. 169). As already stated, the arachnoid extends a distance along the cerebrospinal nerve roots and here the subarachnoid space becomes continuous with the tissue spaces of the nerve sheaths, which in turn communicate with lymphatics. The subarachnoid space also communicates with the tissue spaces within or around the blood vessels which penetrate the central nervous system from the pia. In the larger vessels these *perivascular spaces* or *spaces of Virchow-Robin* lie within the adventitia, being covered externally by prolongations of pial connective tissue. When the smaller neuronal clefts which surround the bodies of nerve cells (Weed), (Fig. 101). Through these channels waste substances produced by the nerve cells may pass out to the subarachnoid space.

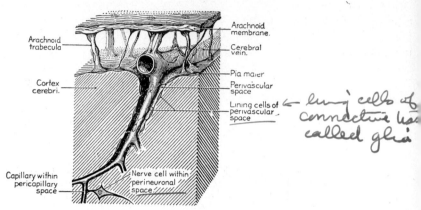

FIG. 101. Diagram of cerebral pia-arachnoid, showing relations of subarachnoid space, perivascular channels and nerve cells. (Weed.)

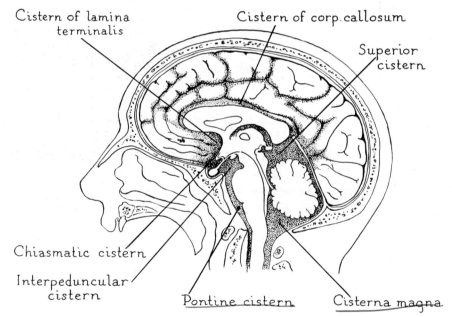

FIG. 102. Diagrammatic view of the main subarachnoid cisterns. (After Bailey.)

vessels are reached, the pial prolongations come to an end, and the perivascular spaces now lie between the vessel wall and the glial membrane. The spaces continue along the finer ramifications of the blood vessels, ultimately communicating with the peri- In the spinal canal there is always a relatively wide subarachnoid space between pia and arachnoid. Below the caudal tip of the spinal cord the space extends to the depth of the dural sac and here contains the filum terminale and descending lumbosacral nerve roots (cauda equina). This region is therefore most suitable for tapping the cerebrospinal fluid (lumbar puncture) since there is no likelihood of injury to the spinal cord. In the cranial cavity the extent of the subarachnoid space shows many local variations, owing to the irregular contour of the brain surface. Over the convex surfaces of the convolutions, the pia and arachnoid are close to each other with only a narrow space between them.

of the medulla to the ventral summit of the cerebellum, forming the large *cisterna magna (cerebello-medullaris)* into which open the foramina of Magendie and Luschka. Ventrally the medullary subarachnoid space widens into the *cisterna pontis*. The midbrain is completely surrounded by cisterns, dorsally by the *cisterna superior*, laterally by the *cisterna ambiens*, and ventrally by the *cisterna interpeduncularis* which extends laterally over the stem of the Sylvian fissure

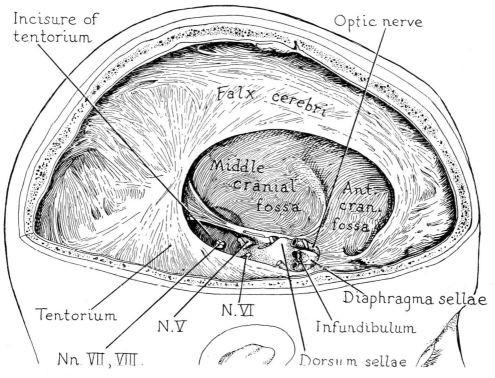

FIG. 103. Interior of cranial cavity after removal of brain, showing dural septa. (After Rauber-Kopsch.)

When passing over sulci the pia dips in while the arachnoid bridges over, hence the subarachnoid spaces are deeper. At the base of the brain and its transition to the spinal cord the arachnoid becomes widely separated from the pia in certain places, giving rise to large cavities, the *subarachnoid cisterns* (Fig. 102). The whole medulla has a rather wide subarachnoid space, but this is most extensive dorsally where the arachnoid passes from the dorsal surface

In front of the interpeduncular cistern is the *cisterna chiasmatica*, followed anteriorly and dorsally by cisterns along the lamina terminalis and the dorsal convex surface of the corpus callosum.

The **cerebrospinal fluid** is a clear colorless fluid apparently identical with the aqueous humor of the eye and other tissue fluids. Its specific gravity is about 1.004–1.007. It contains small amounts of protein and glucose, larger amounts of potassium and sodium chloride, and traces of sulfate, phosphate, calcium and uric acid. Normally a few lymphocytes, about 3–8 per cubic millimeter, are also found. The quantity of the fluid in the adult is around 80–200 cc., but there may be more extreme individual variations. The bulk of the fluid is formed by the activity of the chorioidal cells of the chorioid plexuses and telae and is poured into the ventricles of the brain from which it passes through the foramina of Magendie and Luschka to the cisterns and other subarachnoid spaces. A smaller amount is probably contributed by the nerve cells, the waste products of their metabolic activity reaching the subarachnoid space by way of the perineuronal and perivascular spaces. Whether ependyma and other neuroglia cells also contribute to its formation is not certain. The drainage of the fluid is principally by filtration through the wall of the arachnoid villi into the cerebral venous sinuses. The venous blood is hypertonic to the fluid and its pressure somewhat lower, hence the direction of the drainage is from subarachnoid space to venous channel. Some of the fluid also escapes by way of the perineuronal spaces into the sheaths of the spinal and cranial nerves, ultimately reaching lymphatics and lymph nodes.

The cerebrospinal fluid probably has a mechanical function, serving as a water cushion for the central nervous system and aiding in the maintenance of a relatively constant intracranial pressure. It also plays an important part in removing waste substances from the brain and spinal cord. Changes of the fluid in pathological states, both as to increase and nature of the cells found in it and its altered chemical composition, are of great importance in the diagnosis of many diseases of the nervous system. It is usually withdrawn by a lumbar puncture which taps the subarachnoid space of the cauda equina of the spinal cord. The same puncture is also used for the introduction of therapeutic agents. A block in the free passage of the cerebrospinal fluid from ventricles to subarachnoid space causes internal hydrocephalus.

CHAPTER IX

THE SPINAL CORD

The spinal cord surrounded by its coverings lies loosely in the vertebral canal, extending from the foramen magnum where it is continuous with the medulla oblongata to the lower border of the first lumbar vertebra (Figs. 104, 99). During early development the spinal cord extends to the lower end of the sacrum, but from the fourth month on the vertebral column elongates more rapidly than the cord. The latter, anchored above to the medulla oblongata, is pulled upward in the spinal canal, its caudal tip reaching the third lumbar vertebra at birth and the lower border of the first lumbar in the adult. Variations have been found, the spinal cord terminating as high as the twelfth thoracic or as low as the third lumbar vertebra. It is said to be slightly lower in woman.

The spinal cord is cylindrical in shape, somewhat flattened dorso-ventrally, especially in the cervical portion, and shows two spindle-shaped swellings, the *cervical* and *lumbar* enlargements, comprising those portions of the cord which innervate respectively the upper and lower extremities. In animals without typical limbs there are no enlargements, the spinal cord having a uniform diameter which gradually narrows in its caudal portions. Below the lumbar enlargement the cord rapidly narrows to a cone shaped termination, the *conus medullaris*, from which a slender filament, the *filum terminale*, extends downward to the fundus of the dural sac, at about the level of the second sacral vertebra (Fig. 104). There it penetrates the dura and, invested by a dural process, continues as the *filum durae matris* to the posterior surface of the coccyx to pass into the periosteum of the latter. A prolongation of the central canal of the spinal cord continues into the upper portion of the filum terminale which is otherwise composed mainly of pial connective tissue.

Though the spinal cord is intrinsically a continuous and unsegmented structure, the thirty-one pairs of nerves which arise from it produce an appearance of external segmentation. Each segment is that portion of the cord which furnishes dorsal and ventral root filaments to a single pair of nerves. On this basis there are thirty-one segments corresponding to the nerve pairs, eight cervical, twelve thoracic, five lumbar, five sacral and usually one coccygeal (Fig. 104). The first cervical nerve emerges between the atlas and the occipital bone.

During early development, the "segments" of the spinal cord correspond closely to the respective embryonal vertebrae, and the spinal nerves pass laterally to their intervertebral foramina. Later, when the vertebral column grows more rapidly than the cord, the latter is pulled upward, and the interval between the spinal origin of a nerve and its vertebral exit gradually increases in length. The result is that in the adult where the cord terminates at the lower border of the first lumbar vertebra, the lumbar and sacral nerves have long roots which descend in the dural sac to reach their respective intervertebral foramina (Fig. 104). This bundle of descending roots surrounding the filum terminale resembles a horse's tail and hence is known as the *cauda equina*. The exact relations of the spinal cord segments to the vertebral bodies and processes are shown in Fig. 105.

The length of the spinal cord from its upper limit to the tip of the conus terminalis is about 45 cm. in the male and 43 cm. in the female, contrasted to a length of about 70 cm. for the vertebral column. Its weight is about 35 grams. In the mid-thoracic region the transverse and sagittal diameters

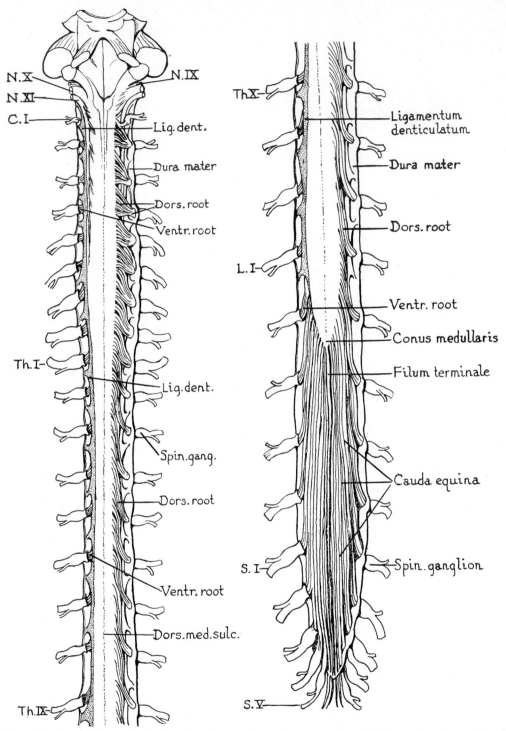

FIG. 104. Dorsal view of spinal cord with ganglia and nerve roots. The dorsal portion of the dura
mater has been removed to show the contents of the dural sac. On the left side the dorsal roots have
been cut to expose the denticulate ligament (*Lig. dent.*) and the ventral roots. The spinal nerves are
indicated by Roman numerals. *C*, cervical; *Th*, thoracic; *L*, lumbar; *S*, sacral. (After Leveillé, from
Hirschfeld's "Système Nerveux".)

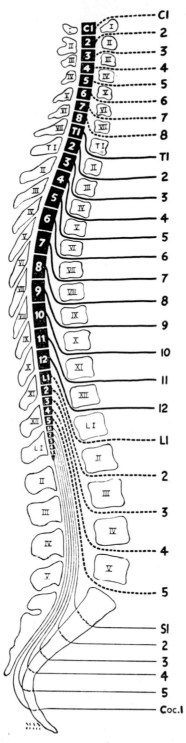

FIG. 105. Diagram of the position of the spinal cord segments with reference to the bodies and spinous processes of the vertebrae.   Note also the place of origin of the nerve roots from the spinal cord and their emergence from the corresponding intervertebral foramina.   (Haymaker and Woodhall.)

are about 10 mm. and 8 mm. respectively; in the cervical enlargement (sixth cervical) 13–14 mm. and 9 mm.; in the lumbar enlargement (third lumbar) about 12 mm. and 8.5 mm.

General topography. When freed from its meninges, the surface of the cord shows a number of longitudinal furrows (Figs. 106, 107). On the ventral side is the deep *ventral median fissure* which penetrates into the cord for a depth of some 3 mm. and into which extends a fold of the pia containing blood vessels. On the dorsal surface is the shallow *dorsal median sulcus*. This sulcus is continuous with a delicate glial partition, the *dorsal median septum*,

incompletely separated halves connected by a narrow median bridge or commissure.

In a transverse section the cord is seen to consist of a centrally placed gray substance surrounded everywhere by a mantle of white (Fig. 107). The latter is composed mainly of closely packed myelinated fibers and hence appears glistening white in the fresh condition. The central substance appears pinkish-gray because besides fibers it contains the numerous unmyelinated cell bodies, dendrites and terminal arborizations, and has a much richer blood supply. The gray substance forms a continuous deeply notched column extending the entire length of the cord (Fig. 106), which in

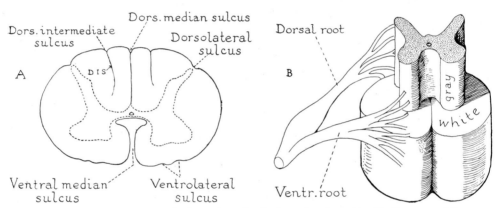

Fig. 106. *A*, section through cervical portion of spinal cord, schematic; *B*, diagram of the gray columns of the cord. *Dis*, dorsal intermediate septum.

which extends into the cord to a depth of 5 mm. and reaches the deep lying gray. More laterally are the *dorsolateral* and *ventrolateral sulci*. The former is a fairly distinct furrow into which the filaments of the dorsal roots enter in a rectilinear manner. The ventrolateral sulcus marks the exit of the ventral root fibers and is hardly distinguishable, since the ventral roots do not emerge rectilinearly but in groups of irregular filaments occupying an area of about 2 mm. in transverse diameter. In the cervical and upper thoracic cord another furrow, the *dorsal intermediate sulcus*, extends between the medial and lateral sulci. The ventral median fissure and dorsal median septum divide the cord into two

section shows the form of a butterfly or of the letter H. The odd-shaped vertical bars form the gray columns of the lateral halves of the cord, the cross bar constitutes the gray commissure containing the central canal. In each half the gray substance extending dorsal to the gray commissure is called the *dorsal column* or *horn*, that extending ventrally is the *ventral column* or *horn*. The portion connecting the two and from which the gray commissure extends is known as the intermediate gray. In the thoracic cord a slender lateral protrusion constitutes the *lateral* or *intermediolateral* column or horn (Figs. 111, 115). In the concavity between dorsal and ventral horn, small processes of gray extend into the white where they become intimately interlaced with longitudinally running fibers, forming the *reticular process* or *reticular formation*, most extensively developed in the cervical portion of the cord.

The gray commissure is divided by the central canal into a dorsal and ventral gray commissure. Immediately surrounding the horn shows a division into an expanded head or *caput* separated by a constricted neck or *cervix* from the *basal* portion which is continuous with the intermediate gray. The head is capped by a light staining area (in Weigert preparations) known as the *gelatinous substance of Rolando*, external to which is a thin zone, the *zona spongiosa*,

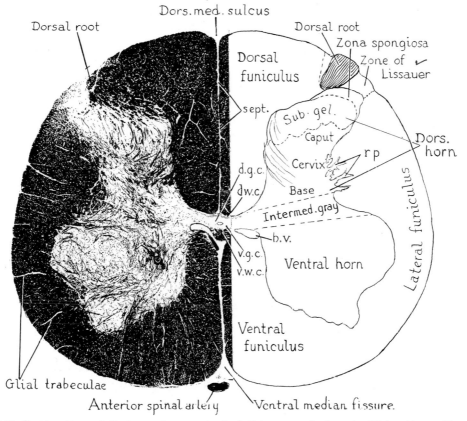

Fig. 107. Section through first sacral segment of adult human spinal cord. Weigert's myelin stain. Photograph. *b.v.*, blood vessel; *d.g.c.*, dorsal gray commissure; *d.w.c.*, dorsal white commissure; *r.p.*, reticular process; *sept.*, dorsal median septum; *sub.gel.*, substantia gelatinosa; *v.g.c.*, ventral gray commissure; *v.w.c.*, ventral white commissure.

central canal is a light granular area composed mainly of neuroglia and known as the central gelatinous substance (substantia gliosa). The dorsal horn extends nearly to the surface of the cord, being separated from the periphery by a narrow zone of white matter, the *zone of Lissauer* or *dorso-lateral fasciculus*, composed of delicate longitudinally coursing myelinated and unmyelinated fibers. In most levels the dorsal containing scattered large nerve cells and a delicate plexus of fine myelinated fibers.

The mantle of white is divided by the entering dorsal and the emerging ventral roots into three main regions: a *dorsal funiculus* lying between the dorsal median septum and dorsal roots; a *lateral funiculus* between the dorsal and ventral roots; and a *ventral funiculus* between the ventral median fissure and the ventral roots. Since the dorsal gray horn extends almost to the periphery of the cord, the dorsal funiculus is quite definitely delimited from the rest of the white. There is, however, no clear boundary between the other two funiculi, the two together really constituting a single U-shaped ventrolateral funiculus. Just ventral to the ventral gray commissure is a bundle of transverse fibers, the *ventral white commissure*, composed of crossing fibers from various nerve cells to be described below. In the dorsal part of the dorsal gray commissure, fine decussating

all the nerve cells and dendrites and portions of myelinated and unmyelinated fibers which generally run in a transverse plane, hence are cut longitudinally in a transverse section of the cord. These fibers are axons of nerve cells passing to the white matter, and terminal portions of fibers in the white entering the gray to terminate there. All synapses are thus in the gray since there alone the cell bodies and dendrites are found. The white matter contains no neuron bodies or dendrites, the nervous elements being confined to myelinated and

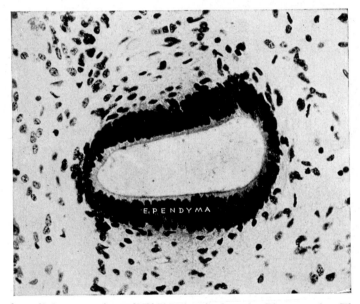

FIG. 108. Ependyma lining central canal of infant's spinal cord. Photograph. The area surrounding the ependyma is the central gelatinous substance (substantia gliosa) in which numerous neuroglia nuclei are seen.

myelinated fibers constitute the *dorsal white commissure*.

FINER STRUCTURE OF GRAY AND WHITE (SUBSTANTIA GRISEA AND SUBSTANTIA ALBA)

The gray and white matter is composed of nervous elements supported by an interstitial framework of neuroglia. The mesodermal structures comprise the blood vessels and their contents, the larger of which are accompanied by prolongations of pial connective tissue. The gray matter contains

unmyelinated fibers and their branches. The fibers are in the main longitudinally arranged but are connected with the gray by the many transverse fibers mentioned above.

The neuroglia. The central canal is lined by a layer of ependymal cells resembling a simple columnar epithelium in ordinary stains (Fig. 108). They have elongated nuclei and their cytoplasm contains neuroglia fibers which extend basally from the cell for some distance to merge with the diffuse glial network which permeates the gray and white matter. The ependymal cells are practically embryonal neuroglia cells (spongioblasts) which have retained their primitive form and position. In the region of the ventral median fissure and dorsal median septum, the basal processes of the ependymal cells actually reach the pia to which they are attached by terminal expansions or end feet, a condition characteristic of all spongioblasts during early development (Fig. 55).

cells and fibers are found in the substantia gelatinosa of Rolando and the zona spongiosa. The neuroglia of the white matter is composed chiefly of fibrous astrocytes whose fibers form a meshwork around the longitudinally coursing myelinated and unmyelinated fibers. Oligodendrocytes and microcytes are found in both gray and white. In the latter, the oligodendrocytes are often seen lying in rows, their delicate processes wrapping around the nerve fibers. Ex-

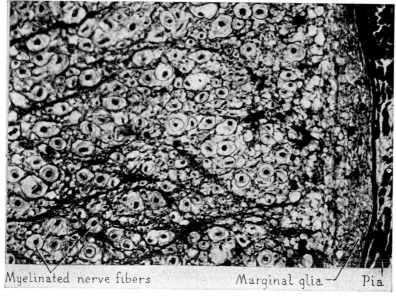

FIG. 109. Portion of white matter and adjacent pia of adult spinal cord. Mallory's phosphotungstic hematoxylin stain. Photograph. Among the myelinated fibers are seen darker staining strands composed of neuroglia cells and fibers. In upper portion of pia is a blood vessel filled with red blood corpuscles.

In most adults the central canal is often obliterated, the ependyma being represented by clumps of apparently rounded cells. Surrounding the ependyma is the clear central gelatinous substance, composed of neuroglia fibers and clumps of fibrous astrocytes which are otherwise rather scarce in the gray matter. In the gray and white matter the neuroglia forms a diffuse network, enveloping the neuron bodies, dendrites and nerve fibers. In the gray it consists mainly of protoplasmic astrocytes with rather few scattered fibrous ones. Special condensations of neuroglia

ternally, the neuroglia condenses to form a narrow peripheral zone, *the marginal glia*, devoid of nerve fibers and composed solely of branching glia cells and their fibers (Fig. 109). This marginal glia forms a continuous investment of the spinal cord, its outer boundary appearing as a thin line, the *superficial glial limiting membrane*, closely applied to the inner surface of the pia. From the marginal glia smaller or larger glial processes extend into the white matter, the largest of them being the dorsal median septum.

The blood vessels which penetrate into

the cord from the pia are always invested by tubular prolongations of the marginal glia forming the perivascular glial membranes which thus everywhere separate the nervous elements from the mesodermal tissues. The clefts between vessel wall and glia constitute the perivascular spaces which communicate with the subarachnoid spaces.

The structural features of neuroglia are difficult to demonstrate, and special stains

nuclei belong to microcytes, the somewhat larger round nuclei to oligodendroglia, while the larger paler ones are those of astrocytes.

The nuclei or cell groups. The gray matter contains numerous multipolar cells of varying size and structure, which may be grouped into two main classes, the *root cells* and the *column cells*. The root cells, situated in the ventral and lateral gray, are the

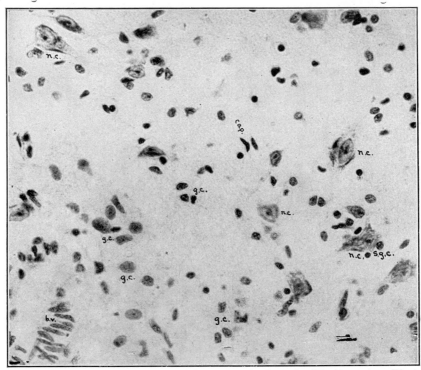

Fig. 110. Portion of intermediate gray of infant's spinal cord. Nissl's stain. Photograph. *bv,* blood vessel with nuclei of circular smooth muscle coat; *cap,* capillary with two endothelial nuclei; *gc,* nuclei of neuroglia cells. The larger pale nuclei belong to astrocytes, the darker smaller round nuclei to oligodendroglia, and the darkest smallest round or elongated nuclei to microglia. *nc,* small and medium sized nerve cells showing Nissl bodies.

are required to bring out the cytoplasm of neuroglia cells and the glia fibers. The nuclei are always seen in preparations stained with basic dyes, scattered through the gray and white matter (Fig. 110). They are easily distinguished from the vesicular nuclei of the medium sized and larger nerve cells, but with greater difficulty from those of the small ones and from the nuclei of connective tissue and endothelium. In general, the smallest most deeply staining

efferent peripheral neurons whose axons pass out of the cord as ventral root fibers to innervate the somatic and visceral effectors. The column cells, on the other hand, are entirely confined to the central nervous system. They constitute the *central, intermediate* or *associative* neurons. The majority send their axons to the white where by bifurcating or bending they form the longitudinal fibers of the white columns. Some are Golgi's type II cells whose short unmyelinated axons do not reach the white but terminate in the gray close to their origin. Those cells whose fibers remain on the same side are known as *tautomeric* or *ipsolateral* column cells, those whose axons cross are *heteromeric, contralateral* or *commissural* cells, while some cells may have axons which split into a crossed and uncrossed fiber (*hecateromeric* cells). The Golgi's type II cells may likewise be *tautomeric* or *heteromeric*, their axons ending in the Golgi cells which obviously are intrasegmental in character.

The nerve cells are not scattered uniformly through the gray, but are organized in more or less definite columns or *nuclei* which may be recognized in transverse sections as separate groups distinguished from others by their location, size, form and internal structure (Figs. 111, 112, 115, 117, 119). Some of these cell groups extend the whole length of the cord, though varying in

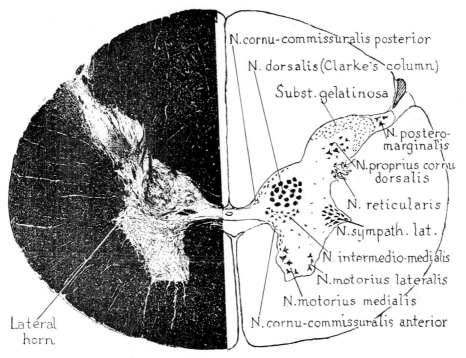

N.cornu-commissuralis posterior
N. dorsalis (Clarke's column)
Subst. gelatinosa
N. postero-marginalis
N. proprius cornu dorsalis
N. reticularis
N. sympath. lat.
N. intermedio-medialis
N. motorius lateralis
N. motorius medialis
N. cornu-commissuralis anterior
Lateral horn

FIG. 111. Section through twelfth thoracic segment of adult human spinal cord. Weigert's myelin stain. Photograph. On the right side the more constant cell columns have been schematically indicated.

the gray of the same side or crossing over to the gray of the opposite side and arborizing there. Some of the longitudinal fibers arising from the column cells, both crossed and uncrossed, may reach the brain as long tracts which are part of suprasegmental pathways. Others ascend or descend a variable distance as intersegmental fibers connecting various levels of the cord. Still others may be very short and terminate within a segment. This is especially true of

extent in different levels. Others may be limited to certain regions only. There is still considerable disagreement as to the distribution and terminology of many cell columns. The following is based mainly on the work of Jacobsohn, Massazza and Bok.

A. The **root cells** are organized into the following groups:

1. *Nuclei motorii cornu ventralis.* These are the groups of somatic motor cells located in the ventral horn, whose axons pass with-

T7 downward fas. cuneatus

out interruption to the striped voluntary muscles. They are the largest cells of the spinal cord reaching a long diameter of well over 100 micra and having a transverse diameter of 30–60μ. They are elongated multipolar cells with 3–10 or even 20 dendrites, a large vesicular nucleus and coarse Nissl bodies. They are largest in the lumbo-sacral and cervical enlargements, smaller in

column. The dorsomedial group is smaller, most distinct in the cervical and lumbar enlargements, and may be altogether missing in the thoracic and sacral portions. The medial motor column innervates the short and long muscles of the spine.

(b) The *lateral* motor cell group innervates the rest of the musculature. In the thoracic segments it is small and undivided

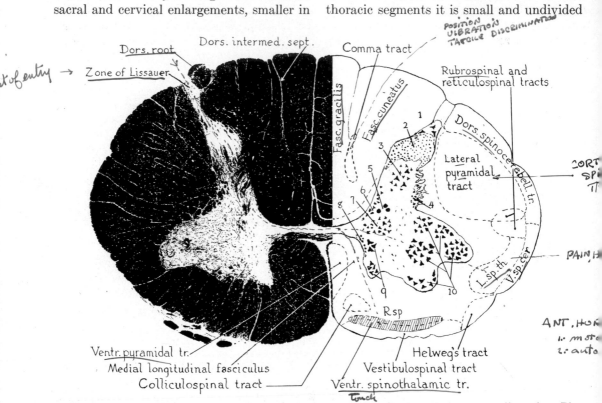

pt of entry →

FIG. 112. Section through adult human spinal cord at level of C7–C8. Weigert's myelin stain. Photograph. On the right side the cell groups (*1–10*) and fiber tracts are diagrammatically indicated. *1*, cellulae posteromarginales; *2*, substantia gelatinosa; *3*, nucleus proprius cornu dorsalis; *4*, nucleus reticularis; *5*, Clarke's column; *6*, nucleus cornucommissuralis posterior; *7*, nucleus intermedio-medialis; *8*, nucleus cornucommissuralis anterior; *9*, nuclei motorii mediales; *10*, nuclei motorii laterales; *L.sp.th.*, lateral spinothalamic tract; *R.sp.*, reticulospinal fibers; *V.sp.cer.*, ventral spinocerebellar tract.

the thoracic levels. Two main groups are distinguished, each of which shows several subdivisions:

(a) The *medial* cell group or column is divisible into a dorsomedial and ventromedial group. The latter extends throughout the whole cord, being most prominent in C1, C2, C4, Th1, Th2, L3, L4, S2, S3. The nucleus of the hypoglossal nerve in the medulla appears to be a continuation of this

and innervates the intercostal and other ventrolateral trunk muscles (Fig. 111). In the cervical and lumbar enlargements it becomes considerably enlarged and a number of sub-groups may be distinguished, accounting for the massive ventral horns found in these regions. It is especially prominent in those segments which participate in the innervation of the most distal portions of the extremities. Here there may be distin-

Lateral spinothalamic tract is used by the sensory fiber to travel up to cortex. (pain heat) (touch)

Ventral

Fasciculus cuneatus & gracilis } vibratory & proprioception. to conscious level

THE SPINAL CORD 97

vo. & Ven. spin cerebellar tract - proprioception to unconscious level.

guished ventrolateral, dorsolateral, ventral (anterior), central, and retrodorsolateral groups (Figs. 112, 117). The exact innervation of the various extremity muscles by each of these groups has not been completely worked out, but in general the more distal muscles are supplied by the more lateral cell groups. Passing thus from the most mesial part of the ventral horn to its lateral periphery, the successive innervation is spine, trunk, shoulder and hip girdle, upper leg and arm, lower leg and arm, the retrodorsolateral group finally supplying the muscles of hand and foot. It is interesting that in all the lateral cell groups the ven-

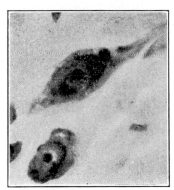

FIG. 113. Two preganglionic sympathetic cells in lateral horn of human spinal cord. Nissl stain. × 800. (Greving, from Moellendorf, Handb. der Mikr. Anat. des Menschen.)

trally placed cells supply the dorsal musculature and *vice versa* (Bok).

2. *Nuclei sympathici.* (Preganglionic autonomic neuron groups.) These are the cells whose axons pass out by way of the ventral roots and white rami communicantes to the various sympathetic ganglia. They are ovoid or spindle-shaped cells with thinner shorter dendrites, vesicular nuclei and finer chromofilic bodies (Fig. 113). They are considerably smaller than the somatic motor cells, ranging in size from 12–45μ. In Weigert preparations they appear to be surrounded by a clear homogenous substance resembling the gelatinous substance of Rolando. They may be divided into the following two groups:

(a) *Nucleus sympathicus lateralis* (*Intermediolateral column*) (Figs. 111, 115). This nucleus really consists of several adjacent cell columns of which the outermost, the apical cell group, projects furthest laterally and constitutes the lateral horn (intermediolateral column). The nucleus begins in the caudal portion of C8, the apical cell group extending to about L2 or L3, the other groups continuing to the conus terminalis. The nucleus is usually divided into a *superior* portion corresponding to the extent of the apical group, and an *inferior* portion continuing into the sacral cord. In the lower sacral segments the inferior nucleus breaks up into irregularly scattered cells which

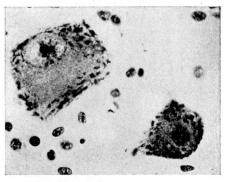

FIG. 114. Two cells from Clarke's column of human spinal cord. Nissl stain. Photograph.

apparently mingle with those of the medial sympathetic nucleus to be described below, the two together occupying a considerable part of the ventral horn.

(b) *Nucleus sympathicus medialis* (*Nucleus myoleioticus*). This nucleus begins about L3, is largest in L5 and continuous to the caudal end of the cord. It lies along the medial border of the ventral horn, but in the lower sacral segments becomes mingled with the inferior lateral sympathetic nucleus (Figs. 117, 119).

The axons of the sympathetic nuclei appear to run into the ventral roots (Bok, 1922; Poliak, 1924). It is at present believed that the axons of the superior lateral nucleus (intermediolateral column) go to the vertebral and prevertebral ganglia of the thoracico-lumbar autonomic system, while the inferior lateral and the medial sympathetic nuclei send their axons to the pelvic ganglia of the sacral autonomic (parasympathetic). It is quite possible that there are other autonomic sympathetic cells, some of which may send their axons through the dorsal roots as vasodilator fibers.

B. **Central cells** (Column cells and Golgi's type II cells). These cells and their proc-

The longest fibers reach the brain as parts of suprasegmental pathways. The cells vary in size, form and internal structure. Some are organized into definite cell groups easily distinguishable in transverse sections, others are scattered irregularly in the gray matter.

The *nucleus posteromarginalis* (*nucleus magnocellularis pericornualis, marginal cells*) forms a thin layer of cells covering the tip

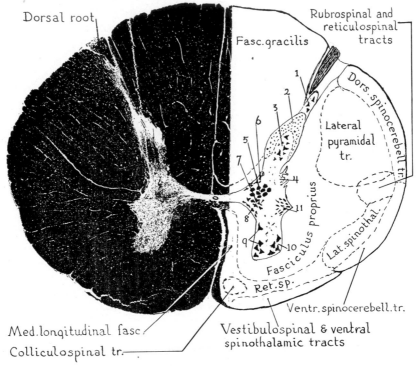

FIG. 115. Section through seventh thoracic segment of adult human spinal cord. Weigert's myelin stain. Photograph. *1*, nucleus posteromarginalis; *2*, substantia gelatinosa; *3*, nucleus proprius cornu dorsalis; *4*, nucleus reticularis; *5*, Clarke's column; *6*, nucleus cornucommissuralis posterior; *7*, nucleus intermedio-medialis; *8*, nucleus cornucommissuralis anterior; *9*, nucleus motorius medialis; *10*, nucleus motorius lateralis; *11*, nucleus sympathicus lateralis; *Ret. sp.*, reticulospinal fibers.

esses are entirely confined to the central nervous system. In the dorsal and intermediate gray especially, they receive the collaterals or direct terminations of dorsal root fibers. They in turn send their axons either directly to ventral horn cells of the same segments, or to the white matter where by bifurcating or bending upward or downward they become longitudinal fibers, forming intersegmental tracts of varying length.

of the dorsal horn and situated in the zona spongiosa. They are large tangentially arranged stellate or spindle-shaped cells reaching a diameter of over 50 micra (Ziehen). Their axons pass into the lateral white and bifurcate into ascending and descending fibers, probably forming intersegmental tracts. The cells are found throughout the cord, most numerous in the lumbosacral segments, less in the cervical and least in the thoracic. In sections 10–20μ thick, their number varies from 1 or 2 in the thoracic to 6 or 10 in the lumbar cord.

Beneath the marginal cells is the *substantia gelatinosa* of *Rolando* (*nucleus sensibilis proprius*) which forms the outer cap-like portion of the head of the dorsal horn. It extends the whole length of the cord, being largest in the lumbosacral and first cervical segments. Its variations in size are to some extent related to the size of the dorsal roots, the increase in the first cervical segment being due to the considerable number of descending fibers from the trigeminal nerve (*see medulla*). The nucleus is composed of rows of small ovoid or polygonal cells with deeply staining nuclei (cells of Gierke), about 6–20μ in diameter. The unmyelinated or finely myelinated axons end in considerable numbers in the substantia gelatinosa or dorsal horn. Others pass into the zone of Lissauer, adjacent lateral white and perhaps also into the dorsal white column. The large number and small size of the cells suggests that they give rise to short, principally intrasegmental fibers. The nucleus constitutes the chief associative organ of the dorsal horn for incoming impulses and probably also forms an important part of the pathway for painful, thermal and perhaps some tactile impulses, either conscious, reflex or both.

The center of the head and cervix is occupied by the *nucleus proprius cornu dorsalis* (*nucleus magnocellularis centralis, nucleus spinothalamicus, nucleus centrodorsalis*). Some are spindle-shaped cells of rather more than medium size, others are large polygonal cells with numerous dendrites, which may approach the size of a motor ventral horn cell. This rather poorly defined cell column is found in all segments, the cells being most numerous in the lumbosacral cord. It seems certain that the long crossed spinothalamic and spinotectal fibers arise from these cells, but axons also pass to the adjacent white of the same side. Lateral to this nucleus, the small and medium sized cells found in the reticular process have been termed the *nucleus reticularis* (Bok). They send their axons to the same as well as to the opposite ventrolateral white.

The *column of Clarke* (*nucleus dorsalis, nucleus magnocellularis basalis, nucleus spinocerebellaris*) is a striking cell column placed in the medial portion of the base of the dorsal horn. The nucleus begins to be well defined in C8 and extends through the thoracic and upper lumbar segments, being most prominent in Th11, Th12 and L1. Below L3 it becomes indistinguishable, though occasional cells are found in the

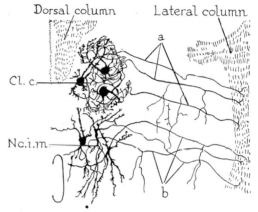

FIG. 116. Clarke's column (*Cl.c.*) and nucleus intermedio-medialis (intermediate gray, *Nc.i.m.*) in transverse section of thoracic cord of new-born mouse. Golgi impregnation. (After Cajal.) *a*, fibers from Clarke's column entering lateral column (dorsal spinocerebellar fibers); *b*, fibers from intermediate gray entering lateral column. Some of these may be ventral spinocerebellar fibers.

lower cord segments as well as in the cervical region. In the uppermost cervical segments it enlarges again and becomes continuous with the nuclei of the dorsal column, especially with the lateral cuneate nucleus. In sections 10–20μ thick, the number of cells ranges from 3 or 4 in the upper thoracic to 10 or 15 in the lower thoracic, with about 20 in Th12 and L1 (Fig. 124). The cells are large, many of them as large as the somatic motor cells. They are multipolar but have an ovoid or spherical shape, with large vesicular, often eccentrically placed nucleus, and coarse chromofilic bodies

Post columns (white)
position
vibration
Tactile discrimination

usually confined to the periphery of the cell body (Fig. 114). Their large thickly myelinated axons pass uncrossed to the lateral white where they ascend to the vermis of the cerebellum as the dorsal spinocerebellar tract (Figs. 116, 124, 125).

In the intermediate gray a rather diffusely organized cell group constitutes the *nucleus intermediomedialis*, as contrasted with the intermediolateral or sympathetic column

commissurales posterior and *anterior* (dorsomedial and ventromedial diffuse cell groups of Jacobsohn). The former in section is a thin cell stripe occupying the medial margin of the dorsal horn and extending along the border of the dorsal gray commissure, lying over the column of Clarke where the latter is present. The other is a similar cell group along the medial surface of the ventral horn and ventral gray commissure. These nuclei

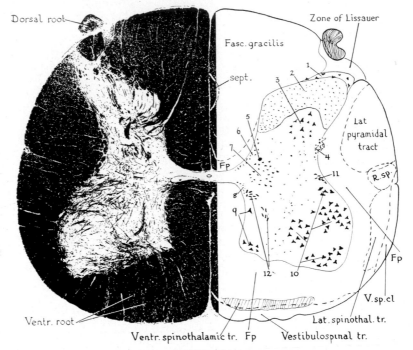

FIG. 117. Section through lower portion of fourth lumbar segment of adult human spinal cord. Weigert's myelin stain. Photograph. *1*, nucleus posteromarginalis; *2*, substantia gelatinosa; *3*, nucleus proprius cornu dorsalis; *4*, nucleus reticularis; *5*, cell from Clarke's column; *6*, nucleus cornucommissuralis posterior; *7*, nucleus intermediomedialis; *8*, nucleus cornucommissuralis anterior; *9*, nucleus motorius medialis; *10*, nucleus motorius lateralis; *11*, nucleus sympathicus lateralis; *12*, nucleus sympathicus medialis; *Fp*, fasciculus proprius; *R.sp.*, rubrospinal and reticulospinal tracts; *sept.*, septomarginal fasciculus; *V.sp.cl.*, ventral spinocerebellar tract.

described under the root cells. The small and medium sized cells, 10–24μ in size, are found in varying numbers throughout the cord but are most numerous in the upper cervical segments. Their axons pass mostly to the lateral white of the same side and are believed in part at least to contribute to the ventral spinocerebellar tract.

Two less definite cell columns extending the length of the cord are the *nuclei cornu-*

consist of small and medium sized spindle-shaped cells whose axons probably form intersegmental tracts in the dorsal and ventral white respectively.

Besides the more organized groups, there are diffusely scattered cells (*cellulae disseminatae*) throughout the gray matter. In the interior of the ventral horn, scattered between the somatic motor cells, these small triangular or spindle-shaped cells are often collectively termed the *nucleus proprius cornu ventralis*. They are most numerous in C5–C8 and L2–L4 and may serve for intranuclear connections.

As a rule, most of the cells except the smallest ones are largest in the lumbosacral cord.

Arrangement of fibers. It has been noted already that the white matter is composed principally of longitudinal fibers while in the gray the fibers have a transverse direction, running from gray to white or *vice versa* (Fig. 121). The reason for the transverse course of these fibers is obvious. The gray matter contains all the cell bodies and dendrites, hence all synapses are in the gray. Any fiber or collateral terminating in any level of the cord enters the gray as a transverse fiber. Similarly, axons arising from column cells leave the gray as transverse fibers to pass into the white where they assume a longitudinal course. The transverse fibers are therefore either fibers of origin or fibers of termination and include in general, (a) root fibers entering or leaving the cord, (b) axons of column cells passing to the white where they become ascending or descending fibers, and (c) collaterals and terminals of fibers of the white matter, which come from other parts of the spinal cord or from the brain and enter the gray to terminate there.

The dorsal roots, as already stated, are composed of coarse thickly myelinated fibers and of finer fibers, many of which are unmyelinated. The former are processes of the larger spinal ganglion cells, bringing in impulses from muscle and tendon spindles, Meissner's corpuscles, Pacinian corpuscles, etc., and probably also from diffuse tactile receptors (position and movement, touch, vibration). The finer myelinated and unmyelinated fibers which are processes of the smaller ganglion cells conduct impulses from diffuse endings, perhaps also from end bulbs and other encapsulated endings (primarily pain and temperature, perhaps also some touch). The dorsal roots break up into a number of filaments or rootlets which enter the cord in a linear manner. Each of these filaments on entering the cord separates into a smaller lateral division composed of fine fibers which enters the zone of Lissauer, and a larger medial division composed of the coarser fibers, which passes into the main portion of the dorsal funiculus lying medial to the dorsal horn (Figs. 122, 123). Each

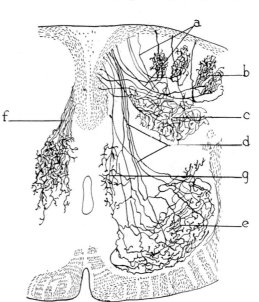

Fig. 118. The more important collaterals from the fibers of the dorsal funiculus. New-born rat. Golgi impregnation. (After Cajal.) *a*, collaterals to substantia gelatinosa and to the nucleus proprius (central nucleus) of dorsal horn. Terminal arborizations of these fibers are seen in substantia gelatinosa (*b*) and nucleus proprius (*c*); *d*, sensorimotor collaterals with terminal arborizations around cells of ventral horn (*e*); *f*, collaterals to intermediate gray (nucleus intermediomedialis); *g*, terminal branching of a collateral from a sensori-motor fiber in intermediate gray.

root fiber bifurcates into a longer ascending and a shorter descending arm as soon as it enters the cord. The fine fibers which pass to the zone of Lissauer divide into very short arms, the longer ascending ones extending only for one or two segments. (Ranson). The coarser fibers of the medial division bifurcate into shorter descending and long ascending arms which run a variable distance and form the majority of the

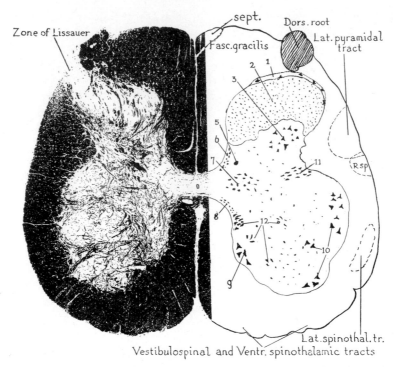

FIG. 119. Section through third sacral segment of adult human spinal cord. Weigert's myelin stain. Photograph. Numbers of cell groups as in Fig. 117. *R.sp.*, rubrospinal and reticulospinal tracts; *sept.*, septomarginal fasciculus.

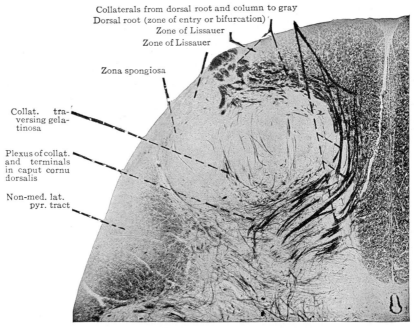

FIG. 120. Portion of transverse section of lumbar spinal cord of five-week old infant, showing entrance of dorsal root and its collaterals. Weigert's myelin stain. Photograph.

longitudinal fibers of the dorsal funiculus. From both the ascending and descending arms, and sometimes also from the root fibers before bifurcation, collateral branches are given off which enter the gray as transverse fibers. More of these are usually given off near the entry of the root fibers than further along the course of the ascending and descending arms. The descending and ascending arms themselves sooner or later also enter and terminate in the gray, terminal plexuses in the caput and cervix of the dorsal horn (Figs. 118, 120). In the thoracic and upper lumbar segments many myelinated collaterals are seen entering the column of Clarke (Figs. 124, 125). Still others can be traced to the intermediate gray, and finally some go directly to the ventral horn as "sensorimotor" or "direct reflex collaterals". By means of the last named collaterals, two-neuron reflex arcs are made possible, but the number of such

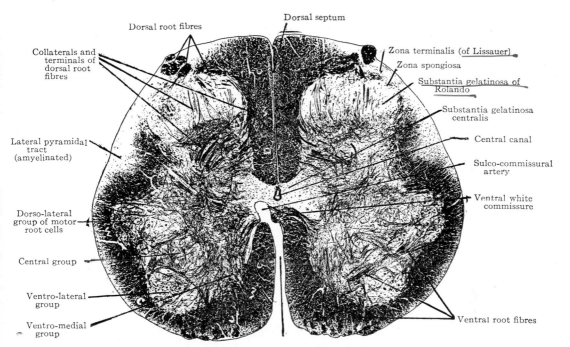

FIG. 121. Section through fourth lumbar segment of spinal cord of five-week infant. Weigert's myelin stain. Photograph ×20. *DWC* (white letters), dorsal white column; *LWC*, lateral white column; *VWC*, ventral white column. The vertical line lies in the ventral median fissure.

the longest arms reaching the medulla before doing so. In any transverse section of the cord, bundles of fine fibers composed of these collaterals and terminals from the entering roots or dorsal funiculus may be seen passing radially through the substantia gelatinosa or sweeping around its mesial side to be distributed to the various cell groups of the gray matter, a few crossing through the dorsal white commissure to the gray of the opposite side. Some terminate in the substantia gelatinosa, others form collaterals terminating directly on the motor cells is relatively small, and most reflexes have at least one additional central neuron interposed between the afferent and efferent peripheral neurons (Fig. 149).

The lateral and ventral funiculi are likewise connected with the gray by many transverse fibers. These are all processes of central cells. They are either axons of column cells entering the white to become ascending or descending longitudinal fibers, or collaterals and terminals of longitudinal

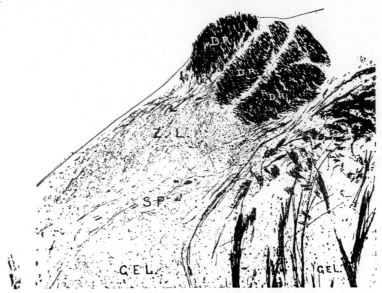

Fig. 122. Portion of transverse section of lumbar cord of five-week infant, showing entry of a dorsal spinal root. Weigert's myelin stain. Photograph. Three bundles of root fibers (*DR*) are seen entering from which the fine fibers separate and pass (arrow) into the zone of Lissauer (*ZL*). *GEL*, substantia gelatinosa through which pass bundles of collaterals of dorsal root fibers. *SP*, zona spongiosa.

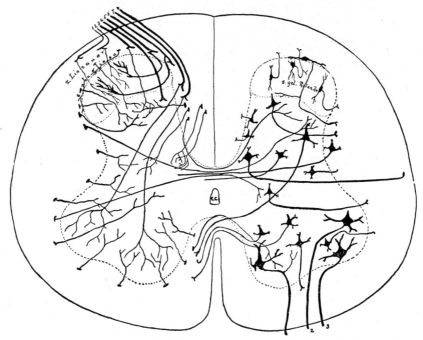

Fig. 123. Section through spinal cord, showing arrangement of collaterals (left) and cell bodies and their axons (right) as seen in Golgi preparations. (After Cajal and Lenhossék.) *1* and *2* represent fine dorsal root fibers passing laterally to the zone of Lissauer. *3* to *8* represent dorsal root fibers passing to the medial coarse-fibered portion of the dorsal white column. Collaterals from *1* and *2* enter the substantia gelatinosa, those from *3* to *8* enter the gelatinosa, head and neck of the dorsal horn, intermediate gray and ventral horn. Some collaterals from dorsal root fibers of other, probably lower, levels are seen leaving the dorsal white column and ending in the dorsal horn, intermediate gray and (most mesially) in the column of Clarke. Preganglionic autonomic root cells are not shown. *cc*, central canal.

fibers coming from other portions of the cord or brain, entering the gray to terminate there. Many of the fibers cross to the opposite side. The ventral white commissure consists of such decussating fibers of column cells which lie near the level of crossing, and perhaps also of some decussating collaterals. The much smaller dorsal white commissure contains a few crossing axons of column cells, collaterals from the dorsal white column and perhaps also from the zone of

from cells of the lateral horn, and constituting preganglionic autonomic fibers. These fine fibers are nearly or entirely absent in the ventral roots of the other segment of the cord.

Variations in structure at different levels. While the general structure described above obtains throughout the cord, the different levels vary considerably as regards the shape and size of the cord, the shape and size of the gray matter and the relative amount of

FIG. 124. Transverse section through low thoracic region of adult spinal cord. Cajal's silver stain. Photograph. a, collaterals from dorsal white column entering Clarke's column.

Lissauer and adjacent portion of the lateral white.

Finally in the ventral part of the cord may be seen the coarser transverse fibers which are axons of the various somatic motor cell groups, gathered into bundles which leave the ventral horn, pass through the white matter and emerge as ventral root fibers (Fig. 121). In the thoracic and upper lumbar segments and in some of the sacral ones, the ventral roots contain also a large number of fine myelinated fibers coming

gray and white. These differences are primarily due to two factors: (1) Variations in size of the nerve roots, causing corresponding variations in the white and especially in the gray matter which receives the afferent fibers and contains the cells of origin of the efferent ones. Thus the larger nerves of the extremities produce the cervical and lumbar enlargements marked primarily by the great increase in the gray columns. Similarly the outflow of the preganglionic sympathetic fibers in the thoracic cord is represented by the lateral horn (intermediolateral column). (2) Since all levels of the cord are connected with the brain by long ascending and descending fibers, there will naturally be an increase in the white matter as we proceed from lower to higher levels, the first cervical containing the largest number of fibers. Some of the variations seen at different levels may be briefly summarized.

There is a considerable increase in the white matter. The gray columns are massive and the ventral horns are bayed out laterally, due to the increase of the lateral motor cell groups. In sections of the *thoracic* cord (Figs. 115, 111) the area is smaller than in the lumbar enlargement, due primarily to the great reduction of the gray. Both dorsal and ventral horns are slender and

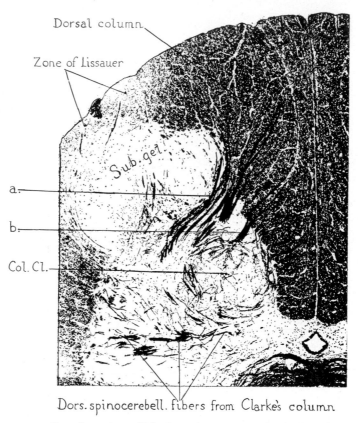

FIG. 125. Transverse section through twelfth thoracic segment of spinal cord of five-week infant. Weigert's myelin stain. Photograph. *a*, collaterals from dorsal column to substantia gelatinosa, intermediate gray and ventral gray; *b*, collaterals from deeper portion of dorsal white column to Clarke's column. *Col. Cl.*, Clarke's column.

In the *third sacral* segment (Fig. 119), the gray columns are massive with a large substantia gelatinosa and a short gray commissure. The white matter is relatively small in amount and the total area of the section is likewise small. The cross-sectional area is much larger in the *fourth* or *fifth lumbar* segment, with a transverse diameter of about 12 mm. and a sagittal of 9 mm. (Fig. 117).

there is a well marked lateral horn (intermediolateral column). On the mesial surface of the base of the dorsal horn is seen the column of Clarke especially prominent in the twelfth thoracic which also has a stouter ventral horn than the more typical thoracic segments (Figs. 124, 125). Myelinated collaterals from the dorsal funiculus may be seen entering Clarke's column to terminate among its cells. From the nucleus coarse myelinated fibers gather at its ventral side and pass outward to the lateral periphery of the cord where they bend upwards as fibers of the dorsal spinocerebellar tract (Figs. 124, 125). The white matter is considerable and increases in amount at successively higher levels. In the midthoracic region the transverse diameter is massive, with lateral extensions accommodating the lateral motor cell groups innervating the upper extremities. The reticular process is prominent, and there is a great increase in the white matter. A more or less complete septum divides the dorsal funiculus into a medial fasciculus gracilis and a lateral fasciculus cuneatus. In the *upper cervical* segments as C2 or C1, the

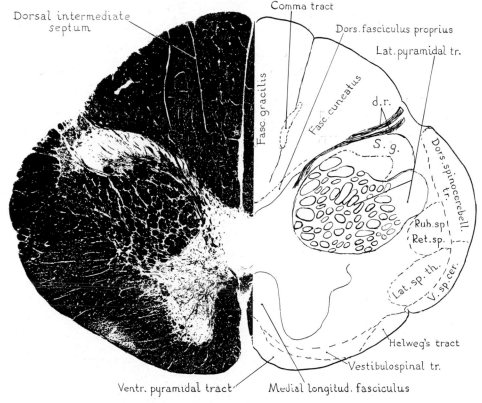

Fig. 126. Section through upper portion of first cervical segment of adult cord. Myelin stain. Photograph. *d.r.*, dorsal root; *Lat.sp.th.*, lateral spinothalamic tract; *Ret.sp.*, *Rub.sp.*, reticulospinal and rubrospinal tracts; *S.g.*, substantia gelatinosa; *V.sp.cer.*, ventral spinocerebellar tract.

about 10 mm., the sagittal about 8 mm. (Ziehen).

The largest area is found in sections of the *cervical enlargement* and especially in C7 and C8 where the transverse and sagittal diameters are about 13–14 mm. and 9 mm. respectively (Fig. 112). The shape of the section is oval, flattened dorsoventrally. The dorsal horn is enlarged though relatively slender, and the ventral horns are again

gray matter becomes again reduced but the area of the section is large, due to the great amount of white matter. The diameter is about 12 mm (Fig. 126).

Blood supply. The blood supply of the spinal cord is derived from two sources. The vertebral arteries, close to their fusion into the basilar artery, give off two pairs of arterial branches. The more rostral pair pass caudally to the ventral surface of the cord and unite in the midline to form the *anterior spinal artery (anterior vertebrospinal artery)*. The caudal pair remain separate, only a few segments of the cord and usually end at the fourth or fifth cervical segments.

More important is the blood supply

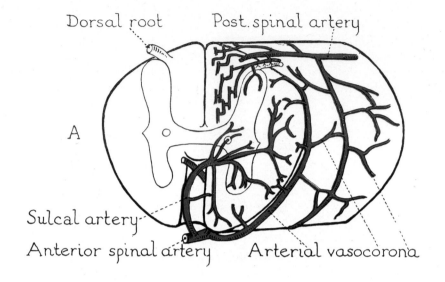

Dorsal root   Post. spinal artery

A

Sulcal artery

Anterior spinal artery   Arterial vasocorona

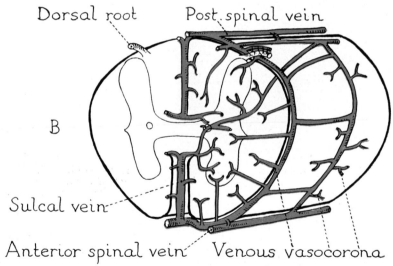

Dorsal root   Post. spinal vein

B

Sulcal vein

Anterior spinal vein   Venous vasocorona

FIG. 127. Diagram of the blood supply of the spinal cord. *A*, arterial; *B*, venous. (After Herren and Alexander.)

pass to the region of the dorsolateral sulcus where each forms the usually paired *posterior spinal artery*. The anterior and posterior spinal arteries thus formed supply through the *radicular* arteries. These are branches of the deep cervical, intercostal, lumbar and sacral arteries, which pass through the intervertebral foramina and after penetrating the dura divide into *anterior* and *posterior radicular arteries*. In early foetal life, each spinal root apparently has its own segmental artery and vein (Elze), but during later development the majority of these vessels fail to reach the spinal cord and merely supply the roots and ganglia. According to Suh and Alexander (1939), the adult cord is supplied by 6–8 anterior radicular and 5–8 posterior radicular arteries, of which the largest one, the *arteria radicularis magna*, is found in the upper lumbar region.

The anterior radicular arteries go the region of the ventral median sulcus and there form the anterior spinal artery or trunk which must be considered as a chain of anastomosing ascending and descending branches of the anterior radicular arteries. This irregular trunk is always narrowest and most poorly developed in the mid-area between two radicular arteries. In the cervical region the trunk anastomoses with that portion of the anterior spinal artery derived from the vertebral arteries.

The posterior radicular arteries similarly give rise to the paired posterior spinal arteries, each consisting of an irregular anastomotic trunk whose continuity is often interrupted. A plexus of finer branching and anastomosing vessels in the pia, the *arterial vasocorona*, connects the dorsal and ventral arterial trunks (Fig. 127 A).

The anterior spinal artery gives off a number of *sulcal* (sulcocommissural) branches which pass dorsally in the ventral fissure and enter the cord alternately to the right and left. Only in the lumbar and sacral segments does an occasional single sulcal artery penetrate into the fissure and divide into a left and right branch. The anterior sulcal arteries are most numerous in the lumbar region and fewest in the thoracic where the segmental blood supply is poorest

and there may be but one sulcal artery to an entire segment (Herren and Alexander, 1939).

The anterior spinal artery through its sulcal branches supplies the ventral and lateral horns, central gray and Clarke's column (Fig. 127 A). It also supplies the ventral and lateral white funiculi including the lateral pyramidal tract. To a smaller degree the lateral white is also supplied by branches from the arterial vasocorona. The posterior spinal arteries feed the dorsal horn and dorsal white column.

The venous distribution is in the main similar to that of the arteries (Fig. 127 B). There are 6–11 anterior and 5–10 posterior radicular veins, one of which, situated in the lumbar region, is of considerably greater caliber and is known as the *vena radicularis magna* (Suh and Alexander). The posterior radicular veins form a more or less distinct posterior median spinal vein or trunk along the whole extent of the cord as well as smaller paired posterolateral trunks. Similarly, an anterior median and paired anterolateral venous trunks are formed from the anterior radicular veins. As in the case of the arteries, a meningeal plexus of veins, the vasocorona, connects the longitudinal trunks. From the anterior spinal vein, sulcal branches pass dorsally in the ventral fissure and enter the cord, each sulcal vessel as a rule supplying both sides of the cord.

The posterior radicular veins (and posterior trunks) drain the dorsal white column, dorsal horn including Clarke's column, and a narrow strip of lateral white immediately adjacent to the dorsal horn (Fig. 127 B). The anterior spinal vein, through the sulcal vessels, drains the sulcomarginal white and the medial portion of the ventral horn. The lateral portions of the ventral horn, the lateral horn, and the ventral and lateral white columns are drained by branches of the venous vasocorona (Fig. 127 B).

CHAPTER X

SEGMENTAL AND PERIPHERAL INNERVATION

SEGMENTAL (RADICULAR) INNERVATION

The "segmental" character of the cord, as evidenced by its spinal nerves, corresponds to the general metamerism of the body, each pair of nerves supplying a body segment (metamere). The ventral roots

area supplied by a single dorsal root and its ganglion is called a *dermatome*.

In the adult, the correspondence between neural and body metameres is easily recognized in the trunk and neck regions where each spinal nerve supplies the musculature and cutaneous area of its own segment.

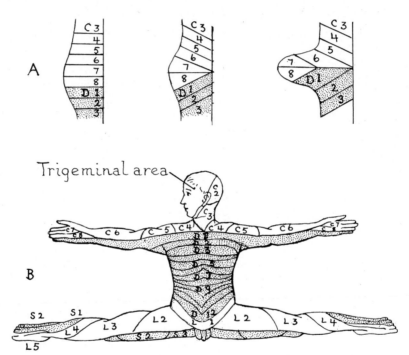

Fig. 128. *A*, schema of migration of metameres during development. (After Bing.) *B*, segmental arrangement of dermatomes. (After Luciani.) *c*, cervical; *d*, thoracic; *l*, lumbar; *s*, sacral.

contain the efferent fibers which go to the somatic musculature (myotomes) and by way of the autonomic ganglia to the blood vessels (vasoconstrictor), visceral muscle and glandular epithelium. The dorsal roots contain all the afferent fibers, superficial, deep and visceral, and probably also some efferent fibers which act as vasodilators of cutaneous bloodvessels. That cutaneous

Here the dermatomes follow one another consecutively, each forming a band encircling the body from the mid-dorsal to the mid-ventral line. In the extremities, however, the conditions are far more complicated. During development the metameres migrate distally into the limb buds and arrange themselves parallel to the long axis of the future limb (Fig. 128). In each extremity, there is thus formed an axial line along which are placed a number of consecutive segments which have wandered out from the axial portions. The result is that in the trunk and neck portion of the adult the fourth cervical dermatome is in contact with the second thoracic, and the second lumbar with the third sacral, the intervening segments having migrated to form the dermatomes of the extremities (Figs. 130, 130A). This mode of migration explains the seemingly confusing arrangement and sequence of the limb dermatomes, and may still be recognized in the adult when the foetal position is approximated (Fig. 128B).

anesthesia. Pictures similar to those of Sherrington were obtained by irritating single roots or ganglia with strychnine and noting the resulting hypersensitive areas (Dusser de Barenne).

Clinically, Head was the first to outline the human dermatomes by studying the areas of eruption and hyperalgesia occurring in Herpes zoster, a disease which often attacks isolated spinal ganglia. More recently Foerster (1933, 1936) has furnished a remarkably complete map of human dermatomes, based on numerous resections of dorsal roots for the alleviation of spastic conditions and on cases of root injury due to

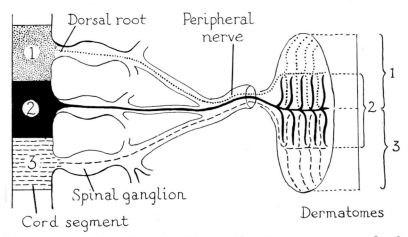

FIG. 129. Diagram of radicular and peripheral innervation of cutaneous areas. Overlapping of the dermatomes. (Modified from Bing.)

Sherrington (1894) experimentally demonstrated in the monkey the exact cutaneous areas supplied by the various dorsal roots. Section of a single root did not produce a marked anesthesia anywhere, so he selected a special root for study and cut two or three adjacent roots above and below. The area of "remaining sensibility" bounded above and below by an area of anesthesia obviously represented the dermatome supplied by the normal root. He found that each dermatome overlapped the sensory cutaneous areas of adjacent roots, being co-innervated by the one above and the one below (Fig. 129), hence at least two contiguous roots had to be sectioned to produce a region of complete

tumors or other causes. They correspond in the main with the fields of Head and show the same overlapping given by Sherrington for monkeys. Most dermatomes are supplied by three, occasionally even four, dorsal roots. The only root whose section produces an area of complete anesthesia is C2, neither C3 nor the trigeminal nerve invading to any considerable extent the back of the head. It is interesting that the overlapping of adjacent dermatomes is greater for touch than for pain and temperature. The distribution of the human dermatomes is shown in Figs. 130, 130A.

The segmental innervation of the striped masculature (myotomes) has likewise been

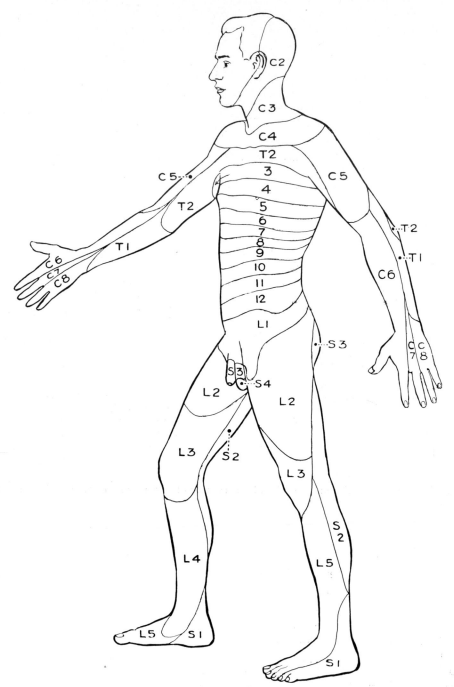

FIG. 130. A ventrolateral view of the human dermatomes. (After Foerster from Haymaker and Woodhall).

worked out, by direct stimulation of ventral roots, by study of the pathological changes which occur in the ventral horn cells when a motor nerve is cut, and by secondary degeneration of peripheral nerve fibers. As in the case of the dermatomes, the majority

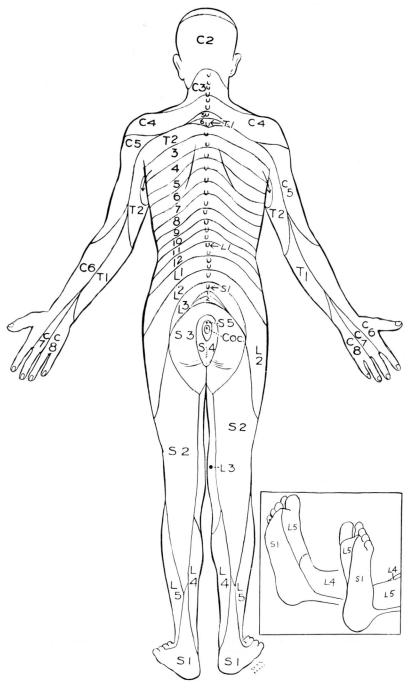

FIG. 130A. Back view of the human dermatomes. (After Foerster from Haymaker and Woodhall.) Arrows in the region of the spinal column point to the spinous processes of the first thoracic, first lumbar and first sacral vertebrae.

of the muscles, especially those of the extremities, are innervated by two or three and occasionally even four ventral roots. Hence injury to a single root may only weaken the muscle or have no apparent effect whatever. Only the very short muscles of the trunk and spinal column and a few others such as the Abductor pollicis, are formed from single myotomes and retain a monosegmental innervation. The peripheral projection of the myotomes coincides in the main with that of the dermatomes.

Following are the locations in the cord of the ventral horn cells which carry out some of the important reflex and other activities.

Movements of the head (by muscles of neck), C1–C4.

Movements of diaphragm (phrenic center), C3–C5.

Movements of upper extremity, C5–Th2.

Biceps tendon reflex (flexion of forearm on percussion of biceps tendon), C5, C6.

Triceps tendon reflex (extension of forearm on percussion of triceps tendon), C6–C8.

Radial periosteal reflex (flexion of forearm on percussion of distal end of radius), C7, C8.

Wrist tendon reflexes (flexion of fingers on percussion of wrist tendons), C8–Th1.

Movements of trunk, Th1–Th12.

Abdominal superficial reflexes (ipsilateral contraction of subjacent abdominal muscles on stroking skin of upper, middle and lower abdomen), upper (epigastric), Th6, Th7; middle, Th8, Th9; lower, Th10–Th12.

Movements of lower extremity, L1–S3.

Cremasteric superficial reflex (elevation of scrotum on stroking skin of inner thigh), L1, L2.

Genital center for ejaculation, L1–L3 (smooth muscle); S3, S4 (striped muscles).

Vesical center for retention of urine, Th12–L2.

Patellar tendon reflex or knee jerk (extension of leg on percussion of patellar ligament), L2–L4.

Gluteal superficial reflex (contraction of glutei on stroking skin over glutei), L4–S1.

Plantar superficial reflex (flexion of toes on stroking sole of foot), L5–S2.

Achilles tendon reflex or ankle jerk (plantar flexion of foot on percussion of Achilles tendon), L5–S2.

Genital center of erection, S2–S4.

Vesical center for evacuation of bladder, S3–S5.

Bulbo-cavernosus reflex (contraction of bulbocavernosus muscle on pinching penis), S3–S4.

Anal reflex (contraction of external rectal sphincter on stroking perianal region), S4, S5, and coccygeal.

PERIPHERAL INNERVATION

While each spinal nerve in a general way supplies its own body segment, there is considerable intermixture and anastomosis of adjacent nerve trunks before they reach their peripheral destination. The primary dorsal rami (Fig. 72) remain relatively distinct, though even here interconnections are common in the cervical and sacral regions. The ventral rami however form far more elaborate connections. Except for the thoracic nerves which largely retain their segmental distribution, the cervical and lumbosacral rami innervating the extremities anastomose and branch to form extensive plexuses in which a radical regrouping of fibers occurs. Each of the peripheral nerves arising from these plexuses now contains fibers contributed from two, three, four or even five ventral rami. As a result the cutaneous areas supplied by the peripheral nerves do not correspond with the cutaneous areas supplied by the individual dorsal roots (dermatomes). Similarly, several ventral roots may contribute fibers to a single muscle, and conversely several muscles may receive fibers from a single ventral root. A knowledge of the cutaneous and muscular distribution of the peripheral nerves is of great importance to the neurologist for determining the segmental level, spinal or radicular, of peripheral nerve injuries, hence the more important morphological features are briefly presented. A more complete account will be found in the larger handbooks of anatomy and clinical neurology.

The **dorsal** or **posterior rami** of the spinal nerves innervate the intrinsic dorsal muscles of the back and neck, which constitute the extensor system of the vertebral column, and the overlying skin from vertex to coccyx. In the middle of the back the cutaneous area roughly corresponds to that of the underlying muscles, but in the upper and lower portions it widens laterally to reach the acromial region above and the region of the great trochanter below. With certain exceptions the dorsal rami have a typical segmental distribution, the field of each overlapping with that of the adjacent segment above and below. Each ramus usually divides into a medial and a lateral branch, both of which may contain sensory and motor fibers, though the lateral branches of the cervical rami are purely motor in character. Deviations are found in the upper two cervical and in the lumbosacral rami. The first or *suboccipital* nerve is purely motor and terminates in the short posterior muscles of the head (rectus capitis and obliquus capitis). The main branch of the second cervical ramus, known as the *greater occipital* nerve ascends to the region of the superior nuchal line where it becomes subcutaneous, and supplies the scalp on the back of the head to the vertex, occasionally extending as far as the coronary suture (Fig. 134). The nerve is joined by a filament from the third cervical ramus. The lateral branches of the upper three lumbar and upper three sacral rami send cutaneous twigs which supply the upper part of the gluteal area, extending laterally to the region of the great trochanter. These branches are usually known as the *superior* (lumbar) and *medial* (sacral) *clunial* nerves (Fig. 134).

The **ventral** or **anterior rami** of the spinal nerves supply the ventrolateral muscles and skin as well as the extremities which are outgrowths of the ventral body wall. With the exception of most thoracic nerves, the ventral rami of adjacent nerves unite and anastomose to form the cervical, brachial and lumbosacral plexuses.

The **cervical plexus** is formed from the ventral rami of the four upper cervical nerves. It furnishes cutaneous nerves for the ventrolateral portions of the neck, the shoulder, the upper part of the breast and the lateral portions of the back of the head. The muscular branches supply the deep cervical muscles of the spinal column, the infrahyoid muscles and the diaphragm. They also aid in the innervation of the trapezius and sternocleidomastoid which are chiefly supplied by the accessory nerve (N.XI).

The mainly sensory cutaneous branches are the larger ones. The *lesser occipital* nerve (*C2*, C3) is distributed to the upper pole of the pinna and to the lateral area on the back of the head, overlapping only slightly the field of the greater occipital nerve (Fig. 134). The *great auricular nerve* (*C3*, C2) supplies the larger lower portion of the pinna and the skin over the angle of the mandible. The *anterior cervical cutaneous* (*C3*, C2) innervates the ventral and lateral parts of the neck from chin to sternum (supra- and infrahyoid region). The *supraclavicular nerves* (*C4*, C3) variable in number of branches, are distributed to the shoulder, the most lateral regions of the neck, and to the upper part of the breast where their end branches overlap with those of the second intercostal nerve (Figs. 133, 134).

The chief muscular nerve is the *phrenic* which supplies the diaphragm and is derived mainly from C4, with smaller contributions from C3 or C5 or from both (Fig. 131). It frequently receives an anastomotic branch from the subclavian nerve of the brachial plexus, which enters the phrenic at a variable height. Hence in high lesions of the phrenic, paralysis of the diaphragm may not occur. The deep cervical muscles are innervated by direct segmental branches from the ventral rami. The lateral and the anterior rectus capitis receive twigs from C1 and C2; the longus capitis from C1–C3; the longus colli from C3–C6; the intertransversarii from all the cervical rami. Branches from C4 also aid in the innervation of the median scalene muscle.

The hyoid muscles, excepting those supplied by the cranial nerves, are innervated by twigs from C1–C3 and probably also from C4 (Foerster). These twigs unite into a common trunk and join the hypoglossal nerve (*ansa hypoglossi*). The geniohyoid and thyreohyoid are supplied entirely from

from C1. The trapezius receives its main contributions from C3 and C4, perhaps also from C1 and C2. The nerve filaments form one or more bundles which are often incorporated in the supraclavicular cutaneous nerves, and are distributed to the upper portion of the muscle. The middle and

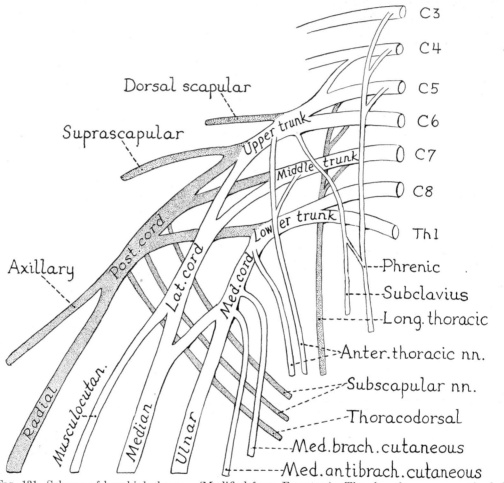

FIG. 131. Schema of brachial plexus. (Modified from Foerster.) The dorsal nerves are stippled

C1; the sternohyoid, sternothyreoid and omohyoid from C2, C3 and C4. The cervical plexus also aids in the innervation of the sternocleidomastoid and trapezius muscles which are mainly supplied by the accessory nerve, and of the levator scapulae. The last two muscles are related to the shoulder girdle. The sternocleidomastoid receives twigs from C2 and C3, to a smaller extent

lower portions appear to be solely innervated by the accessory nerve (Foerster). The levator scapulae is supplied from C3–C5.

Paralysis of the neck muscles as a result of peripheral injuries is relatively rare and is usually associated with involvement of the spinal cord.

The brachial plexus. The nerves supplying the upper extremity and forming the brachial plexus are derived as a rule from the ventral rami of the four lower cervical and the first thoracic nerves with a small contribution from the fourth cervical (Fig. 131). There are however considerable variations. If the contribution from the fourth cervical is strong and that of the first thoracic negligible the plexus belongs to the *prefixed* type. It is called *postfixed* when the fourth cervical does not participate at all, but the contribution of the first thoracic is strong and in addition the second thoracic sends a branch to the plexus. Between these extremes there are many intermediate conditions, depending on the stronger or weaker participation of the fourth cervical on the one hand and the first thoracic on the other. These variations are probably dependent on embryological factors. The limb buds of both arms and legs may vary in longitudinal extent and especially in their relative position to the neuraxis. The more cephalic the position of the limbs, the more cephalic will be the nerves contributing to the plexus, and *vice versa* (Stookey).

The ventral rami supplying the plexus give rise to three *primary trunks.* C5 and C6 unite to form the *upper trunk*; C8 and Th1 form the *lower*, while C7 is continued as the *middle trunk.* Then passing underneath the region of the clavicle, each trunk splits into a dorsal and a ventral division. The dorsal divisions of all three trunks fuse to form the *posterior cord* or *fasciculus* placed behind the axillary artery. The ventral divisions of the upper and middle trunk form the *lateral fasciculus*, while the ventral division of the lower trunk is continued as the *medial fasciculus* (Fig. 131).

Many of the nerves supplying the shoulder muscles are given off directly from the ventral rami or from the primary trunks and their branches before these unite to form the secondary fasciculi. Here also dorsal and ventral nerves are formed. Thus the *dorsal scapular* nerve supplying the rhomboids arises from the dorsal surface of C5; the *long thoracic* nerve to the serratus an-

terior from the dorsal surface of C5, C6, C7. From the upper trunk emerge dorsally the *suprascapular* nerve (C4, C5, C6) for the supraspinatus and infraspinatus; ventrally the small nerve to the subclavius (C5, C6). The roots of the *anterior thoracic* nerves (C5–Th1) which innervate the pectoralis major and minor arise in part from the ventral surface of the upper and middle trunks, in part from the medial fasciculus (Fig. 131).

The three large peripheral nerves of the arm, radial, median and ulnar, are formed in the following manner. The posterior fasciculus which receives contributions from all the plexus nerves, gives off the *thoracodorsal* (C6–C8) and the *subscapular* nerves (C5–C8), the former supplying the latissimus dorsi, the latter the teres major and subscapularis. Then it splits into its two terminal branches, the larger *radial* and the smaller *axillary* nerve. The lateral and medial fasciculi each split into two branches, thus forming four nerve trunks. The two middle branches, one from the lateral and one from the medial fasciculus, unite to form the *median* nerve. The outer branch derived from the lateral fasciculus becomes the *musculocutaneous nerve.* The large innermost branch derived from the medial fasciculus gives off the purely sensory *medial brachial cutaneous* and *medial antibrachial cutaneous* nerves, and is then continued as the *ulnar* nerve (Figs. 131, 132).

A brief reference to embryological conditions will aid in explaining the formation of the plexus. During early development the primitive muscle mass of the limb is split into a dorsal and a ventral layer, separated by the anlage of the humerus. The primary ventral nerve rami invading the limb likewise split into dorsal and ventral branches to supply the corresponding muscles and the overlying skin. Within the primitive musculature, many simple muscles fuse to form larger and more complex ones and become supplied by two or more spinal nerves, with resulting interlacing of nerve fibers and plexus formation. Such fusion usually occurs within the dorsal or the ventral musculature and the muscles are innervated respectively by dorsal or ventral nerves. However at the cephalic (preaxial) and the caudal (postaxial) border of the limb some muscles may be derived from both the dorsal and ventral musculature. These are shoulder. The nerves arising from the dorsal plate are the dorsal scapular, long thoracic, suprascapular, subscapular, thoracodorsal, axillary and radial. Those from the ventral plate include the subclavian, anterior thoracic, musculocutaneous, median, ulnar, and the purely sensory medial brachial and medial antibrachial cutaneous nerves.

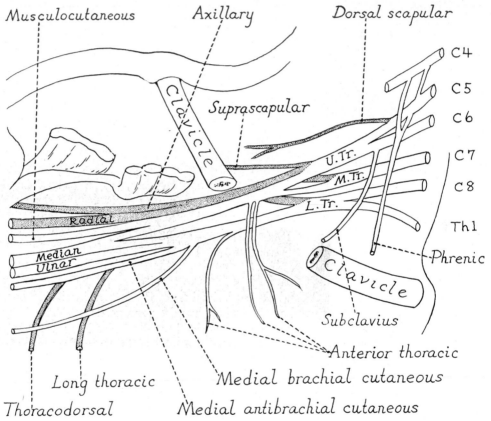

FIG. 132. The brachial plexus. (After a dissection by Borchardt.) The dorsal nerves are stippled. U.Tr., M.Tr., L.Tr., upper, middle, and lower trunk.

then supplied by both dorsal and ventral nerves. A well known example is the brachialis muscle which receives branches from the radial and musculocutaneous nerves. Thus the plexus primitively shows a division into a dorsal and a ventral plate, the former innervating the dorsal or extensor half of the arm and the dorsal shoulder muscles, the latter supplying the volar or flexor half and the ventral muscles of the

In very rare instances this primitive division into dorsal and ventral plates may persist in the adult and give rise to the arm nerves without the formation of the primary plexus trunks.

Following is a summary of the peripheral distribution of the principal arm nerves, including the segmental supply of the individual muscles. The cutaneous areas are shown in figs. 133, 134.

The *axillary* nerve supplies motor branches to the deltoid (C4–C6) and teres minor (C5, C6) and sends the *lateral brachial cutaneous* nerve to the skin of the upper outer surface of the arm, mainly the deltoid region (Figs. 133, 134). In complete section of the nerve, abduction of the arm without external rotation is practically impossible. The sensory loss is less extensive than the area supplied, due to the overlap of neighboring cutaneous nerves.

The *radial* nerve (C5–Th1) supplies motor branches to all the extensors of the elbow, hands and fingers, to the brachioradialis, supinator and abductor pollicis longus. In addition it usually sends a twig to the brachialis. Its cutaneous branches, all distributed to the dorsal surface of the extremity, are the *posterior brachial cutaneous nerve* to the arm, the *dorsal antibrachial cutaneous* to the forearm, and the *superficial ramus* to the radial half of the dorsum of the hand and fingers to the proximal interphalangeal joints (Fig. 134). The muscular branches are given off to the muscles in the following order:

Triceps and Anconeus, C7, C8, Th1.
Brachioradialis, C5, C6.
Extensor carpi radialis longus, C6, C7.
Supinator, C5, C6.
Extensor digitorum communis, (C6), C7, C8.
Extensor carpi radialis brevis, C7.
Abductor pollicis longus, C7, C8.
Extensor carpi ulnaris, C7, C8.
Extensor digiti quinti proprius, C7, C8.
Extensor pollicis longus, C7, C8.
Extensor pollicis brevis, C8, Th1.
Extensor indicis proprius, C8, Th1.

Injuries of the radial nerve will give variable symptoms depending on the height of the lesion. Complete section of the nerve above all its branches will produce inability to extend the elbow, wrist, fingers and thumb, with wrist drop as the most striking feature. The sensory loss is most marked on the dorsum of the hand in the territory supplied by the superficial ramus. The anesthesia is negligible on the arm, but is usually present in a narrow strip on the dorsal surface of the forearm from elbow to wrist. The limited sensory loss is due to overlap of adjacent cutaneous nerves.

The *musculocutaneous* nerve (C5–C7) sends muscular branches to the coracobrachialis (C6, C7), biceps (C5, C6) and brachialis (C5, C6), and continues as the *lateral antibrachial cutaneous* nerve to supply the radial half of the forearm, both dorsal and volar (Figs. 133, 134). In complete section of the nerve flexion and supination of the forearm are weakened. The lateral portion of the brachialis may be spared since it receives as a rule a branch from the radial nerve, and in addition flexion can still be produced by the brachioradialis. The sensory loss is variable in extent. It is poorly defined dorsally, due to overlap with the dorsal antibrachial cutaneous nerve of the radial. On the volar side it is more extensive and more nearly approximates the territory supplied by the nerve.

The *median* nerve (C6–Th1, sometimes also C5) supplies all the muscles on the volar surface of the forearm except the flexor carpi ulnaris and the ulnar heads of the flexor digitorum profundis. In the hand its branches go to the outer lumbricals (I, II) and to the muscles of the thenar eminence, excepting the adductor pollicis and deep head of the flexor pollicis brevis. The sensory innervation is practically limited to the hand, comprising the volar surface of the thumb, index and middle fingers and the radial half of the fourth finger, with corresponding portions of the palm (Fig. 133). Dorsally the nerve supplies the two distant phalanges of the index, middle and radial half of the fourth finger. An inconstant *palmar* branch is distributed to the radial half of the volar surface of the wrist, but this area is usually completely overlapped by the antibrachial branch of the musculocutaneous nerve. The order of the muscular branches is about as follows:

Pronator teres, C6, C7.
Flexor carpi radialis, C6–C8.
Palmaris longus, (C7), C8, Th1.

Flexor digitorum sublimis, C7–Th1.

Flexor digitorum profundis, radial head, (C7), C8, Th1.

Flexor pollicis longus, (C7), C8, Th1.

Pronator quadratus, C8, Th1.

arm will affect all its branches. Complete interruption causes severe impairment of pronation of the forearm and weakened flexion of the wrist. The wasting of the thenar eminence and the abnormal position

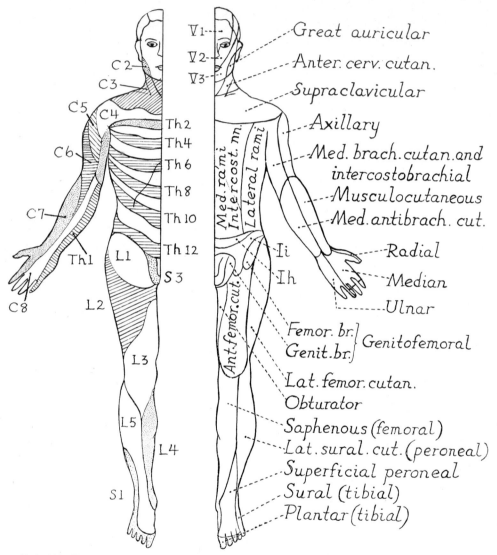

Fig. 133. Dermatomes (left) and cutaneous fields of peripheral nerves. Front view.
Ih, iliohypogastric; Ii, ilioinguinal

Flexor pollicis brevis, superficial head, C8, Th1.

Abductor pollicis brevis, C8, Th1; opponens pollicis, C8, Th1.

Lumbricales I and II, (C7), C8, Th1.

Injury to the nerve along its course in the

of the thumb may give the hand a characteristic appearance. Normally the thumb is partially rotated and its metacarpal bone is in a more volar plane than the other metacarpals. In injury of the median nerve the rotation is lost, the thumb is extended and now lies in the same plane as the rest of the palm (simian hand).

Flexion of the index finger is practically abolished, and is only slightly compensated by the flexor action of the interossei at the metacarpophalangeal joint. The middle finger is more variably affected. In the thumb flexion of the terminal phalanx is completely lost, as are abduction and opposition of the thumb. Make-shift movements of opposition, without abduction and rotation, can still be effected by the adductor pollicis and the deep head of the flexor brevis (pseudo-opposition). The motor defects are especially brought out in making a fist. The fourth and fifth fingers flex, the thumb and index finger, and to a variable degree the middle finger remain partially extended.

Disturbances of cutaneous sensibility occur in the area supplied by the nerve. Complete anesthesia is however much smaller in extent and is most constant on the volar surface of the index and middle finger.

The *ulnar* nerve (C8, Th1, some fibers also from C7) supplies in the forearm the flexor carpi ulnaris and the ulnar heads of the flexor digitorum profundis. In the hand it is distributed to the adductor pollicis, the deep head of the flexor pollicis brevis, the interossei, the two inner lumbricals, and the muscles of the hypothenar eminence. It gives off three cutaneous branches. The *palmar cutaneous* branch supplies the ulnar half of the volar surface of the wrist, an area extensively overlapped by the medial antibrachial cutaneous nerve. The *dorsal* branch goes to the ulnar half of the dorsum of the hand and little finger and to the proximal phalanx of the fourth and ulnar half of the middle finger. The *superficial volar* branch supplies the volar surface of the fifth and ulnar half of the fourth finger and the corresponding ulnar portion of the palm (hypothenar region), (Figs. 133, 134). The muscle branches are given off in the following order:

Flexor carpi ulnaris, (C7), C8, Th1.

Flexor digitorum profundis, ulnar heads, (C7), C8, Th1.

Palmaris brevis, C8, Th1.

Hypothenar muscles, C8, Th1:

Abductor digiti quinti.

Flexor digiti quinti brevis.

Opponens digiti quinti.

Interossei, C8, Th1.

Adductor pollicis, C8, Th1.

Flexor pollicis brevis, deep head, C8, Th1.

Lumbricales III and IV, C8, Th1.

As in the case of the median, injury to the ulnar nerve in the arm region will affect its whole distribution. Flexion of the wrist is weakened, as are also flexion of the fourth and fifth fingers and adduction of the thumb. There is marked wasting of the hypothenar muscles and of the interossei. The paralysis of these small muscles is practically most disturbing, making it exceedingly difficult to execute the finger movements required for writing, sewing and other skilled activities. The interossei flex the basal phalanges and extend the middle and distal ones. Hence paralysis of the interossei may cause an overextension of the basal phalanges by the extensor digitorum communis, and a flexion of the middle and distal ones by the flexor digitorum sublimis (claw hand).

Sensory disturbances are variable, corresponding in the main to the anatomical distribution. Total anesthesia is as a rule limited to the little finger and hypothenar region.

The *medial antibrachial cutaneous* nerve (C8, Th1) supplies the medial half of the forearm, both dorsal and volar (Figs. 133, 134). The extent of the sensory deficits caused by injury varies in individual cases. On the volar side it often reaches to the middle of the arm. On the dorsal side it is smaller than the area of supply.

The *medial brachial cutaneous* nerve (Th1) is usually associated with the *intercostobrachial* nerve derived from the second and often also from the third thoracic (intercostal) nerves. The two nerves supply the axillary region and the inner surface of the arm, the area being considerably larger on the volar than on the dorsal surface (Figs. 133, 134). The area is extensively overlapped by adjacent cutaneous nerves. Injury to one or the other produces negligible

of the injury and on whether the primary trunks or secondary cords are involved. In injury of the trunks the symptoms are segmental in character, and two main types of symptom complexes may be recognized,

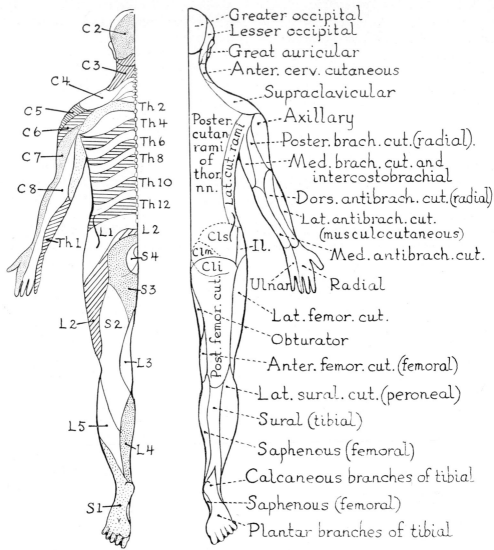

Fig. 134. Dermatomes (left) and cutaneous fields of peripheral nerves. Back view. Cls, Clm, Ci, superior, medial, and inferior clunial nerves; Il, iliohypogastric nerve.

symptoms or none at all. In injury of both the anesthesia is limited to the axillary region and medial surface of the upper arm.

Injuries of the brachial plexus. The motor and sensory deficits of plexus lesions vary considerably, depending on the extent

affecting respectively the upper or the lower primary trunk. The upper type (syndrome of Duchenne-Erb) involves the muscles supplied by C5 and C6, namely the deltoid, biceps, brachialis, brachioradialis, supinator, teres major, teres minor, supraspinatus and infraspinatus. There is difficulty in the elevation and external rotation of the arm, and practical loss of flexion and supination of the forearm. Owing to the overlap of adjacent roots, the sensory deficit is as a rule limited to the deltoid region and outer aspect of forearm.

The lower type (syndrome of Klumpke or of Duchenne-Aran) is relatively rare and affects primarily the small muscles of the hand innervated by C8 and Th1. The palmaris longus and the long digital flexors are usually also involved, hence the chief disabilities are in the finger and wrist movements. The sensory defects are along the inner aspect of the arm, forearm and hand. If the preganglionic sympathetic fibers of the first thoracic root are included in the injury, there will be drooping of the eyelid, diminution of the pupil and narrowing of the palpebral fissure (Horner's syndrome, see p. 161).

Injuries of the secondary cords produce symptoms similar to those of peripheral nerves, except that several peripheral nerves are affected at the same time. Thus a lesion of the posterior cord will involve the radial and axillary nerves, and often also the thoracodorsal and subscapular. Interruption of the lateral cord will affect the musculocutaneous and the lateral portion of the median nerve, while injury to the medial cord will involve the ulnar and the medial portion of the median nerve as well as the medial brachial and antibrachial cutaneous nerves. The motor and sensory disabilities resulting from injury of these nerves have already been discussed.

The lumbosacral plexus. The plexus innervating the lower extremity is as a rule formed by the primary ventral (anterior) rami of L1–S2 and the larger portion of S3, frequently with a small contributing branch from Th12. As in the case of the brachial plexus there are considerable variations. The plexus is *prefixed* when supplied by Th12–S2, *postfixed* when formed from L2–S4, with many intermediate conditions, the

maximum shift in either direction rarely exceeding the extent of a single spinal nerve. These conditions are probably determined by the individual variations in the position of the limb buds during development. According to Foerster (1929) prefixed plexuses are rare, since in none of his cases did faradic stimulation of the twelfth thoracic nerve produce a contraction of a single muscle in the lower extremity.

The lumbosacral plexus, excluding the pudendal and coccygeal portions which are not distributed to the leg, is conveniently subdivided into an upper *lumbar* and a lower *sacral* plexus, without however any definite line of demarcation. The lumbar plexus is formed by L1, L2, L3 and the larger part of L4, and there is usually a communicating branch from Th12 (Fig. 135). The more extensive sacral plexus is supplied by the smaller portion of L4 (furcal nerve) which joins L5 to form the stout lumbosacral trunk, and by S1, S2 and the greater portion of S3 (Fig. 136). Except for the uppermost portion supplied mainly by L1, where the conditions are somewhat obscure, both plexuses show an organization into dorsal and ventral divisions. The arrangement is however simpler than in the arm plexus. The undivided lumbosacral primary rami do not form interlacing trunks but split directly into dorsal and ventral divisions related respectively to the primitive dorsal and ventral musculature of the leg. The peripheral nerves to the extremity are then formed by the union of a varying number of dorsal or of ventral divisions (Figs. 135, 136). In the lumbar plexus the ventral divisions give rise to the iliohypogastric (ventral branch), ilioinguinal, genitofemoral and obturator nerves; the dorsal to the iliohypogastric (dorsal branch), femoral, and lateral femoral cutaneous nerves. According to Eisler the saphenous nerve and the medial portions of the anterior cutaneous nerves, both of which are branches of the femoral, likewise belong to the ventral division. In the sacral plexus the ventral divisions furnish the tibial nerve and the nerve to the hamstring muscles; the dorsal divisions form the common peroneal and the superior and inferior gluteal nerves. The posterior femoral cutaneous nerve which supplies the back of the thigh receives fibers from both dorsal and ventral divisions. As in the case of the arm, muscles derived from both the dorsal and the ventral primitive musculature, are innervated by both dorsal and ventral divisions. Thus the biceps femoris

is distributed to the inner surface of the thigh (Figs. 133, 134), the area being extensively overlapped by adjacent cutaneous nerves. The muscle branches are as fol'ows:

Obturator externus, L4.

Adductor magnus, L2, L4; lower portion, L5, S1 (sciatic nerve).

Adductor brevis, L2–L4.

Adductor longus, L2–L4.

Gracilis, L2–L4.

(Pectineus, L2–L4).

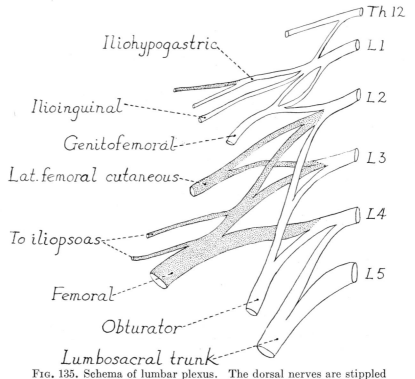

FIG. 135. Schema of lumbar plexus. The dorsal nerves are stippled

receives branches from the tibial as well as peroneal portions of the sciatic nerve.

Following is a summary of the peripheral distribution of the principal leg nerves including the segmental supply of the individual muscles. The cutaneous areas are shown in figs. 133, 134.

The *obturator* nerve (L2–L4) supplies the adductor muscles of the thigh and the gracilis, and sends an inconstant branch to the pectineus which is more often innervated by the femoral nerve. Its cutaneous branch

In injury of the nerve, adduction of the thigh is severely weakened but not completely lost since the adductor magnus also receives fibers from the sciatic nerve. The sensory defects usually involve only a small triangular area of the anatomical field.

The *femoral* nerve (L2–L4, also L1) sends motor branches to the extensors of the leg, the iliopsoas, the sartorius and usually also to the pectineus. Occasionally a branch may go to the adductor longus. The cutaneous branches are the *anterior femoral cutane-*

ous nerves for the thigh and the *saphenous* nerve for the leg and foot (Figs. 133, 134). The former supply the ventral and ventromedial surface of the thigh, comprising a relatively large autonomous sensory field. The saphenous nerve sends an infrapatellar branch to the skin in front of the knee-cap and is then distributed to the medial side of the leg, the lowermost terminal branches going to the medial margin of the foot to about the proximal phalanx of the great toe. The order of muscular branches is as follows:

Iliopsoas, L1–L4, mainly L1, L2.

Pectineus, L2–L4.

Sartorius, L1–L3.

Quadriceps femoris:

    Rectus femoris, L2–L4

    Vastus lateralis and vastus intermedius, L2–L4

    Vastus medialis, L2–L4

Injury of the nerve causes inability to extend the leg. If the lesion is high enough to involve the iliopsoas, flexion of the thigh is severely impaired. Sensory disturbances are manifested throughout the field of supply with relatively large areas of total anesthesia. If the thigh nerves alone are involved the anesthesia is most extensive on the ventral surface of the thigh above the knee. In isolated lesions of the saphenous nerve, the anesthetic field extends on the inner surface of the leg from just below the knee to the medial margin of the foot.

The *lateral femoral cutaneous* nerve (L2, L3) supplies the lateral half of the thigh, both dorsal and ventral, extending from the lateral buttock region to the knee (Figs. 133, 134). In spite of considerable overlapping with adjacent cutaneous nerves, injury produces a considerable strip of anesthesia on the lateral aspect of the thigh.

The cutaneous areas supplied by the *iliohypogastric* (L1), *ilioinguinal* (L1) and *genitofemoral* (L1, L2) nerves are shown in figs. 133, 134. The iliohypogastric and ilioinguinal also send motor fibers to the internal oblique and transverse muscles. Sensory loss due to injury of any one of these nerves is relatively small or lacking altogether, but such lesions frequently cause neuralgia.

The *sciatic* nerve (L4–S3), the largest nerve in the body, is the chief continuation of all the roots of the sacral plexus. It is in reality composed of the two main leg nerves, the tibial and the common peroneal, enclosed for a variable distance within a common sheath (Fig. 136). Emerging from the greater sciatic foramen, or while still within it, the nerve sends branches to the main external rotators of the thigh, comprising the obturator internus, the gemelli and the quadratus femoris (L5, S1, S2). Lesions of these nerves are comparatively rare and little is known of their clinical symptoms, but there is probably only a weakening of external rotation, since other external rotators are available. In the region of the thigh branches are given off to the flexors of the knee (hamstring muscles) and to the adductor magnus, the latter being also innervated by the obturator nerve. These branches, all derived from the tibial portion of the sciatic, often spring from a common trunk which either runs independently or is loosely incorporated in the medial side of the sciatic nerve. An additional branch arising much lower from the common peroneal nerve supplies the short head of the biceps femoris. In injuries of the hamstring nerves flexion of the knees is severely impaired, but some flexion may still be produced by the action of the gracilis and probably also of the sartorius.

The sciatic splits into its two terminal nerves at greatly varying levels of the thigh regions. The muscular branches of the common trunk are as follows:

Quadratus femoris, obturator, gemelli, L5, S1, S2.

Semitendinosus, L5–S2.

Semimembranosus, L5–S2.

Biceps femoris, long head, L5–S2.

Biceps femoris, short head, S1, S2 (common peroneal nerve).

The *tibial* nerve (L4–S3) supplies the dorsal calf muscles concerned with plantar flexion and inversion of the foot and with plantar flexion of the toes, and the intrinsic muscles of the sole which aid in maintaining the arch of the foot. One cutaneous branch given off in the thigh, the *sural* nerve, is distributed to the dorsal and medial surface supply the back and medial margin of the heel, the plantar surface of the foot and toes and the dorsal surface of the distal phalanges (Figs. 133, 134). The muscle branches are as follows:

Gastrocnemius, S1, S2.

Plantaris, S1, S2.

Popliteus, L5, S1, S2.

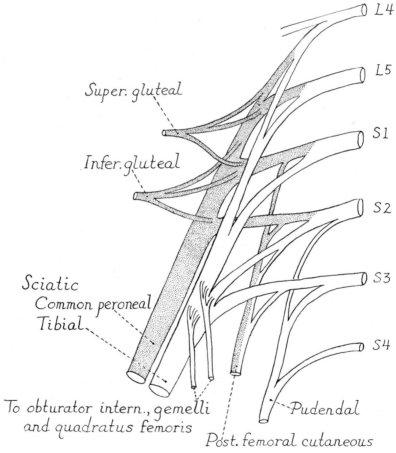

Super. gluteal

Infer. gluteal

Sciatic
Common peroneal
Tibial

To obturator intern., gemelli
and quadratus femoris

Pudendal

Post. femoral cutaneous

L4

L5

S1

S2

S3

S4

Fig. 136. Schema of sacral plexus. The dorsal nerves are stippled

of the calf where it is extensively overlapped by the end branchings of the saphenous and lateral sural (peroneal) nerves. The terminal branches of the sural (*lateral calcaneal*) supply the outer margin of the heel and a triangular area on the outer surface of the foot to about the lower portion of the Achilles tendon. Direct terminals of the tibial nerve (*medial calcaneal* and *plantar*)

Soleus, S1, S2.

Tibialis posterior, L4, L5.

Flexor digitorum longus, S1, S2.

Flexor hallucis longus, S1, S2.

Muscles of the sole:

Flexor digitorum brevis, S2, S3.

Interossei and lumbricales, S1–S3.

Flexor brevis and abductor digiti quinti, S1–S3.

Abductor hallucis, S1–S3.

Flexor hallucis brevis, S1–S3.

Adductor hallucis, S1–S3.

Complete interruption of the tibial nerve above all its branches will abolish plantar flexion of foot and toes and severely impa r inversion of the foot   Atrophy of the sole muscles will increase the concavity of the plantar arch (pes cavus). Sensory disturbances are negligible in the calf region in which only a narrow strip may show reduced sensitivity. Total anesthesia is found on the sole of the foot, the plantar surface of the toes and on the heel, and often on a triangular area on the outer surface of the foot.

The *common peroneal* nerve (L4–S2) supplies the lateral and ventral muscles of the leg and the dorsal muscles of the foot, effecting dorsal flexion and eversion of the foot and dorsal flexion of the toes. The chief cutaneous nerves are the *lateral sural cutaneous* and the *superficial peroneal* nerve (Figs. 133, 134). The former, given off in the thigh, is distributed to the outer side of the leg from the knee region to nearly the outer margin of the sole where it invades the territories of the superficial peroneal and sural nerves. The superficial peroneal supplies the dorsum of the foot and toes to the distal phalanges and a portion of the ventral surface of the leg. A small branch of the deep peroneal nerve is distributed to the adjacent surfaces of the great and second toe. The muscle branches are as follows:

Peroneus longus, L5–S2.

Peroneus brevis, L5–S2.

Tibialis anterior, L4, L5.

Extensor digitorum longus, L5, S1.

Peroneus tertius, L5, S1.

Extensor hallucis longus, L5, S1.

Extensor digitorum brevis, S1, S2.

Extensor hallucis brevis, S1, S2.

Complete section of the peroneal nerve causes paralysis of dorsal flexion and eversion of the foot and of dorsal flexion (extension) of the toes. The most striking feature is the inability to elevate the foot and toes (foot-drop). If the condition is prolonged, shortening of the Achilles tendon will produce a permanent plantar overflexion and the foot will assume the appearance of equinovarus. Sensory defects will be found on the dorsum of the foot, the outer part of the leg, and the skin between the great and second toe. The extent is much smaller than the anatomical field, since both foot and leg areas are extensively overlapped by the adjacent cutaneous nerves.

The *superior gluteal* nerve (L4–S1) supplies the gluteus medius, gluteus minimus and tensor fasciae latae, which abduct the hip and rotate it internally. These movements will be impaired by injury to the nerve.

The *inferior gluteal* nerve (L5–S2) is distributed to the gluteus maximus which is the strongest extensor of the hip. Injury causes wasting of the buttock. There is difficulty in rising from a sitting position, wa king uphill or climbing stairs, where powerful contraction of the muscle is required for raising the body.

The *posterior femoral cutaneous* nerve (S1–S3) gives off several branches (*inferior clunial*) which supply the lower portions of the buttocks where they overlap with the branches of the lumbar and sacral dorsal rami (superior and medial clunial nerves), (Fig. 134). Another small branch (*perineal*) goes to the lower innermost part of the buttock and the dorsal surface of the scrotum (or labia majora) and reaches the inner surface of the thigh. The main stem supplies the dorsal aspect of the thigh, often extending considerably below the knee and widely overlapping with adjacent nerves. Injuries produce a relatively broad strip of anesthesia on the dorsal surface of the thigh from buttocks to the level of the knee-cap.

Regeneration of injured peripheral nerves. Our knowledge of the processes of degeneration and regeneration has been greatly increased in recent years by intensive investigations on mammalian nerves under various experimental conditions and by clinical and surgical studies of the many peripheral nerve injuries resulting from the war. Seddon (1944) distinguishes three types of nerve injury: (1) Complete anatomical division (*neurotmesis*), practically always demanding surgical intervention, such as suture, for a more or less successful recovery. The recovery is however never complete since many of the regenerating fibers fail to reach their respective end organs. (2) Injuries in which the continuity of the nerve fibers is broken but the sheath and supporting tissue remain intact (*axonotmesis*), due to crush or severe compression. There is complete degeneration of the severed nerve fibers as in neurotmesis, and the clinical symptoms such as loss of sensation and movement, wasting of muscles and reaction of degeneration, are likewise the same. But since the damaged nerve fibers are in close anatomical contiguity, spontaneous regeneration always leads to good recovery. (3) Temporary impairment or block, with varying degree of paralysis but with persistence of normal electrical excitability (*neurapraxia*). The nerve fibers are not severed, hence there is no peripheral degeneration. Recovery is rapid, beginning in a few weeks and usually completed in two or three months. The three types may appear as separate entities or in various combinations. Since the clinical symptoms of neurotmesis and axonotmesis are the same until recovery begins, surgical exploration is usually indicated to determine the nature of the injury. (Stookey and Scarff).

After primary suture of the peroneal nerve in the rabbit it takes about seven days for the growing axon tips of the central stump to traverse the scar of the gap and reach the peripheral stump (Gutmann, Guttmann, Medawar and Young). After crush the "scar" delay is about 5 days. Then the fastest tips grow at the rate of 3.5 mm. a day after suture, 4.4 mm. after a crush. The growing axons reach their respective end organs before the return of function which is "dependent on all the processes of maturation leading to functional completion", hence there is a further delay before advance in recovery begins. The total latent period in the rabbit is about 36 days after suture and 20 days after a crush. In man the process may be somewhat slower, though a rate of 4.4 mm. a day for growing axons was found after a crush of one of the digital nerves (Bowden and Gutmann). However, the rate of functional regeneration appears to fall off with the distance traversed, and the variable delay due to the nature of the scar has likewise to be considered. According to Bowden and Gutmann, a justifiable assumption for axonal growth in man is about 3 mm. per day, with an average latent period of 20 days after axonotmesis and 50 days after suture.

A knowledge of the histological changes is of great importance for intelligent surgical repair. Many growing axon tips, after traversing the gap, may enter a single neurilemma tube (band fiber). Only one of these usually goes to functional completion, gradually increasing in thickness and becoming myelinated. The others apparently atrophy and disappear. Fewer fibers enter a peripheral stump which has degenerated for a long time, and myelinization is considerably retarded. There are other serious disadvantages when sutures are delayed for too long a period. While true degenerative changes and fragmentation of muscle fibers probably do not occur till the end of the third year after denervation, there is extreme shrinkage of the muscle fibers and a great increase in connective tissue. This makes it difficult or even impossible for growing axons to find and make connections with degenerating nerve fibers. Hence the chances for recovery are poor even before muscle degeneration has started. After three years the changes in muscle tissue can no longer be reversed by re-innervation (Bowden and Gutmann). It is important also that the sensory and motor end organs be re-innervated before the neuri emma tubes leading to them are blocked by proliferating connective tissue, and before the end organs themselves disintegrate and finally disappear a together. While the growing axons, after long atrophy, will ultimate y make new contacts with the shrunken muscle fibers and form end plates, the process is slow and incomplete, and the new end plates are often simple axonal thickenings surrounded by a number of nuclei. From the evidence it is concluded that a delay of two or three months before suture will not hinder recovery, but that greater delays, especially over six months or longer, will seriously interfere with the reparative processes or even prevent them altogether. After three years any degree of recovery is apparently impossible.

CHAPTER XI

THE FIBER TRACTS OF THE SPINAL CORD

The ascending and descending fibers of the spinal cord do not run in a haphazard manner but are organized into more less distinct functional bundles which occupy definite areas in the white matter. When such bundles consist of fibers having the same origin, termination and function they are known as *tracts*. When composed of a mixture of functionally distinct fibers they are usually termed *fasciculi*. The various tracts and fascicles are not sharply demarcated, but on the contrary show considerable overlapping and intermingling. In general, the long fibers are peripherally placed, the shorter lying nearest the gray matter.

In determining the fiber tracts, the method of secondary or Wallerian degeneration has been especially valuable (Fig. 137). When a nerve fiber is cut, not only does the part severed from the cell body undergo complete degeneration, but the cell body itself exhibits certain pathological changes, such as central chromatolysis, swelling and nuclear eccentricity (p. 39). Thus if the cord is cut at some particular level, all the ascending fibers will degenerate above that level ("ascending" degeneration) being severed from their cell bodies located below the cut, and the cells of the cut fibers will show the pathological changes mentioned (Fig. 49). On the other hand, below the level of injury the descending fibers will degenerate ("descending" degeneration) since their cell bodies are placed above the cut. In the same way the central continuations of the dorsal root fibers may be determined by following their secondary degeneration in the cord after cutting the dorsal roots proximal to the spinal ganglia (Fig. 137). In this case the chromatolysis will occur in the spinal ganglion cells. The location of the neuron bodies which give rise

to the ventral roots may be similarly determined by cutting the latter and ascertaining which cell bodies in the cord show the regressive changes of axonal degeneration. By the extensive use of this method, both experimentally and in cases of human injury, the origin, course and termination of many important tracts have been definitely established.

THE LONG ASCENDING TRACTS

I. **The dorsal white column.** (*Fasciculus gracilis and fasciculus cuneatus*.) Since the dorsal funiculus and zone of Lissauer are predominantly composed of dorsal root fibers, both the ascending and descending course of these fibers will be described under this heading.

It has been noted that each dorsal root just before entering the cord, separates into a lateral fine-fibered and a medial coarse-fibered portion. The former composed of finely myelinated and unmyelinated fibers passes to the zone of Lissauer where the fibers bifurcate into short ascending and descending arms only a segment or so in length. The coarser fibers of the medial portion enter the dorsal white column just medial to the dorsal horn and likewise bifurcate into ascending and descending arms of variable but often considerable length, many of the ascending ones passing upward the whole extent of the spinal cord to terminate in the medulla. As these fibers ascend they are gradually displaced medially and somewhat dorsally by the ascending arms of the dorsal roots entering at successively higher levels, thus effecting a segmental arrangement of fibers in the dorsal column (Fig. 139). At any level of the cord, the most medial fibers close to the dorsal septum are the longest and come from

130

the lowermost dorsal roots. Progressing laterally the fibers represent successively higher dorsal roots, those of the uppermost root lying closest to the medial surface of

of Burdach) (Figs. 112, 138, 141, 142). The former contains the long ascending root fibers from the sacral, lumbar and lower thoracic ganglia, i.e. from the lower ex-

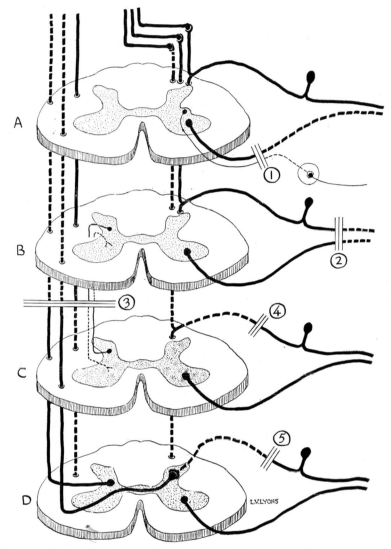

FIG. 137. Diagram illustrating the secondary degeneration of nerve fibers separated from their neuron bodies by lesions of the spinal roots or spinal cord. (After a figure from Ranson.) A,B,C,D, various levels of spinal cord. 1,2,3,4,5, various lesions severing nerve fibers. The portions undergoing secondary degeneration are indicated by broken lines.

the dorsal horn. In the cervical region the now massive dorsal funiculus is divided by the dorsal intermediate septum into a medial *fasciculus gracilis* (column of Goll) and a lateral *fasciculus cuneatus* (column

tremity and lower portion of the trunk. The fasciculus cuneatus consists of similar fibers from the upper thoracic and cervical ganglia representing upper trunk, upper extremity and neck. The fibers of the fasciculus gracilis and fasciculus cuneatus terminate respectively in the nucleus gracilis and nucleus cuneatus of the medulla.

Since many ascending arms are relatively short, it is evident that only a portion of the root fibers terminate in the medulla, the others ending in the dorsal gray column at various intermediate levels. Those which

(Brouwer), receiving principally impulses from the arms and legs. In animals without extremities they are poorly developed and consist mainly of shorter fibers. When we consider the great importance of the upper extremity, especially the hand, as an organ for discriminative sensibility and acquisition of skill, and the lower extremity

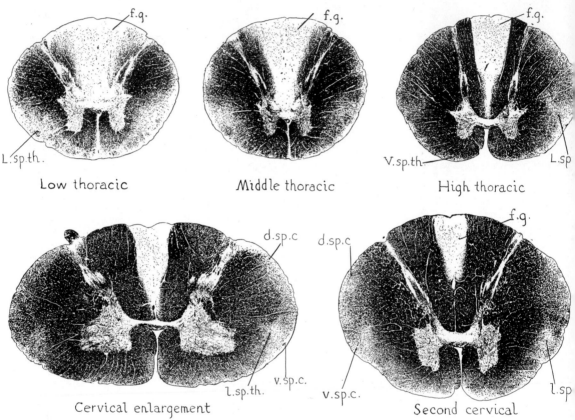

Low thoracic   Middle thoracic   High thoracic

Cervical enlargement   Second cervical

FIG. 138. Transverse sections of a human spinal cord which had been crushed some time previously in the lumbo-sacral region. Weigert's myelin stain. Photographs. *d.sp.c.*, dorsal spinocerebellar tract; *f.g.*, fasciculus gracilis; *l.sp.th.*, lateral spinothalamic tract; *v.sp.c.*, ventral spinocerebellar tract. In the dorsal column the progressive diminution of the degenerated area is due to the passing into the gray of the short and medium ascending arms of the lumbo-sacral dorsal root fibers. Also the progressive increase of normal fibers, next to the dorsal horn, is due to the addition of ascending arms of dorsal root fibers entering the cord above the injury.

reach the bulb constitute the first relay of an important afferent pathway to the cerebral cortex. According to Winkler, they come primarily from the lumbosacral and cervical segments, the thoracic contributing relatively few long arms to the medulla.

The dorsal white columns are among the newer acquisitions of the nervous system

for the maintenance of erect posture, it is not surprising that this phylogenetically younger fiber system constitutes the principal path for the conduction of discriminative (epicritic) sensibility related to cortical function.

The long fibers of the dorsal column convey impulses from the proprioceptors which give rise to sensations of position and movement. They also conduct impulses from tactile receptors necessary for the proper discrimination of two points simultaneously applied (spatial discrimination) and for exact tactile localization. Rapidly successive stimuli produced by the application of a tuning fork to bone or faradic current to skin, which give rise to the sense of vibration (temporal discrimination), are likewise conducted along these fibers.

Lesions of the dorsal column will naturally abolish or diminish these forms of sensibility, the symptoms appearing on the same side as the lesion. Mere contact and pressure are apparently normal, but tactile localization is poor, and two-point discrimination and vibratory sense are lost or greatly diminished. There is loss of appreciation of

is a three-neuron pathway (Fig. 143). In general, one cerebral hemisphere represents the opposite half of the body, as regards sensation and movement. In the sensory pathways the crossing occurs as a rule in the second neuron (Fig. 143).

The descending arms of the dorsal roots, also varying in length, likewise become displaced medially and somewhat dorsally as they pass to lower segments of the cord. They are relatively short fibers but some may descend a distance of ten or more segments. In the cervical and most of the thoracic cord they form a small plug-shaped bundle, the *fasciculus interfascicularis* or *comma tract of Schultze*, lying about the middle of the dorsal funiculus (Figs. 140, 148). In the lumbar region they descend near the middle of the dorsal septum in the *no clinical importance*

   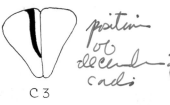

Th 11   Th. 9   Th 2   C 3   *position of descending cords*

FIG. 139. Ascending degeneration after section of dorsal roots L1, Th12 and Th11. Marchi method. (After Foerster.)

differences in weight and inability to identify objects placed in the hand by feeling them. These symptoms are most acute on the fingers and more acute on the extremities than on the trunk. Position and movement sense is severely affected, especially in the distal parts of the extremities, and as a rule accompanied by a diminution of muscular tone (hypotonia). Small passive movements are not recognized as movements at all but as touch or pressure. But even in long excursions the direction and extent of the movement are not perceived or only very poorly. With the loss of muscle sense there is inability to perform voluntary active movements properly, the latter being clumsy, uncertain and incoordinated (sensory or dorsal column ataxia).

The proprioceptive-discriminative touch-vibratory pathway from periphery to cortex

septomarginal fasciculus (*oval area of Flechsig*) which in the sacral cord occupies a small triangle near the dorsomedian periphery (*triangle of Phillippe-Gombault*, Figs. 140, 117, 119). Besides the descending root fibers, the above named fascicles also contain descending fibers from cells of the dorsal horn. *lumbar* *sacral*

The zone of Lissauer (*fasciculus dorsolateralis*) is composed of fine myelinated and unmyelinated arms of the dorsal root fibers which convey impulses of pain and temperature. Mingled with them are fibers from the substantia gelatinosa and marginal cells, which likewise ascend or descend for only a few segments. These are probably associative in character, connecting near parts of the dorsal horn.

II. **The spinothalamic and spinotectal tracts** arise from the large cells of the dorsal horn (nucleus centrodorsalis) and probably also from similar cells of the intermediate gray. The majority of the axons cross obliquely in the ventral commissure, the decussation extending through the height of one segment, and ascend in the ventral and ventrolateral white of the opposite side as

especially with the lateral spinothalamic fibers go to the roof of the midbrain as the *spinotectal* or *spinocollicular* fibers.

The lateral spinothalamic tract lying just mesial to the ventral spinocerebellar tract is the larger and more concentrated of the two, and contains more numerous long fibers

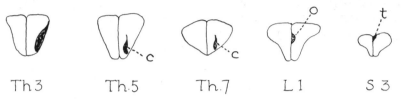

Th 3   Th.5   Th.7   L 1   S 3

FIG. 140. Descending degeneration after section of dorsal roots C3–Th3. Marchi method. (After Foerster.) The degenerating fibers occupy successively the comma tract (*c*), the oval bundle of Flechsig (*o*) and the triangle of Phillippe-Gombault (*t*). The last two constitute the septomarginal fasciculus.

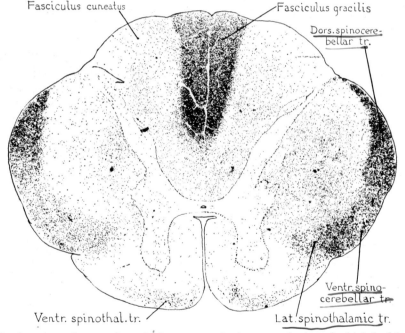

FIG. 141. Section through second cervical segment of a human spinal cord which had been crushed several weeks previously in the upper lumbar region. Marchi stain for degenerating fibers. Photograph. The ascending degenerating fibers are seen as black granules.

the *lateral* and *ventral spinothalamic tracts* (Figs. 138, 141, 142). A smaller number of uncrossed fibers ascends on the same side in similar locations. Only a portion of the fibers go directly to the thalamus, many terminating in the reticular formation of the medulla and pons and reaching the thalamus by several relays. Still others intermingled

going directly to the thalamus. The ventral spinothalamic, spread diffusely near the ventral periphery and ventral median sulcus, is composed mainly of short fibers. In cases of secondary degeneration, relatively few fibers can be traced above the medullary levels.

The lateral spinothalamic tract conveys

"Syringomyelia" is growth in central gray to interfere with second order neurons.

THE FIBER TRACTS OF THE SPINAL CORD   135

impressions of pain and temperature. As in the case of the dorsal white column, the fibers show a segmental arrangement, the most lateral fibers representing the lowest portion of the body, the more medial ones related to the upper portions. There is evidence that the paths for pain and temperature are distinct within the tract, the temperature fibers lying more dorsally (Foerster and Gagel), but the two are so closely associated that cord injuries will ordinarily affect both of them.

usually some recovery of painful sensibility, due undoubtedly to the presence of uncrossed spinothalamic fibers and perhaps also other more obscure compensatory pathways. The same applies to temperature. Bilateral section is necessary to produce a more complete and enduring sensory loss.

The ventral spinothalamic (and spinoreticular) fibers are believed to convey impulses of touch and pressure, supplementing the tactile path of the dorsal white column. Hence injury to this tract produces little if

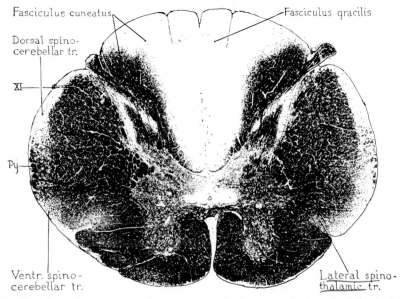

Fig. 142. Section through second cervical segment of a human spinal cord which had been crushed some time previously in the lower cervical region. Weigert's myelin stain. Photograph. Owing to the high level of the injury, practically all the fibers of the spinocerebellar and spinothalamic tracts have undergone degeneration; also all ascending root fibers in dorsal column except those of dorsal root fibers which have entered above the upper level of the lesion (about C6). Py, aberrant pyramidal fibers; XI, root fibers of spinal accessory nerve.

Unilateral section of this tract produces a complete loss of pain and temperature (analgesia and thermoanesthesia) on the opposite side of the body, extending upward to a level one segment below that of the lesion, due to the oblique crossing of the spinothalamic fibers. The anesthesia involves the superficial and deep portions of the body wall and extremities, but not the viscera which apparently are bilaterally represented. The anogenital region likewise is not markedly affected. After a variable period there is

any disturbance in tactile sensibility, though such may be ascertained by more precise methods of investigation (heightened threshold, reduction of touch and pressure points per unit skin area). The signs, if any, are more marked on the opposite side, but may also appear on the same side. The whole tract is rather diffusely organized. There are few direct fibers to the thalamus, impulses reaching the latter through several neuronal relays, and bilateral representation is considerable. Touch is the form of sensation least apt to be completely abolished in cord lesions.

Discriminative sensibility is undisturbed though it is maintained by some that tactile localization is conducted by these fibers (Head, Stopford). On the other hand, the

It is evident from the above that the sensory impulses brought in by the dorsal roots are organized in the spinal cord into two main systems, discriminative (epicritic) and affective (vital, protopathic), the former related to the long fibers of the dorsal

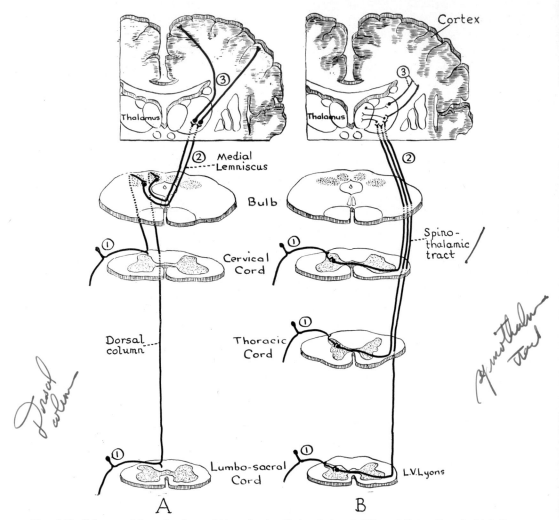

FIG. 143. Scheme of dorsal column (A) and spinothalamic tract (B) and the paths of which they are a part. (1) first neuron (spinal ganglionic); (2) second neuron (medial lemniscus in A, spinothalamic in B); (3) third neuron (thalamocortical).

pleasant or unpleasant character of sensation is definitely related to conduction in the ventrolateral columns. In bilateral destruction of these columns, there is apparently complete loss of these affect qualities such as itching, tickling and libidinous feeling (Foerster).

column, the latter to the shorter root fibers and the ventrolateral column. Discriminative sensibility carried by the longest fibers remains uncrossed in the spinal cord. Pain and temperature brought in by the shortest fibers in the zone of Lissauer cross almost at once *via* the lateral spinothalamic tract.

dorsal & ventral spinocerebellar are unconscious proprioception.

The rest of tactile sense (mere contact and pressure) is carried upward in the dorsal column by ascending root fibers of varying length which terminate in the gray of the cord and connect with the ventral spino-thalamic neurons at various intermediate levels (Stopford). This distribution of afferent impulses accounts for the curious sensory dissociation occurring in hemi-section of the spinal cord (Brown-Sequard) where there is loss of pain and temperature on the opposite half of the body below the level of lesion, while the sense of position and movement, two-point discrimination and vibration are lost on the same side as the lesion.

It is probable that cells of the substantia gelatinosa are intercalated between the fine root fibers which conduct pain and the neurons of the lateral spinothalamic tract, accounting perhaps for the high threshold and diffuse character of pain reactions.

III. **The dorsal spinocerebellar tract** (*tract of Flechsig, direct cerebellar tract*) is a prominent uncrossed fiber bundle lying along the dorsolateral periphery of the cord, bounded medially by the lateral pyramidal tract (Figs. 141, 142, 148). Its fibers arise from the cells of Clarke's column, pass laterally to the white matter of the same side and there ascend the whole length of the cord. In the medulla they form part of the inferior cerebellar peduncle and pass to the cerebellum, terminating in both the cephalic and caudal portion of the vermis. The tract appears first in the upper lumbar cord, L3 or L2, and increases in size until the upper limit of Clarke's column has been reached.

Since the column of Clarke is not present to any extent in the sacral and lower lumbar regions of the cord, impulses destined for the cerebellum are carried upward by the large myelinated ascending arms of the dorsal roots which give off bundles of collaterals to Clarke's column when the latter nucleus is reached (Figs. 124, 125). But even in the thoracic cord the dorsal root fibers usually ascend a few segments before sending collaterals to Clarke's column.

This uncrossed pathway from periphery to cerebellum is composed of two neurons, the spinal ganglion cells and the cells of Clarke's column (Fig. 144). The proprioceptive impulses transmitted by the dorsal spinocerebellar tract come mainly from the trunk and lower extremities.

IV. **The ventral spinocerebellar tract** is likewise situated along the lateral periphery of the cord, extending from the ventral limits of the direct cerebellar tract to about the exit of the ventral roots (Figs. 141, 142, 148). Mesially it is in intimate contact with the lateral spinothalamic tract, the two together constituting the *anterolateral fasciculus of Gower*. The tract is more diffusely organized than the direct cerebellar, and is composed of finer fibers which probably arise from cells scattered through the intermediate gray (intermediomedial nucleus) and perhaps also from cells in the base of the dorsal horn. The majority of the fibers are uncrossed, but a smaller number come from cells of the opposite side. The tract appears in the upper sacral or lower lumbar cord and naturally increases as it passed upward. The fibers of this tract reach the cerebellum by a somewhat different route, ascending considerably higher than the dorsal spinocerebellar tract, and then turning back along the outer side of the superior cerebellar peduncle to terminate in the cephalic portion of the vermis. This path to the cerebellum is likewise composed of two neurons (Fig. 144), but is partly crossed and partly uncrossed. The proprioceptive impulses conducted by the tract come from all parts of the body including the neck and upper extremities.

The spinocerebellar tracts convey to the cerebellum impulses from the muscle, tendon and joint receptors, which enable the cerebellum to exercise its regulative tonic and synergizing influence upon the voluntary muscles. Injury to these tracts, especially the direct cerebellar, results in reduced

lat. to lat. spino thalamic tract

muscular tone and in an incoordination of muscular action producing disturbances of posture and movement (cerebellar ataxia or asynergia). There is no sensory loss of position and movement, the impulses to the cerebellum remaining on an unconscious level.

central gyrus of the cerebral cortex (motor area, area 4 of Brodmann), in larger part from other cells of this and adjacent frontal areas (premotor area, area 6) and probably also from other cortical areas. They converge in the corona radiata and pass downward through the internal capsule, basis

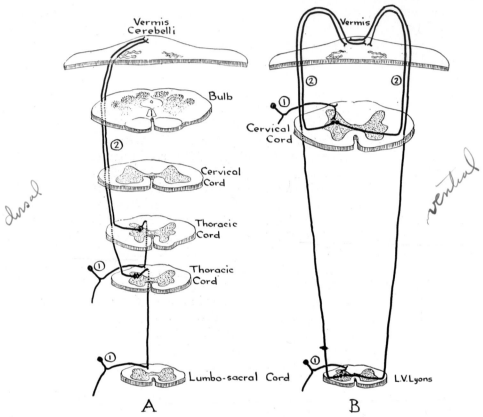

Fig. 144. Scheme of dorsal (*A*) and ventral (*B*) spinocerebellar tracts and the paths of which they are a part. (*1*) spinal ganglionic neurons; (*2*) spinocerebellar neurons.

THE LONG DESCENDING TRACTS

I. **The corticospinal or pyramidal tracts** constitute the most important and conspicuous descending fiber bundles of the cord, each composed, according to the latest counts, of over a million fibers (Lassek and Rasmussen, 1940). Some of the fibers are very large, having a caliber of 10–25 micra, but the great majority are much finer and have a thickness of 1–10 micra. The fibers arise in part from the giant pyramidal cells of Betz in the pre-

pedunculi, pons and medulla, giving off terminals to the motor nuclei of the cranial nerves. In the medulla the tracts come to the surface as the ventral pyramids. At the junction of medulla and cord, the fibers undergo an incomplete decussation giving rise to two tracts in each half of the spinal cord, a *lateral or crossed pyramidal* and a *ventral uncrossed or direct pyramidal* tract (Fig. 176).

The majority of the fibers, 75–90 per cent, cross in the pyramidal decussation and descend in the dorsal part of the lateral funiculus as the lateral or crossed pyramidal tract, lying between the dorsal spinocerebellar tract and the lateral fasciculus proprius (Figs. 145, 146, 147). It comes to the surface in the lumbar and sacral regions where the dorsal cerebellar tract is lacking. In the uppermost cervical segments some fibers occupy for a short distance an aberrant position outside the dorsal spinocerebellar fibers (Fig. 142). The tract extends to the lowermost part of the cord, constantly diminishing in size

its size shows considerable variations, due to the fact that the proportion of decussating fibers is not constant. In extreme cases they may be altogether absent, practically all of the fibers crossing in the pyramidal decussation. In other isolated cases, the pyramidal fibers of one or both sides may not cross at all and give rise to huge ventral pyramidal tracts.

Besides the two tracts discussed, there are other uncrossed corticospinal fibers which form the *ventrolateral pyramidal tract*

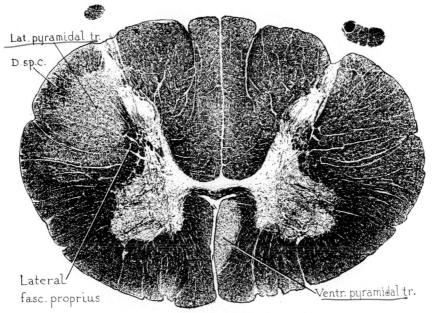

FIG. 145. Transverse section through cervical enlargement of spinal cord of hemiplegic man. Weigert's myelin stain. Photograph. The lateral pyramidal tract of one side and the ventral pyramidal tract of the other side are degenerated. *d.sp.c.*, dorsal spinocerebellar tract.

as more and more fibers leave to terminate in the gray matter.

A smaller portion of the pyramidal fibers descends uncrossed as the ventral or direct pyramidal tract (bundle of Türck), occupying an oval area adjacent to the ventral median sulcus (Figs. 145, 147). It normally extends only to the upper thoracic cord, though fibers have been traced to the lower thoracic and even lumbar region, thus innervating primarily the muscles of the upper extremities and neck. This tract is found only in man and the higher apes and

of Barnes ("Fibres pyramidales homolaterales superficielles" of Déjérine). The bundle is composed of rather fine fibers which descend more ventrally in the lateral funiculus, in or near the area occupied by the tract of Helweg (see below).

The fibers of the lateral pyramidal tract terminate in the gray of the same side. The termination of the direct tract is not fully ascertained. It is probable that most fibers cross individually through the ventral commissure to terminate on the opposite side, a smaller number ending on the same side. The majority of all pyramidal fibers are not projected directly on the ventral horn cells but terminate in arborizations around intercalated cells in the intermediate or ventral gray. Only a relatively small number (10–20 per cent) come in direct synapse with the motor cells (Hoff and Hoff, 1934).

It is evident from the above that the corticospinal system is primarily a crossed one, but nevertheless has considerable

lower. Myelinization of the fibers begins around birth and is not fully completed until the end of the second year.

The pyramidal tract conveys to the spinal cord impulses which result in volitional movements, especially those isolated individual movements of finger, hand, etc., which form the basis for the acquisition of skill. Destruction of the tract therefore produces a loss of voluntary movement, most marked in the distal parts of the

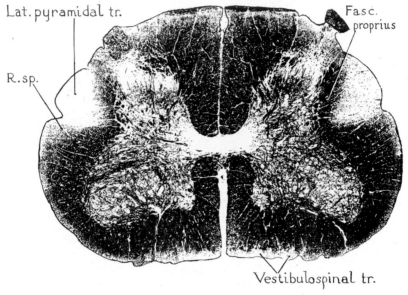

Lat. pyramidal tr.

Fasc. proprius

R.sp.

Vestibulospinal tr.

Fig. 146. Section through fourth lumbar segment of a human spinal cord which had been crushed some time previously in the lower cervical region. Weigert's myelin stain. Photograph. The degenerated long descending tracts are unstained. Note that the lateral pyramidal tract reaches the lateral periphery of the cord. *R.sp.*, rubrospinal and reticulospinal tracts.

homolateral representation through the ventrolateral tract of Barnes and the fibers of the direct pyramidal tract which end on the same side. Hoff and Hoff (1934) conclude that in the chimpanzee, 20–25 per cent of the fibers establish ipsolateral connections.

It has been estimated that about 55 per cent of all pyramidal fibers end in the cervical cord, 20 per cent in the thoracic, and 25 per cent in the lumbosacral (Weil and Lassek, 1930). This would suggest that pyramidal control over the upper extremity is much greater than over the

extremities, the proximal joints and grosser movement being less severely and less permanently affected. At the sudden onset of the "stroke", there is at first a loss of tone in the affected muscles. But after a period of days or even weeks the muscles gradually become more resistant to passive movement (spasticity), and the deep kinetic reflexes, especially in the leg, are increased in force (hyperreflexia). On the other hand, the superficial reflexes, such as the abdominals, cremasteric and normal plantar, are lost or diminished. In the case of the plantar reflex, stimulation of the sole is followed by

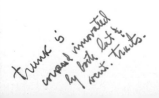

trunk is crossed innervated by both lat. & vent. tracts.

dorsiflexion of the big toe instead of the normal plantar flexion (sign of Babinski), a symptom invariably present in injury of the pyramidal tract. In time there may be considerable restitution, especially for the grosser movements, the residual defects being most marked in the distal parts of the extremities.

The belief that the spasticity usually occurring in human hemiplegia is due to the release of lower neural centers from pyram-

areas than was formerly supposed, and originating in part only from the giant pyramidal cells of Betz in the precentral gyrus. These cells are relatively few in number, about 25,000 according to Campbell, some 34,000 in the more careful recent count of Lassek (1940). They probably furnish the larger fibers, 10–25 micra in diameter, whose number has been estimated around 40,000 (Lassek and Rasmussen, 1940). The more numerous finer fibers

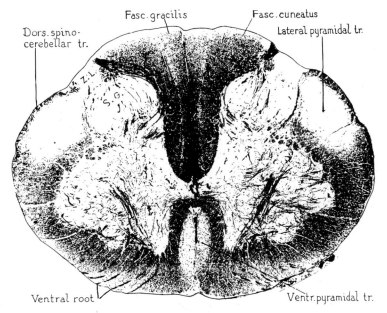

Fasc. gracilis

Fasc. cuneatus

Dors. spino-cerebellar tr.

Lateral pyramidal tr.

Z.L.

S.G.

Ventral root

Ventr. pyramidal tr.

FIG. 147. Section through cervical enlargement of spinal cord of seven to eight months human foetus. Weigert's myelin stain. Photograph. The pyramidal tracts are unmyelinated at this stage, hence are unstained. *S.G.*, substantia gelatinosa; *Z.L.*, zone of Lissauer.

idal control, is not shared by some investigators. Ablation of the motor area (area 4) in monkeys and chimpanzees produces paralysis of a flaccid character, and only when the premotor area (area 6) is also involved, is there increased resistance to passive movement (Fulton and Kennard). These investigators conclude therefore that the spasticity is due to "extrapyramidal" motor pathways descending in close conjunction with the pyramidal tracts.

It must be remembered, however, that the pyramidal tract is a complex fiber system arising from more extensive cortical

come in considerable part from the premotor area (area 6) and perhaps from other cortical regions (Häggquist, Kennard, Foerster). Thus there are at least two components in the pyramidal tract, a large-fibered component from the motor area, and a fine-fibered one from the motor, premotor and perhaps other areas. Lesions of the entire pyramidal tract involve both components, ablation of the motor area alone destroys only the large-fibered one (Häggquist, 1937). It is probable that the fibers of the Betz cells are concerned with the finer isolated movements of the

(handwritten margin notes: Betz #4 fine musculature #6 rough musculature; upper motor lower mo)

distal parts of the extremities, which are primarily affected in pyramidal lesions. The more numerous finer fibers may be related to grosser movement and tonic control, and injury to them may be the cause of the increase in muscle tone and the more active deep reflexes. These fibers are not however "extrapyramidal". They form an integral part of the pyramidal tract, its largest portion indeed, descending unin-

(ventral horn cells) which directly innervate the striped muscle. The symptoms of pyramidal lesion, characterized by loss of volitional movement, spasticity, increased deep reflexes, loss of superficial reflexes, and the sign of Babinski, are therefore often designated as "upper motor neuron" paralysis (spastic or supranuclear paralysis). In "lower motor neuron" paralysis, there is loss of all movement, reflex and voluntary,

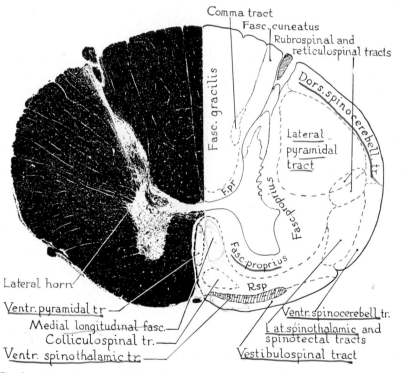

FIG. 148. Section through second thoracic segment (lower portion) of adult human spinal cord. Weigert's myelin stain. Photograph. The principal fiber tracts are indicated schematically on the right side. *F.pr.*, fasciculus proprius; *R.sp.*, reticulospinal fibers.

terruptedly from cerebral cortex through the medullary pyramids to the spinal cord. They come from cortical areas which also send true extrapyramidal tracts, i.e., tracts which are relayed in subcortical nuclei before reaching the cord, and which perhaps have functions similar to the fine-fibered component of the pyramidal tract.

The pyramidal cells and their axons constitute the "upper motor neurons" in contrast to the "lower motor neurons"

with loss of tone and rapid atrophy of the affected muscles.

Paralysis of both arm and leg on one side is termed a *hemiplegia*, that of a single limb a *monoplegia*. *Diplegia* denotes the paralysis of two corresponding parts on opposite sides, such as both arms, though when both legs are involved the term *paraplegia* is often used. Paralysis of all four extremities is usually known as *tetraplegia*.

II. **The vestibulospinal tract** originates

from the lateral vestibular nucleus of the medulla which receives fibers from the vestibular division of the eighth nerve and from the cerebellum, and descends uncrossed along the ventral periphery of the cord, intermingled with ascending fibers of the ventral spinothalamic tract (Figs. 146, 148). It is reduced in man, but its fibers have been traced to the lowermost part of the cord, all terminating in the ventral gray. Fewer fibers, both crossed and uncrossed, also pass down more mesially in the ventral white column as part of the medial longitudinal fasciculus to be described below (Fig. 148).

The vestibulospinal tracts bring to the ventral horn cells impulses from the vestibular mechanism of the ear and from the cerebellum. These probably exert a tonic influence upon the musculature of the trunk and extremities which aid in maintaining position and equilibrium, especially in correlation with positions of the head. Examples of their activity are seen in the tendency to fall after being rapidly rotated, and in the "past-pointing" reaction. In the latter, after being rotated in a certain direction, vertical voluntary movements tend to deviate in that direction and the person misses objects he endeavors to touch with his eyes closed.

III. **The rubrospinal tract** is a small fiber bundle arising from certain large cells of the red nucleus (nucleus ruber) situated in the tegmentum of the midbrain. The fibers cross immediately and descend to the cord where they lie ventral to and intermingled with the lateral pyramidal tract (Figs. 146, 148). They terminate in the dorsal part of the ventral horn. Conspicuous in most mammals, it is greatly reduced in man, and its course is not fully ascertained. The fibers of this tract have been definitely traced in man to the thoracic levels (Stern, 1938).

IV. **The colliculospinal (tectospinal) tract** originates in the colliculi of the midbrain

roof, decussates and descends to the cord where it lies in the ventral part of the ventral funiculus (Fig. 148). The fibers end in the ventral horn, mainly in the upper portion of the spinal cord, relatively few descending to lower levels. The tract, small in man, conveys impulses which mediate reflex activity of the muscles, especially the neck muscles, in response to optic and perhaps also auditory stimuli.

V. **The medial longitudinal fasciculus.** In the dorsal part of the ventral funiculus are found diffusely organized descending fiber bundles of mixed constitution (Figs. 148, 112). Some come from the interstitial nucleus of Cajal (interstitiospinal) and from the nucleus of the posterior commissure (commissurospinal), two nuclei located in the tegmentum of the midbrain just cephalad to the oculomotor nucleus. These fibers are mainly uncrossed. Other fibers, both crossed and uncrossed, are axons from cells of the lateral and perhaps other vestibular nuclei (medial vestibulospinal). All the fibers terminate in the ventral horn. In the brain stem these various fibers form a well defined bundle, the medial longitudinal fasciculus, from which a considerable number of fibers are continued into the ventral white of the upper cervical cord. Below that region the fibers are few in number and difficult to follow, but some of them have been traced to the lumbar levels of the cord.

VI. **The reticulospinal tracts** are fairly extensive but diffuse fiber bundles which originate from large cells scattered through the reticular formation of the medulla, pons and midbrain. Both crossed and uncrossed fibers are present, all terminating in the ventral horn. According to Papez (1926), a predominantly uncrossed lateral bundle descends in close relation with the rubrospinal and lateral pyramidal tracts (Figs. 148, 146, 112). Other chiefly uncrossed fibers descend in the ventral white funiculus, close to the medial longitudinal fasciculus, while a mainly crossed bundle is found between the vestibulospinal tract and the ventral fasciculus proprius (Figs. 148, 112, *R.sp.*).

VII. **The tract of Helweg** (*olivospinal tract*) is a complex tract composed of fine fibers which stain lightly with the Weigert method. Some of the fibers undoubtedly originate in the inferior olivary nucleus of the medulla and terminate in the ventral horn of the upper cervical cord. Others which come from higher brain regions have in part been identified with the ventrolateral pyramidal tract described by Barnes and Déjérine. According to some, there are also present ascending spino-olivary fibers. The tract as a whole is only found in the upper cervical cord where it forms a light staining triangular area on the periphery just lateral to the ventral roots (Fig. 126). It disappears below the fourth or fifth cervical segments, but individual fibers have been traced to lower cord levels.

It is evident that the ventral horn cells, which constitute the "final common path" to the muscles, are not only stimulated by pyramidal impulses, but are also under the influence of various other descending tracts which impinge upon them, directly or through intercalated neurons. The rubrospinal, reticulospinal, colliculospinal, vestibulospinal, etc., may be collectively termed *extrapyramidal* tracts and constitute the older motor descending systems from higher neural centers before the evolution of the pyramidal system. They not only exert a regulatory control over reflex and other automatic activities, but are able to produce the grosser synergic movements of a volitional nature. These latter movements have been partly superseded by and blended with the pyramidal movements, but partly still exist independently and persist in a modified form when the pyramidal tract is destroyed. It is probable that the recovery of the larger, grosser movements after pyramidal injury is in part due to the fuller utilization of the old motor tracts.

Descending autonomic tracts. The descending tracts described in the preceding pages are parts of pathways ultimately reaching the voluntary striped muscles through the somatic ventral horn cells. The spinal cord also contains descending fibers which come in relation with the intermediolateral column and other preganglionic cell groups for the innervation of visceral structures (smooth muscle, heart muscle and glandular epithelium). The highest coordinating center of this pathway is the hypothalamus which in turn is under the influence of the associative apparatus of the cerebral cortex and thalamus. Other important autonomic centers lie in the tegmentum of the midbrain and pons and in the medulla. The descending paths are diffuse and are probably interrupted by relay neurons. In the cord these fibers descend mainly in the ventral and ventrolateral portion of the white, in close relation to the fasciculi proprii.

THE FASCICULI PROPRII

Equally important as the long ascending and descending tracts are the shorter fiber systems which form part of the intrinsic reflex mechanism of the cord. In its simplest form a spinal reflex arc may consist of only two neurons, an afferent peripheral neuron (spinal ganglion cell) and an efferent peripheral neuron (ventral horn cell) with a single synapse in the gray (Fig. 149). These monosynaptic reflexes are as a rule uncrossed and usually involve only one segment or closely adjacent ones, i.e., they are primarily intrasegmental reflexes. It is quite probable that some of the periosteal and tendon reflexes and the tonus-maintaining stimuli from a muscle back to itself, are represented by such arcs.

There are, however, only few collaterals of dorsal root fibers which terminate directly on ventral horn cells (Hoff, 1932; Foerster, 1933). Hence in most reflex arcs there is at least one central or associative neuron interposed between the afferent and efferent peripheral neurons (Fig. 149). These cen-

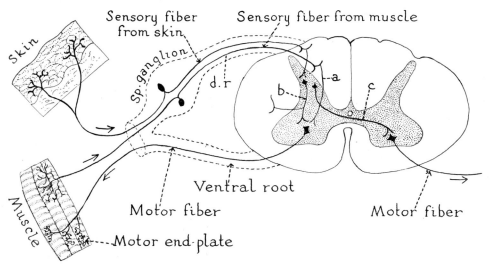

FIG. 149. Diagram illustrating two-neuron and three-neuron intrasegmental spinal reflexes, crossed and uncrossed. *a*, collateral of dorsal root fiber; *b*, associative (tautomeric) cell; *c*, commissural cell.

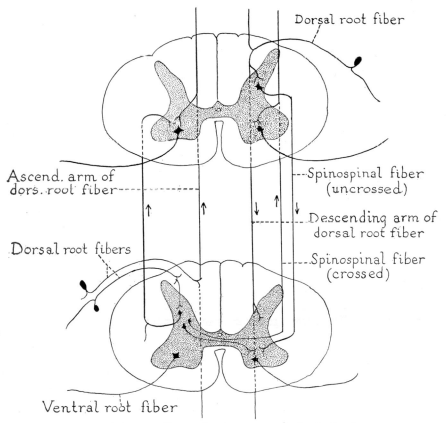

FIG. 150. Diagram illustrating intersegmental spinal reflex arcs

tral cells then send their axons to the motor cells of the same segment or to higher and lower segments for the completion of various intersegmental arcs (Fig. 150). Many of the fibers are axons of tautomeric associative cells, which ascend or descend in the white of the same side. Others come from heteromeric (commissural) cells and pass to the white of the opposite side. All these ascending and descending fibers, crossed and uncrossed, which begin and end in the spinal cord and connect its various levels, constitute the *spinospinal* or *fundamental* columns (*fasciculi proprii*) of the spinal cord (Figs. 148, 115, 117). To this spinal reflex mechanism also belong the descending root fibers of the interfascicular and septomarginal bundles previously described, and the collaterals and many terminals of ascending root fibers. Impulses entering the cord at any segment may travel along these fibers to higher or lower levels before connecting directly or through associative neurons with the ventral horn cells (Fig. 150).

The spinospinal fibers are found in all the white funiculi, dorsal, ventral and lateral. They occupy the area adjacent to the gray matter, between the latter and the more peripherally placed long fiber tracts with which they naturally intermingle. They are most numerous in the ventrolateral white columns. In the dorsal funiculus they form a narrow zone along the dorsal commissure and adjacent portions of the dorsal horn known as the *cornucommissural tract* (Fig. 148). Other fibers are found in the zone of Lissauer and in the interfascicular and septomarginal bundles. In general, the shortest fibers lie nearest the gray and connect adjacent segments. The longer fibers lie more peripherally and continue up or down through several or many segments.

It must be kept in mind that there are no *isolated* reflexes, and that every neural reaction involving any given arc always influences and is influenced by other parts of the nervous system. Studies of foetal behavior suggest that local reflexes have secondarily differentiated in a nervous system primitively organized for the production of generalized or total rather than local activities (Coghill, Herrick and Coghill, Hooker).

The activities of the spinal cord are under the dominant control of the brain, and its independence as a reflex center is greatly diminished in man. In acute total transection of the spinal cord, its intrinsic reflex mechanism temporarily collapses. Below the level of injury there is not only the expectable voluntary paralysis and sensory loss, but there is also complete loss of muscle tone and absence of all reflexes, somatic and visceral. This condition, known as "spinal shock", is undoubtedly due to the sudden severance of all descending tracts from the brain.

After a variable period the spinal mechanism recovers to some extent. The flexor reflex appears first, somewhat later weak extensor movements may likewise be elicited. The bladder may empty itself both automatically and on stimulation of the sole of the foot or the thigh. In man the recovery is slight and as a rule only temporary. After a while the reawakened activities gradually subside and disappear altogether, with death intervening. In other mammals, "spinal shock" is less severe, and recovery of spinal activities is greater and more enduring.

CHAPTER XII

THE PERIPHERAL PORTIONS OF THE AUTONOMIC SYSTEM

Those portions of the central and peripheral nervous system primarily concerned with the regulation of visceral activities are often collectively termed the *visceral* or *vegetative* nervous system in contrast to the *somatic* or *cerebrospinal*. The visceral reactions initiated in the main by internal changes acting on the visceroceptors and taking effect in the smooth musculature and glands are to a large extent involuntary and unconscious. Such visceral reactions as do reach the conscious level are vague and poorly localized and of a predominantly affective character. Tactile sensibility is practically absent, and temperature is apparently appreciated only in certain places such as oesophagus, stomach, colon and rectum. On the other hand, distention or muscular spasms of the walls of the hollow viscera or blood vessels may produce severe distress or acute pain, and it is probable that the constant stream of afferent visceral impulses gives rise to the general feeling of internal well-being or of *malaise*.

The division of the nervous system into a somatic and visceral portion, convenient from a physiological standpoint, does not imply the presence of two anatomically distinct systems. They are merely two aspects of a single integrated neural mechanism, closely interrelated both centrally and peripherally. The higher brain centers regulate both somatic and visceral functions and throughout most neural levels there is intermingling and association of visceral and somatic neurons. Peripherally, visceral efferent fibers are found in all the spinal and many of the cranial nerves, and the visceral afferent fibers have their cell bodies in the cerebrospinal ganglia. Moreover, visceral reflexes may be initiated by impulses passing through afferent somatic fibers and coming from any receptor, and conversely visceral changes may give rise to active somatic movement.

The autonomic system. Interposed in the efferent peripheral pathway from the central nervous system to the visceral structures are aggregations of nerve cells, known as the *autonomic ganglia*. The cells of these ganglia are in synaptic relation with fibers from the spinal cord or brain, and send out axons which terminate in the visceral effectors: smooth muscle, heart muscle and glandular epithelium. Thus unlike striped muscle, which is directly innervated by axons of centrally placed neurons, the transmission of impulses from the central nervous system to the viscera always involves two systems of neurons. The first neuron situated in the brain or spinal cord sends its fine myelinated axon as a *preganglionic* fiber to some autonomic ganglion to synapse with one or more ganglionic cells. The usually unmyelinated axons of the autonomic ganglion cells then pass as *postganglionic* fibers to the visceral effectors. It is therefore evident that even the simplest visceral reflex arc will involve at least three neurons: afferent, efferent preganglionic visceral, and efferent post ganglionic visceral neurons (Fig. 151).

All these "nerve cells and nerve fibers, by means of which efferent impulses pass to tissues other than multinuclear striated muscle" form the *autonomic system* as defined by Langley (1921). By this definition, the autonomic represents only the peripheral motor portion of visceral innervation. The visceral afferent fibers which run by way of the autonomic but have their cell bodies in the cerebrospinal ganglia are not included in this system, nor are the higher brain centers which influence and regulate

147

vegetative activities. In recent years, there has been a tendency to make the term "autonomic" more synonymous with "visceral" or "vegetative" and to include the whole neural apparatus, both peripheral and central, concerned with visceral functions.

The autonomic ganglia which have a wide distribution in the visceral periphery, may be placed in three groups: the *vertebral* or *lateral*; the *prevertebral* or *collateral*; and

they innervate. The ganglia show extreme variations as to size and compactness of organization. They may be organized into anatomically distinct encapsulated structures, as in the case of the sympathetic trunks and the autonomic ganglia of the head; they may form extensive plexuses of nerve cells and fibers, as in the intramural intestinal plexuses; or they may be found as small ganglionic masses or scattered cell groups within or near the walls of visceral

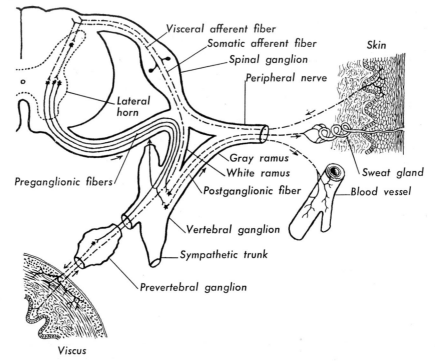

Fɪɢ. 151. Diagram of neural reflex arcs involving sympathetic system. (Bailey's Histology)

the *terminal* or *peripheral* ganglia. The vertebral ganglia are arranged in a segmental fashion along the ventrolateral surface of the vertebral column and connected with each other by longitudinal fibers to form the two *sympathetic trunks* or ganglionated cords. The collateral ganglia are irregular aggregations of cells found in the mesenteric neural plexuses surrounding the abdominal aorta and larger visceral arteries, while the terminal ganglia are located within or close to the structures

structures, as in the heart, bronchi, pancreas and urinary bladder.

Three outflows of preganglionic fibers connect the central nervous system with the autonomic ganglia (Fig. 152). The *cranial outflow* contains efferent visceral fibers from the oculomotor, facial, glossopharyngeal and vagus nerves, these fibers going only to the terminal autonomic ganglia. The *thoracicolumbar outflow* is composed of fibers from the lateral sympathetic nucleus (intermediolateral column) of the spinal cord, which pass out by way of the ventral roots of the thoracic and upper two or three lumbar nerves, a few passing also through the eighth cervical. These fibers leave the ventral roots as the white rami communicantes, enter the sympathetic trunk and end in the vertebral ganglia of the trunk or in the collateral mesenteric ganglia. The *sacral outflow* contains efferent visceral fibers from the inferior lateral and medial sympathetic nuclei of the spinal cord, which pass through the ventral roots of the second, third and fourth sacral nerves and go to the terminal ganglia associated with the pelvic viscera.

Most of the viscera receive a double autonomic innervation, the effects of the two being as a rule antagonistic. One is through the thoracicolumbar division which supplies all the visceral structures of the body. The other innervation is by the cranial or sacral divisions. The former supplies the visceral structures of the head and the thoracic and abdominal viscera with the exception of the pelvic organs which are supplied by the sacral division. The latter, like the cranial autonomic, is antagonistic to the thoracicolumbar. The cranial and sacral divisions have other features in common. They react in a similar manner to certain drugs. They have no white rami communicantes which enter the sympathetic trunk, but their preganglionic fibers run directly to the terminal ganglia. The autonomic thus comprises two main divisions: the *thoracicolumbar* or *sympathetic* system and the *craniosacral* or *parasympathetic* system.

The sympathetic system. The sympathetic trunks are two ganglionated cords symmetrically placed along the ventrolateral aspects of the vertebral column and extending from the base of the skull to the coccyx (Figs. 152, 154). The cervical portion contains three ganglia probably formed by the fusion of originally eight segmental ganglia. The superior cervical ganglion is the largest autonomic ganglion

and is situated near the second and third cervical vertebrae. The small middle cervical ganglion, often absent, may lie near the sixth cervical vertebra or close to the inferior cervical ganglion (Fig. 155). The latter, placed at the lower border of the seventh cervical vertebra, frequently fuses with the first thoracic ganglion to form the stellate ganglion. In the thoracic, lumbar and sacral portions the ganglia are segmentally arranged. There are 11–12 thoracic, 3–4 lumbar and 4–5 sacral ganglia. In the sacral portion, the two trunks gradually approach each other and fuse at the coccyx into the unpaired coccygeal ganglion.

The prevertebral ganglia are irregular ganglionic masses situated in the mesenteric neural plexuses surrounding the visceral branches of the aorta. The largest are the coeliac ganglia, the others comprise the superior mesenteric, aorticorenal, phrenic and inferior mesenteric ganglia (Fig. 156). These will be described in relation to the coeliac and subsidiary plexuses.

The sympathetic ganglia receive preganglionic fibers from the spinal cord through the ventral roots of the eighth cervical, all the thoracic and the upper two or three lumbar nerves. These fibers leave the ventral roots, pass through the white rami communicantes and enter the sympathetic trunk where they have two general destinations: (a) They terminate in the vertebral ganglia, either the one which they enter first, or they pass up or down in the sympathetic cord giving off collaterals, and terminating in vertebral ganglia above or below the level of their entrance (Fig. 153). The fibers from the eighth cervical and the upper five or six thoracic pass mainly upward. Those from the middle thoracic (Th7–10) pass up or down, while those of the lumbar and lowest thoracic pass only downward. (b) Other preganglionic fibers do not synapse in the vertebral ganglia but merely pass through them and emerge as the splanchnic nerves (efferent rami) to terminate in the prevertebral ganglia (Figs.

153, 156). Thus while the sympathetic   synapse occurring either in the vertebral
pathway from the spinal cord to the viscera   *or* prevertebral ganglia (Langley).

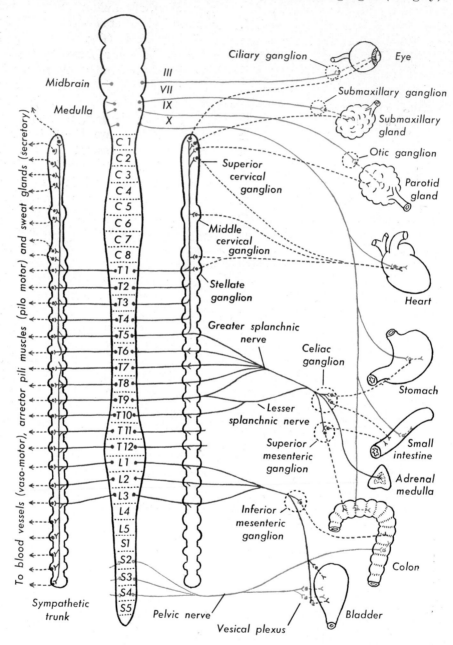

FIG. 152. Diagram showing general arrangement of the autonomic system. (Bailey's Histology.)
Sympathetic shown in red, parasympathetic in blue. Solid lines represent preganglionic fibers, broken
lines postganglionic fibers. For clearness the sympathetic fibers to the blood vessels, hair and sweat
glands are shown separately on the left side.

always involves two neurons, there are   While the white rami communicantes are
apparently never more than two, the   limited to the thoracic and upper lumbar

nerves, each spinal nerve receives a gray ramus communicans from the sympathetic trunk. These consist of unmyelinated fibers which innervate the blood vessels, hair and glands of the body wall. There is some histological evidence that fine unmyelinated fibers also terminate in striped muscle fibers arise numerous gray strands composed of postganglionic fibers (Fig. 154). These are distributed as gray rami to the adjacent cranial nerves (IX, X, XII) and to the upper three or four cervical nerves, to the pharynx and to the external and internal carotid arteries around which the fibers form

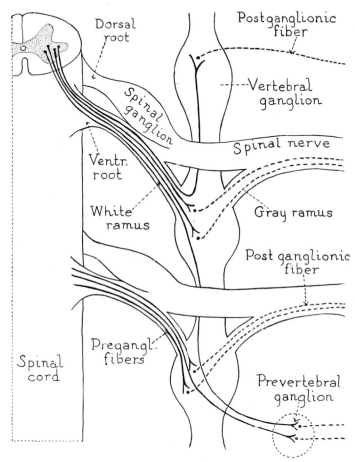

Fig. 153. Diagram of portion of sympathetic trunk, showing course of preganglionic and postganglionic fibers. (After Edinger.)

where they form accessory motor end plates (Boeke). The suggestion that these are of sympathetic origin has been opposed by many investigators.

The cervical sympathetic ganglia receive ascending preganglionic fibers from the white rami of the eighth cervical and upper thoracic nerves, most of them going to the superior cervical ganglion. From the latter corresponding plexuses (Fig. 155). From these plexuses the fibers accompany the branches of the cranial nerves and supply the dilator muscle of the iris, the smooth muscle portion of the levator palpebrae, the orbital muscle of Müller; the blood vessels, sweat glands and hairs of the head and face, and the lacrimal and salivatory glands. Another important branch passes as the

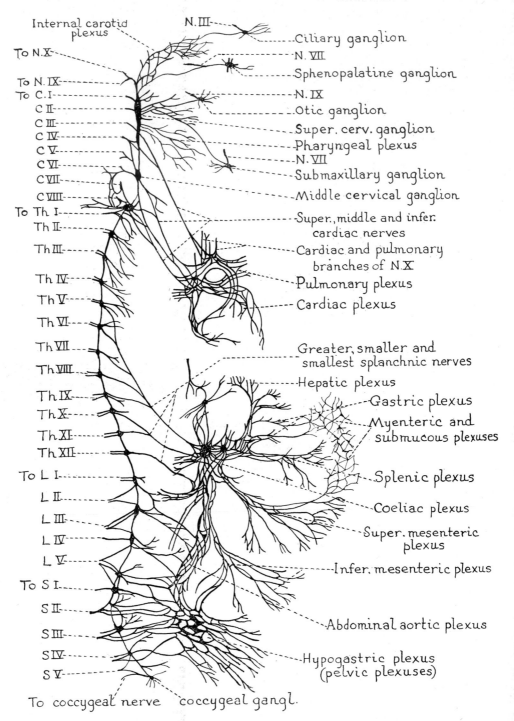

Internal carotid plexus
N. III
Ciliary ganglion
To N.X
N. VII
To N. IX
Sphenopalatine ganglion
To C. I
N. IX
C II
Otic ganglion
C III
Super. cerv. ganglion
C IV
Pharyngeal plexus
C V
N. VII
C VI
C VII
Submaxillary ganglion
C VIII
Middle cervical ganglion
To Th I
Super., middle and infer. cardiac nerves
Th II
Th III
Cardiac and pulmonary branches of N.X
Th IV
Pulmonary plexus
Th V
Cardiac plexus
Th VI
Th VII
Greater, smaller and smallest splanchnic nerves
Th VIII
Hepatic plexus
Th IX
Gastric plexus
Th X
Myenteric and submucous plexuses
Th XI
Th XII
Splenic plexus
To L I
Coeliac plexus
L II
L III
Super. mesenteric plexus
L IV
L V
Infer. mesenteric plexus
To S I
S II
Abdominal aortic plexus
S III
S IV
Hypogastric plexus (pelvic plexuses)
S V
To coccygeal nerve coccygeal gangl.

FIG. 154. Diagram of the sympathetic nervous system including some of the parasympathetic ganglia and the main autonomic plexuses. (Modified from Morris-Jackson.)

superior cervical cardiac nerve to the cardiac plexuses innervating the heart. The middle cervical ganglion, when lying at the level of the sixth cervical vertebra, supplies gray rami to the 5th and 6th cervical nerves, and at times also to the 4th and 7th. When absent or when placed close to the inferior cervical ganglion, these nerves receive their gray rami from the sympathetic trunk (Fig. 155). The inferior cervical ganglion furnishes gray rami to the 7th and 8th cervical and the first thoracic nerves, occasionally also to the 6th cervical. Thus a single ganglion may supply two or more of the lower cervical nerves, and a single nerve may be supplied by two ganglia. Potts (1925) has found that the lower four cervical nerves may each receive three gray rami derived from the sympathetic trunk and the middle and inferior cervical ganglia. In addition, the middle and inferior ganglia give off respectively the middle and inferior cardiac nerves which go to the heart by way of the cardiac plexuses (Fig. 154).

The thoracic, lumbar and sacral ganglia furnish gray rami to the remaining spinal nerves. Delicate branches from the upper five or six thoracic ganglia go to the cardiac plexuses as the thoracic cardiac nerves, while fibers from the stellate ganglion (and inferior cervical) reach the pulmonary plexuses to innervate the bronchial musculature and blood vessels of the lungs. Shorter mediastinal branches from both the thoracic and lumbar ganglia form plexuses around the thoracic and abdominal aorta. In addition to these, there are two, sometimes three, important branches known as the *splanchnic nerves* which arise from the thoracic portion of the trunk, pierce the diaphragm and terminate in the prevertebral ganglia of the mesenteric plexuses. The *greater splanchnic nerve* arises by roots from the fifth to the ninth thoracic ganglia and goes to the coeliac plexus. The *lesser splanchnic* usually arises by two roots from the tenth and eleventh ganglia and either unites with the greater splanchnic or con-

tinues as an independent nerve to that portion of the coeliac plexus which surrounds the roots of the renal arteries and there terminates in the aorticorenal ganglion (Fig. 156). A *smallest splanchnic nerve* sometimes arises from the last thoracic ganglion and goes to the renal plexus. Often this nerve is represented by a branch from the lesser splanchnic. The splanchnic nerves, though appearing as branches of the thoracic ganglia, are in reality composed of preganglionic fibers from the white rami which merely pass through the sympathetic trunk on their way to the coeliac ganglia (Figs. 152, 154).

The *coeliac* plexus is an extensive plexus surrounding the roots of the coeliac and superior mesenteric arteries. It extends cranially to the diaphragm, caudally to the renal arteries and laterally to the suprarenal bodies. It becomes continuous above with the thoracic, below with the abdominal aortic plexuses. From the main plexus are given off paired and unpaired subsidiary plexuses which accompany the branches of the coeliac and superior mesenteric arteries and other branches of the abdominal aorta. The paired ones include the phrenic, suprarenal and spermatic (or ovarian), while the gastric, hepatic, splenic and superior mesenteric plexuses are unpaired. Within the coeliac plexus are found two relatively large ganglionic masses of flattened semilunar shape, the *coeliac ganglia*, lying on either side of the coeliac artery and connected with each other by delicate fiber strands (Fig. 156). Occasionally the two may be so close as to form a single unpaired ganglion encircling the artery. Other ganglionic masses found in the plexus include the paired aorticorenal ganglia and the superior mesenteric ganglion lying near the roots of their respective arteries, and the small phrenic ganglion present only on the right side at the junction of the phrenic nerve with the phrenic plexus (Fig. 156). All these ganglia receive preganglionic fibers from the splanchnic nerves.

Caudally the coeliac plexus becomes continuous with the abdominal aortic plexuses lying on either side of the aorta (Fig. 154). From these plexuses nerve strands pass to *inferior mesenteric ganglion* (Fig. 156). Still further caudally the abdominal aortic plexuses are continued into the unpaired *hypogastric* or *pelvic plexus* which also receives

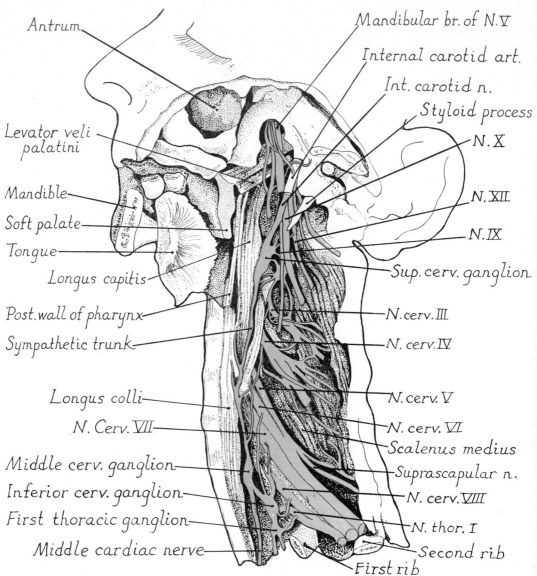

FIG. 155. Lateral view of the left cervical sympathetic trunk and its connections. (Somewhat modified from Potts)

the root of the inferior mesenteric artery and form the inferior mesenteric plexus which surrounds that artery and its branches. Within this plexus and lying close to the root of the artery is another prevertebral ganglionic mass known as the strands from the inferior mesenteric plexus. On entering the pelvis the plexus breaks up into a number of subsidiary plexuses surrounding the rectum, bladder and accessory genital organs. The preganglionic fibers supplying the pelvic organs come from the white rami of the two or three upper lumbar nerves and from the lowest thoracic one, pass through the corresponding ganglia

The parasympathetic system. The preganglionic fibers of the craniosacral division form synaptic relations only with the termi-

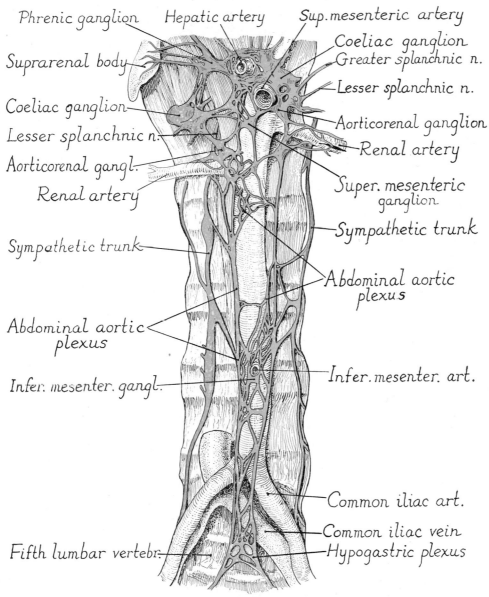

Phrenic ganglion Hepatic artery Sup. mesenteric artery

Coeliac ganglion

Greater splanchnic n.

Suprarenal body

Lesser splanchnic n.

Coeliac ganglion

Aorticorenal ganglion

Lesser splanchnic n.

Renal artery

Aorticorenal gangl.

Super. mesenteric ganglion

Renal artery

Sympathetic trunk

Sympathetic trunk

Abdominal aortic plexus

Abdominal aortic plexus

Infer. mesenter. art.

Infer. mesenter. gangl.

Common iliac art.

Common iliac vein

Fifth lumbar vertebr.

Hypogastric plexus

FIG. 156. Portion of the abdominal sympathetic trunk and related plexuses. (Henle)

of the sympathetic trunk and terminate in the inferior mesenteric ganglion. The cells of this ganglion then send postganglionic fibers which pass by way of pelvic and inferior mesenteric plexuses to the pelvic viscera.

nal ganglia. In the cephalic region there are four such ganglia topographically related to the branches of the trigeminal nerve (Figs. 152, 154). The *ciliary ganglion* lying against the lateral surface of the optic nerve receives preganglionic fibers from the oculomotor nerve (III) and sends post-ganglionic to the sphincter of the iris and the smooth muscle of the ciliary body. The *sphenopalatine ganglion* in the spheno-palatine fossa and the *submaxillary ganglion* lying over the submaxillary gland receive fibers from the intermediate portions of the facial nerve (VII). These fibers pass by way of the greater superficial petrosal nerve to the sphenopalatine ganglion, and by way of the chorda tympani to the submaxillary ganglion. The latter is usually broken up into a submaxillary and a sublingual portion. The sphenopalatine ganglion sends post-ganglionic fibers to the lacrimal glands and to the blood vessels and glands of the mucous membranes of the nose and palate. Postganglionic fibers from the submaxillary ganglion go to the submaxillary and sub-lingual glands and probably also to the mucous membrane of the floor of the mouth. The *otic ganglion* situated mesially to the mandibular nerve receives preganglionic fibers from the glossopharyngeal nerve (IX) by way of the lesser superficial petrosal nerve and sends postganglionic fibers to the parotid gland. All of the cephalic ganglia also receive nerve filaments from the superior cervical ganglion, passing by way of the internal and external carotid plexuses. These, however, do not synapse with the ganglionic cells but merely pass through to furnish the sympathetic innervation of the same structures.

The largest preganglionic source of the cranial autonomic is furnished by the vagus nerve (X) which supplies the pharynx, larynx and practically all the thoracic and abdominal viscera except those in the pelvic portion. In the thorax these preganglionic fibers enter the pulmonary and cardiac plexuses to be distributed to the terminal (intrinsic) ganglia of the heart and bronchial musculature, from which short post-ganglionic fibers go to the heart and bronchial muscle. In the abdomen the vagus fibers go to the oesophagus and stomach and pass through the coeliac and

its subsidiary plexuses to end in the terminal ganglia of the intestine, liver, pancreas and probably also the kidneys. In the ali-mentary canal these terminal ganglia form the extensive ganglionated plexuses of Auerbach (myenteric) and of Meissner (submucosal) which extend the whole length of the digestive tube from the upper portion of the oesophagus to the internal sphincter of the anus. These plexuses are com-posed of numerous small aggregations of ganglion cells intimately connected to each other by delicate transverse and longitudinal fiber bundles. From these cells post-ganglionic fibers terminate in the smooth muscle and glandular epithelium. The alimentary innervation of the vagus extends to the descending colon.

The sacral autonomic consists of pre-ganglionic fibers from the second, third and fourth sacral nerves which form the pelvic nerve (N. erigens) and go to the terminal ganglia of the pelvic plexuses and to the myenteric and submucosal plexuses of the descending colon and rectum. Post-ganglionic fibers from these ganglia then supply the effectors of the pelvic organs including the urinary bladder, descending colon, rectum and external generative organs. The sacral autonomic thus in-nervates those viscera not supplied by the vagus.

The enteric plexuses differ from the other autonomic plexuses in one important respect. They apparently contain some mechanism for local reflex action, since coordinated peristalsis occurs on stimulation of the gut after section of all the nerves which con-nect them with the central nervous system. The nature of this reflex mechanism is not fully understood.

It is evident from the above that all the autonomic plexuses consist of complicated intermixtures of sympathetic and para-sympathetic fibers which are difficult to distinguish morphologically. It must, how-ever, be emphasized again that the sympa-thetic preganglionic fibers are interrupted in the vertebral and prevertebral ganglia, while the parasympathetic ones pass by way of the plexuses to the terminal ganglia.

In addition to the craniosacral outflow, it is believed by many investigators that efferent parasympathetic fibers from the spinal cord pass through the dorsal roots as vasodilators of the cutaneous blood vessels. Stimulation of the distal end of a cut dorsal root causes vasodilation and a rise in tem-

Fig. 157. Section through portion of thoracic ganglion of sympathetic trunk. Bielschowsky's silver stain. (R. L. Müller.)

perature in the skin of the corresponding dermatome, and recently it has been shown that centrifugal discharges occur normally at the proximal ends of cut sensory nerves (Tönnies). The anatomical data are still inadequate and conflicting. Some have definitely demonstrated efferent fibers in the dorsal roots of many forms (Fig. 67), others have been unable to locate them. The balance of evidence suggests the existence of such fibers, but their origin and peripheral distribution are still obscure. If established, the body wall as well as the viscera would receive a double autonomic innervation.

Afferent visceral fibers. There are numerous receptors in the viscera whose afferent fibers, myelinated or unmyelinated, travel centrally by way of the autonomic system. The largest myelinated fibers come principally from Pacinian corpuscles, the smaller myelinated and the unmyelinated ones from the diffuse visceral receptors. All these fibers have their cell bodies in the cerebrospinal ganglia. The peripheral processes of the spinal ganglion cells pass through the white rami communicantes, enter the sympathetic trunk and run uninterruptedly to the viscera by way of the splanchnic nerves and the upper lumbar sympathetic roots. The vagus likewise sends afferent fibers to the heart and other viscera and similar fibers are found in the facial and glossopharyngeal nerves. Some maintain that there are also afferent autonomic cells whose dendrites act as visceral receptors and whose axons do not enter the spinal cord but terminate in the spinal ganglia (Dogiel). Such neurons, if actually present, would furnish a simple anatomical explanation of "referred pains", since by this means visceral stimuli could be directly transferred to the cell bodies of somatic spinal ganglionic neurons.

Structure of autonomic ganglia. The autonomic ganglia are cellular aggregations of varying size and shape, each surrounded by a connective tissue capsule. Trabeculae extending from the capsule form an internal framework which contains numerous, often pigmented, cells between which are irregular plexuses of myelinated and unmyelinated fibers (Fig. 157). Besides these ganglia, isolated autonomic cells or non-encapsulated aggregations of such cells are found widely distributed throughout the viscera.

The autonomic cells are typically multipolar, though bipolar and unipolar cells are occasionally found. The size of the cells fluctuates between 20–60 micra and the number of their branching dendrites is exceedingly variable, as few as three or four in some and as many as twenty in others. The cells have a clear spherical or ovoid nucleus, delicate neurofibrils and fine chromofilic bodies. Binucleated or even multinucleated cells are not uncommon. Most of the cells are surrounded by cellular capsules similar to those surrounding the spinal ganglion cells.

Some of the cells have short dendrites which ramify within the capsules. These are numerous in the autonomic ganglia of

ganglionic fibers. The extracapsular dendrites end in similar end arborizations at varying distances from the cell body, which may likewise interlock with those of other cells. These long dendrites together with preganglionic fibers and axons of autonomic cells form the intricate fiber plexuses between the cells. Many autonomic cells, especialy in the terminal ganglia, have long slender dendrites almost indistinguishable from axons, and some of these have been regarded as afferent autonomic cells (Dogiel).

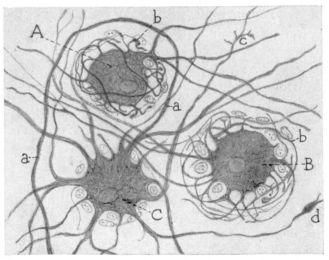

Fig. 158. Human sympathetic cells. (Cajal.) *A,B*, cells whose dendrites (*b*) form a pericellular plexus. *C*, cell with long dendrites. *a*, axon; *c,d*, terminal portions of dendrites. Cajal's silver stain.

man (Fig. 158). Others have long slender dendrites which pierce the capsule and run for varying distances in the intercellular plexuses. Some cells possess both short and long processes. The intracapsular dendrites may arborize symmetrically on all sides of the cell or they may form "glomerular" structures on one side. These "glomeruli" are often formed by the interlocking dendritic processes of two or more cells, and all the cells so interlocked are enclosed within a single capsule (Fig. 159A). Such cells probably receive in common terminal arborizations of pre-

Most of the axons of the autonomic ganglion cells are unmyelinated, but myelinated ones are found in many places, as in the ciliary ganglion. Some axons are partly myelinated and partly unmyelinated. All are postganglionic fibers terminating in the visceral effectors.

Numerous preganglionic fibers end in synaptic relation with the bodies and dendrites of the autonomic cells. They are fine myelinated fibers which may branch repeatedly within the ganglion and form pericellular arborizations, the terminal fibrils ending by neurofibrillar rings or loops on the cell body (Fig. 160). More common than such axosomatic synapses are the axodendritic ones where the preganglionic fibers end in diffuse arborizations in contact with the ramifications of the intracapsular and extracapsular dendrites. The preganglionic character of the several endings

tions with several or even a large number of autonomic neurons (Fig. 159B).

Functional considerations. Gaskell has pointed out that whenever a visceral structure is innervated by both the sympathetic and parasympathetic, the effects of the two are as a rule antagonistic. The sympathetic

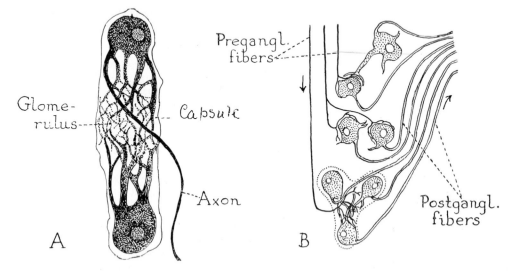

FIG. 159. *A*, Glomerulus formed by dendrites of two sympathetic cells. (After Cajal.) *B*, Diagram showing ways by which one preganglionic fiber may come into relation with two or more sympathetic ganglion cells. (After Ranson and Billingsley.)

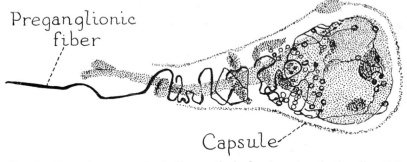

FIG. 160. Terminations of a preganglionic fiber on the body of a sympathetic cell. (After Huber)

described above has been demonstrated experimentally, since they degenerate and disappear when the appropriate preganglionic fibers, such as the vagus or white rami, are cut (Larsell; Ranson and Billingsley), (Fig. 161). There is convincing anatomical evidence that a single preganglionic fiber may form synaptic rela-

dilates the pupil, accelerates the heart, inhibits intestinal movements and contracts the vesical and rectal sphincters. The parasympathetic constricts the pupil, slows the heart, furthers peristaltic movement and relaxes the above named sphincters. The apparently haphazard effects on involuntary muscle produced by each autonomic division in different organs, contraction in one, inhibition in another, are more readily explained when *all* the activities of the two systems are taken in consideration. The parasympathetic deals primarily with anabolic activities concerned with the pres-

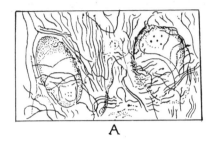

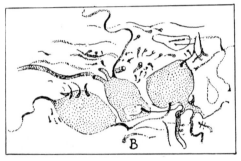

Fig. 161. *A*, Three cells from superior cervical ganglion of a dog showing fibers of the intercellular plexus wrapped around them. *B*, Three cells from the superior cervical ganglion of a dog in which the sympathetic trunk had been cut 58 days before the dog was killed. The fine fibers of the intercellular plexus have disappeared. These fibers are thus the terminations of preganglionic fibers which pass from the cord to the cells of the superior cervical ganglion. (After Ranson and Billingsley.)

ervation of bodily energy and the resting of vital organs. In the words of Cannon, "a glance at these various functions of the cranial division reveals at once that they serve for bodily conservation; by narrowing the pupil they shield the retina from excessive light; by slowing the heart rate they give the cardiac muscle longer periods for rest and invigoration; and by providing for the flow of saliva and gastric juice, and by supplying the necessary muscular tone for the contraction of the alimentary canal, they prove fundamentally essential to the processes of proper digestion and absorption,

by which energy-yielding material is taken into the body and stored. To the cranial division . . . belongs the great service of building up reserves and fortifying the body against times of need and stress." The sacral division supplements the cranial by ridding the body of its intestinal and urinary wastes.

On the other hand, stimulation of the sympathetic equips the body for the intense muscular action required in offense and defense. It is a mechanism of "war" quickly mobilizing the existing reserves of the body. This is especially brought out in emergencies or emotional crises. The eyes dilate and the rate and force of the heart is increased. The blood vessels of the viscera and the skin are constricted, the blood pressure raised, and the blood driven to the striped muscles, lungs, heart and brain. The hairs stand on edge, perhaps to frighten the enemy, and sweat is poured over the surface to cool a body overheated by violent muscular action. The peaceful activities are slowed down or even paralyzed, the blood drained from the huge intestinal reservoir, peristalsis and alimentary secretion inhibited, the urinary and rectal outlets blocked by contraction of their sphincters.

The two systems are reciprocally innervated and their actions integrated to fit the demands of any given situation. The parasympathetic activities are primarily initiated by internal changes in the viscera themselves. The sympathetic is in considerable part activated by exteroceptive impulses passing over the somatic afferent fibers and initiated by favorable or unfavorable changes in the external environment.

The preganglionic fibers of the sympathetic arise from a continuous cell column of the spinal cord, and a single fiber may form synaptic relations with many cells in different vertebral ganglia or in the prevertebral ones. Both types of ganglia are placed at considerable distances from the organs innervated, and from them relatively small numbers of postganglionic fibers are distributed to extensive visceral areas. Such a mechanism permits a wide radiation of impulses, hence sympathetic discharges are profuse and expressed in widely spread visceral effects. Thus the stimulation of a thoracic ventral root or white ramus will cause erection of hair and vasoconstriction in five or six or even more segmental skin areas.

In the parasympathetic the preganglionic neurons are represented by more isolated cell groups, whose fibers pass out in separate nerves and go directly to the terminal ganglia within or near the organs. Parasympathetic action is therefore more discrete, and limited in effect to the portion stimulated. Thus stimulation of the glossopharyngeal nerve will increase parotid secretion and stimulation of the oculomotor will constrict the pupil, in each case without the appearance of other parasympathetic effects. Similarly, stimulation of the distal end of a cut dorsal root will cause vasodilation limited to the corresponding dermatome.

Section of the cervical sympathetic trunk or of the upper thoracic white rami causes a number of symptoms clinically known as Horner's syndrome. There is a constriction of the pupil (myosis), drooping of the eyelid (ptosis) and a sinking in of the eyeball (enophthalmos), accompanied by vasodilation and dryness of the skin of the face. The reason for the enophthalmos is not clear. It is commonly believed to be due to paralysis of the orbital muscle of Müller, a band of smooth muscle lying obliquely on the floor of the orbit, whose contraction supposedly causes a slight protrusion of the eyeball (exophthalmos). The muscle is vestigial in man and according to many ophthalmologists is incapable of effecting even the slightest exophthalmos.

SOME IMPORTANT PERIPHERAL AUTONOMIC PATHWAYS
Eye

(a) *Parasympathetic.* Preganglionic fibers from nucleus of Edinger-Westphal in midbrain by way of third nerve to ciliary ganglion. Postganglionic fibers from cells of ciliary ganglion to ciliary muscle and sphincter of iris.

Function: Contraction of pupil and accommodation to near and far vision.

(b) *Sympathetic.* Preganglionic fibers from cells of lateral sympathetic nucleus in spinal cord passing by way of upper two or three thoracic white rami and sympathetic trunk to superior cervical ganglion. Postganglionic fibers from the latter ganglion *via* the internal carotid plexus and long and short ciliary nerves to the radial muscle fibers of the iris.

Function: Dilation of pupil.

Submaxillary, sublingual and lacrimal glands

(a) *Parasympathetic.* Preganglionic fibers from superior salivatory nucleus of medulla by way of facial nerve, chorda tympani and lingual nerve to submaxillary ganglion; by way of facial nerve and great superficial petrosal nerve to sphenopalatine ganglion. Postganglionic fibers from submaxillary ganglion to submaxillary and sublingual glands; from sphenopalatine ganglion *via* zygomatic and maxillary nerves to lacrimal gland.

Function: Increases secretion.

(b) *Sympathetic.* Preganglionic fibers from lateral sympathetic nucleus in spinal cord passing by way of upper thoracic white rami and sympathetic trunk to superior cervical ganglion. Postganglionic fibers from that ganglion by way of external and internal carotid plexuses to submaxillary, sublingual and lacrimal glands.

Function: Some increase in lacrimal secretion; apparently some increase of thick viscid salivary secretion.

Heart

(a) *Parasympathetic.* Preganglionic fibers from dorsal motor nucleus of vagus by way of vagus nerve and its cardiac branches and cardiac plexus to intrinsic ganglia of heart. Postganglionic fibers from these ganglia to heart muscle.

Function: Cardiac inhibition.

(b) *Sympathetic.* Preganglionic fibers from lateral sympathetic nucleus of cord by way of the white rami of the upper four or five thoracic nerves to the cervical and upper thoracic ganglia. Postganglionic fibers from these ganglia *via* cervical and thoracic cardiac nerves to heart muscle.

Function: Cardiac acceleration.

Lungs and bronchi

(a) *Parasympathetic.* Preganglionic fibers from dorsal motor nucleus of vagus by way of vagus nerve and its pulmonary branches to intrinsic ganglia of trachea, bronchi and lung. Postganglionic fibers from these ganglia to musculature and glands of bronchial tree.

Function: Constriction of bronchi and secretion of mucus.

(b) *Sympathetic.* Preganglionic fibers from lateral sympathetic nucleus through upper thoracic white rami to stellate ganglion. Postganglionic fibers from stellate ganglion *via* pulmonary plexuses to bronchial musculature and blood vessels.

Function: Dilatation of bronchi.

Gastrointestinal tract to descending colon, pancreas, liver

(a) *Parasympathetic.* Preganglionic fibers from dorsal motor nucleus of vagus by way of vagus nerve and its corresponding branches to the terminal ganglia of the digestive tube, pancreas and liver. Postganglionic fibers from the latter to smooth muscle and glands of these organs.

Function: Excites peristalsis of digestive tube and gall bladder. Increases secretion of gastrointestinal and pancreatic juices.

(b) *Sympathetic.* Preganglionic fibers from lateral sympathetic nucleus *via* white rami from the fifth to twelfth thoracic nerves and splanchnic nerves to coeliac and related ganglia. Postganglionic fibers from the latter to smooth muscle and glands of the digestive tube and to pancreas.

Function: Inhibits peristalsis of digestive tube and gall bladder. Vasoconstriction of intestinal blood vessels. Little effect on pancreatic secretion.

Descending colon and rectum, urinary bladder

(a) *Parasympathetic.* Preganglionic fibers from inferior lateral and from medial parasympathetic nuclei of cord by way of second, third and fourth sacral nerves and pelvic nerve to terminal ganglia of colon, rectum and urinary bladder. Postganglionic fibers from the latter to the smooth muscle of those organs.

Function: Excites peristalsis of colon and rectum and inhibits internal anal sphincter. Excites detrusor muscle and inhibits vesical sphincter with resulting urination.

(b) *Sympathetic.* Preganglionic fibers from lateral sympathetic nucleus by way of lumbar white rami and continuing uninterruptedly through the lumbar ganglia and abdominal aortic plexuses to inferior mesenteric ganglion and perhaps to smaller scattered ganglia in hypogastric plexus. Postganglionic fibers from these ganglia to smooth muscle of descending colon, rectum and bladder.

Function: Inhibits peristalsis of colon and rectum and excites contraction of anal sphincter. Inhibits detrusor muscle of bladder and excites contraction of internal sphincter with consequent retention of urine.

Cutaneous blood vessels, sweat glands and arrector pili muscles

(a) *Parasympathetic.* The anatomical pathway of such parasympathetic fibers, if at all present, has not been demonstrated. There is some evidence that vasomotor fibers leave the cord in the dorsal roots and act as vasodilator fibers of cutaneous blood vessels. The origin and course of these fibers are still obscure.

(b) *Sympathetic*.   Preganglionic fibers from lateral sympathetic nucleus by way of thoracic and lumbar white rami to all the ganglia of the sympathetic trunk. Postganglionic fibers from superior cervical ganglion by way of the external and internal carotid plexuses and by way of gray rami of upper cervical nerves to blood vessels, sweat glands and hair muscles of the head and neck. Postganglionic fibers from all other trunk ganglia via gray rami and corresponding spinal nerves to blood vessels, sweat glands and hair muscles of trunk and extremities.

Function: Vasoconstriction, excitation of erector pili muscles and of sweat gland secretion.

CHAPTER XIII

GENERAL CONSIDERATIONS OF THE BRAIN. THE ANATOMY
OF THE MEDULLA AND PONS

The brain which almost completely fills the cranial cavity is composed of five main parts: the endbrain (telencephalon), interbrain (diencephalon), midbrain (mesencephalon), and hindbrain (rhombencephalon), the last named comprising the medulla oblongata (myelencephalon) and callosum (Fig. 162). On entering the medulla the central canal of the cord expands into the broad but shallow *fourth ventricle* of the hindbrain, which is orally continuous with the narrow channel of the midbrain, known as the *iter* or *cerebral aqueduct*. The iter in turn empties into the

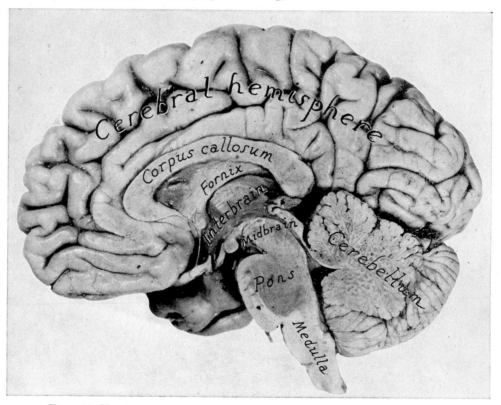

Fig. 162. Hemisected human brain seen from the medial surface. Photograph

the pons and cerebellum (metencephalon). Endbrain, interbrain and midbrain together constitute the cerebrum whose largest and most striking structures are the cerebral hemispheres which practically cover all other parts of the brain and are connected to each other by a massive commissure, the corpus deep cleft-like *third ventricle* of the interbrain, which on each side communicates with the more spacious *lateral ventricle* of the hemisphere by a small opening, the *interventricular foramen*.

When the cerebral hemispheres and cerebellum are dissected off, the remaining basal portions of the brain constitute the so-called "brain stem" (Figs. 166, 167, 168). In such preparations there will naturally be seen the cut surfaces of the fiber bundles which connect the brain stem with the detached portions. The massive bundle connecting the brain stem with the cerebral hemisphere is known as the *internal capsule*, the three smaller bundles connecting it with the cerebellum are known as the *cerebellar peduncles*.

The complex structure and peculiarities of the brain as distinguished from the spinal cord depend on two main factors: (a) the nature of the receptors and effectors of the head connected to the brain by the cranial nerves, and (b) the development of extensive higher coordinating mechanisms in the central nervous system of the head.

The cranial nerves. The metamerically or segmentally arranged spinal nerves have in general a uniform constitution, both as to their peripheral components and central connections. Each nerve, primitively supplying a single body segment (metamere), is both afferent and efferent. The afferent fibers bringing in impulses from somatic and visceral receptors have their cell bodies in the spinal ganglia and enter the cord by the dorsal roots. The efferent somatic and visceral fibers arise from cells in the ventral and lateral columns of the cord and leave by the ventral roots. Thus a typical spinal nerve contains fibers for all types of receptors and effectors: somatic afferent, visceral afferent, visceral efferent and somatic efferent. Since the striped muscles of the body differentiate from the myotomic portion of the somite, the spinal nerves are often known as myomeric nerves, though the term "myomeric" refers technically to only the somatic motor portion of the nerve.

Within the cord, the similar components of the various spinal nerves tend to be associated into functional columns. As stated in a previous chapter, each lateral wall of the neural tube at an early stage of development becomes differentiated into a dorsal or *alar* and a ventral or *basal* plate, separated from each other by a longitudinal furrow, the *sulcus limitans*. The receptive or "sensory" cell groups which constitute the nuclei of termination for the afferent fibers, develop in the alar plate, the more medial cell groups related to afferent somatic, the more lateral ones to afferent visceral fibers. The motor cell groups constituting the nuclei of origin of the efferent fibers differentiate in the basal plate, and here again the medial groups furnish efferent somatic, and the lateral groups efferent visceral fibers. Thus in the adult cord there is found a general territorial organization of functional columns, the dorsal half being afferent or receptive, the ventral half efferent or motor, each having its somatic and visceral divisions (Fig. 65).

The cranial nerves do not show a similar uniformity, the individual nerves varying widely in the composition of their functional components. Some are entirely sensory, some are mainly motor, while others resemble the mixed spinal nerves in having both afferent and efferent fibers. Among the factors responsible for these differences are (a) the reduction or absence of true metamerism in the head; (b) the presence of the complex special sense organs of the nose, eye and ear; and (c) the great expansion of visceral structures, due to the presence in this region of the mouth, pharynx, respiratory organs and heart. Some of the mixed cranial nerves (VII, IX, X) supplying this region contain practically only visceral components and are connected to that part of the brain (medulla oblongata) in which are found the intrinsic centers for the regulation of digestive, respiratory and cardiac activities. In a general way the twelve pairs of cranial nerves may be placed into three groups: myomeric (metameric), branchiomeric and special sensory.

In the region of the head the formation of somites (metamerism) is greatly reduced, but along the medulla and midbrain are

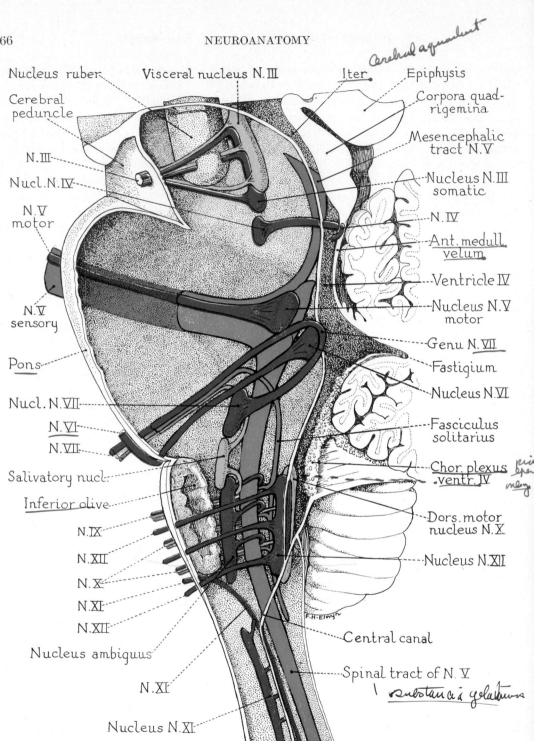

Nucleus ruber

Visceral nucleus N. III

Iter *Cerebral aqueduct*

Epiphysis

Cerebral peduncle

Corpora quadrigemina

N. III

Mesencephalic tract N. V

Nucl. N. IV

Nucleus N. III somatic

N. V motor

N. IV

Ant. medull. velum

N. V sensory

Ventricle IV

Nucleus N. V motor

Pons

Genu N. VII

Fastigium

Nucl. N. VII

Nucleus N. VI

N. VI

Fasciculus solitarius

N. VII

Salivatory nucl.

Chor. plexus *pia* ventr. IV *mesg*

Inferior olive

N. IX

Dors. motor nucleus N. X

N. XII

Nucleus N. XII

N. X

N. XI

N. XII

Nucleus ambiguus

Central canal

N. XI

Spinal tract of N. V

substancia gelatinosa

Nucleus N. XI

N. XI

FIG. 163. Nuclei and intramedullary course of some of the cranial nerves, somewhat schematic, viewed from the median sagittal surface. The right brain stem is represented as a hollow from which all other brain substance has been removed. (After Braus-Elze.) *Red,* somatic motor and special visceral motor components (to striped muscle); *yellow,* general visceral motor; *blue,* sensory components.

found several masses of paraxial mesoderm which are considered as homologous to the myotomes of the body. The most caudal of these, probably representing the fusion of three or four neck myotomes which have migrated into the occipital region of the head, differentiates into the striped muscles of the tongue and is supplied by the *hypoglossal nerve* (XII). The upper less distinct mass, also known as the premandibular "somite", gives rise to the striped extrinsic muscles of the eyeball which are innervated by the oculomotor (III), trochlear (IV) and abducens (VI) nerves. The oculomotor also furnishes general visceral efferent fibers to the smooth intrinsic muscles of the iris and ciliary body. The above named striped muscle groups constitute the somatic muscles of the head derived from myotomic mesoderm, and the nerves supplying them may be considered as *myomeric* or *metameric*, similar to those of the spinal cord. However these nerves are mainly motor and have no distinct ganglia or afferent roots, hence they are really comparable only to the ventral roots of spinal nerves. The nuclei which give rise to their fibers may be regarded as upward extensions of the somatic efferent column of the cord, and their roots emerge in line with the ventral spinal roots (Figs. 165, 166).

The cranial nerves connected with the general visceral receptors and effectors of the head, but also mediating somatic sensibility from the face and forehead, develop phylogenetically in relation to the *branchial* or *visceral arches* which in the lower aquatic vertebrates carry the respiratory organs or gills. These *branchiomeric* nerves include the trigeminal (V), facial (VII), glossopharyngeal (IX) and vagus (X), whose roots emerge on the lateral surface of the brain along a line intermediate between those of the dorsal and ventral spinal roots (Figs. 165, 166). They contain both afferent and efferent fibers which however leave the brain together and are not separated into dorsal and ventral roots. Attached to

their roots are typical ganglia (cranial ganglia) from whose unipolar cells the afferent fibers arise. These comprise the *Gasserian* or *semilunar* for the trigeminal, the *geniculate* for the facial, the *superior* and *petrosal* for the glossopharyngeal, and the *jugular* and *nodosal* for the vagus.

The functional composition of the branchiomeric nerves are not the same for all of them. The sensory root of the trigeminal nerve constitutes the *general somatic afferent* nerve of the head, mediating touch, pain and temperature from the face, forehead and ectodermal mucous membranes of the mouth and nose. The afferent fibers of the seventh, ninth and tenth nerves, on the other hand, are related to visceral sensibility, conveying *general afferent visceral* impulses from the pharynx, larynx, thoracic and abdominal viscera, and also the *special afferent visceral* impulses from the taste buds. The special receptors of taste are not aggregated in the form of a definite anatomical structure as is the case with the other organs of special sense. In lower aquatic forms taste buds are found not only in the mouth, but along the region of the gills and other parts of the body surface. Though limited to the oral cavity in the higher forms, they are still scattered over a relatively large area such the dorsum of the tongue and region of the epiglottis, and during development may be found also in other portions of the mouth and pharynx. This wider distribution is reflected in the "segmental" innervation of the taste buds, gustatory impulses reaching the brain by way of three branchiomeric nerves.

On the efferent side the branchiomeric nerves likewise show individual variations. The seventh, ninth and tenth nerves supply all the *general visceral efferent* fibers to the glands and visceral muscle of the pharynx, larynx and thoracic and abdominal organs. These are naturally preganglionic fibers which reach the visceral effectors after a relay in some autonomic ganglion. All the branchiomeric nerves however contribute *branchiomotor* or *special visceral efferent* fibers to a group of striped muscles which are developed from the mesoderm of the branchial arches, designed in water living forms to effect movement of the gills. These are masticatory muscles derived from the first or mandibular arch and innervated by the motor trigeminal nucleus; the facial muscles related to the second or hyoid arch and

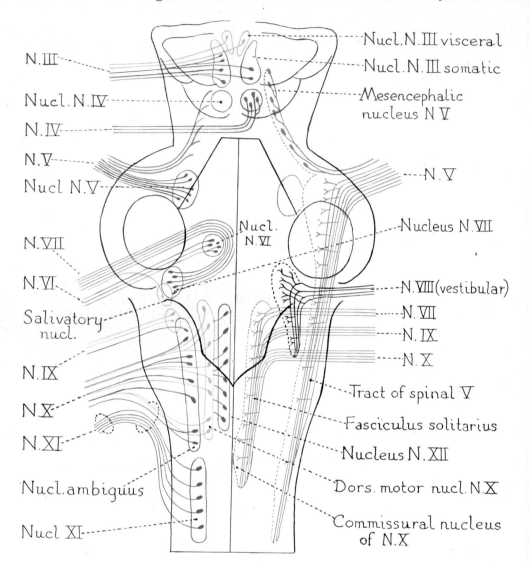

N.III

Nucl.N.IV

N.IV

N.V

Nucl N.V

N.VII

N.VI

Salivatory nucl.

N.IX

N.X

N.XI

Nucl.ambiguus

Nucl XI

Nucl.N.III visceral

Nucl.N.III somatic

Mesencephalic nucleus N V

N.V

Nucl. N.VI

Nucleus N.VII

N.VIII(vestibular)

N.VII

N.IX

N.X

Tract of spinal V

Fasciculus solitarius

Nucleus N.XII

Dors. motor nucl. N.X

Commissural nucleus of N.X

FIG. 164. Diagram showing nuclei of origin, nuclei of termination and intramedullary course of the cranial nerves, projected on the dorsal surface of the brain stem. (Modified from Van Gehuchten.) *Red*, special somatic motor and special visceral motor (to striped muscle); *yellow*, general visceral motor; *blue*, general sensory (somatic and visceral); *black*, special somatic sensory (proprioceptive).

striped voluntary muscles innervated like the somatic muscles directly from the central nervous system, but on account of their derivation and function they are known as *special visceral muscles*. They comprise the supplied by the motor facial nucleus; and the striped muscles of the pharynx and larynx, derived from the third and fourth arches and innervated by the branchiomotor nucleus (nucleus ambiguus) of the ninth and tenth nerves (Figs. 163, 164). With these is usually included a part at least of the sternocleidomastoid and trapezius muscles innervated by the accessory nerve (XI). While these are skeletal muscles concerned with the turning of the head and raising of the shoulder, there is evidence that they are in part at least derived from the branchial mesoderm (Straus and Howell), hence the purely motor accessory nerve is usually included with the branchiomeric series.

Finally there are the purely afferent *nerves of special sense*, related to the nose, eye and ear. The olfactory nerve (I) is composed of special visceral afferent fibers which are the central processes of bipolar cells in the olfactory epithelium of the nose. The fibers pass through the cribriform plate and end in the olfactory bulb of the forebrain. The "optic" nerve (II) consists of special somatic afferent fibers from the retina, which after partial decussation in the optic chiasm end in the interbrain and midbrain. Since the retina is an evaginated portion of the brain and contains nerve cells as well as photoreceptors, the "optic" nerve is really a fiber tract connecting two portions of the brain. The acoustic nerve (VIII) which conveys special somatic afferent impulses from the ear to the hindbrain, is composed of two portions, cochlear and vestibular. The former conducts impulses from the cochlea, its fibers arising from the bipolar cells of the *spiral ganglion*. The vestibular branch brings impulses from the vestibule, saccule and semicircular canals, and its fibers originate similarly from the bipolar cells of the *vestibular ganglion* or *ganglion of Scarpa*. The two branches unite for a short distance into the single acoustic nerve but split again on entering the hindbrain, each having its separate terminals. Another nerve probably belonging to this group is the more recently discovered *nervus terminalis*. Its fibers arise from the mucous membrane of the nasal septum, pass through the cribriform plate and continue as a slender strand along the medial border of the olfactory bulb

and tract to terminate in the basal olfactory area of the brain. It has a ganglion lying medial to the olfactory bulb, and scattered nerve cells are also found along its peripheral root. Its function is not fully understood.

It is obvious from the above that in addition to the general somatic and visceral components, the cranial nerves also contain the special somatic and visceral components related to the organs of special sense and the striped branchial musculature. No single cranial nerve has all these components, and some may have only one. In the main, the general somatic afferent is represented by N.V., the general somatic efferent by Nn. III, IV, VI and XII, and the special visceral efferent component supplying the branchiomeric striped muscles by Nn.V, VII, IX, X and XI. The general visceral afferent and efferent components are represented by Nn.VII, IX, and X, and these also carry the special visceral afferent fibers from the taste buds which may be regarded as more concentrated and localized receptors of general visceral sensibility. The special visceral afferent fibers of smell are represented by N.I, and the special somatic afferent fibers of vision, hearing and head position are related respectively to the "optic" nerve (N.II) and to the cochlear and vestibular branches of N.VIII.

The central connections of the cranial nerves are similar to those of the spinal cord, but while in the latter the sensory and motor columns are continuous, the sensory and motor nuclei of the cranial nerves are represented by discontinuous spatially separated cell columns (Figs. 163, 164). The afferent fibers after entering the brain usually bifurcate into ascending and descending arms, but here the descending ones are the longer, and many descend without bifurcation. These descending central continuations of the cranial nerves are known as their *spinal* or *descending* tracts, such as the spinal trigeminal tract or the spinal vestibular tract (Figs. 163, 164). Fibers of similar function, though brought in by widely separated nerves, tend to become associated within the brain. Thus the visceral afferent fibers from Nn.VII, IX and X form a common descending bundle known as the fasciculus solitarius (Figs. 163, 164). All the afferent fibers, whether descending or ascending, are accompanied by groups or columns of cells which form their terminal or "sensory" nuclei, just as the dorsal column of the cord constitutes the terminal nucleus of the

the effectors innervated by these nerves. Like the motor cells of the cord they receive fibers from various segmental and suprasegmental centers for the voluntary and reflex kinetic and tonic control of the cranial muscles. These fibers constitute the so-called "bulbar" tracts, as the corticobulbar, rubrobulbar or vestibulobulbar, in contrast to the corticospinal, rubrospinal and vestibulospinal tracts which go to the motor

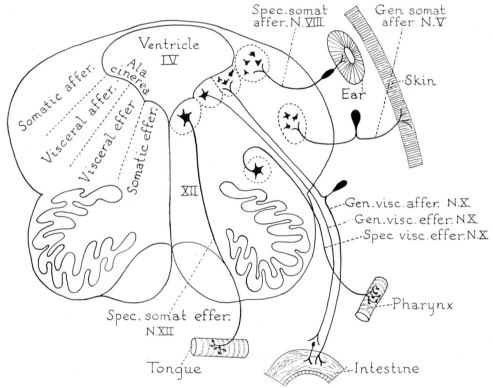

Fig. 165. Diagrammatic section through the medulla showing the functional components of the cranial nerves and the cell columns to which they are related

afferent spinal nerves. From these terminal nuclei arise secondary fibers which either go to motor nuclei for reflex connections, or form parts of secondary pathways to the pallium and other suprasegmental structures.

The motor nuclei of the cranial nerves are similar in structure and function to the motor cell groups of the ventral horn. They constitute the lower motor neurons of the brain stem, the final common pathway to

nuclei of the cord. Lesions of the motor cranial nuclei or of their fibers produce a lower motor neuron paralysis characterized by complete loss of movement, loss of tone and atrophy of the muscles affected.

Like the spinal cord, the brain stem shows a territorial organization into functional columns, most marked in the hindbrain where the sulcus limitans persists as a definite landmark in the adult (Figs. 163, 164, 165). In this region the central canal is expanded into the fourth ventricle and the dorsal walls (alar plates) diverge laterally and come to lie in nearly the same plane as the basal plates, but the relations of the sensory and motor columns remain the same (Fig. 165). Most medially in the ventricular floor is the somatic motor column composed of the motor nuclei of Nn.XII, VI, IV, and III. Lateral to this the visceral motor area is composed of two nuclear columns, a dorsal and a ventral one. The dorsal is the general efferent visceral column innervating glandular epithelium and visceral muscle and is represented mainly by the dorsal motor nucleus of the vagus. The ventral or special visceral efferent (branchiomotor) is composed of the motor nuclei of Nn.V and VII and the ventral motor nucleus (nucleus ambiguus) of Nn.IX and X. The motor nucleus of the accessory nerve (N.XI), found in the lower medulla and upper cord may be regarded as the caudal continuation of the branchiomotor column.

The afferent columns lie lateral to the sulcus limitans. The visceral afferent column is represented by the nucleus of the fasciculus solitarius which receives the visceral fibers of Nn.VII, IX and X. In the somatic afferent column, placed most laterally, are found the terminal nucleus of the trigeminal nerve representing general somatic sensibility, and the cochlear and vestibular nuclei receiving special somatic afferent impulses from the cochlea and the vestibular sense organ.

Suprasegmental structures. Besides its intrinsic associative system mediating segmental and intersegmental reflex activities, the brain contains extensive higher coordinating centers of a suprasegmental character. These structures are developed from the dorsal wall of certain portions of the brain and are composed of enormous numbers of association neurons usually arranged in the form of an external layer or *cortex* of complex cellular constitution. Within them terminate afferent pathways from all parts of the body, and from them arise efferent paths controlling and qualifying the reflex and other activities of the body. The most extensive of these is the pallium or cerebral cortex, others are the cerebellum and the roof (tectum) of the midbrain, though the latter is much reduced in man. The corpus striatum and parts of the thalamus, though having no cortical structure, may likewise be regarded as suprasegmental. In man the suprasegmental structures form by far the largest portion of the brain, and will be studied in detail in subsequent chapters.

THE ANATOMY OF THE PONS AND MEDULLA

The *medulla oblongata* or *cerebral bulb* is the conically expanded upward continuation of the spinal cord, extending from the foramen magnum to the caudal margin of the pons and having a length of about 28 mm. Its width at the lower end is approximately that of the uppermost cervical cord, about 9–12 mm. Proceeding upward it rapidly expands until in the most rostral portion the lateral diameter is around 24 mm. Both length and width however show individual variations within considerable limits.

The substance of the medulla in reality extends to the midbrain with which it becomes continuous, but this upper portion of the hindbrain is covered ventrally by a massive protuberance, the *pons*, which on each side is connected to the cerebellum by a stout fiber bundle, the *brachium pontis* (Fig. 166). It is usual to include the hindbrain structures thus covered as belonging to the pons, but actually the latter consists of two structurally and functionally distinct parts. The dorsal portion known as the *tegmentum of the pons* is the direct continuation of the medulla oblongata. The *basilar portion* or pons proper together with the brachia pontis are parts of phylogenetically newer pathways connecting the pallium and cerebellum, superimposed ventrally on the older structures of the medulla.

In its caudal portion the medulla has the

general form of the spinal cord and its narrow channel which is a continuation of the central canal is completely surrounded by thick walls. Toward the middle of the

in the same plane (Fig. 167). The triangular or V-shaped recess thus formed constitutes the bulbar portion of the fourth ventricle communicating caudally with the

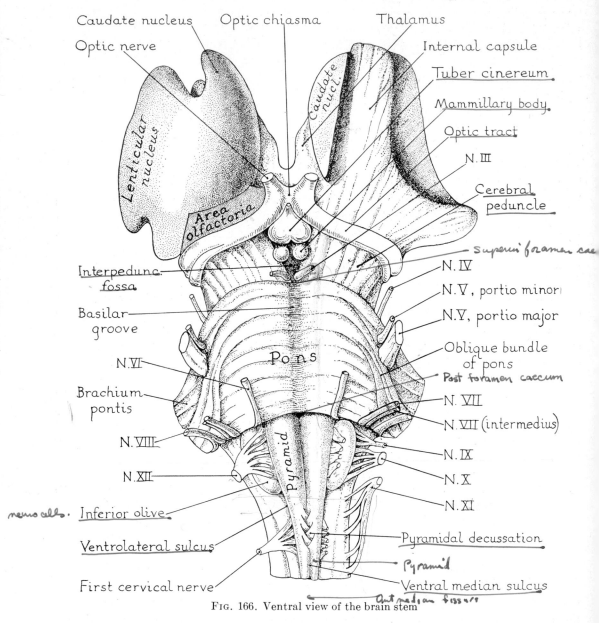

FIG. 166. Ventral view of the brain stem

medulla however, the dorsal walls, down to the central canal, begin to diverge laterally and become bent outward until in the widest portion near the junction of medulla and pons, the dorsal and ventral walls lie nearly

central canal and roofed over by a thin membrane, the *tela chorioidea*, which is attached laterally to the diverging columns. The tela is composed of an internal layer of ependymal epithelium to which is fused externally a richly vascular layer of pial connective tissue. When the tela is stripped off to expose the ventricular floor, its torn edges of attachment are seen as delicate seams or bands, the *taeniae*, extending from the region of the lateral recess to the caudal angle of the ventricle where they fuse to form a small triangular plate, the *obex* (Fig. 167).

The ventral and dorsal median sulci of the spinal cord are continued into the medulla and divide the latter into two symmetrical halves. In the most caudal portion of the bulb the ventral sulcus is partially obliterated by obliquely crossing fiber bundles constituting the pyramidal decussation through which the largest part of the corticospinal fibers reaches the lateral funiculus (Fig. 166). Above the decussation the sulcus deepens and flanked on either side by a tapering longitudinal prominence, continues to the caudal border of the pons where it ends in a somewhat expanded blind pit, the *foramen caecum posterior*. The tapering prominence on each side of the sulcus is the medullary *pyramid*, composed now of the entire corticospinal tract.

Dorsolateral to the pyramid in the rostral portion of the bulb is a prominent ovoid body, the *inferior olive*, caused by a convoluted mass of gray matter situated just below the surface (Fig. 166). It is bounded medially by the preolivary sulcus which is a continuation of the ventrolateral sulcus of the cord, laterally by the deeper postolivary groove which may be considered as the laterally shifted continuation of the dorsolateral sulcus. Emerging from the ventrolateral sulcus are the roots of the abducens (VI) and hypoglossal (XII) nerves, the former at the junction of medulla and pons, the latter arising by many rootlets between the pyramid and olive. The uppermost filaments of the ventral root of the first cervical nerve likewise emerge from the most caudal part of this sulcus. In the region of the olive and also somewhat caudal to it, many fine fiber bundles may be seen emerging from the ventral median sulcus and

also from the preolivary groove; which pass superficially over the pyramid and olive and reach the dorsolateral surface of the medulla (Fig. 168). These *ventral external arcuate fibers*, as will be seen later, arise from certain gray masses of the bulb and go to the cerebellum by this superficial route.

Emerging from the wide postolivary sulcus are the roots of the facial (VII), glossopharyngeal (IX) and vagus (X) nerves. The facial emerges at the junction of medulla and pons, the numerous filaments of the ninth and tenth in the region of the olive. Caudal to these but in the same line of emergence are the rootlets of the accessory nerve (XI), which arise in part from the caudal portion of the medulla, in part from the upper five or six cervical segments of the cord. The acoustic nerve (VIII) enters the brain at the caudal border of the pons, immediately lateral to the roots of the facial nerve (Fig. 166).

In the lower portion of the medulla up to the opening of the fourth ventricle, the dorsal surface is similar to that of the spinal cord, showing continuations of the dorsal median sulcus and of the gracile and cuneate fasciculi. Toward the caudal end of the fourth ventricle these fasciculi expand into ovoid eminences, known respectively as the *clava* and *tuberculum cuneatum* (Fig. 167). The swellings are caused by the appearance within the fascicles of large cell groups in which the fibers of the dorsal column terminate. The *nucleus gracilis* lies below the clava, the *nucleus cuneatus* below the cuneate tubercle. Lateral to the fasciculus cuneatus the narrow zone of Lissauer likewise gradually enlarges into the *tuberculum cinereum* or *eminentia trigemini*. This as will be seen later is due to the expansion of the substantia gelatinosa which extends into the medulla and is there covered superficially by descending fibers of the trigeminal nerve. At the caudal angle of the ventricle the clava, cuneate tubercle and trigeminal eminence diverge laterally and the cuneate and trigeminal tubercles appear to fuse with another prominent ridge, the *restiform body* or *inferior cerebellar peduncle*. Actually these tubercles have no connection at all

lateral border of the ventricle, passes underneath the lateral recess to be described below, and then turns dorsally to enter the

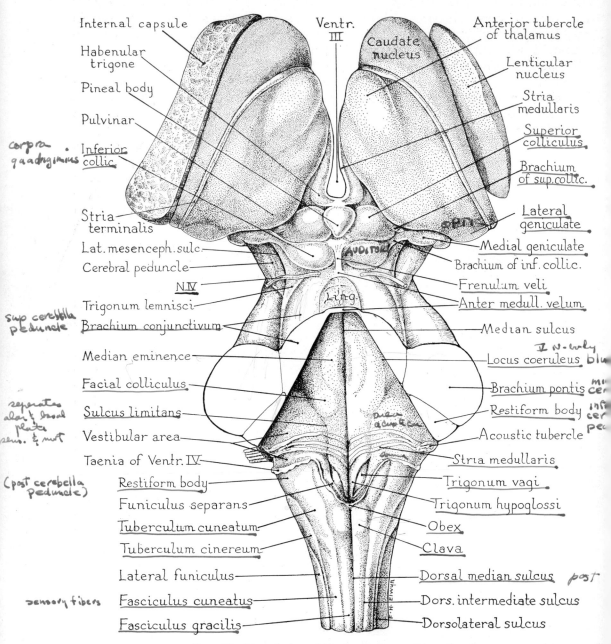

Internal capsule

Habenular trigone

Pineal body

Pulvinar

corpra quadrigimus · Inferior collic.

Stria terminalis

Lat. mesenceph. sulc.

Cerebral peduncle

N. IV

Trigonum lemnisci

sup cerebella peduncle · Brachium conjunctivum

Median eminence

Facial colliculus

separates along basal plate sens. & mot

Sulcus limitans

Vestibular area

Taenia of Ventr. IV

(post cerebella peduncle) · Restiform body

Funiculus separans

Tuberculum cuneatum

Tuberculum cinereum

Lateral funiculus

sensory fibers · Fasciculus cuneatus

Fasciculus gracilis

Ventr. III

Caudate nucleus

Anterior tubercle of thalamus

Lenticular nucleus

Stria medullaris

Superior colliculus

Brachium of sup. collic.

Lateral geniculate

Medial geniculate

Brachium of inf. collic.

Frenulum veli

Anter medull. velum

Median sulcus

II N-body blu · Locus coeruleus

Brachium pontis mi cer

Restiform body inf cer pe

Acoustic tubercle

Stria medullaris

Trigonum vagi

Trigonum hypoglossi

Obex

Clava

Dorsal median sulcus   post

Dors. intermediate sulcus

Dorsolateral sulcus

Ling.

AUDITORY

FIG. 167. Dorsal view of the brain stem. *Ling.*, lingula

with the peduncle but are merely covered superficially by it. The restiform body is a stout fiber bundle which runs along the

cerebellum. It constitutes the main connection of the cerebellum with the spinal cord and medulla, and among its constituents are

restiform body

the dorsal spinocerebellar tract and the external arcuate fibers previously mentioned.

The **pons proper** is a mass of cells and fibers placed transversely on the ventral surface of the hindbrain between the medulla and the cerebral peduncles, from both of which it is sharply marked off by the inferior and superior pontile sulci (Fig. 166). Viewed externally it appears as a broad band of predominantly transverse fibers, having a length of 20–30 mm. and a width of 30–36 mm. On each side the fibers become aggregated into a stout bundle, the *brachium pontis* or *middle cerebellar peduncle*, which passes dorsally and somewhat caudally into the cerebellar hemispheres. The pyramidal tracts which in the pons are located beneath the superficial pontile fibers, form longitudinal bulges on the ventral surface enclosing between them a shallow groove, the *basilar sulcus*, in which is lodged the basilar artery. The trigeminal nerve (N.V.) emerges from the lateral portion of the pons about midway between the superior and inferior borders. A line connecting the exits of the trigeminal and facial nerves marks the transition from pons to pontile brachium.

Not all the superficial fibers run transversely into the brachium pontis. An *oblique bundle* from the middle or rostral portion runs obliquely downward along the medial border of the trigeminal roots toward the exits of N.VII and N.VIII (Fig. 166). Some of the fibers probably enter the brachium pontis, others pass between the seventh and eighth nerves and end in a slight swelling, the pontobulbar body, on the lateral surface of the restiform body.

Along the rostral border of the pons are often found one or two fiber strands known as the *fila lateralia* or *taenia pontis* (Fig. 168). Their complete course and termination are not clear. They may be detached bundles of the pons which have a separate and aberrant course to the cerebellum, or they possibly represent connections between the pons and certain midbrain structures.

In a general way the ventral structures of the hindbrain such as pons, pyramids and larger portion of the inferior olives, belong to the newer parts of the brain (neëncephalon), related to the pallium and cerebellar hemispheres. The dorsal portions of the medulla and the tegmentum of the pons are mainly composed of the phylogenetically older structures belonging to the palencephalon. This topographical arrangement of new and old structures is characteristic of the brain stem as a whole.

The fourth ventricle. The fourth ventricle is the broad but shallow cavity of the hindbrain, extending from the middle of the medulla where it is continuous with the central canal to the cerebral aqueduct of the midbrain. Its floor is formed by the dorsal surface of the medulla and pontile tegmentum, its roof by the anterior medullary velum, a portion of the cerebellum, the posterior medullary velum and the tela chorioidea (Figs. 163). At its widest portion just behind the brachium pontis, it is continued on each side into a tubular *lateral recess* which curves laterally over the restiform body and extends along a portion of the cerebellum known as the peduncle of the flocculus to the basal surface of the brain (Fig. 169).

The white substance of the cerebellum which forms part of the roof splits at an acute angle into two thin white lamina, enclosing between them a peak-like recess, the *fastigium* or roof recess of the fourth ventricle (Figs. 163, 239). One lamina, the *anterior medullary velum*, extends rostrally to the midbrain and forms the roof of the superior or pontile portion of the ventricle. The other layer, the *posterior medullary velum*, passes caudally for a short distance and then becomes continuous with the *tela chorioidea* which as already stated roofs the lower or medullary portion. From the tela the *chorioid plexus* projects into the ventricle. This is composed of irregular nodular evaginations of the tela chorioidea containing vascular loops covered by a modified glandular ependymal epithelium. These vascular tufts are evaginated in the form of two longitudinal ridges placed near the midline and extending from the most caudal portion of the ventricle to the inferior medullary velum to which the tela is attached. From each of these ridges another strip of chorioid plexus extends practically at right angles through the whole length of the lateral recess (Fig. 163). At its distal end each recess opens into the subarachnoid roof (Fig. 169). Through these three openings the cerebrospinal fluid produced by the various chorioid plexuses of the brain ventricles escapes into the subarachnoid spaces.

The rhomboid or diamond shaped floor of the fourth ventricle is known as the *rhom-*

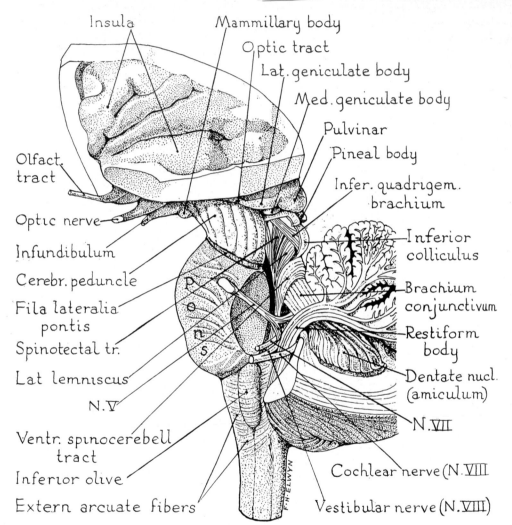

FIG. 168. Lateral view of the brain stem, partially dissected to show some of the fiber tracts. (Modified from Büttner, after Elze)

space by a small *lateral aperture* or *foramen of Luschka* through which protrudes a portion of the chorioid plexus which elsewhere is always limited to the ventricular cavities of the brain. A similar but medially placed aperture, the foramen of Magendie, is found in the most caudal part of the ventricular

boid fossa (Fig. 167). It is widest at its lateral angles where it is continued into the lateral recesses. The apex of its rostral angle is directed toward the midbrain, that of the caudal angle toward the central canal. The pointed caudal end of the fossa, on account of its resemblance to a pen, is called the *calamus scriptorius*. The upper larger triangular area belongs to the pons, and its lateral walls and lateral portions of the roof are formed by the *superior cerebellar peduncles* or *brachia conjunctiva*, two fiber bundles which emerge from the cerebellum above the lateral recess and extend to the midbrain approaching each other as they proceed rostrally. The roof of this part of the ventricle, as already stated, is completed by the anterior medullary velum which is

vestibular nerve. The apex of this area extends into the lateral angle of the floor and there swells into a small eminence, the *tuberculum acusticum*, caused by a subjacent terminal nucleus of the cochlear nerve (Fig. 167). From the region of the acoustic tubercle a varying number of whitish strands may be seen running transversely or obliquely toward the midline where they disappear in the median sulcus of the fossa. These are the *striae medullares* or *striae*

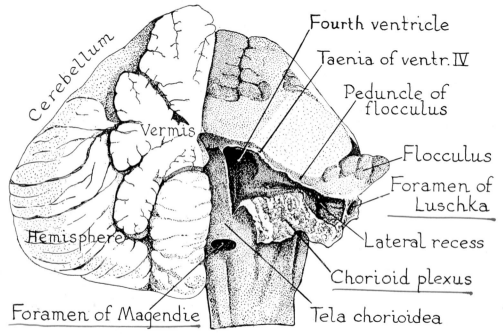

FIG. 169. The fourth ventricle partially opened, viewed from the right. The right half of the cerebellum has in large part been removed. (After Spalteholz)

attached to the medial borders of the superior cerebellar peduncles (Fig. 167). The lower triangular area belongs to the medulla and is bounded laterally by the clava, cuneate tubercle and restiform body.

The rhomboid fossa is divided into two symmetrical halves by the *median sulcus* which extends the whole length of the ventricular floor. Another groove, the *sulcus limitans* divides each half into a medial longitudinal ridge, the *median eminence*, and a lateral triangular area, the *area vestibularis*, beneath which lie the terminal nuclei of the

cerebellares whose significance will be discussed later. The region of the floor traversed by the striae medullares is sometimes called the intermediate portion of the rhomboid fossa and is continuous on each side with the lateral recess.

The median eminence, produced largely by subjacent motor nuclei of the cranial nerves, is narrow in the lower part of the fossa but widens in a rostral direction. The tapering caudal portion is called the *trigonum hypoglossi* because of the underlying nucleus of the hypoglossal nerve. Above the striae medullares it expands into a rounded eminence, the *colliculus abducentis* (*colliculus facialis, eminentia teres*) caused by the underlying nucleus of the sixth nerve and the root of the seventh nerve which here passes dorsally over the abducens nucleus. The deepened portion of the sulcus limitans lateral to the facial colliculus is the *superior fovea*. Extending from this fovea to the midbrain along the lateral border of the floor is a somewhat depressed narrow field of bluish color, the *locus caeruleus*, sub-

jacent to which is a column of pigmented cells.

Lateral to the hypoglossal trigone is another triangular or oval area, the *ala cinerea* or *trigonum vagi*, beneath which lie the dorsal nuclei of the vagus nerve. The deepening of the sulcus limitans in this region is often known as the inferior fovea. A white stripe, the funiculus separans, composed of neuroglial tissue, separates the ala cinerea from the *area postrema*, a narrow zone bordering on the lateral wall of the ventricle. The significance of this area is not known.

CHAPTER XIV

THE INTERNAL STRUCTURE OF THE MEDULLA

The relatively uniform picture seen in any section of the spinal cord is rapidly altered in the medulla oblongata and there the changes continue from level to level. The centrally placed H-shaped gray matter of the cord becomes broken up into more or less definite cell groups distributed throughout the whole area of the section. The white matter no longer surrounds the gray as a continuous peripheral mantle of longitudinal fibers but is now composed of fiber bundles intermingled with the gray masses and characterized by numerous transversely or obliquely running fibers, the whole constituting the *reticular formation* of the medulla, pons and upper portion of the brain stem. An understanding of these bewildering changes may best be gained by the study of a closely graded series of transverse sections in which the appearance and changing relationships of the various structures can be followed continuously. The series selected is that of a one month baby in which myelinization of several fiber systems is still incomplete, hence many tracts may be distinguished from others by the relative intensity of their staining capacity. Thus the fully myelinated fibers stain black in myelin stains, while others, as the pyramidal tract, are only partly myelinated and appear gray. Still others, such as the pontile fibers, are entirely unmyelinated and practically remain unstained. Whenever necessary, adult sections have been introduced to bring out structures not easily seen in the infant.

At the junction of the spinal cord and medulla (Fig. 170) the picture is still typical of the upper cervical cord, though with certain significant modifications. The substantia gelatinosa has increased in size and in the zone of Lissauer coarser myelinated

fibers have made their appearance. The zone at this level is a mixed bundle, consisting in part of fine ascending root fibers of the uppermost cervical nerves, in part of coarser descending fibers of the trigeminal nerve (N.V), which enter at a much higher level (pons) and descend in the dorso-lateral fasciculus to terminate in the substantia gelatinosa.

The lateral pyramidal tract is detaching itself from the the lateral white column and has invaded the gray. It is broken up into a number of obliquely or transversely cut bundles between which are strands of gray matter, and partially separates the dorsal from the ventral gray. The central gray has increased in amount and is expanding dorsally.

In the ventral gray are the somatic motor cells of the first cervical nerve, whose axons emerge as ventral root fibers. These cells extend for a short distance into the medulla where they are known as the supraspinal nucleus (Jacobsohn, Fig. 175). Dorsal and lateral to them is the nucleus of the spinal accessory nerve (N.XI), some roots of which are present at this level. The accessory nerve is often divided into a bulbar and spinal portion, forming respectively the internal and external branches of the nerve (Fig. 185). The former is in reality composed of displaced caudal fibers of the vagus nerve which emerge together with the spinal portion and then return to the vagus. The spinal portion constitutes the accessory nerve and supplies the sternocleidomastoid and portions of the trapezius muscles. It originates from a cell column in the ventral horn extending from the fifth or sixth cervical segments to about the middle of the pyramidal decussation. Caudally the cells of the column are in the lateral part of the

XI supply trap. & sterno[...]
bulbar & spinal portion

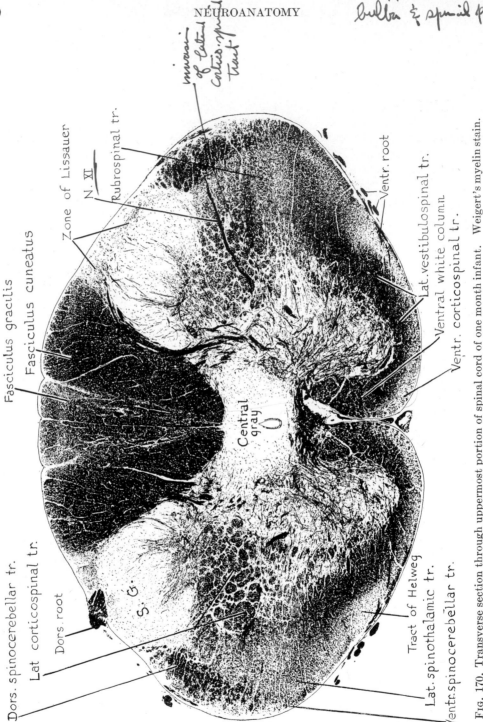

invasion of lateral corticospinal tract

Rubrospinal tr.

N. XI

Zone of Lissauer

Fasciculus cuneatus

Fasciculus gracilis

Dors. spinocerebellar tr.

Lat corticospinal tr.

Dors. root

S. G.

Central gray

Ventr. root

Lat. vestibulospinal tr.

Ventral white column

Ventr. corticospinal tr.

Tract of Helweg

Lat. spinothalamic tr.

Ventr. spinocerebellar tr.

Fig. 170. Transverse section through uppermost portion of spinal cord of one month infant. Weigert's myelin stain. Photograph. S. G., substantia gelatinosa.

ventral horn, but in the oral portion the cells assume a more central position. The root fibers arch dorsally and laterally, some of them first ascending within the cord for a distance, and emerge on the lateral aspect of the cord in a series of rootlets extending as low as the fifth or sixth cervical segments (Figs. 171, 185). The rootlets unite to

turns the head to the opposite side, in lesions of the XIth nerve the head will have a tendency to deviate to the side of the injury.

In the white matter the fiber tracts have the same arrangement as in other sections of the cervical cord. The dorsal column shows a massive fasciculus cuneatus and a

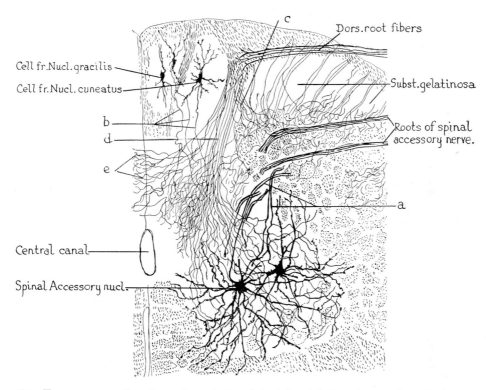

FIG. 171. Transverse section through medulla of foetal cat below decussation of the pyramids Golgi impregnation. (After Cajal.) *a*, axons from cells of spinal accessory nucleus forming fibers of spinal accessory nerve; *b*, axons from cells of nucleus gracilis and nucleus cuneatus forming media lemniscus fibers. Collaterals from dorsal white column to substantia gelatinosa and other parts of dorsal horn *c*, to intermediate gray and nucleus of spinal accessory *d*, crossing to opposite side in dorsal commissure *e*.

form a common trunk (external branch) which ascends in the spinal canal and makes its cranial exit through the jugular foramen together with the vagus and glossopharyngeal nerves. The nucleus of N.XI, like all motor nuclei, receives terminations of fibers bringing to it reflex, cerebellar, extrapyramidal and pyramidal influences related to cephalogyric movements. Since contraction of the sternomastoid muscle

somewhat smaller fasciculus gracilis. In the latter, lighter areas represent the caudal tip of the nucleus gracilis in which the whole tract ultimately terminates. In the peripheral part of the lateral and ventral white columns are the dorsal and ventral spinocerebellar, the olivospinal (Helweg) and ventral pyramidal tracts. Somewhat deeper are the rubrospinal, spinothalamic and vestibulospinal tracts. The ventral white contains the medial longitudinal fasciculus and, more ventrally, the colliculospinal fibers. The shorter intersegmental (spinospinal) tracts lie close to the gray matter.

dal tract are crossing the midline to join the ventral pyramidal tract of the opposite side, and in their passage through the gray are cutting off the ventral horn from the rest of the gray matter. In a series of

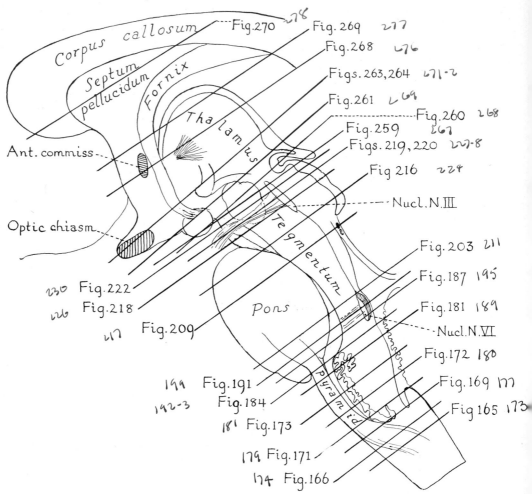

FIG. 172. Outline of paramedian sagittal section of brain stem, showing level and plane of the transverse sections of the figures indicated. For identification of structures see Fig. 265.

Sections of medulla through pyramidal decussation (motor decussation) (Figs. 173, 174)

The most conspicuous features are the decussation of the pyramidal tracts, the appearance of the dorsal column nuclei and the beginning of the gray reticular formation. The central gray dorsal to the central canal has greatly increased in amount.

Bundles of fibers from the lateral pyrami-

ascending sections the decussation is naturally seen in the reverse. The pyramidal tract is a massive descending fiber bundle arising from cells in the motor and premotor cortex. In the pyramidal decussation most of the fibers cross to the dorsolateral portion of the cord where they descend as the lateral or crossed pyramidal tract (Fig. 176). The rest of the fibers remain in their original ventral position as

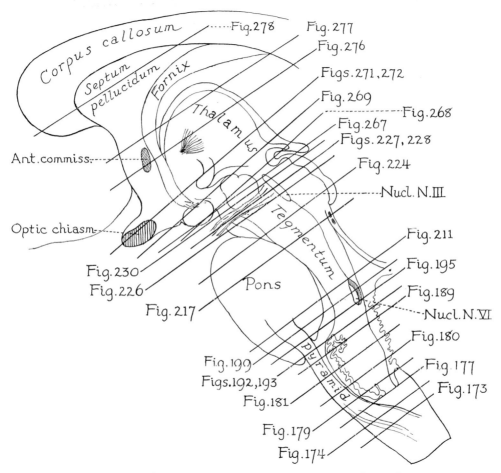

Corpus callosum
Fig. 278
Fig. 277
Fig. 276
Figs. 271, 272
Septum pellucidum
Fornix
Fig. 269
Fig. 268
Thalamus
Fig. 267
Figs. 227, 228
Fig. 224
Ant. commiss.
Nucl. N. III
Tegmentum
Optic chiasm
Fig. 211
Fig. 195
Fig. 230
Fig. 226
Pons
Fig. 189
Nucl. N. VI
Fig. 217
Fig. 180
Pyramid
Fig. 199
Figs. 192, 193
Fig. 177
Fig. 173
Fig. 181
Fig. 179
Fig. 174

NOTE: Refer to this figure for correct references to other figures in the book

the uncrossed or ventral tract. Some uncrossed fibers pass to the lateral tract of the same side. The fibers cross in interdigitating bundles having a downward as well as transverse direction, hence the bundles are cut obliquely and in any section there may be more pyramidal fibers on one side than on the other. The pyramidal decussation forms the anatomical basis for the voluntary

contains ascending spinal root fibers but is composed of descending afferent fibers of the trigeminal nerve (N.V), which terminate directly or by collaterals in the gelatinous substance. This fiber bundle now constitutes the *tract of the spinal* or *descending V* and the substantia gelatinosa similarly becomes the *terminal nucleus of the spinal V.*

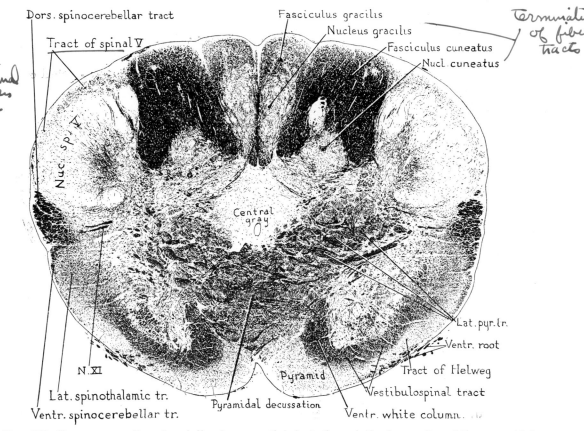

FIG. 173. Transverse section of medulla of one month infant, through the decussation of the pyramidal tracts. Weigert's myelin stain. Photograph. *Lat.pyr. tr.*, lateral pyramidal tract

tary motor control of one half of the body by the opposite cerebral hemisphere. Injury of the pyramidal tract anywhere above the decussation will cause the pyramidal symptoms already described on the contralateral extremities.

The greatly enlarged substantia gelatinosa is capped externally by the zone of Lissauer whose fibers are constantly increasing in number. The zone no longer

The ventral horn is still recognizable and as before contains the motor nuclei of the first cervical and accessory nerves. The rest of the gray, between gelatinous substance and ventral horn, has lost its definite form and continuity and is now composed of a mixture of scattered nuclear masses and fiber bundles, the latter mainly composed of the short intersegmental fibers which in the cord were placed next to the gray. This area of closely intermingled gray and white substance is known as the *reticular formation*.

In the dorsal white columns nuclear masses have appeared in the fasciculi gracilis and cuneatus. These are the nuclei of the dorsal column, known respectively as the *nucleus gracilis* and *nucleus cuneatus*, in

The nucleus gracilis is larger with consequent diminution of the gracile fasciculus. As progressively higher levels are reached, more and more fibers will terminate in these nuclei with constant increase in the size of the latter and corresponding decrease in the size of the dorsal columns. At the caudal tip of the inferior olive, the whole fasciculus

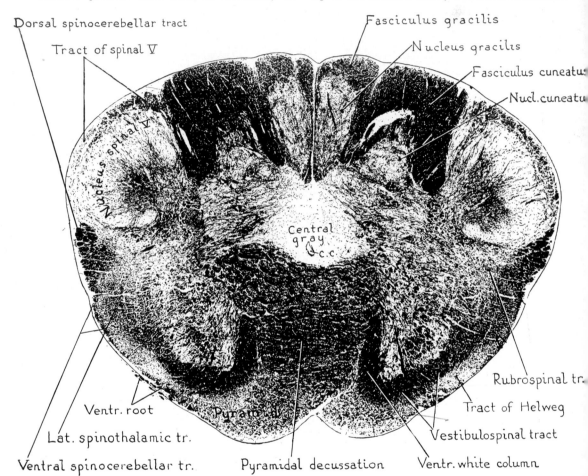

FIG. 174. Transverse section of medulla of one month infant, through upper portion of pyramidal decussation. Weigert's myelin stain. Photograph. *c.c.*, central canal

which the fibers of the dorsal column end. Their termination marks the ending of that system of fibers which has been traced upward from their origin in the spinal ganglia, the completion of the course of the peripheral afferent neurons with long ascending arms. The fasciculus cuneatus is still massive and its nucleus small in these levels.

gracilis and most of the fasciculus cuneatus have been replaced by their respective nuclei. The secondary tracts which arise from these nuclei are better seen in higher levels.

The tracts of the lateral and ventral white columns occupy the same relative positions, though the shorter intersegmental fibers

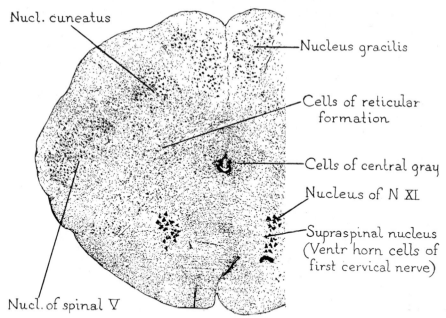

Nucl. cuneatus

Nucleus gracilis

Cells of reticular formation

Cells of central gray

Nucleus of N XI

Supraspinal nucleus (Ventr. horn cells of first cervical nerve)

Nucl. of spinal V

Fig. 175. Section through medulla of one month infant, about same level as Fig. 166. Cresylviolet Photograph, with cell groups blocked in schematically

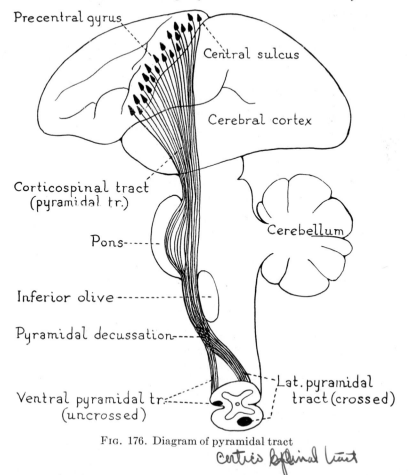

Precentral gyrus

Central sulcus

Cerebral cortex

Corticospinal tract (pyramidal tr.)

Cerebellum

Pons

Inferior olive

Pyramidal decussation

Ventral pyramidal tr. (uncrossed)

Lat. pyramidal tract (crossed)

Fig. 176. Diagram of pyramidal tract

have become part of the reticular formation. The ventral white column has been pushed laterally by the pyramidal decussation.

Section of medulla through the decussation of the medial lemniscus (sensory decussation) (Fig. 177)

The most conspicuous features are the large extent of the nuclei gracilis and cuneatus, the decussation and formation of the medial lemniscus and the increase of the gray reticular formation. Elements belonging to the hypoglossal (N.XII) and vagus (N.X) nerves have appeared in the central gray. Ventral to the central canal is the nucleus of the hypoglossal nerve and dorsolateral to it the dorsal nucleus of the vagus. Dorsal to the central canal is the commissural nucleus of the vagus. These nerves are best studied at somewhat higher levels.

The pyramidal fiber bundles have completely decussated and now form the massive medullary pyramids on either side of the deep median ventral sulcus.

In the dorsal column the nucleus gracilis has reached its greatest extent, practically all of the fibers of the fasciculus gracilis having terminated between this and the preceding level. The nucleus cuneatus is likewise much larger, though still covered by a considerable portion of the cuneate fasciculus. From these nuclei new myelinated fibers arise which as *internal arcuate fibers* sweep ventrally around the central gray, cross in the midline or *raphé*, and at once turn upward to form the ascending fiber bundle known as the *medial lemniscus* or *fillet* (*bulbothalamic tract*) which terminates in the ventral nuclei of the thalamus. This tract constitutes the second neuron of the dorsal column pathway conveying muscle sense and discriminative touch, and the decussation of the medial lemniscus is the basis for the sensory representation of one half of the body by the opposite cerebral hemisphere. Injury to one medial lemniscus above the decussation will hence cause the characteristic dorsal column disturbances on the contralateral side.

Lateral to the nucleus cuneatus is a group of larger cells resembling in structure those of the column of Clarke. This group is known as the *lateral* or *external cuneate nucleus* (magnocellular nucleus of the dorsal column, nucleus of Monakow), (Figs. 177, 178, 179). Its fibers do not participate in the formation of the medial lemniscus but course over the dorsolateral periphery as *dorsal external arcuate* fibers to enter the cerebellum at a higher level. This nucleus may be regarded as a medullary extension of Clarke's column, whose fibers supplement the dorsal spinocerebellar tract, conveying uncrossed impulses to the cerebellum from the muscles of the upper extremity and neck.

The *tract of the spinal V* has increased in size. As already stated, the afferent root of the trigeminal nerve enters the brain stem at a much higher level (pons) but many of its fibers descend as the tract of the spinal V which occupies the region of the zone of Lissauer. In its descent the tract becomes progressively smaller as more and more of its fibers end in the terminal nucleus of the spinal V which is an upward continuation of the substantia gelatinosa extending rostrally to the mid-pontile region. Hence in a series of ascending sections the tract will continue to increase to the level of entry of the trigeminal nerve. These descending fibers convey sensory impulses, primarily pain and temperature, from the face, forehead and mucous membranes of the mouth and nose, hence injury to the tract will cause a diminution of these sensations on the same side of the face. From the terminal nucleus arise fibers which form the secondary trigeminal tracts. The fibers arise, a few at each level, and many cross to the opposite side where they ascend in the reticular formation to terminate in the thalamus. These trigeminothalamic fibers constitute the second neuron system in the sensory pathway from face to cortex. Other uncrossed fibers ascend and descend on the

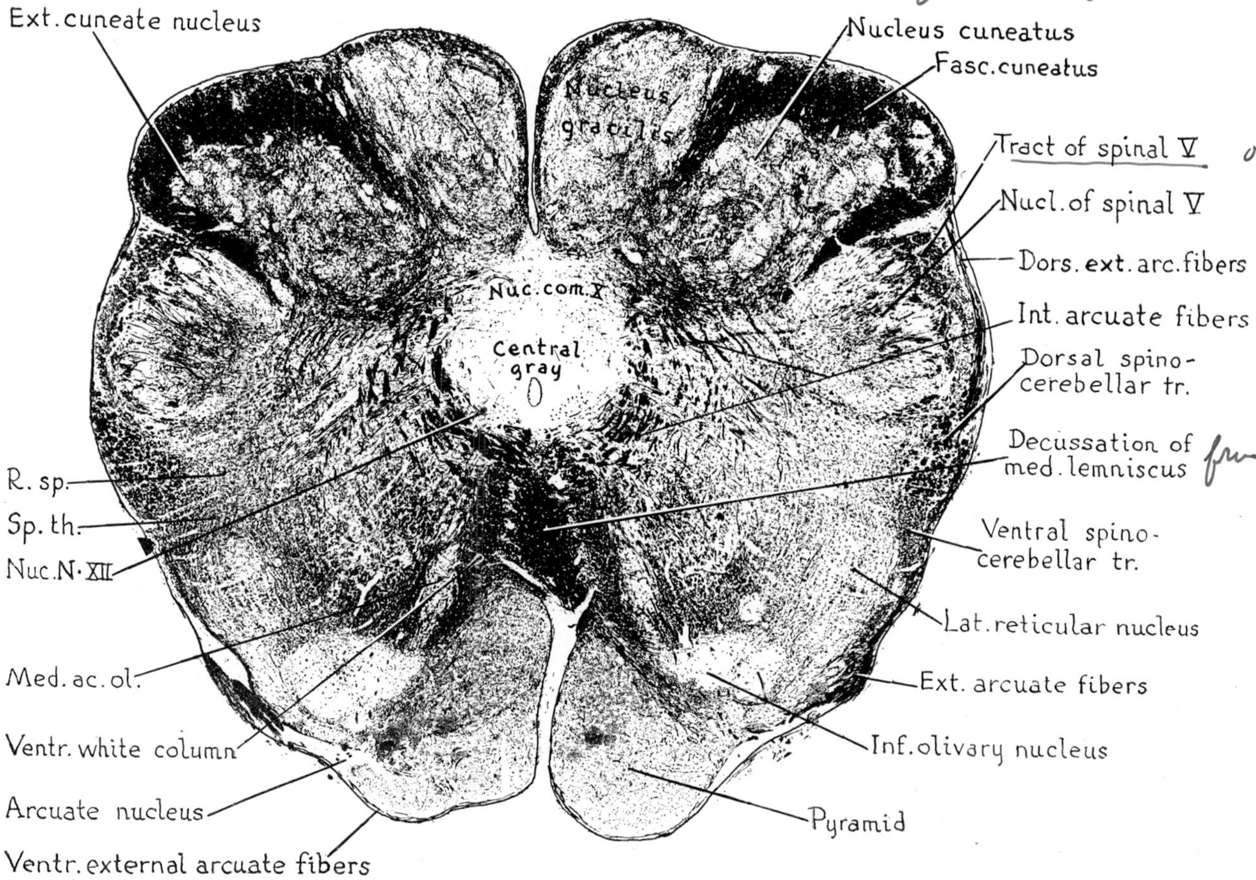

FIG. 177. Transverse section of medulla of one month infant, through the decussation of the medial lemniscus. Weigert's myelin stain. Photograph. *Med.ac.o.*, medial accessory olivary nucleus; *Nuc.com.X*, nucleus commissuralis; *R.sp.*, rubrospinal tract; *Sp.th.*, spinothalamic tract.

Handwritten annotations in margins:

Nucleus gracilis & cuneatus take — place of fasciculi —

old zone of Burdach

fn. [Pyramidal] tracts

Labels around figure: Ext. cuneate nucleus; Nucleus cuneatus; Fasc. cuneatus; Tract of spinal V; Nucl. of spinal V; Dors. ext. arc. fibers; Int. arcuate fibers; Dorsal spino-cerebellar tr.; Decussation of med. lemniscus; Ventral spino-cerebellar tr.; Lat. reticular nucleus; Ext. arcuate fibers; Inf. olivary nucleus; Pyramid; Ventr. external arcuate fibers; Arcuate nucleus; Ventr. white column; Med. ac. ol.; Nuc. N. XII; Sp. th.; R. sp.; Nucleus gracilis; Nuc. com. X; Central gray same side, forming reflex connections with the motor nuclei of the hypoglossal, vagus, facial and other cranial nerves (Figs. 215, 216). Since the spinal V is located not far from the spinothalamic tract, injury to the dorsolateral region of the medulla produces the curious clinical picture of an alternating hemianalgesia and hemithermoanesthesia of the face and body. There is loss or diminution of pain and temperature on the same side of the face and on the opposite side of the body and neck.

The gray of the spinal cord is now replaced by the much increased reticular formation composed of gray matter and longitudinal fiber bundles. Through it course many transverse fibers representing the beginnings or endings of the longitudinal bundles, such as the internal arcuate fibers of the medial lemniscus and secondary trigeminal fibers. In the peripheral portion of the reticular formation, the long tracts of the lateral and ventral columns retain their relative positions but the ventral white is now situated dorsal to the pyramids and lateral to the medial lemniscus.

The **reticular formation** contains numerous cells which are organized in more or less definite groups. In the central and medial portion the cells are diffusely arranged. Many of them are medium sized or small, but scattered among them are found unusually large cells or aggregations of such cells with coarse chromofilic bodies and generally resembling the structure of motor cells. In the upper portions of the medulla and in the pons there are greater condensations of such cells and there also the cells are largest. These large cells, whose number throughout the brain stem is considerable, are collectively known as the *motor reticular nucleus*. Their axons, in large part uncrossed, usually split into ascending and descending branches. Many descend to the spinal cord as reticulospinal fibers, others go to the motor nuclei of the cranial nerves (reticulobulbar fibers). They

receive collaterals or terminals from secondary afferent neurons (medial lemniscus, secondary trigeminal, etc.), from the nucleus ruber and tectum of the midbrain, the corpus striatum and perhaps also from the cerebral cortex, and hence represent intermediate links between the above-named structures and the motor peripheral neurons. They form an extensive if diffuse old motor system, an important part of the extrapyramidal pathway. Some of the reticulospinal and reticulobulbar fibers which descend from the midbrain are believed to play a part in the regulation of extensor tonus of the antigravity muscles. Intermingled with the large cells are smaller ones whose connections are poorly understood. They are probably intersegmental in character and may represent relays in central autonomic or visceral pathways. The reticular formation, like the spinospinal system of the cord, may be regarded as the intrinsic associative system of the medulla, mediating important bulbar reflexes and also forming relay stations in longer conduction paths from and to higher centers. In a general way, the large cells are related to somatic pathways discharging on striped skeletal muscle, while many of the smaller cells are probably parts of central visceral (autonomic) pathways.

More laterally in the reticular formation close to the ventral spinocerebellar tract is the *lateral reticular nucleus* (Figs. 178, 183), usually subdivided into a ventral and a dorsal nucleus. The ventral is the larger and is best developed in the caudal portion of the olivary region (Figs. 179, 180). They appear to be relay stations in the spinocerebellar pathway, receiving terminals of the ventral spinocerebellar tracts. Their axons cross the median raphé, then (as ventral external arcuate fibers) pass over the ventral surface of the pyramid and olive to reach the dorsolateral periphery of the medulla and enter the cerebellum at a higher level (reticulocerebellar fibers).

Fewer fibers pass to the cerebellum uncrossed.

On the basal aspect of the pyramid is the *arcuate nucleus* whose position varies somewhat in different levels (Figs. 178, 183). In the oral portion of the medulla the nucleus enlarges considerably (nucleus precursorius pontis) and appears to become continuous with the nucleus of the pons. It receives fibers from the lateral reticular nucleus and probably also from the gracile and cuneate nuclei, and sends axons as

Sections of medulla through lower and middle portions of inferior olivary nucleus (Figs. 179, 180, 181)

These represent the most characteristic pictures of the medulla, passing dorsally through the fourth ventricle and showing three large surface eminences: the pyramids, inferior olives and restiform bodies. The central canal has opened into the fourth ventricle, narrow at first but widening progressively in higher levels as the dorsal walls of the medulla diverge more and more

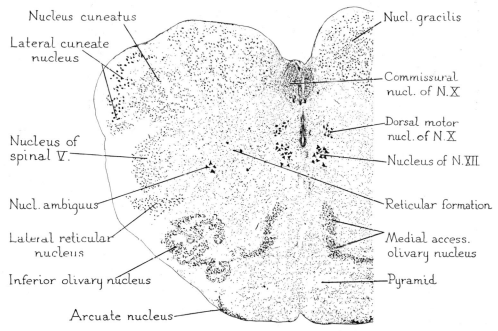

FIG. 178. Section through medulla of one month infant, about same level as Fig. 169. Cresylviolet Photograph, with cell groups blocked in schematically

ventral external arcuate fibers to the cerebellum (arcuatocerebellar), (Fig. 182). Thus in this portion of the medulla there is formed a new though relatively small system of afferent cerebellar fibers arising in the lateral cuneate, lateral reticular and arcuate nuclei.

Dorsolateral to the pyramids new nuclear masses have appeared which become more extensive in the succeeding levels. They represent the caudal tip of the inferior olivary complex.

laterally. The thin non-nervous roof is formed by the tela chorioidea and chorioid plexus. The central gray is now spread out on the ventricular floor. On the latter are seen the eminentia media, here the *trigonum hypoglossi* occupied by the nucleus of the XIIth nerve; the *trigonum vagi* or *ala cinerea* containing certain vagal nuclei, and lateral to this the *area vestibularis* occupied by the medial vestibular nucleus (Figs. 181, 183).

The nucleus gracilis whose oral tip is still cut in the lowest section (Fig. 179), has

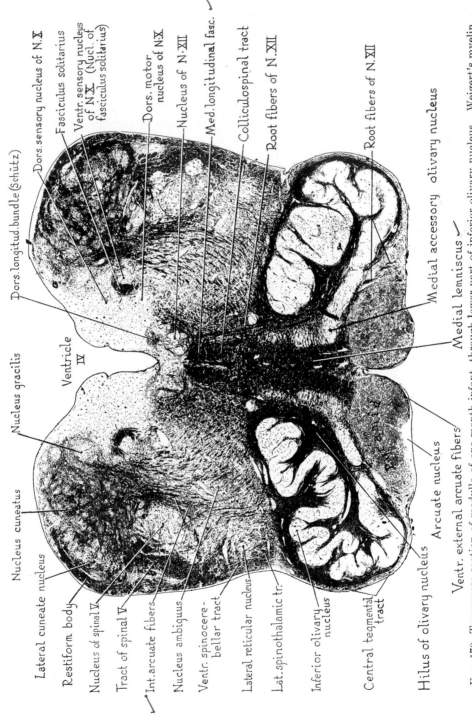

Dors. sensory nucleus of N. X

Fasciculus solitarius

Ventr. sensory nucleus of N. X (Nucl. of fasciculus solitarius)

Dors. motor nucleus of N. X

Nucleus of N. XII

Med. longitudinal fasc.

Colliculospinal tract

Root fibers of N. XII

Root fibers of N. XII

Medial accessory olivary nucleus

Medial lemniscus

Dors. longitud. bundle (Schütz)

Nucleus gracilis

Ventricle IV

Nucleus cuneatus

Lateral cuneate nucleus

Restiform body

Nucleus of spinal V

Tract of spinal V

Int. arcuate fibers

Nucleus ambiguus

Ventr. spinocerebellar tract

Lateral reticular nucleus

Lat. spinothalamic tr.

Inferior olivary nucleus

Central tegmental tract

Hilus of olivary nucleus

Ventr. external arcuate fibers

Arcuate nucleus

Fig. 179. Transverse section of medulla of one month infant, through lower part of inferior olivary nucleus. Weigert's myelin stain. Photograph

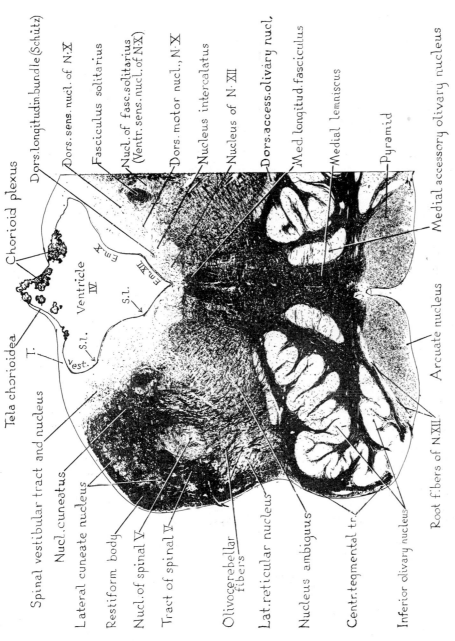

Tela chorioidea

Chorioid plexus

Dors.longitudin.bundle (Schütz)

Dors.sens.nucl. of N.X

Fasciculus solitarius

Nucl.of fasc.solitarius
(Ventr.sens.nucl.of NX)

Dors.motor nucl., N.X

Nucleus intercalatus

Nucleus of N.XII

Dors.access.olivary nucl.

Med.longitud.fasciculus

Medial lemniscus

Pyramid

Medial accessory olivary nucleus

Ventricle IV

Em.X

Em.XII

S.l.

S.l.

Vest.

T.

Spinal vestibular tract and nucleus

Nucl.cuneatus

Lateral cuneate nucleus

Restiform body

Nucl.of spinal V

Tract of spinal V

Olivocerebellar fibers

Lat.reticular nucleus

Nucleus ambiguus

Centr.tegmental tr.

Inferior olivary nucleus

Root fibers of N.XII

Arcuate nucleus

FIG. 180. Transverse section of medulla of one month infant, through inferior olivary nucleus, somewhat higher than Fig. 179. Weigert's myelin stain. Photograph. *Em.X.*, eminentia vagi (ala cinerea); *Em.XII*, eminentia hypoglossi; *S.l.*, suleus limitans; *T*, taenia of fourth ventricle; *Vest.*, area vestibularis.

entirely disappeared in the higher ones, and the larger nucleus cuneatus is similarly diminishing in size. Both nuclei, while present, continue to furnish internal arcuate fibers to the medial lemniscus which now constitutes a conspicuous ventral fiber bundle placed on either side of the raphé (midline) between the olivary nuclei and dorsal to the pyramids. The lateral cuneate nucleus is still large and ventral to it are the tract and nucleus of the spinal V.

The dorsal spinocerebellar tract is leaving its lateral position and is turning dorsally, and together with olivocerebellar fibers (see below) is beginning to form the *restiform body* occupying the dorsolateral periphery of the bulb external to the cuneate nucleus and spinal V (Figs. 179–181). This fiber bundle when fully built up forms the major portion of the *inferior cerebellar peduncle*, composed of afferent fibers to the cerebellum from the cord and medulla, which enters the cerebellum at a higher level.

The most striking new structure is the convoluted gray band of the *inferior olivary nucleus*, appearing in section as a much folded bag with the opening or hilus directed mesially. Placed near the hilus is the *medial accessory olivary nucleus* and near the dorsal aspect of the main nucleus is the *dorsal accessory olivary nucleus*. The main nucleus is composed of relatively small round or pear-shaped cells with numerous short and richly branching dendrites. Their axons form the olivocerebellar fibers distributed to all parts of the opposite side of the cerebellum. The fibers fill the interior of the bag-shaped nucleus, emerge from the hilus, cross through the medial lemniscus and pass through or around the opposite olivary nucleus. Then they turn dorsolaterally and, gathered into more compact bundles, traverse or surround the spinal V and enter the restiform body. The accessory nuclei and the most medial portion of the main nucleus are phylogenetically the oldest (paleo-olive) and send their fibers to the cerebellar vermis (paleocerebellum).

The larger convoluted portion of the main nucleus (neo-olive) is related principally to the cerebellar hemisphere (neocerebellum). As more and more olivocerebellar fibers are given off, the restiform body assumes massive proportions and forms a prominent bulge on the dorsolateral surface of the medulla (Figs. 181, 189). Thus the **restiform body** is composed of the olivocerebellar, dorsal spinocerebellar and to a smaller extent of the external arcuate fibers from the cuneate, arcuate and lateral reticular nuclei (Fig. 182).

The main olivary nucleus is always surrounded by a dense band of myelinated fibers, the *amiculum olivae*, composed in large part of axons terminating in the nucleus. These are principally fibers of a rather extensive tract arising in the upper portion of the midbrain (nucleus ruber, reticular formation) and perhaps also from the globus pallidus and other regions, and known as the *central tegmental tract*. This tract is well developed in man, and together with the olivocerebellar fibers constitutes a newer pathway linking the corpus striatum and thalamus to the newer portion of the cerebellum. The amiculum also contains efferent olivary fibers which descend to the upper cervical cord as the olivospinal tract of Helweg. Some of these may be spino-olivary fibers. The tract of Helweg disappears when the olivary levels are reached.

The ventrolateral tracts of the reticular formation have been pushed dorsally by the olivary nuclei. The ventral spinocerebellar, rubrospinal and spinothalamic tracts occupy the lateral periphery between the restiform body and olive. The vestibulospinal fibers are scattered along the dorsal surface of the olive, and the remnants of the ventral white column now lie on either side of the raphé directly above the medial lemniscus. Its dorsal compact portion constitutes the *medial longitudinal fasciculus*, a descending fiber bundle of mixed origin. In these levels the fasciculus contains fibers from two nuclei in the tegmentum of the midbrain

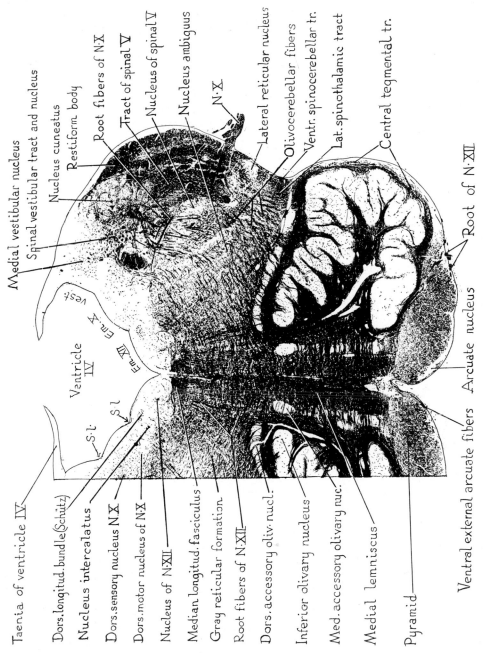

Medial vestibular nucleus
Spinal vestibular tract and nucleus
Nucleus cuneatus
Restiform body
Root fibers of N·X
Tract of spinal V
Nucleus of spinal V
Nucleus ambiguus
N·X
Lateral reticular nucleus
Olivocerebellar fibers
Ventr. spinocerebellar tr.
Lat. spinothalamic tract
Central tegmental tr.
Root of N·XII

Taenia of ventricle IV
Dors. longitud. bundle (Schütz)
Nucleus intercalatus
Dors. sensory nucleus N·X
Dors. motor nucleus of N·X
Nucleus of N·XII
Median longitud. fasciculus
Gray reticular formation
Root fibers of N·XII
Dors. accessory oliv. nucl.
Inferior olivary nucleus
Med. accessory olivary nuc.
Medial lemniscus
Pyramid

Ventral external arcuate fibers
Arcuate nucleus

Ventricle IV
Em·IX Em·X Vest.
S·L
S·L

FIG. 181. Transverse section of medulla of one month infant, through middle of olive. Weigert's myelin stain. Photograph. *Em. X*, eminentia vagi (ala cinerea); *Em. XII*, eminentia hypoglossi; *S.L.*, sulcus limitans; *Vest.*, area vestibularis.

(interstitial nucleus and nucleus of the posterior commissure) and fibers from the vestibular nuclei (medial vestibulospinal). Ventral to the medial longitudinal fasciculus is the more loosely organized *predorsal bundle* composed of colliculospinal (tecto-spinal) fibers.

dominate and the fiber bundles are more loosely arranged. The root fibers of the hypoglossal nerve mark the boundary be-tween the two. In the most dorsal position on either side of the raphé is a band of small cells, the *dorsal paramedian nucleus,* lying immediately beneath the ependyma and

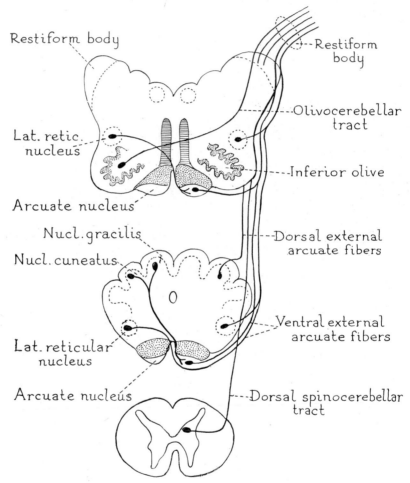

Restiform body

Restiform body

Olivocerebellar tract

Lat. retic. nucleus

Inferior olive

Arcuate nucleus

Nucl. gracilis

Nucl. cuneatus

Dorsal external arcuate fibers

Ventral external arcuate fibers

Lat. reticular nucleus

Arcuate nucleus

Dorsal spinocerebellar tract

Fig. 182. Diagram showing composition of restiform body

The **reticular formation** has reached its fullest extent and contains the above-named long tracts. It may now be divided into two portions: (a) the white reticular forma-tion near the raphé and containing the compact fiber bundles of the medial lemnis-cus, medial longitudinal fasciculus and tecto-spinal tract; and (b) the gray reticular formation in which the gray masses pre-

extending the whole length of the fourth ventricle (Fig. 183). Its lateral extension in the central gray of the ventricular floor, at this level lying dorsal to the hypoglossal nucleus, has been distinguished by some as a separate nuclear column, the *nucleus eminentiae teretis (eminentiae mediae).* Fur-ther ventrally and extending into the inter-olivary region is a larger cell complex, the nucleus (or nuclei) of the raphé (Fig. 183). This nucleus becomes especially large in the uppermost portion of the medulla where it is also known as the inferior central nucleus. A thin discontinuous cell stripe, the *retro-pyramidal nucleus (nucleus conterminalis)*, placed between pyramid and olive probably represents a lateral extension of the raphéal nuclei (Fig. 183).

more medially placed in the higher levels. A group of closely packed medium sized cells placed on the dorsolateral aspect of the restiform body constitutes the caudal portion of the *pontobulbar* nucleus (Fig. 183). Proceeding rostrally, this cell column assumes a more and more ventral position, until at the junction of pons and medulla it forms a fairly large cell mass now placed

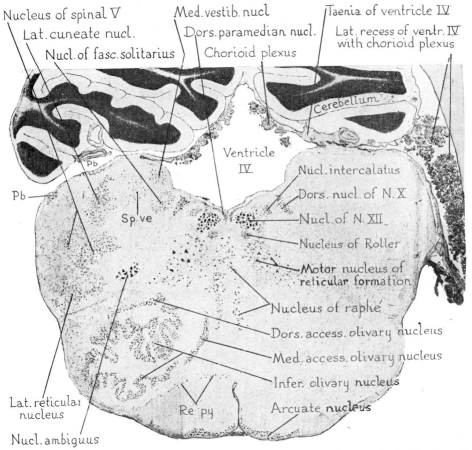

FIG. 183. Section through mid-olivary region of adult medulla. Cresylviolet. Photograph, with schematic representation of main cell groups. *Pb.*, pontobulbar nucleus; *Re.py.*, retropyramidal nucleus; *Sp.ve.*, spinal vestibular nucleus (nucleus of descending vestibular nerve).

In the gray reticular formation the motor reticular nucleus is represented by considerable condensations of large cells surrounded by scattered smaller ones (Fig. 183). The lateral reticular nucleus is best developed in this portion and contributes external arcuate fibers to the restiform body.

The arcuate nucleus is large and becomes

ventral to the inferior cerebellar peduncle (Fig. 192). The cells of this nucleus which thus partly encircles the restiform body resemble in structure those of the pons and are regarded by some as outlying parts of the pontile nuclei.

The cranial nerves of this portion are the *hypoglossus* (N.XII), the *vagus* (N.X) and the *descending vestibular tract or root* of the *acoustic nerve* (N.VIII).

The hypoglossal nerve. is a motor nerve supplying the special somatic striped musculature of the tongue. It also appears to contain some afferent proprioceptive fibers since the muscle spindles of the tongue degenerate on section of the nerve. These afferent fibers may in part be derived from inconstant ganglion cells found on the hypoglossal roots (Langworthy) but their principal source is still obscure. During foetal life the nerve apparently contains dorsal

ending in the nucleus. The root fibers gather on the ventral surface of the nucleus, forming a series of rootlets which pass ventrally lateral to the medial lemniscus and emerge on the surface in the ventrolateral (preolivary) sulcus between pyramid and olive.

The terminal fibers form a delicate plexus within and around the nucleus. Some are pyramidal fibers effecting voluntary movements of the tongue, which go in part to the nucleus of the same side, in larger part cross to the opposite nucleus. Others are

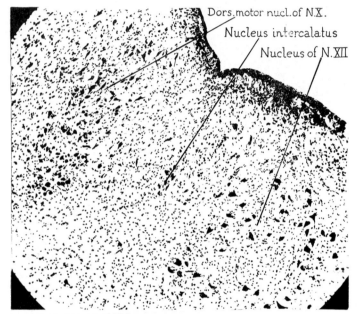

FIG. 184. Some of the nuclei in the floor of the fourth ventricle, about same level as Fig. 183. Medulla of three months infant. Cresylviolet. Photograph

root fibers related to a small ganglion (Froriep) but these disappear in a later period.

The nucleus of N.XII forms a column of typical multipolar motor cells, some 18 mm in length and occupying the central gray of the median eminence. The column begins below the caudal tip of the olive and extends rostrally to the region of the striae medullares. Within the nucleus can be seen coarse myelinated fibers which are the root fibers of the motor cells, and a network of finer fibers representing terminals of axons

secondary glossopharyngeal, vagal and trigeminal fibers mediating reflex tongue movements in response to stimuli from the lingual mucous membrane (taste, touch, temperature, pain). Fibers from olfactory centers and from the medial vestibular nucleus likewise terminate in the hypoglossal nucleus coming in part from a descending bundle of of fine myelinated fibers found in the central gray dorsolateral to the hypoglossal nucleus and known as the *dorsal longitudinal bundle of Schütz* (dorsal tegmental tract, Figs. 179, 180, 181). The constitution of this tract is not fully worked out. Some fibers appear to come directly from the hypothalamus, others from the dorsal tegmental nucleus of the midbrain. In the medulla, fibers from the medial vestibular nucleus are added. Some of its fibers terminate in the hypoglossal nucleus, either directly or through intercalated neurons (nucleus intercalatus, nucleus prepositus). Others probably come in relation with the motor and secretory nuclei of the vagus and glossopharyngeus.

Injury to the hypoglossal nerve will naturally produce a lower motor neuron an upper motor neuron (pyramidal, spastic) hemiplegia of the contralateral half of the body, especially the extremities.

The vagus nerve (N.X) is both efferent and afferent. It contains (a) general somatic afferent fibers distributed through the auricular branch of the vagus to the skin in back of the ear and the posterior wall of the external auditory meatus. These have their cell bodies in the *jugular ganglion* of the vagus nerve (ganglion of the root). (b) General visceral afferent fibers from the pharynx, larynx, trachea, oesophagus, and from the thoracic and abdominal vis-

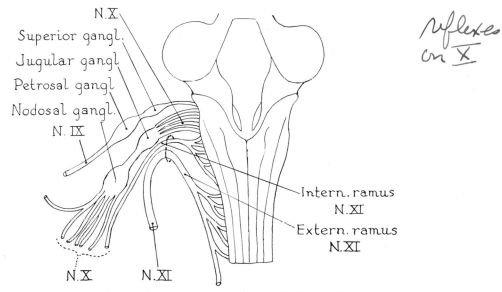

N.X
Superior gangl.
Jugular gangl.
Petrosal gangl.
Nodosal gangl.
N. IX

Intern. ramus
N.XI
Extern. ramus
N.XI

N.X   N.XI

reflexes on X

FIG. 185. Diagrammatic sketch of the roots of nerves IX, X and XI. (After Bendz)

paralysis of the ipsilateral half of the tongue, with loss of all movement, loss of tone and degenerative atrophy of the muscles affected. Since the genioglossus muscle effects an extension of the tongue to the opposite side, the tongue when protruded will deviate to the side of the injury.

The juxtaposition of the emerging root fibers of N.XII and the pyramidal tract is the anatomical basis of the *inferior* or *hypoglossal alternating hemiplegia* resulting from ventral lesions of this area. This consists of a lower motor neuron paralysis of the ipsilateral half of the tongue combined with cera; also some special visceral afferent fibers from scattered taste buds in the region of the epiglottis. The cell bodies of the visceral fibers are in the larger *nodosal ganglion* (ganglion of the trunk). (c) General visceral (preganglionic) efferent fibers to terminal parasympathetic ganglia innervating the thoracic and abdominal viscera. (d) Special visceral efferent (branchiomotor) fibers to the striped voluntary muscles of the larynx and pharynx.

gut

throat

The *dorsal motor nucleus* (preganglionic) occupies the medial portion of the trigonum vagi or ala cinerea (Figs. 167, 179–181).

It is a column of cells somewhat longer than the hypoglossal nucleus, extending both orally and caudally a little beyond the latter, the oral portion belonging to the glossopharyngeal nerve (N.IX) emerging at a somewhat higher level. The nucleus is composed of relatively small spindle-shaped cells among which are larger ones with coarser chromofilic bodies and scattered pigmented cells. The functional significance of the several cell types is not clear. According to one view (Winkler), the large-celled portion innervates the smooth muscle of the visceral walls, especially the stomach, and the small cells the heart and the smooth muscle of the mucosal blood vessels of the head. The cells which give rise to secretory fibers have not been definitely determined for the vagus, but probably lie more ventrally in the dorsal part of the reticular formation. In the more rostral portion of the medulla, a group of such cells is known as the *inferior salivatory nucleus*, contributing secretory fibers to the glossopharyngeal nerve (see below). The axons of the cells from the dorsal nucleus pass ventrolaterally, traverse the nucleus and tract of the spinal V and emerge on the lateral surface of the medulla between the olive and the restiform body.

The dorsal motor nucleus contains relatively few myelinated fibers, indicating that many of the terminals entering it are unmyelinated. These are principally secondary fibers from the sensory nuclei of the glossopharyngeal and vagus nerves, from olfactory centers, and from the medial vestibular nucleus. Through the latter vomiting could be effected by excessive vestibular stimulation. Terminals from central autonomic tracts linking the thalamus and cortex with the nucleus must likewise be present since emotional states may give rise to nausea, vomiting and changes in heart beat.

The *ventral motor* nucleus or *nucleus ambiguus* is a column of cells placed in the reticular formation about halfway between the nucleus of the spinal V and the inferior olive (Figs. 183, 180, 181). It extends from about the caudal border of the lemniscus decussation to the level of the striae medullares, the uppermost portion contributing fibers to the glossopharyngeal nerve. The nucleus is composed of typical multipolar lower motor neurons whose axons go directly to the striped muscles of the larynx and pharynx. These axons have an arched intramedullary course (Figs. 163, 187). They pass obliquely dorsally and medially, join the other fibers of the vagus, and then bending abruptly outward pass with them to the lateral surface of the medulla. Some cross the midline to leave by the root of the opposite side (Obersteiner). The nucleus receives various terminals, among which are both crossed and uncrossed pyramidal fibers for the voluntary control of swallowing and phonation. Others appear to come from the lateral columns (Marburg) and secondary trigeminal tracts. The nucleus should receive stimuli from the pharyngeal and laryngeal muscles themselves for proprioceptive tonic control; secondary vagal, glossopharyngeal and trigeminal fibers which convey stimuli from the oral, pharyngeal and respiratory mucosa mediating various reflexes such as coughing, vomiting, pharyngeal and laryngeal reflexes; and perhaps also fibers conveying cerebellar and extrapyramidal impulses.

The afferent fibers of the vagus enter along with the efferent ones. The few cutaneous fibers coming from the external ear apparently terminate in the nucleus of the spinal V, the latter thus forming the terminal nucleus for all the general somatic afferent impulses brought in by the cranial nerves. The more numerous afferent visceral fibers pass dorsomedially and either end immediately in terminal nuclei or bend sharply and form a long descending bundle known as the *fasciculus solitarius* (tract of the descending IX and X) (Figs. 163, 164). This bundle gives off collaterals and terminals *en route*, constantly diminishing in size until caudal to the fourth ventricle many of the remaining fibers decussate dorsal to the central canal (Fig. 187). The fasciculus solitarius is not formed by the vagus alone but receives contributions of afferent visceral fibers from the glossopharyngeal and facial nerves. The glossopharyngeal fibers convey taste impulses from the posterior third of the tongue, those of the facial bring in similar impulses from the anterior two-thirds of the tongue. Though entering at

sensation from the organs innervated by the vagus.

The fibers of the fasciculus solitarius end in two main terminal nuclei, the *dorsal sensory nucleus of the vagus* and the *nucleus of the fasciculus solitarius (ventral sensory nucleus,* Figs. 179, 186). The dorsal nucleus is a column of small cells placed medial to the fasciculus in the central gray of the trigonum vagi, lateral to the dorsal motor nucleus, and extends from the middle of the

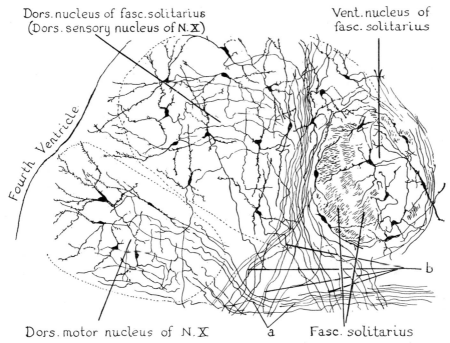

Fig. 186. The various vagus nuclei in the floor of the fourth ventricle. Medulla of new-born cat. Golgi impregnation. (After Cajal.) *a,* efferent (preganglionic) root fibers from dorsal motor nucleus; *b,* fibers from the sensory nuclei forming secondary vagoglossopharyngeal tracts.

higher levels, these fibers descend to form the upper portion of the fasciculus solitarius to be joined in the levels studied by the larger contingent from the vagus (Fig. 164). Just as the spinal V constitutes a descending bundle of somatic afferent fibers, so does the fasciculus solitarius represent a descending bundle of visceral afferent fibers. The upper portion, especially above the entry of N.X, is almost entirely related to taste, the lower portion represents general visceral

pyramidal decussation to the upper third of the olive. The ventral nucleus lies ventrolateral to and also within the fascicle and in the uppermost portions completely surrounds the fasciculus. It is composed of both small and large cells, the latter mainly aggregated in the lateral portion. The nucleus forms a long column over an inch in length, extending upward almost to the inferior border of the pons and downward some distance below the fourth ventricle. Here the nucleus of each side becomes continuous with a median nuclear mass, the *commissural nucleus of N.X*, placed dorsal to the central canal (Fig. 187) and in which terminate many crossed fibers of the fasciculus solitarius. The uppermost enlarged portion of the nucleus solitarius which receives the taste fibers from N.VII and N.IX is also known as the *gustatory nucleus*.

The secondary fibers forming part of the afferent taste pathways to the thalamus and

calated neurons. Others relaying impulses from the pharyngeal, respiratory and alimentary mucous membranes go to the nucleus ambiguus for pharyngeal and laryngeal reflexes; to the dorsal motor nucleus, phrenic nucleus in the cervical cord and the nuclei of the costal muscles in the thoracic cord, involved in coughing, vomiting and respiration. The connection with the cord centers of the respiratory muscles is prob-

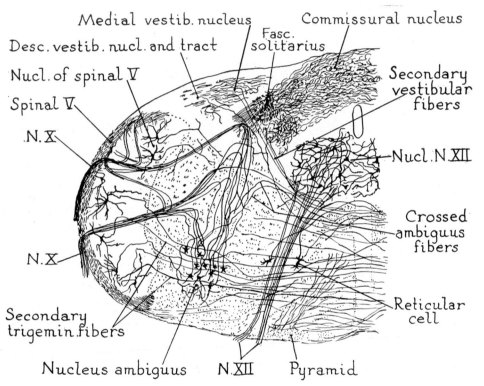

FIG. 187. Transverse section through medulla of mouse four days old, at level of hypoglossal nucleus and nucleus ambiguus. Golgi silver impregnation. (After Cajal)

cortex are not well established. They appear to be both crossed and uncrossed fibers which ascend in the dorsal part of the reticular formation and possibly join the medial lemniscus (Allen). Other secondary fibers from the sensory nuclei of N.X and N.IX go to various motor nuclei of the cranial and spinal nerves. As already stated, such fibers go to the hypoglossal ard salivatory nuclei for lingual and secretory reflexes, either directly or through inter-

ably in part only by long secondary fibers (solitariospinal), in larger part by intercalated reticular neurons in the vicinity of the nucleus solitarius (reticulospinal fibers). This whole region, including the sensory nuclei of the vagus and the adjacent portion of the reticular formation, is known as the reflex *"respiratory center"*. The secondary and reticular cells of this "center" are not only activated by afferent vagal and other neural impulses, but are affected directly by changes in the blood content (CO₂ accumulation, etc.) in such a manner as to effect the needed changes in respiration (Fig. 188).

The glossopharyngeus (N.IX), though emerging at a somewhat higher level (Figs. 185, 189), is intimately related to the vagus, the two having common intramedullary nuclei of origin and termination and similar functional components. Some of its con-

in the superior ganglion and they apparently terminate in the nucleus of the spinal V. (b) Visceral afferent fibers whose cell bodies are in the petrosal ganglion. Some are general visceral afferent fibers of touch, pain and temperature supplying the mucous membrane of the posterior portion of the tongue, tonsil and Eustachean tube. More numerous are the special visceral afferent fibers from the taste buds on the posterior

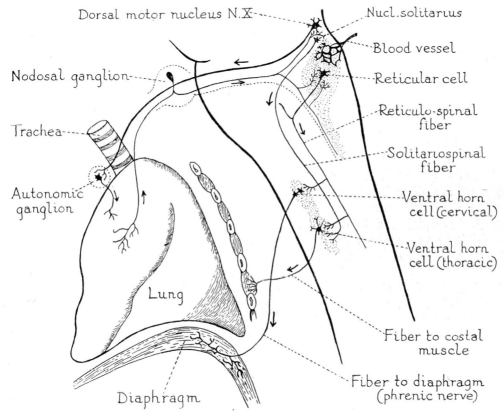

FIG. 188. Diagram of the intrinsic neural mechanism of respiration. (After Cajal and Herrick)

nections have already been mentioned. Like the vagus, it is both afferent and efferent. The afferent fibers have their unipolar cell bodies in the small *superior ganglion* placed within the jugular canal and the larger extracranial *petrosal ganglion*. The nerve contains (a) a few general somatic afferent fibers from the skin in back of the ear, distributed through the auricular branch of the vagus nerve. Their cell bodies are

third of the tongue. After entering the medulla, these fibers contribute to the upper portion of the fasciculus solitarius and terminate in the nucleus of the latter which is fairly large rostrally and known as the gustatory nucleus. (c) General visceral efferent fibers, principally preganglionic secretory fibers to the parotid gland. These originate in the inferior salivatory nucleus already mentioned (Figs. 163, 164), the

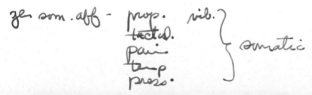

glandular homologue of the dorsal motor nucleus, and by way of the lesser superficial petrosal nerve reach the otic ganglion whence they are relayed to the parotid gland. (d) *Special efferent visceral* fibers arising from the rostral portion of the nucleus ambiguus aid in the innervation of the pharyngeal striped muscle, going to the superior constrictor and to the stylopharyngeus muscle. The secondary fiber systems originating from the sensory glossopharyngeal nuclei have been described with the vagus nerve.

Lesion of the vagus nerve causes an ipsilateral paralysis and anesthesia of the larynx and pharynx with loss of the laryngeal and pharyngeal (gagging) reflexes. There is difficulty in swallowing (dysphagia) and hoarseness (dysphonia). If the glossopharyngeal is also involved there will be ipsilateral loss of taste on the posterior portion of the tongue. The visceral disturbances are difficult to diagnose, but usually there is an acceleration of the heart beat (tachycardia) due to destruction of the inhibitory vagus fibers.

Another bundle of descending afferent fibers is the *descending* or *spinal vestibular root* lying dorsolateral to the fasciculus solitarius (Figs. 164, 181). The fibers are arranged in small bundles (area fasciculata) accompanied by cells which constitute their terminal nucleus, the *nucleus of the descending or spinal vestibular tract.* Occupying the floor of the ventricle medial to the vestibular root and lateral to the trigonum vagi is another terminal nucleus of the vestibular nerve, the *medial* or *triangular vestibular nucleus.* The vestibular nerve and its central connections will be fully described in higher levels.

In the central gray of the ventricular floor are several nuclear masses whose functions and connections are not fully understood. The *nucleus intercalatus* placed between the hypoglossal and the dorsal motor vagus nucleus (Figs. 183, 184) is composed of small cells among which are clumps of larger ones. It is probably a relay station in intersegmental visceral reflex pathways, gustatory, olfactory and others. It receives secondary vago-glossopharyngeal fibers, fibers from the medial vestibular nucleus and the bundle of Schütz, and probably sends fibers to the hypoglossal and salivatory nuclei and to the dorsal motor nucleus of the vagus. According to some, it is a detached portion of the medial vestibular nucleus.

The *nucleus* of *Roller*, also known as the "sublingual nucleus", lies ventral to the hypoglossal nucleus (Fig. 183) and is composed of small densely packed cells. It is considered by some to be a condensation of reticular cells, by others to be related to the medial vestibular nucleus. Like the nucleus intercalatus, it is probably a station for intersegmental visceral pathways.

Section of medulla through lateral recess and entrance of cochlear nerve
(Fig. 189)

The fourth ventricle has reached its maximum width and is here continued into its lateral extensions, the *lateral recesses*, passing external to the restiform body and the dorsal and ventral cochlear nuclei which form its medial walls. The lateral wall of each recess is formed by a dense fiber bundle, the *peduncle* of the *flocculus*, related to the floccular lobe of the cerebellum which here becomes continuous with the lateral surface of the medulla. The nerves of this level are the *glossopharyngeus* (N.IX) and the *cochlear root* of the *acoustic nerve* (N.VIII).

The hypoglossal and the dorsal motor vagus nucleus have disappeared but the most rostral portion of the nucleus ambiguus is usually still present and contributes efferent fibers to the glossopharyngeal nerve. The afferent fibers of N.IX are entering on the lateral aspect of the medulla, ventral to the restiform body, traverse the spinal V and pass to the fasciculus solitarius, some terminating in the nucleus of that

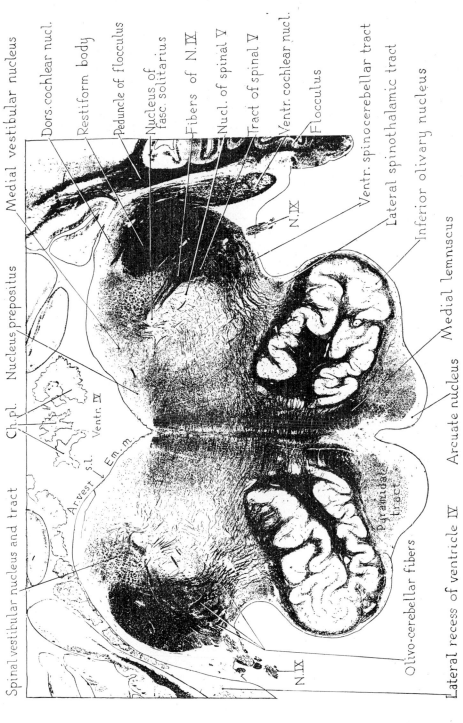

Spinal vestibular nucleus and tract
Nucleus prepositus
Medial vestibular nucleus
Dors. cochlear nucl.
Restiform body
Peduncle of flocculus
Nucleus of fasc. solitarius
Fibers of N.IX
Nucl. of spinal V
Tract of spinal V
Ventr. cochlear nucl.
Flocculus
Ventr. spinocerebellar tract
Lateral spinothalamic tract
Inferior olivary nucleus
Medial lemniscus
N.IX
Ch. pl.
Ventr. IX
Em. m.
Ar. vest. s.l.
Pyramidal tract
N.IX
Olivo-cerebellar fibers
Lateral recess of ventricle IV
Arcuate nucleus

Fig. 189. Transverse section of medulla of one month infant, through cochlear nuclei and ninth nerve. Weigert's myelin stain. Photograph. *Ar. vest.*, area vestibularis; *Ch. pl.*, chorioid plexus; *Em. m.*, eminentia media (teretis); *S. l.*, sulcus limitans

tract here known as the gustatory nucleus, others descending to lower levels. The fasciculus solitarius is now very small and just above the entrance of N.IX can no longer be distinguished as a definite bundle, consisting of only a few descending afferent root fibers of N.VII.

The root fibers of the *cochlear nerve*, conveying impulses from the organ of Corti in the cochlea, enter at the extreme lateral angle of the medulla and terminate at once in two nuclear masses, the *ventral* and *dorsal cochlear nuclei*, the latter forming a prominence, the *tuberculum acusticum* on the floor of the rhomboid fossa. The ventral nucleus is composed of rather large ovoid or rounded cells with dark-staining protoplasm. In the dorsal nucleus, the cells are smaller and fusiform (Fig. 190). The secondary cochlear (auditory) fibers arising from these cells are not well seen until the cephalic end of the cochlear nuclei is reached.

The descending vestibular root and its terminal nucleus is large and forms a triangular area wedging ventrally between the restiform body and the nucleus of the spinal V. The medial vestibular nucleus has likewise enlarged and occupies practically all the ventricular gray lateral to the sulcus limitans. Secondary vestibular fibers from these nuclei form internal arcuate fibers which either enter the reticular formation of the same side or pass toward the raphé to become incorporated in the medial longitudinal fasciculus of the same and opposite side (Fig. 191). It is probable that those from the descending nucleus convey vestibular (and cerebellar) impulses to the voluntary muscles for the regulation of postural tone, while those from the medial nucleus form part of vestibular visceral reflexes such as nausea and vomiting after excessive vestibular stimulation.

The main olivary nuclei are still large and send many bundles of olivocerebellar fibers to the opposite restiform bodies which have grown to massive proportions. The arcuate nuclei practically envelop the pyramids and may now represent the most caudal portion of the pontile nuclei (*nucleus precursorius pontis*, Ziehen). In favorable preparations the *striae medullares* (*striae cerebellares*) are seen passing transversely over the ventricular floor and dipping into the raphé. These fibers, or at least the most superficial ones, are apparently not secondary auditory fibers from the cochlear nuclei as was formerly believed. According to some (Winkler, Brouwer), they arise from the arcuate nucleus, cross and ascend dorsally in the raphé and then pass laterally over the ventricular floor to terminate in the flocculus of the cerebellum (arcuato-cerebellar tract). According to others, many of the fibers originate in the ponto-bulbar nucleus and go to the opposite side of the cerebellum (Marburg).

With the disappearance of the cuneate nucleus, the medial lemniscus has reached its fullest extent, forming a vertical band of fibers on either side of the raphé, in intimate contact with the ventrally lying pyramid. The longest fibers of the "medial" or "ventral" spinothalamic tract whose course is difficult to trace in the medulla are probably now incorporated in the medial lemniscus. In the ventral portion of the lemniscus, here as well as in lower and higher levels, are seen bundles of lighter staining fibers. These are aberrant descending fibers detached from the pyramids, which either go to the more caudally lying motor nuclei of the cranial nerves (hypoglossal, accessory, ambiguus) or rejoin the pyramids lower down. The whole system of pyramidal fibers innervating the cranial motor nuclei is known as the *corticobulbar* or *corticonuclear tract* (aberrant pyramidal tract). Owing to the close proximity of the pyramid and medial lemniscus in the interolivary region of the medulla, injury of this area may affect both tracts and produce a more or less severe contralateral anesthesia (touch, muscle sense, vibration) and hemiplegia (upper motor neuron paralysis) of the body and extremities.

The reticular formation is large and similar in structure to that of the previous level. The medial longitudinal fasciculus and predorsal bundle are now partially separated from the medial lemniscus by lighter areas occupied by the nucleus of the raphé which here and in somewhat higher

dorsally toward the vestibular nuclei from which they originate. Conspicuous transverse fibers in the reticular formation are the olivocerebellar and the secondary vestibular and trigeminal fibers.

Extensive lesions of the gray reticular formation throughout the medulla often produce the sympathetic disturbances already described as the syndrome of Horner,

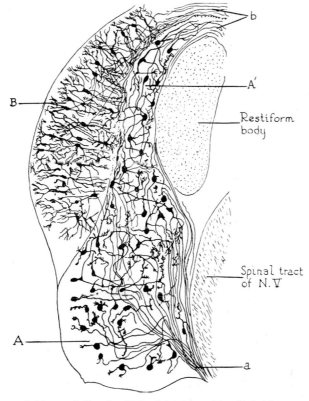

FIG. 190. Cochlear nuclei in medulla of rabbit eight days old. Golgi impregnation. (After Cajal.) *A*, ventral cochlear nucleus and its dorsal extension or tail (*A'*); *B*, dorsal cochlear nucleus (tuberculum acusticum); *a*, axons from ventral nucleus passing ventrally and medially to become fibers of the trapezoid body; *b*, axons from dorsal nucleus and tail of ventral nucleus passing dorsally and medially to form the superficial and intermediate trapezoid fibers.

levels increases in size and spreads laterally into the reticular formation (inferior central nucleus, nucleus pterygoideus). The rubrospinal, spinothalamic and ventral spinocerebellar tracts are in the same position, but the vestibulospinal tract is moving from the dorsal surface of the olive to a more internal position. Its fibers cannot usually be distinguished but are bending

characterized by constriction of the pupil (myosis) and drooping of the eyelid (ptosis). The disturbances are apparently due to interruption of central autonomic tracts which connect higher autonomic centers with the lateral horn of the upper thoracic cord.

As already stated, there is found in the superficial gray of the median eminence a

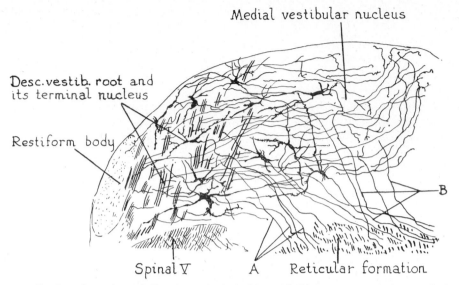

FIG. 191. Section through medulla of mouse four days old showing some of the vestibular nuclei. Golgi impregnation. (After Cajal.) *A*, uncrossed secondary vestibular fibers; *B*, decussating secondary vestibular fibers.

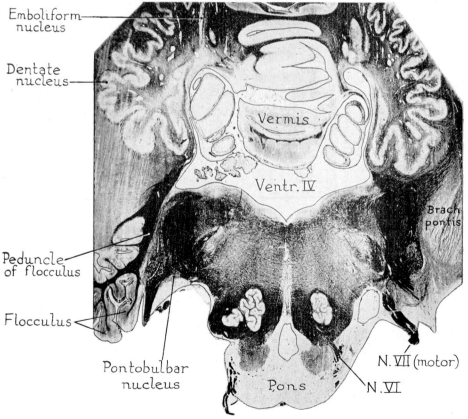

FIG. 192. Section through medulla and portion of cerebellum of one month infant, at level of caudal border of pons. Weigert's myelin stain. Photograph

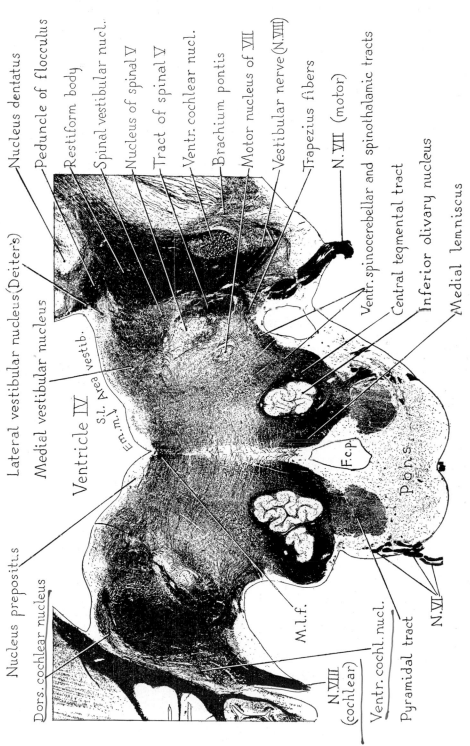

Nucleus dentatus
Peduncle of flocculus
Restiform body
Spinal vestibular nucl.
Nucleus of spinal V
Tract of spinal V
Ventr. cochlear nucl.
Brachium pontis
Motor nucleus of VII
Vestibular nerve (N.VIII)
Trapezius fibers
N. VII (motor)

Ventr. spinocerebellar and spinothalamic tracts
Central tegmental tract
Inferior olivary nucleus
Medial lemniscus

Lateral vestibular nucleus (Deiters)
Medial vestibular nucleus
Ventricle IV
S.l. Area vestib.
Em.m.

Nucleus prepositus
Dors. cochlear nucleus

M.l.f.

N. VIII (cochlear)
Ventr. cochl. nucl.
Pyramidal tract
N. VI

F.c.p.
Pons

FIG. 193. Transverse section of medulla of one month infant, through caudal border of pons. Weigert's myelin stain. Photograph. *Em.m.*, eminentia media; *F.c.p.*, foramen caecum posterior; *M.l.f.*, medial longitudinal fasciculus

stripe of closely packed small cells known as the nucleus eminentiae teretis (eminentiae medialis). Incorporated in this small-celled column at several places are groups of larger cells, the most conspicuous of which is the *nucleus prepositus* now found in the place previously occupied by the hypoglossal nucleus (Figs. 189, 193). The nucleus extends from the oral limits of the hypoglossal nucleus to about the caudal limit of the abducens nucleus. It is composed of numerous relatively large cells and fewer smaller cells, resembling those of the nucleus intercalatus with which it apparently becomes continuous in more caudal levels. Like the nucleus intercalatus, it is believed by some to have intimate relations with the medial vestibular nucleus. It is probably a relay station in olfactory and other visceral reflex pathways, receiving fibers from the bundle of Schütz, medial vestibular nucleus and other less known sources, and sending fibers to the reticular formation, probably also to the hypoglossal, dorsal motor vagus and secretory nuclei.

Section of hindbrain at level of junction of medulla and pons (Figs. 192, 193)

The section which is cut somewhat obliquely, the right side being higher than the left, is immediately in front of the lateral recess, and the roof of the fourth ventricle is now formed by the cerebellum, a portion of which is shown in Fig. 192. In the cerebellum are seen a portion of the *vermis* and two of the internal cerebellar nuclei, the *nucleus dentatus* and *nucleus emboliformis*. On the left side the cochlear nuclei are overhung laterally by a portion of the cerebellum known as the *flocculus*, from the interior of which a dense deeply staining fiber bundle, the *peduncle of the flocculus*, extends dorsally along the cochlear nuclei. This peduncle, as already mentioned, forms the outer wall of the lateral recess (Fig. 189).

On the right (higher) side the restiform body is bending dorsolaterally and entering the white substance of the cerebellum. It is covered externally by a broad band of fibers, the *brachium pontis* or *middle cerebellar peduncle*, which medially becomes continuous with the pons whose caudal tip now covers the ventral surface of the medulla and practically envelops the pyramidal tract. The blind end of the ventral median sulcus overhung by the pons is known as the *foramen caecum posterior*.

The greatly reduced olivary nucleus is flanked laterally by the considerably augmented central tegmental tract whose fibers terminate in the olive. The medial lemniscus now in contact with the dorsal surface of the pons is flattening dorsoventrally and curving laterally along the ventral surface of the inferior olive. The lighter staining area separating it from the medial longitudinal fasciculus and predorsal bundle is occupied by the inferior central nucleus (nucleus of the raphé).

The cochlear nerve has disappeared on the right side, but the oral tip of the ventral cochlear nucleus is still visible and gives rise to secondary cochlear (trapezius) fibers which course medially along the dorsal border of the pons and can be traced better in the next level. A few fibers of the *vestibular nerve* are entering the medulla and are passing between the restiform body and the spinal V to the vestibular area. This area, besides the large medial vestibular nucleus now includes the large-celled *lateral vestibular nucleus* of Deiters lying dorsal to the restiform body.

In the lateral portion of the reticular formation is the caudal tip of the motor nucleus of the facial nerve, occupying a position similar to that of the nucleus ambiguus. Emerging at the junction of the medulla and pons are the roots of the facial (N.VII) and abducens (N.VI) nerves. The former emerges medial to the vestibular nerve and in line with the glossopharyngeal, the latter between the pyramid and the olive.

CHAPTER XV

THE INTERNAL STRUCTURE OF THE PONS

The rostral portion of the hindbrain which is the direct continuation of the medulla oblongata, and the caudal portion of the midbrain are covered ventrally by a massive band of cells and fibers constituting the *pons Varolii*. Hence in sections of this region two parts may be distinguished, a dorsal and a ventral (Fig. 194). The dorsal portion known as the *tegmentum* of the pons

Sections through caudal portion of pons and pontile tegmentum (Figs. 195, 199, 200)

The roof of the now narrower fourth ventricle is formed by the cerebellum. Within the latter may be seen a portion of the vermis and the four pairs of internal cerebellar nuclei (Figs. 199, 211). The most lateral of these is the *nucleus dentatus*, a convoluted band of gray resembling the

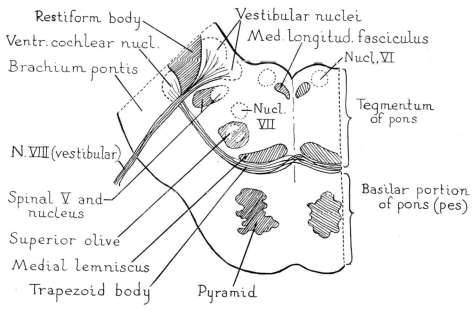

Restiform body
Ventr. cochlear nucl.
Brachium pontis
Vestibular nuclei
Med. longitud. fasciculus
Nucl. VI
Nucl. VII
Tegmentum of pons
N. VIII (vestibular)
Spinal V and nucleus
Superior olive
Medial lemniscus
Trapezoid body
Pyramid
Basilar portion of pons (pes)

FIG. 194. Diagrammatic section of pons at level of entrance of vestibular nerve

(tegmentum of the hindbrain) is the direct continuation of the medulla and besides its own new structures contains the upward prolongations of those already studied in lower levels, with the exception of the pyramidal tracts. The ventral part which now includes the pyramidal tracts forms the *basilar portion* of the pons or *pons proper*. In strict usage the term *pons* is referable to the basilar portion only.

inferior olive, and medial to this the *nucleus emboliformis, nucleus globosus* and nucleus *fastigii* or *tecti*. The fastigial nucleus receives fibers from the cortex of the cerebellar vermis and is intimately related with the vestibular nerve and nuclei. The dentate and emboliform nuclei receive fibers principally from the cerebellar hemispheres, and their axons form an efferent cerebellar fiber cable, the *superior cerebellar peduncle* or *brachium conjunctivum*, conveying cerebellar impulses to the contralateral midbrain and thalamus. The superior peduncle is not fully formed in the lower pontile levels.

The basilar portion of the pons

The basilar portion or pons proper consists of transverse and longitudinal fibers between which there are numerous groups of small and medium sized polygonal cells, the *pontile nuclei*. The longitudinal fibers comprise (1) the pyramidal tracts (corticospinal and corticobulbar) which descend through the pons and while there give off a number of fibers to the motor nuclei of the cranial nerves. The main body passes through the pons to enter the medullary pyramids (Fig. 176). Compactly arranged near the caudal border of the pons, the pyramidal fibers become broken up into a number of bundles separated by the transverse pontile fibers. At the rostral margin of the pons the pyramidal fibers are again organized into a compact mass which forms part of the cerebral peduncle of the midbrain. The pyramidal tract is believed to give off some collaterals or even terminals to the pontile nuclei (Cajal). (2) Other longitudinal fibers which likewise descend from the pallium terminate within the pontile nuclei themselves and are known as the *corticopontile* or *palliopontile fibers*. They arise from the cortex of the frontal lobe (frontopontile), from the temporal and parietal cortex (temporo- and parietopontile) and probably also from some portions of the occipital lobe, and descend uncrossed to end in the homolateral nuclei of the pons. Numerous in the upper portion of the pons where they form considerable bundles difficult to distinguish from the pyramidal tracts (Fig. 218), their number gradually diminishes as more and more of the fibers terminate in the pontile nuclei until in the most caudal portions only a few of them are left. The corticopontile fibers and the transverse fibers to be described below do not become

myelinated till some time after birth and hence are not distinguishable in brain sections of a four weeks infant. They are shown in Fig. 218.

The transverse fibers are axons of cells of the pontile nuclei, which cross almost entirely to the opposite side and unite to form a massive bundle, the *brachium pontis* or *middle cerebellar peduncle*. They pass dorsal and ventral to the pyramidal tract, the dorsal ones forming the *deep layer*, and the ventral ones the *superfical layer* of the pons. The brachia pontis sweep dorsally and somewhat caudally into the cerebellum, lying external to the restiform bodies, and are distributed principally to the cortex of the cerebellar hemispheres. The pons is thus a relay station in an extensive and phylogenetically new two-neuron pathway from the cerebral cortex to the cerebellar hemispheres. The first one is a cortical neuron sending an uncrossed corticopontile fiber to the pons. The second is a pontile neuron sending a crossed pontocerebellar fiber *via* the brachium pontis to the cerebellum.

Some of the transverse fibers connect the cerebellum with the reticular formation of the tegmentum (tegmentocerebellar). Fibers passing vertically in the raphé from tegmentum to pons are undoubtedly continuations of such transverse fibers. Other more laterally placed vertical fibers are pyramidal fibers which enter the tegmentum to innervate the motor nuclei of the cranial nerves (corticobulbar or aberrant pyramidal fibers, Fig. 212).

The pontile nuclei are numerous closely packed cellular aggregations of varying extent placed between the transverse and longitudinal fibers (Fig. 196). In the caudal region the cells form a ring around the compact pyramidal tract, more rostrally the latter is broken up into smaller bundles by islands of pontile cells. In a general way the cells may be grouped into lateral, medial, dorsal and ventral nuclear masses. In the lateral groups the polygonal cells

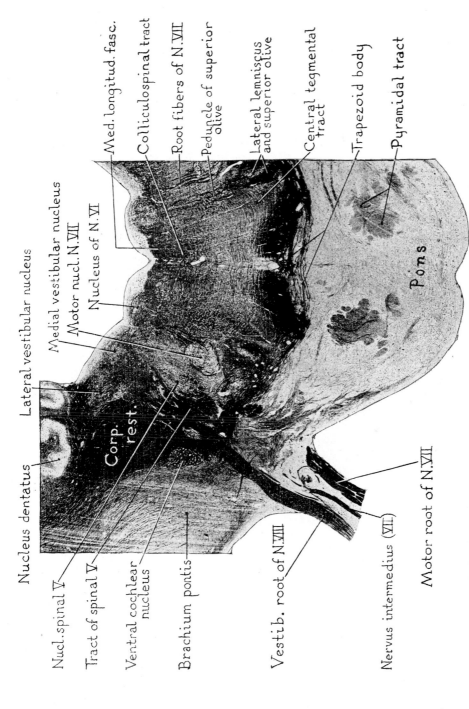

Nucleus dentatus

Lateral vestibular nucleus

Medial vestibular nucleus

Motor nucl. N.VII

Nucleus of N.VI

Med. longitud. fasc.

Colliculospinal tract

Root fibers of N.VII

Peduncle of superior olive

Lateral lemniscus and superior olive

Central tegmental tract

Trapezoid body

Pyramidal tract

Pons

Nucl. spinal V

Tract of spinal V

Ventral cochlear nucleus

Brachium pontis

Corp. rest.

Vestib. root of N.VIII

Nervus intermedius (VII)

Motor root of N.VII

Fig. 195. Section of pons and pontile tegmentum of one month infant, through vestibular and facial nerve roots.   Weigert's myelin stain.   Photograph.   *Corp. rest.*, restiform body

are relatively large or medium sized, in the paramedian region they are as a rule smaller. Their dendrites ramify around adjacent cell bodies, their axons, almost entirely crossed, form the brachium pontis. Among these cells are found curiously shaped Golgi Type II cells whose dendrites are beset with numerous hair-like processes and whose short, branching axons terminate in the vicitnity of the cell body.

(Fig. 200). As already stated this tract constitutes a system of descending fibers terminating principally in the inferior olive. The exact origin of the fibers has not been fully ascertained. Most of them probably come from the upper tegmentum of the midbrain, in part from the oral portion of the nucleus ruber, in part from the reticular formation of that region (rubroolivary and tegmentoolivary). Many descend directly

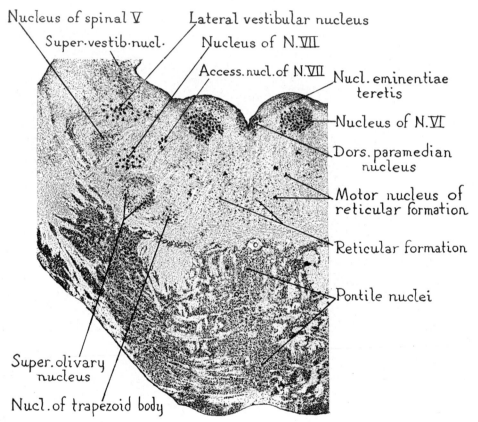

FIG. 196. Section through pons and pontile tegmentum of three months infant. About same level as Fig. 195. Cresylviolet. Photograph, with schematic representation of cell groups

The pontile tegmentum

The inferior olivary nucleus is no longer present and the olivocerebellar fibers are here entering the cerebellum as part of the restiform body covered externally by the brachium pontis. The **central tegmental tract** at first occupies the ventral part of the reticular formation but in higher levels gradually shifts to a more central position

to the olive, others are relayed in the reticular formation. Some fibers may come from the globus pallidus (Spatz). The tract, extensive in man, appears to be a link in a newer pathway connecting the corpus striatum and thalamus with the cerebellum, but its functional significance is poorly understood. Intermingled with the olivary fibers are probably descending and ascending fibers of other functionally distinct systems.

The medial lemniscus no longer compressed between the two inferior olives has lost the form of a longitudinal column and now appears as a flattened elliptic mass extending transversely, in close contact with the dorsal border of the pons. It is widely separated from the medial longitudinal fasciculus and colliculospinal tract, the interval being occupied by the enlarged nucleus of the raphé, here known as the nferior central nucleus. The tract and

teretis). More ventrally is the enlarged nucleus of the raphé (inferior central nucleus), and scattered through the reticular formation are the large cells constituting the motor reticular nucleus. The lateral reticular nucleus furnishing arcuate fibers to the cerebellum has disappeared.

Secondary cochlear fibers and related nuclei. A striking feature in sections of these and somewhat higher levels is the *trapezoid body*, a conspicuous bundle of transversely running fibers in the ventral portion of the tegmentum. These fibers

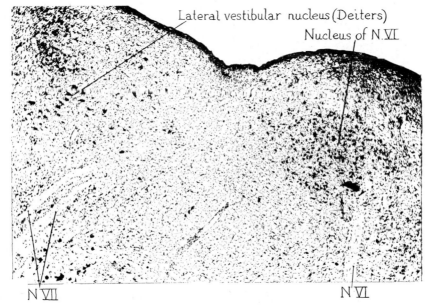

FIG. 197. Nucleus of sixth nerve and lateral vestibular nucleus. Pontile tegmentum of three months baby. Cresylviolet. Photograph

nucleus of the spinal V, the spinothalamic and ventral spinocerebellar tracts are in the same position but are now separated from the surface by the pons and pontile brachium. The uncrossed vestibulospinal fibers are emerging from their nucleus of origin (lateral vestibular nucleus) and cannot be distinguished easily.

The reticular formation is extensive and contains the various nuclear masses already described. In its dorsal portion are the dorsal paramedian nucleus and the nucleus of the median eminence (nucleus eminentiae

arise principally from the ventral cochlear nucleus and in a convex arc sweep medially toward the raphé. Most of them cross to the opposite side passing through or ventral to the medial lemniscus and reach the ventrolateral portion of the tegmentum where they turn sharply in a longitudinal direction to form a new ascending fiber bundle, the *lateral lemniscus* or *lateral fillet*. The turn is made just dorsolateral to a nuclear mass known as the *superior olive*. The dorsal cochlear nucleus likewise gives rise to secondary fibers which cross in a more dorsal position close to the floor of the fourth ventricle to join the lateral lemniscus, but these do not form a conspicuous bundle and are difficult to distinguish from the secondary vestibular fibers which arise from the adjacent vestibular nuclei (Figs. 190, 198, 209).

nucleus composed of medium sized polygonal cells, and a wedge-shaped medial or accessory nucleus of closely packed somewhat larger fusiform cells (Fig. 201). The superior olive receives collaterals or terminals of secondary cochlear fibers and contributes fibers to the trapezoid body and lateral

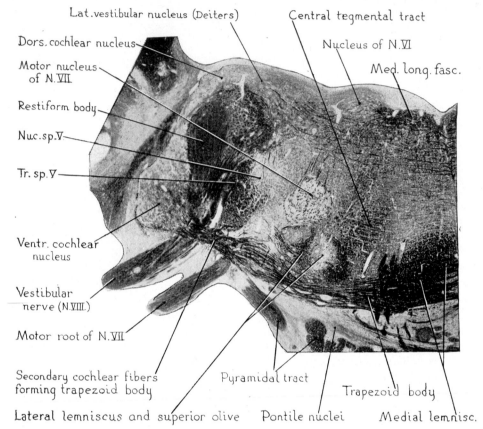

FIG. 198. Section of left half of pons and pontile tegmentum of three years old child whose brain showed a complete absence of the left cerebellar hemisphere and middle cerebellar peduncle. Weigert's myelin stain. Photograph. (Strong.) The origin of the trapezoid fibers from the ventral cochlear nucleus is clearly shown.

Closely related to the trapezoid body are several cellular aggregations of which the most prominent is the nuclear complex of the *superior olive*. This is a cellular column, about 4 mm. long, extending from the level of the facial nucleus to the motor nucleus of the trigeminal nerve, in close contact ventrally with the lateral portion of the trapezoid body. It contains several distinct cell groups: an S-shaped lateral chief

lemniscus. From its dorsal surface a bundle of fibers, the *peduncle of the superior olive*, passes dorsomedially toward the abducens nucleus, some ending in that nucleus, others going to the reticular formation and probably to the medial longitudinal fasciculus (Fig. 195).

Other smaller cellular aggregations related to the trapezoid body are difficult to see in Weigert preparations (Fig. 201). They include the *trapezoid nucleus*, scattered among the trapezoid fibers medial to the superior olive, and the *internal* and *external preolivary nuclei* lying ventral to the superior olive. All these nuclei appear to be intercalated in the secondary cochlear (auditory) pathways.

The new cranial nerves appearing in these sections are the vestibular root of N.VIII, the facial nerve (N.VII) and the abducens nerve (N.VI). The facial nerve is composed of two portions: a medial large *motor root* innervating the facial musculature, and lateral to this a slender strand known as the *nervus intermedius* or *nerve of Wrisberg* (glossopalatine nerve, Fig. 195). The intermediate nerve contains both afferent and efferent visceral fibers.

The afferent *vestibular root fibers* enter at the caudal border of the pons, pass between the restiform body and the spinal V and reach the field previously occupied by the descending vestibular tract whose fibers form a downward continuation of the root. Scattered large cells in this area form the *lateral vestibular nucleus* of *Deiters*. The medial vestibular nucleus is still present, and dorsal to the lateral nucleus, at the extreme angle of the fourth ventricle, is the *superior vestibular nucleus* (Figs. 195–197, 199). As in previous levels the vestibular nuclei are sending out secondary fibers which either enter the reticular formation of the same side or pass to the raphé to become incorporated in the medial longitudinal fasciculus of the same and opposite side. Other fibers are seen passing from the vestibular area to the cerebellum, coursing close to the fourth ventricle (Figs. 199, 211). These are in part vestibular root fibers and secondary fibers from the vestibular nuclei which go to the cerebellum, in part descending fibers from the cerebellum to the vestibular nuclei and to other cells in the reticular formation. These ascending and descending fibers which connect the vestibular area with the cerebellum constitute the

internal or *juxtarestiform* portion of the inferior cerebellar peduncle.

The *motor nucleus of N.VII* appears as as a pear-shaped gray mass in the lateral part of the reticular formation immediately dorsal to the superior olive (Figs. 195, 196). Within it may be seen the usual plexus of fine terminals and the coarser fibers which give origin to the facial root. The root fibers form a rather complicated intramedullary loop whose continuity can not be seen in any one section (Figs. 163, 164). Emerging as fine bundles of fibers from the dorsal surface of the nucleus they proceed dorsomedially to the floor of the ventricle. There they form a compact longitudinal bundle which ascends for a distance of about 2 mm. medial to the abducens nucleus and dorsal to the medial longitudinal fasciculus. At the oral extremity of the abducens nucleus the bundle makes a sharp lateral turn over the dorsal surface of that nucleus, forming the *facial genu* or bend, and then proceeds ventrolaterally and caudally to emerge on the lateral aspect of the caudal border of the pons (Fig. 195). While near the midline some of the fibers may possibly cross over to join the nerve of the opposite side (Obersteiner).

The *nucleus of N.VI* is a rounded gray mass placed in the lateral part of the median eminence of the fourth ventricle and together with the genu of the facial nerve forms the rounded prominence in the ventricular floor known as the *colliculus abducentis* or *colliculus facialis* (Fig. 199). Its root fibers emerge from the medial surface and proceed directly ventrad to the border of the tegmentum where they bend caudally for a short distance to emerge at the caudal border of the pons. This kink in the root fibers just dorsal to the pons is due to the relatively late embryological development of the pontile nuclei. The root fibers at first emerge directly but are later carried backward by the pontile cells which migrate caudally from a more cephalic position.

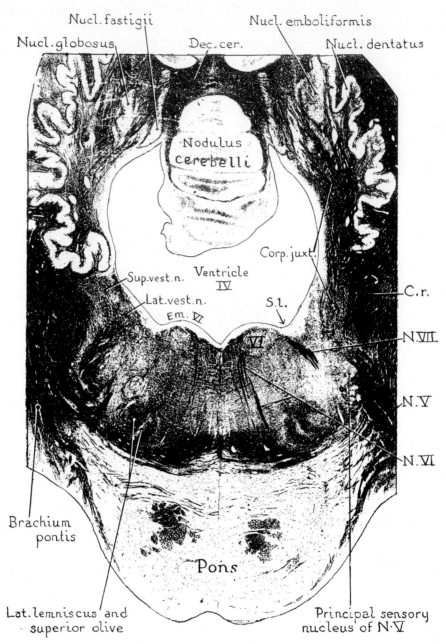

Nucl.fastigii   Nucl.emboliformis

Nucl.globosus   Dec.cer.   Nucl.dentatus

Nodulus
cerebelli

Corp.juxt.

Sup.vest.n.   Ventricle
IV

Lat.vest.n.   S.l.   C.r.

Em.VI   N.VII

VI   N.V

N.VI

Brachium
pontis

Pons

Lat.lemniscus and
superior olive   Principal sensory
nucleus of N.V

FIG. 199. Section through pons, pontile tegmentum and part of cerebellum, just below entrance of trigeminal nerve. One month infant. Weigert's myelin stain. *C.r.*, restiform body; *Corp.juxt.*, juxtarestiform body; *Dec.cer.*, cerebellar decussation; *Em.VI*, eminentia abducentis; *S.l.*, sulcus limitans; *VI*, nucleus of sixth nerve.

The cranial nerves of this region and their central connections and significance may now be discussed in a more comprehensive manner.

The acoustic nerve (N.VIII, N. acusticus) is composed of two parts:—(a) the *cochlear nerve* which supplies the cochlea and is concerned with hearing, and (b) the *vestibu-*

lar nerve which innervates the utricle, saccule and semicircular canals and is concerned with postural and equilibratory functions (Fig. 202). The two run together as the acoustic nerve from the internal auditory meatus to their entrance into the brain stem at the lateral aspect of the

nerve. Its fibers originate in the *spiral ganglion*, an aggregation of bipolar cells situated in the modiolus of the cochlea. The longer central processes of these cells form the cochlear nerve, the short peripheral ones end in relation to the hair cells of the organ of Corti (Fig. 203). The

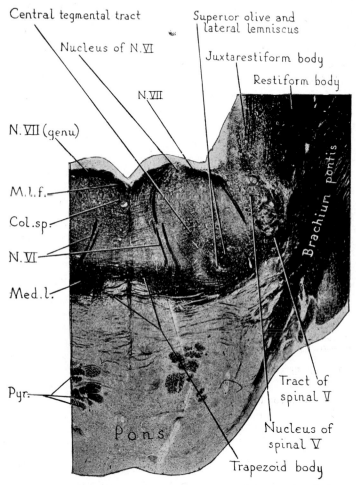

FIG. 200. Section of pons and pontile tegmentum of one month infant, just below entrance of trigeminal nerve. Weigert's myelin stain. Photograph. *Col.sp.*, colliculospinal tract; *M.l.f.*, medial longitudinal fasciculus; *Med.l.*, medial lemniscus; *Pyr.*, pyramidal tract.

caudal border of the pons. Here they separate again, each having its own central connections.

The cochlear nerve and the auditory pathways. The cochlear nerve is the larger portion of N.VIII and enters the brain at a somewhat lower level than the vestibular

cochlear nerve on entering the brain terminates in two nuclear masses, the *ventral* and the *dorsal cochlear nucleus*, placed on the external surface of the restiform body just caudal to the point where the latter turns to enter the cerebellum (Figs. 189, 193). The dorsal nucleus forms an elevation, the *tuberculum acusticum*, on the most lateral portion of the ventricular floor.

The *secondary cochlear* (auditory) pathways to the cerebral cortex are quite complex and there is still considerable uncertainty regarding their exact composition and course. From the ventral cochlear nucleus arises a strong bundle of fibers which course medially along the ventral border of the pontile tegmentum and form the *trapezoid body* (Fig. 204). Many of these pass through or ventral to the medial lemniscus, cross the raphé and reach the dorsal to the restiform body (Figs. 190, 204). Some run close to the floor of the fourth ventricle as dorsal trapezoid fibers (decussation of Monakow), cross the midline and then dip ventrally to join the lateral lemniscus of the opposite side. Others dip more deeply into the reticular formation (intermediate trapezoid fibers, decussation of Held), then decussate and join the lateral lemniscus. Both dorsal and intermediate fibers may give off collaterals or terminals to the superior olivary and trapezoid nuclei. A considerable num-

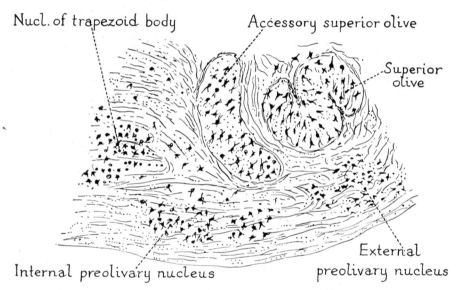

FIG. 201. Composite view of secondary acoustic nuclei of rabbit, reconstructed from Nissl preparations. (After Cajal)

dorsolateral border of the opposite superior olive where they turn upward to form a longitudinal ascending bundle known as the *lateral lemniscus* or *lateral fillet*. Other trapezoid fibers terminate in the homolateral and contralateral nuclei of the superior olive and of the trapezoid body, two nuclear masses interposed in the secondary cochlear pathway. From these nuclei arise fibers which join the lateral lemniscus of the same and the opposite side.

From the dorsal cochlear nucleus and also from the dorsomedial part of the ventral nucleus fibers arise which pass medially, ber of these fibers ascend in the lateral lemniscus of the same side.

Interposed in the course of the lateral lemniscus in the upper portion of the pons, are other more diffuse cellular aggregations which constitute the *nucleus of the lateral lemniscus* (Fig. 204). To these the lemniscus contributes some terminals or at least collaterals, and probably receives additional fibers from them. The lateral lemniscus then reaches the midbrain where a considerable portion terminates either directly or by collaterals in the inferior colliculus, some fibers reaching the colliculus of the opposite side through the commissure of the inferior colliculi. The rest of the lateral lemniscus fibers continue to the medial geniculate nucleus of the thalamus from which fibers are projected to the transverse temporal gyri of the cerebral cortex (auditory cortex). From the inferior colliculus fibers likewise pass to the medial geniculate body, joining the fibers of the lateral lemniscus, and together with these constituting the *brachium of the inferior colliculus (inferior quadrigeminal brachium)*

ventral cochlear nuclei and lateral lemniscus, (3) superior olive and lateral lemniscus, (4) inferior colliculus and its brachium, and (5) medial geniculate nucleus and geniculo-cortical fibers (auditory radiations). Whether all these nuclei contribute fibers which carry impulses ultimately reaching the cortex is not fully settled. There is some good evidence (Winkler) that the dorsal and intermediate trapezoid fibers (dorsal decussations of Monakow and Held) which arise from the dorsal cochlear nucleus,

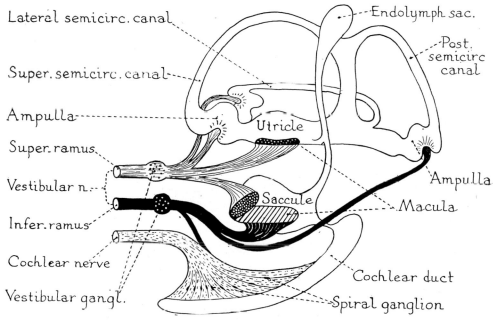

FIG. 202. Diagram showing innervation of the membranous labyrinth of the rabbit. (After de Burlet from Kolmer)

(Fig. 204). Some collicular fibers probably pass directly to the temporal cortex.

It is evident from the above that the hearing pathway has a more complex composition than the sensory systems heretofore studied, receiving contributions from a number of intercalated nuclear masses, and that it has a considerable ipsilateral representation. It is quite difficult to state the number of neurons involved in the auditory pathway from periphery to cortex, but the principal ones are: (1) spiral ganglion and cochlear nerve, (2) dorsal and

and from the dorsomedial portion of the ventral nucleus pass directly to the medial geniculate body and thence by a third neuron system to the cortex. This three-neuron path may be the path of hearing, the other nuclei of the cochlear pathway subserving reflex functions.

The *reflex* cochlear connections are likewise complex and many of them have not been fully determined. Probably all the nuclei intercalated in the auditory pathway, —superior olive, trapezoid nucleus, nucleus of the lateral lemniscus, inferior colliculus, are involved in these reflex circuits, sending fibers to the various motor nuclei for reflex movements in response to cochlear stimulation (sound). From the superior olive arises a fiber bundle known as the peduncle of the superior olive. Some of the fibers pass dorsomedially to the abducens nucleus for reflex turning of eyes. Others course in the reticular formation or enter the medial longitudinal fasciculus and go to the nucleus of the facial nerve and to the nuclei innervating the neck muscles and perhaps other spinal muscles (closing of the eye to loud noise, stapedius reflex, turning

superior one, the latter may possibly be concerned with auditory as well as optic reflexes.

Destruction of the cochlear nerve or of both cochlear nuclei will naturally cause complete deafness on the same side. Since the secondary cochlear pathways are both crossed and uncrossed, lesions of the lateral lemniscus or of the auditory cortex effect a bilateral diminution of hearing (partial deafness) usually more marked in the contralateral ear. Removal of one temporal lobe causes an impairment of sound localization on the opposite side, especially as

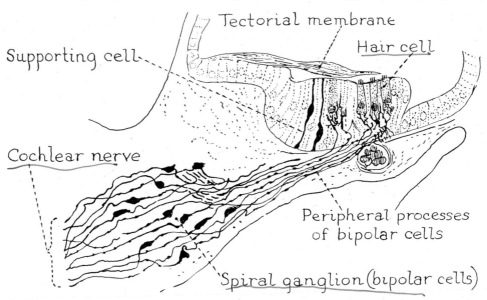

FIG. 203. Section through the spiral ganglion and organ of Corti of five day mouse. (After Cajal)

of head to sound, etc.). The nucleus of the lateral lemniscus gives rise to fibers which decussate and ascend in the lateral lemniscus to the inferior colliculus of the opposite side. Other fibers from this nucleus enter the reticular formation of the pons (Cajal) to be distributed to various motor nuclei, but their course is not well understood. The inferior colliculus probably contributes fibers to the colliculobulbar and colliculospinal (tectospinal) tracts, though according to some these tracts originate solely in the superior colliculus (Rasmussen). Since the inferior colliculus also sends fibers to the

regards judgment of the distance from which the sound is coming (Penfield and Evans, 1935).

The vestibular nerve and its central connections. The vestibular portion of the inner ear, concerned with equilibratory functions, consists of three semicircular canals, the utricle and the saccule (Fig. 202). The semicircular canals are arranged at right angles to each other, representing approximately the three planes of space. At one end each canal has a dilatation, the *ampulla*, containing a patch of sensory epithelium, the *crista ampullaris*, charac-

of colliculus — fn refers
geniculate body — primarily fn sens'l.

terized by the presence of special neuro-epithelial cells, the *hair cells*, which constitute the vestibular receptors. The utricle and saccule have each likewise a similar and saccule together constitute the so-called "otolith organ".

The cristae are stimulated by movement, and especially by rotatory (angular) move-

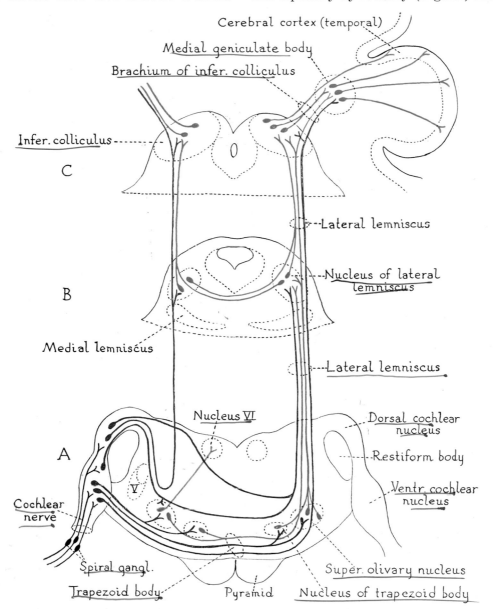

FIG. 204. Diagram of the auditory pathway. *A*, medulla; *B*, isthmus; *C*, midbrain

patch of sensory epithelium, the *macula utriculi* and *macula sacculi*, but here the hair cells are in contact with a gelatinous covering containing small calcareous crystals or particles, the *otoliths*. Hence utricle

ment, the pressure changes resulting from the displacement of the endolymph providing the adequate stimuli for the hair cells. The utricular macula is an organ of static sense, concerned mainly with the orienta-

STatic

tion of the individual with regard to gravity. Macular impulses convey information concerning the position of the head in space, the hair cells being stimulated by the otolithic particles whose position varies under the influence of gravity. The functions of the saccular macula is not fully understood. Destruction of both sacculae does not apparently produce any disturbance in equilibrium (De Kleijn and Versteegh), and it has been suggested that they might possibly be concerned with cochlear rather than

dorsally between the restiform body and the spinal trigeminal tract, and at some distance from the floor of the fourth ventricle most of them divide into short ascending and longer descending branches, the latter forming the descending vestibular tract broken up into a number of fascicles. Some, of the root fibers continue without interruption to the cerebellum, terminating in the nucleus fastigii, the cortex of the flocculonodular lobe and probably also in other portions of the posterior vermis (uvula),

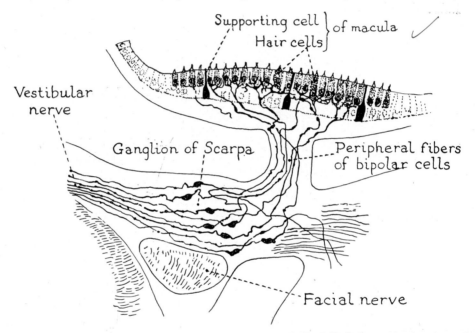

Fig. 205. The ganglion of Scarpa and terminations of the peripheral branches of its bipolar cells in a macula.   Foetus of mouse near term.   (After Cajal)

vestibular function, perhaps serving as an organ for registering bone vibration in the head (Tait).

The maculae and cristae are innervated by the vestibular ganglion (ganglion of Scarpa), an aggregation of bipolar cells located in the internal auditory meatus. The shorter peripheral processes of these cells go to the maculae and cristae (Figs. 202, 205), the longer central ones form the vestibular nerve which enters the medulla somewhat higher and medial to the cochlear nerve. The vestibular root fibers pass

constituting the direct vestibular tract to the cerebellum.   The other vestibular fibers end in four terminal nuclei which can not all be seen in any one section: the *descending* or *spinal* vestibular nucleus, the *medial* or *principal* vestibular nucleus (nucleus triangularis, nucleus of Schwalbe), the *superior* vestibular nucleus (nucleus angularis, nucleus of von Bechterew), and the *lateral* vestibular nucleus of Deiters.   The ascending fibers terminate mainly in the superior and medial nuclei, the descending ones in the lateral and spinal nuclei.   According to

portions of nucleus not important

some the lateral nucleus receives only collaterals of vestibular root fibers (Cajal), according to Winkler the lateral nucleus does not receive any direct vestibular fibers at all but only through the intermediation of the medial nucleus.

Some direct vestibular fibers or collaterals are also believed to go to the ventral cochlear nucleus and superior olive (Held, Winkler) and to the abducens nucleus (Ferrier-Turner).

The descending (spinal) vestibular nucleus is composed mainly of medium sized cells among which there are also many small ones. It extends from the zone of entry of the nerve caudally to about the upper limit of the nucleus gracilis. The lateral nucleus is a scattered mass of large multipolar cells (nucleus magnocellularis) resembling the large "motor" cells of the reticular formation and is by many considered as an aggregation of such cells. It is found in the lateral ventricular floor in the region of entry of the vestibular nerve and extends to the rostral level of the abducens nucleus. The superior nucleus lies somewhat dorsal to the lateral nucleus with which it is continuous, in the angle of the floor and lateral wall of the ventricle, extending from about the level of the abducens nucleus to the principal sensory nucleus of the trigeminal nerve. The cells are of medium size and contain coarse chromofilic bodies. The medial nucleus is the largest and occupies most of the floor of the area vestibularis. Its rostral and caudal boundaries are difficult to delimit, appearing in lower levels than the lateral nucleus and becoming lost near the upper boundary of the abducens nucleus. It is composed mainly of small cells, hence it is also known as the *nucleus parvocellularis*.

The terminal vestibular nuclei give rise to secondary vestibular tracts which go primarily to the cerebellum and to the motor nuclei of the cranial and spinal nerves. In addition to the root fibers which go directly to the cerebellum, vestibulocerebellar fibers (nucleocerebellar) pass to the same and opposite nucleus fastigii and to the cortex of the flocculonodular lobe, uvula and lingula. These fibers originate primarily in the superior, and to a lesser extent in the lateral vestibular nucleus, and it is possible that the other vestibular nuclei may likewise contribute similar fibers (Fig. 206). From the fastigial (and globose) nuclei of the cerebellum crossed and uncrossed fibers pass to the medulla and terminate mainly in the vestibular nuclei, some ending in the reticular formation or even descending to the cervical cord (fastigiobulbar or cerebellobulbar tract). The direct vestibular root fibers, the vestibulocerebellar and fastigiobulbar fibers course medial to the restiform body and collectively constitute the internal segment of the inferior cerebellar peduncle or *juxtarestiform body* (Fig. 206). Thus while the restiform body is composed primarily of afferent cerebellar fibers, the juxtarestiform portion contains both afferent and efferent ones, all of which are related to the vestibular mechanism. It is obvious that the vestibular nuclei are not only relay stations in vestibulobulbar and vestibulospinal reflexes, but serve also as parts of afferent and efferent cerebellar pathways.

The secondary vestibular fibers which go to the motor nuclei of the brain and spinal cord are organized into several bundles (Figs. 206, 207). The uncrossed (lateral) vestibulospinal tract has already been discussed. It arises principally from the lateral vestibular nucleus, to a slighter extent from the descending nucleus. The fibers enter the reticular formation of the same side, pass downward along the dorsal surface of the inferior olive and enter the spinal cord where they descend throughout its whole length in the ventral funiculus. The tract mediates reflex responses of the trunk and limb muscles to vestibular stimulation.

From the superior, medial and descending nucleus, and probably from the lateral as well, internal arcuate fibers pass to the medial longitudinal fasciculus of the same and the opposite side where many bifurcate into ascending and descending arms, while others turn up or down without bifurcation (Fig. 207). The ascending fibers go primarily to the midbrain (vestibulomesencephalic), especially to the nuclei of N.VI, N.IV and N.III which innervate the ocular muscles. Some terminate in the interstitial nucleus of Cajal and the nucleus of the posterior commissure (nucleus of Darkschewitsch). The descending fibers are distributed to the nuclei of N.XI and to the upper cervical cord innervating the neck

descending arms. Most of the fibers from the descending nucleus apparently cross and descend in the opposite fasciculus.

From the medial (triangular) nucleus there also arise fibers which pass to the reticular formation of the same and opposite side (trianguloreticular bundle of Spitzer) and reach the visceral motor nuclei of the cranial nerves such as the dorsal motor nucleus of N.X, the secretory nuclei and other autonomic cell groups, mediating various reflexes as vomiting and pallor on excessive vestibular stimulation. Many of these

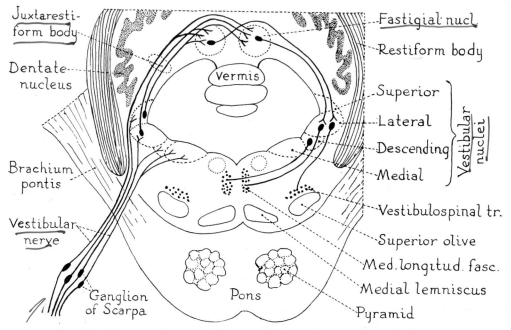

FIG. 206. Diagram of some of the central connections of the vestibular nerve

musculature. These fibers bring the eye and neck muscles under reflex vestibular control. The exact contributions of the different vestibular nuclei to the medial longitudinal fasciculus are not fully ascertained for man, but appear to be as follows in some of the animals studied (Rasmussen, 1932; Buchanan, 1937). The superior nucleus furnishes ascending fibers to the fasciculus of the same side. Fibers from the medial nucleus, and probably from the lateral also, mainly cross the opposite side where they bifurcate into ascending and

fibers enter the dorsal longitudinal bundle of Schütz and are relayed in the nucleus intercalatus or nucleus interpositus before reaching the visceral nuclei. In a general way the superior, lateral and descending nuclei composed of large and medium sized cells and constituting the lateral vestibular column are concerned with somatic vestibular control, while the small-celled medial nucleus is in addition extensively associated with reflex visceral activities in response to vestibular stimulation.

Secondary vestibular pathways to the

cortex of the temporal lobe undoubtedly exist, but their course and the exact location of the vestibular cortex are not fully ascertained. Such vestibulocortical connections would explain the dizziness or vertigo which in man is a frequent symptom of vestibular disease. In animals (cats and

(Aronson). Spiegel has also shown that the electrical action currents led off from the temporal lobe increased in strength during vestibular stimulation. The important researches of Winkler have suggested a probable cortical pathway. According to this investigator the fibers supplying the maculae

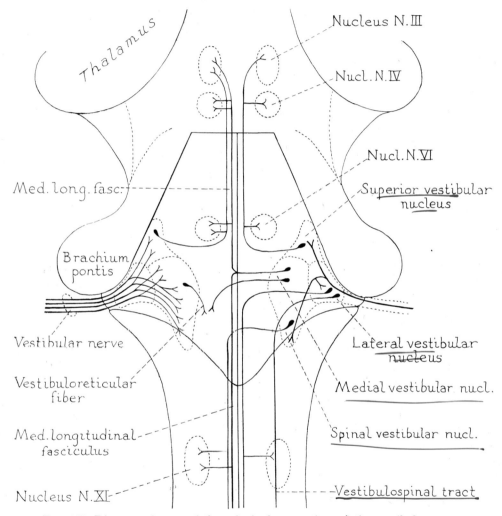

FIG. 207. Diagram of some of the principal connections of the vestibular nerve

dogs) it has been experimentally shown that vestibular impulses reach the cortex. When the temporal convolutions are sensitized by painting with strychnine, stimulation of the labyrinth by rotation produces convulsive movements (Spiegel), but these movements fail to appear if the eighth nerve is destroyed

of the utricle and saccule terminate only in part in the vestibular nuclei, another portion terminating in the ventral part of the ventral cochlear nucleus. From the latter nucleus secondary fibers (trapezoid fibers) proceed to end in part in the superior olivary and trapezoid nuclei of the same and oppo-

site side and in part to form the ventrolateral portion of the lateral lemniscus where
some of the fibers reach the inferior colliculus and are thence projected to the temporal
cortex, either directly or after a relay in the
medial geniculate body. The lateral lemniscus would thus be a link in both the
auditory and vestibular cortical pathways.

The mechanisms governing equilibrium
i.e. the maintenance of appropriate positions of the body in space, are largely of a
reflex character and are activated by afferent
impulses from several sources. Among the
more important of these are the general
proprioceptive impulses from the muscles
of the eyes, neck, trunk and lower limbs, and
the special proprioceptive impulses from
the vestibular sense organ of the ear (labyrinth). Impulses from the retina which
reach the cerebral cortex and contribute to
the conscious perception of visual space are
likewise important aids in proper spatial
orientation. In this equilibratory complex
the labyrinth constitutes a highly specialized
proprioceptor stimulated by the *position* or
changes in position of the head. When the
head is moved, either by contraction of the
neck muscles or by the shifting of the body as
a whole, the cristae are stimulated and
through the central vestibular connections
effect the reflex compensatory adjustments
of the eyes and limbs needed for the particular movement (kinetostatic reflexes). The
new attitude, as long as the position of the
head remains unchanged, is then sustained
by reflexes originating in the macula of the
utricle and initiated by the gravitational
pull of the otolithic membrane on the macular hair cells (static reflexes).

The vestibulospinal tracts and perhaps
also other descending fibers from the reticular formation of the medulla exert a strong
excitatory influence on the tonus of the extensor (anti-gravity) muscles. Normally
this is kept down by impulses from higher
centers passing through the pyramidal and
extrapyramidal tracts (rubrospinal, reticulospinal). In animals, when the influence

of these centers is removed by a transection
of the brain stem anywhere above the level
of the vestibular nuclei and below the
superior colliculi of the midbrain, the extensor tonus of the limbs, neck and tail is
tremendously augmented, giving rise to
the condition of "decerebrate rigidity".
The rigidity is abolished by the destruction
of the vestibular nuclei or the vestibulospinal tracts.

Abnormal stimulation or irritative lesions
of the vestibular nerve or of its central connections produce forced movements of the
body such as falling, and kinetic deviations
expressed in *past-pointing* and the rhythmic
oscillations of the eyeballs known as *nystagmus.* In severe cases there may be vertigo
and visceral disturbances as vomiting,
nausea, sweating and vasomotor changes.

**The facial nerve (N.VII, intermedio-
facial).** The facial nerve is both afferent
and efferent (Fig. 208). It contains (a)
special visceral efferent (branchiomotor)
fibers to the striped superficial muscles of
the fáce and scalp (mimic musculature), the
platysma, stylohyoid, posterior belly of
digastric and stapedius. (b) General visceral efferent (preganglionic) fibers which go
to the submaxillary and sphenopalatine
ganglia and supply the submaxillary, sublingual and lacrimal glands and the mucous
membrane of the nose and roof of the mouth.
(c) Special visceral afferent fibers of taste
from the anterior two thirds of the tongue,
which have their cell bodies in the *geniculate
ganglion.* (d) There are probably a few
general somatic afferent fibers from cells in
the geniculate ganglion which together with
similar fibers from N.IX and N.X aid in
the innervation of the external auditory
meatus and the skin back of the ear.

The fibers supplying the facial muscles
form the large motor root. The afferent
and efferent visceral fibers constitute the intermediate nerve of Wrisberg which emerges
between the motor facial root and the vestibular nerve (Fig. 195). According to some
the intermediate nerve is entirely afferent,

the efferent preganglionic fiber forming part of the motor root.

There are some observations which suggest that the facial nerve may carry impulses of deep pain and deep pressure from the face (Hunt). In some cases where the trigeminal nerve was cut for the relief of facial neuralgia, deep pain due to heavy pressure apparently persisted, and on the other hand such pain is sometimes diminished in lesions of the facial nerve (L. E. Davis). The

aspect of the pons as the motor root. The nucleus is composed of a number of distinct cell groups which probably innervate specific facial muscles but the exact distribution of their fibers has not been fully worked out. In a general way a dorsal and several ventral groups may be recognized. The dorsal furnishes fibers to the superior branch of the nerve supplying the frontalis, orbicularis oculi and corrugator supercilii. The ventral groups, passing from the most media

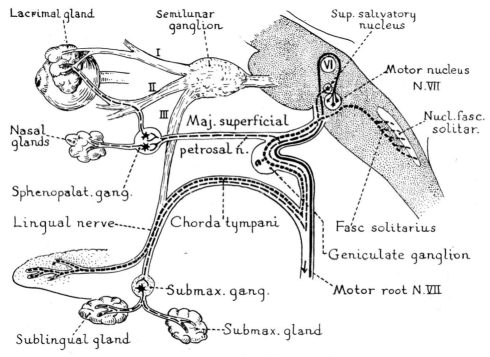

Fig. 208. Diagram showing components of facial nerve (intermediofacial). (After Villiger.) *I*, ophthalmic, *II*, maxillary, and *III*, mandibular ramus of trigeminal nerve

question is not fully settled, but recent investigations indicate that both deep and superficial pain are probably mediated exclusively by the trigeminal nerve (Smyth).

The *motor (branchiomotor) nucleus* of N.VII is a column of typical multipolar motor cells, about 4 mm. long, occupying a lateral position similar to that of the nucleus ambiguus (Figs. 163, 195). The axons of the cells leave the nucleus on its dorsal surface, loop around the abducens nucleus as already described and emerge on the lateral

to the most lateral, probably innervate respectively the stapedius, the platysma and the muscles of the ear, mouth and face. A small group of similar motor cells found dorsomedial to the main nucleus is known as the *accessory facial nucleus*. It may perhaps send fibers to the phylogenetically older muscles innervated by N.VII, such as the stylohyoid, posterior belly of the digastric and the stapedius.

The nucleus receives terminals from many sources. Among these are (1) secondary trigeminal fibers, perhaps also direct collaterals from the spinal V, for the corneal and other trigeminofacial reflexes. (2) Secondary and tertiary fibers from the superior olive and other acoustic nuclei for acousticofacial reflexes, such as closing of eyes to loud noise and the stapedius reflex. (3) Fibers from the superior colliculi (blinking reflex). (4) Corticobulbar (pyramidal) fibers for voluntary facial movement. These fibers detach themselves from the pyramidal tract at or above the level of the facial nucleus and stream fountain-like into the latter, going to both the same and the opposite side (Sand, Spitzer and Karplus). (5) Terminals or collaterals from extrapyramidal systems, representing the emotional control of the facial musculature. These probably come from the corpus striatum, substantia nigra and thalamus, either directly or by way of the reticular formation (reticulobulbar) and the medial longitudinal fasciculus.

The *visceral motor nucleus* also known as the *superior salivatory nucleus* is difficult to distinguish and is apparently represented by a scattered group of cells in the lateral part of the reticular formation. The cells extend caudally to the oral tip of the nucleus ambiguus, the more caudal cells constituting the inferior salivatory nucleus of the glossopharyngeal nerve (Yagita). In Fig. 163 these two cell groups are indicated schematically as a single nuclear column. The superior salivatory nucleus and probably other accessory cells send out preganglionic fibers which leave the brain stem by way of the intermediate nerve. Some pass *via* the chorda tympani to the submaxillary ganglion whence they are relayed to the submaxillary and sublingual glands. Others enter the greater superficial petrosal nerve and reach the sphenopalatine ganglion from which postganglionic secretory and vasomotor fibers go to the lacrimal gland and to the mucous membrane of the nose and roof of the mouth (Fig. 208). The terminals ending in the superior salivatory nucleus

which elicit lacrimal and salivary reflexes are not well known on account of the obscurity and the diffuse character of the nucleus, but they are probably similar to those of N.IX and N.X.

The *afferent visceral fibers* of N.VII, conveying principally taste impulses from the anterior portion of the tongue, form the main component of the nervus intermedius. As already stated (p. 199) these fibers enter the fasciculus solitarius and terminate in the upper portion of the nucleus of that bundle (nucleus gustatorius). The secondary fiber systems from the nucleus solitarius have been discussed in relation to the vagus and glossopharyngeus.

Lesions of the facial nerve produce a total ipsilateral paralysis of facial movements, both reflex and voluntary, with atrophy and RD. Emotional expression is completely lost. There is inability to wrinkle the forehead, to close the eye, to show the teeth, puff out the cheek or whistle. The palpebral fissure is widened, the angle of the mouth droops. It is obvious that the corneal and blinking reflexes are lost since the motor arc of these reflexes is destroyed. If the stapedius is involved there is increased sensitivity of hearing (hyperacusis), especially toward deep tones. Lesion of the nervus intermedius will cause an ipsilateral loss of taste on the anterior two thirds of the tongue.

In pyramidal lesions of one side of the face (upper motor neuron paralysis) the upper facial muscles concerned with wrinkling the forehead, frowning or closing of eyes, appear to be little affected, while there is marked weakness in the lower face, especially in the perioral region. The generally accepted explanation is that the cell groups of the motor nucleus supplying the upper face and forehead receive a bilateral pyramidal innervation i.e. both crossed and uncrossed fibers, while the pyramidal innervation of that part of the nucleus supplying the lower face is predominantly crossed.

The mimetic or emotional innervation of

the face is to a large extent involuntary. While in purely pyramidal lesions of one side of the face the patient has difficulty in showing his teeth or whistling, spontaneous laughing or crying and other emotional expression is unaffected and may at times be actually accentuated on the paralyzed side. The innervation is probably by fibers from the globulus pallidus, substantia nigra

cens is primarily a motor nerve innervating the external rectus muscle of the eye ball, but may possibly contain some afferent proprioceptive fibers from that muscle, from scattered ganglion cells found along the root (Tozer and Sherrington). The nucleus forms a column of typical somatic motor cells, about 3 mm. long, placed in the lateral part of the median eminence. The root

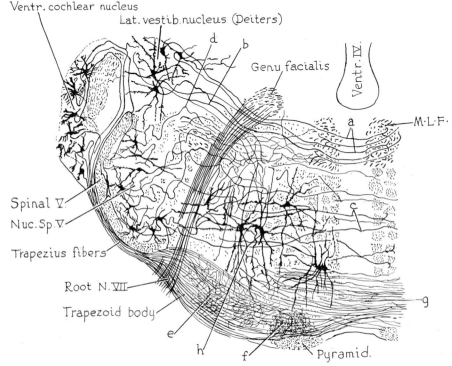

Fig. 209. Transverse section through medulla of new-born mouse at level of emergence of facial nerve. Golgi impregnation. (After Cajal.) *a*, decussating fibers of secondary vestibular tract (from Deiters' nucleus); *b*, uncrossed fiber of secondary vestibular tract; *c*, decussating secondary trigeminal fibers; *d*, uncrossed secondary trigeminal fiber in dorsal part of reticular formation; *e*, collaterals from trapezoid body terminating in superior olivary nucleus, *f*, collaterals from trapez. body terminating in trapezoid nucleus; *g*, decussating trapezoid fibers, the more dorsal ones are from the opposite side; *h*, large (premotor) cells of the reticular formation; *M.L.F.*, medial longitudinal fasciculus.

and diencephalon, which reach the facial nucleus directly or through intercalated neurons of the reticular formation. When these extrapyramidal connections are destroyed, as in lesions of the globus pallidus or substantia nigra, the emotional play of the facial muscles is reduced or lost and the face assumes a frozen or mask-like appearance.

The abducens nerve (N.VI). The abdu-

fibers as already stated pass directly ventrad to emerge at the caudal border of the pons in close relation to the pyramidal tract. The nucleus receives crossed and uncrossed vestibular fibers through the medial longitudinal fasciculus for vestibular control of lateral eye movement; fibers from the superior olive for reflex lateral turning of eyes to sound; pyramidal (corticobulbar) fibers for voluntary movement; and probably fibers from the colliculi, globus pallidus and other extrapyramidal sources by way of the medial longitudinal and predorsal fasciculi.

All ocular movements, whether lateral, vertical or rotatory, require the reciprocal activity of both eyes. In movements of lateral gaze the external rectus of one eye and the internal rectus of the other must contract simultaneously. The central mechanism securing conjugate lateral movement has not been demonstrated with certainty but appears to be as follows. In the reticular formation close to the motor cells of the abducens nucleus, are small groups of cells which send fibers to the oculomotor nucleus by way of the medial longitudinal fasciculus (Fig. 210). The exact course of these *internuclear* or *interocular* fibers has not been fully determined. They may cross and ascend to the oculomotor nucleus of the opposite side, or more probably they ascend uncrossed to the ipsilateral oculomotor nucleus which then sends crossed root fibers to the opposite internal rectus. Any impulses effecting lateral eye movement, whether vestibular, auditory, pyramidal or extrapyramidal, first impinge on these intercalated cells and through the fibers of the latter are related to both the abducens and the oculomotor nucleus. These cell groups, sometimes termed the *parabducens nucleus*, and their fibers are often referred to as the pontile "center for lateral gaze".

Lesions of the sixth nerve cause an ipsolateral paralysis of the external rectus with consequent *internal strabismus* (squint) due to the unopposed action of the internal rectus. The other eye is unaffected and is able to move in all directions. When the abducens nucleus itself is affected there may occur a paralysis of *lateral gaze* toward the side of the injury and both eyes are turned to the opposite side (conjugate deviation). This is due to the fact that in nuclear lesions the central mechanism (parabducens cells) connecting the sixth and third nuclei is likewise injured. Consequently there is not only a paralysis of the ipsolateral external rectus but the oculomotor also no longer receives impulses to cooperate in lateral gaze. Since the lateral gaze mechanism of the opposite side is intact, both eyes will be pulled over to that side.

Owing to the proximity of the emerging root fibers of N.VI and the pyramidal tract, lesions in this place result in a so-called middle alternating hemiplegia similar to that noted for N.XII. There is a lower motor neuron paralysis of the ipsilateral external rectus muscle with internal strabismus and inability to turn the eye outward, and a contralateral upper motor neuron (pyramidal) paralysis of the trunk and extremities.

The medial longitudinal fasciculus (Fig. 210). This fasciculus together with the predorsal bundle which is functionally related to it, represents a complex system of fibers which are among the earliest to myelinate during foetal development. It extends as a definite bundle from the most oral portion of the midbrain to the lower portion of the medulla where the fibers become incorporated in the ventral funiculus of the spinal cord. How far they descend in the latter is not definitely determined. The majority undoubtedly end in the upper cervical segments supplying the neck muscles, but some may descend to lower levels, a few reaching the lumbar and perhaps even the sacral segments. Below the level of the vestibular nuclei the fibers are all descending, above that level the bundle contains both ascending and descending fibers.

Though of complex constitution the medial longitudinal fasciculus nevertheless constitutes a certain functional entity, relating impulses from various sources to the motor nuclei of the cranial nerves and of the upper cervical cord, especially to those of the eye and neck muscles concerned with oculogyric and cephalogyric movements. Among the more important components of the fasciculus are the following: (1) Descending fibers from the *interstitial nucleus* (interstitiospinal) and the *nucleus of the posterior commissure* or *nucleus of Dark-*

colliculi and probably also from the substantia nigra, the interstitiospinal and commissurospinal fibers bring the eye and neck

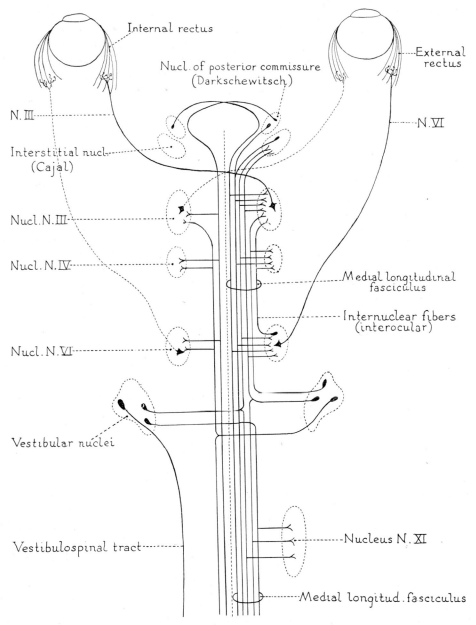

FIG. 210. Diagram showing some of the important components of the medial longitudinal fasciculus

schenitsch (commissurospinal), two nuclei situated in the most oral portion of the midbrain tegmentum. Since these nuclei receive fibers from the globus pallidus, superior

muscles under extrapyramidal control. It is possible that in part at least the mimetic control of the facial muscles is mediated by these fibers. (2) Secondary vestibular fibers, both crossed and uncrossed, which ascend to the nuclei of Nn. VI, IV and III, and descend to the nucleus of N.XI and the ventral horn of the upper cervical cord, bringing the eye and neck muscles under reflex vestibular control. Some of the vestibular fibers terminate in the interstitial and commissural nuclei (Fig. 210). (3) Internuclear fibers connecting the abducens with the oculomotor nucleus, which form part of the central mechanism securing conjugate lateral eye movements. (4) Fibers from the superior olive to the abducens and the facial nucleus mediating reflex facial and lateral gaze movements in response to sound. (5) Tectobulbar and tectospinal fibers from the superior colliculi for optic reflexes. These descend mainly in the more loosely arranged predorsal bundle but are functionally a part of the same system. Besides the above fibers there are others originating in the reticular formation (reticulobulbar and reticulospinal) which descend in or near the medial longitudinal fasciculus and are especially numerous in the predorsal bundle. Finally, it is the belief of some authorities that the corticobulbar (pyramidal) fibers innervating the eye muscles join the medial longitudinal fasciculus to reach the nuclei of those muscles.

Section of pons and pontile tegmentum through roots of trigeminal nerve (Figs. 211, 212)

The fourth ventricle is narrower, its roof still formed by the cerebellum in which may be distinguished the deep cerebellar nuclei. The right side is somewhat lower and still shows the restiform body and brachium pontis. Fibers of the juxtarestiform body connect the superior vestibular nucleus with the roof nuclei of the cerebellum. On the left side the section is above the restiform body, and the superior cerebellar peduncle (corpus conjunctivum) arising primarily from the dentate nucleus is now a large fiber bundle forming the dorsolateral wall of the fourth ventricle.

The basilar portion is larger than the tegmentum and as before contains the transverse and longitudinal fibers and the pontile nuclei. The pyramidal and corticopontile tracts are broken up into numerous bundles, and a number of vertical or perpendicular fibers are seen passing from the pons to the tegmentum. Those within the raphé are probably continuations of transverse pontile fibers which connect the tegmentum with the cerebellum (tegmentocerebellar, perhaps also cerebellotegmental). The more laterally placed perpendicular bundles are aberrant pyramidal (corticobulbar) fibers going directly or indirectly to some of the cranial motor nuclei, in part perhaps to the motor nucleus of N.V (Fig. 212).

In the tegmentum the central tegmental tract is assuming a more central position. The medial lemniscus is traversed by numerous fibers of the now strongly developed trapezoid body, and the lateral lemniscus is a well formed bundle in the ventrolateral part of the tegmentum, in close relation to the superior olive which is still visible in the right (lower) half of the section. On that side the superior vestibular nucleus is also still present, connected to the roof nuclei of the cerebellum by fibers of the juxtarestiform body (Fig. 211). On the left side the superior olive and superior vestibular nucleus have practically disappeared. The spinothalamic and ventral spinocerebellar tracts are in their usual position, as are the large medial longitudinal and predorsal fasciculi. Dorsolateral to the medial longitudinal fasciculus are the longitudinally cut fibers of the facial genu.

The reticular formation is somewhat diminished. The nucleus of the medial eminence (eminentia teres) lies dorsal to the facial genu. In the region of the raphé are extensive cellular aggregations. In the ventral portion between and immediately above the medial lemniscus, is the *reticular tegmental nucleus* of the pons which is really a continuation of the inferior central nucleus seen in lower levels (Figs. 214, 219). It is considered by some as a medial tegmental extension of the pontile nuclei which it resembles, but contains also large multipolar

tively small cells most prominent in the upper pontile levels (Figs. 217, 219). More laterally the reticular formation is rather

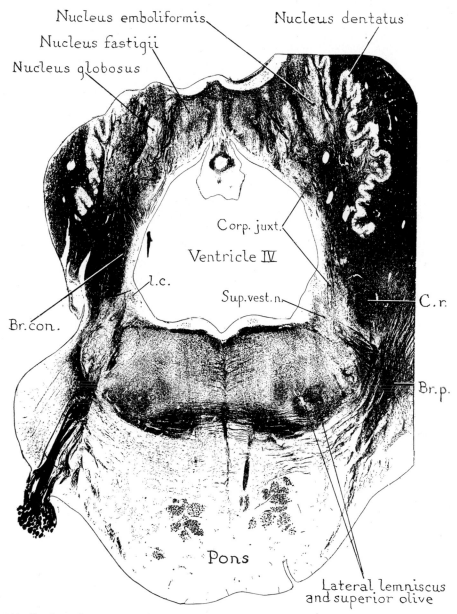

FIG. 211. Section of pons, pontile tegmentum and part of cerebellum, through root of trigeminal nerve. One month infant. Weigert's myelin stain. Photograph, ×6½. *Br.con.*, brachium conjunctivum; *Br.p.*, brachium pontis; *C.r.*, corpus restiforme; *l.c.*, locus caeruleus; *Sup. vest.n.;* superior vestibular nucleus.

cells not found in the pons. More dorsally in the rapheal region is the *superior central nucleus*, a closely packed aggregation of rela-

poor in cells, but scattered among them are the large cells which form the motor reticular nucleus.

The afferent root fibers of the trigeminal nerve pass through the pons and reach the tegmentum where many are seen terminating in the cephalic end of the terminal nucleus of N.V (Fig. 212). This is a large gray mass known as the ' main" or "principal" sensory nucleus of N.V and is broken up into several cellular groups lying dorsolateral to the entering fibers (Fig. 214). Medial to this is the oval motor nucleus of N.V whose coarse efferent fibers are seen

cerebral aqueduct, extending the whole length of the midbrain (Figs. 219, 220). In every section a few such cells may be seen lying medial to the mesencephalic tract. The significance of these cells and their fibers is discussed below.

The trigeminal nerve (N.V). The trigeminal nerve is both afferent and efferent. The afferent fibers convey general somatic impulses of touch, pain and temperature from the skin of the face and forehead, from

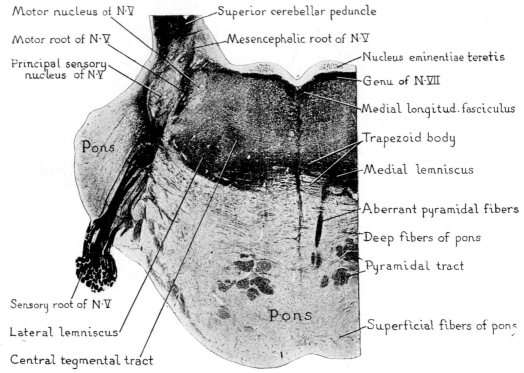

Fig. 212. Section of pons and pontile tegmentum of one month infant through entrance of trigeminal nerve. Weigert's myelin stain. Photograph, × 8

passing out internal to the afferent ones, between the motor and sensory nuclei. Another small bundle of root fibers is seen running dorsally from the motor root toward the angle of the ventricular floor where they turn upward and form a longitudinal bundle extending to the upper portion of the midbrain (Figs. 212, 217). This is the *mesencephalic tract* or *root of N.V* whose fibers arise from large unipolar cells placed in the lateral part of the central gray matter of the

the ectodermal mucous membrane of the nose and oral cavity and from the meninges (dura mater), and proprioceptive fibers from the masticatory muscles and perhaps also from some other muscles of the head. The efferent branchiomotor (special visceral) fibers supply the musculature of the jaw, the tensor tympani and tensor veli palatini. The afferent fibers constitute the large sensory root or portio major of the nerve. The efferent fibers together with the proprioceptive afferent ones form the smaller motor root or portio minor, also known as the masticator nerve.

The afferent fibers with the exception of the proprioceptive ones have their cell bodies in the large, flattened, crescent-shaped *semilunar* or *Gasserian ganglion* placed on the cerebral surface of the petrous bone in the middle cranial fossa and composed of typical unipolar ganglion cells. The peripheral processes of these cells form portion of temple, and the mucous membrane of the nose, upper jaw, upper teeth and roof of mouth to the palatopharyngeal arc. The sensory fibers of the mandibular branch are distributed to the lower lip, chin, posterior portion of cheek and temple, external ear, and to the mucous membrane of the lower jaw, lower teeth, cheeks, anterior two-thirds of the tongue and floor of the mouth. All three branches contribute sensory fibers to the dura which in part is also

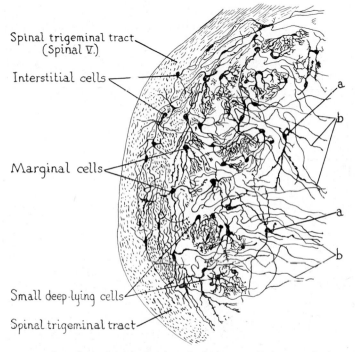

FIG. 213. Transverse section through spinal trigeminal tract and its terminal nucleus. Newborn rabbit. Golgi impregnation. (After Cajal.) *a*, large stellate cell; *b*, axons from cells of terminal nucleus forming crossed and uncrossed secondary trigeminal tracts.

the three main divisions of the trigeminal nerve: ophthalmic, maxillary and mandibular. The first two are wholly sensory, but in the mandibular branch is also incorporated the entire motor root supplying the jaw muscles. The ophthalmic branch innervates the forehead, upper eyelid, cornea, conjunctiva, dorsum of nose and the mucous membrane of the nasal vestibule and of the frontal sinus. The maxillary division supplies the upper lip, lateral and posterior portions of the nose, upper cheek, anterior innervated by fibers from the tenth, ninth and seventh nerve (posterior fossa, Penfield and McNaughton).

The central processes of the semilunar ganglion cells form the sensory root which passes through the pons and enters the tegmentum where many fibers divide into short ascending and long descending arms. Others descend or ascend without bifurcation (Windle). The short ascending fibers and their collaterals terminate in the "main" sensory nucleus lying dorsolateral to the entering fibers. The long descending arms form the spinal trigeminal tract whose longest fibers reach the uppermost segments of the cord, giving off terminals and collaterals to the nucleus of the spinal V *en route*. The nucleus of the spinal V is thus a long column of cells, rostrally in contact with the main sensory nucleus, caudally merging with the substantia gelatinosa of the cord. The tract of the spinal V lies lateral to the nucleus and has a superficial position in the medulla, appearing as a continuation of the zone of Lissauer. In the pons it is separated from the surface by the transverse fibers of the brachium pontis.

Within the spinal tract there is a definite topographical grouping of fibers from the three main peripheral divisions. The ophthalmic fibers are most ventral and descend to the most caudal levels, some reaching the second or third cervical segments. The maxillary fibers are central in the tract and descend to near the caudal limit of the medulla. The mandibular are most dorsally placed and do not reach a level below the oral tip of the dorsal vagus nucleus.

There is considerable clinical evidence that lesions of the spinal tract result chiefly in loss or diminution of pain and temperature in the area innervated by the trigeminal, while tactile sensibility is apparently unaffected. Since many of the trigeminal root fibers bifurcate into ascending and descending arms, it would seem that an afferent fiber may conduct more than one kind of a sensory impulse, a matter of great theoretical importance. The question is not completely settled on anatomical grounds, but it is probable that the nonbifurcating descending fibers mediate exclusively pain and temperature, while the bifurcating ones convey tactile sensibility. Hence in lesions of the spinal V many tactile fibers may be destroyed but the ascending arms of these fibers would still reach the main sensory nucleus, and touch remain intact. Clinically there is no doubt that pain and temperature are handled entirely

by the spinal V while touch and two-point discrimination are in large part related to the main sensory nucleus.

Another source of afferent trigeminal fibers is a slender column of cells found in the lateral portion of the central gray of the upper fourth ventricle and cerebral aqueduct, and extending to the oral limit of the midbrain (Figs. 215, 220). This so-called *mesencephalic nucleus* of N.V is composed of large unipolar cells resembling those of the cerebrospinal ganglia. Their axons form a slender sickle-shaped bundle, the *mesencephalic tract of N.V*, whose fibers descend to the level of the motor trigeminal nucleus where they give off collaterals to the motor cells and then emerge as part of the motor root (Fig. 215). There is evidence that the cells of the mesencephalic nucleus are sensory in character (Johnston) and that their fibers convey proprioceptive impulses from the masticatory muscles, especially from the masseter, temporal and pterygoid (Allen and Thelander). They may be regarded as afferent peripheral neurons which have been "retained" within the central nervous system i.e. have failed to migrate out to the root ganglia. Besides the mesencephalic nucleus, scattered ganglion cells found along the motor root likewise furnish proprioceptive fibers. Some of these apparently innervate the mylohyoid (Allen).

Some authorities believe that deep sensibility of the lingual, facial and ocular muscles is likewise mediated by the fifth nerve, perhaps by fibers of the mesencephalic root. It has already been seen that this is probably not the case with the tongue and eye muscles which in part at least receive proprioceptive fibers through their own nerves, from external ganglion cells found along the roots. Whether there are also central or "retained" cells in the case of these muscles is not known. Deep sensibility of the face is largely handled by the trigeminal nerve (Smyth) but may be supplemented from other sources perhaps from afferent fibers of the facial nerve. There is much that is still obscure about the innervation of the muscles and other deep structures of the head.

The *motor nucleus of N.V* or *nucleus masticatorius* is an ovoid column of typical multipolar motor cells, lying medial to the main sensory nucleus. Its coarse efferent fibers emerge internal to the entering sensory root and pass underneath the semilunar ganglion to become incorporated in as mastication, participation in the act of speech, etc.; and fibers exercising extrapyramidal control whose course is not fully known. In close vicinity of the motor nucleus are two small groups of cells known as the *intertrigeminal* and *supratrigeminal nuclei* (de Nó). Their significance is not clear. They receive collaterals from the mesencephalic nucleus. Their axons in turn send collaterals to the masticator nucleus and then proceed to the *locus caeruleus*

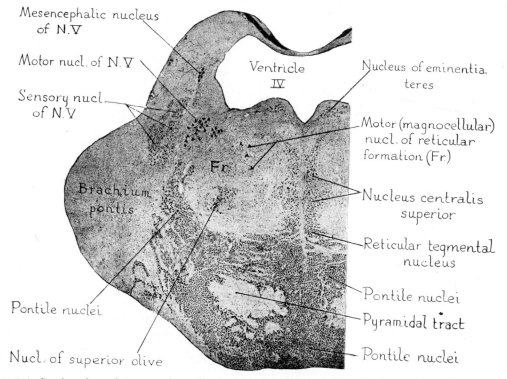

Fig. 214. Section through pons and pontile tegmentum of one month infant, about same level as Fig. 204. Cresylviolet. Photograph, with cell groups schematically blocked in

the mandibular branch. Among the terminals ending in the nucleus are collaterals from the mesencephalic root and other afferent fibers of N.V furnishing a two-neuron arc for reflex proprioceptive control of the jaw muscles; secondary trigeminal fibers, both crossed and uncrossed for reflex control of the jaw muscles by superficial stimuli, especially from the lingual and oral mucous membrane; crossed and uncrossed pyramidal fibers for voluntary movements such (*nucleus pigmentosus pontis*), an aggregation of pigmented cells located in the upper portion of the pons and lower part of the midbrain (Figs. 219, 220). Since the locus caeruleus gives origin to a fiber bundle which descends as far as the nucleus intercalatus of the medulla, it is probable that this mechanism furnishes a connection between the motor nucleus of N.V and the salivatory nuclei, relating mastication with salivary secretion.

Secondary trigeminal pathways. From the main sensory nucleus and nucleus of the spinal V arise the secondary *sensory* and *reflex* trigeminal fibers. The sensory or trigeminothalamic tracts are somewhat obscure but appear to be as follows:—From the lemniscus. In the pons they shift laterally and come to lie near the spinothalamic tract. In this region therefore, the pain and temperature tracts from the face and body lie close together. Fibers from the

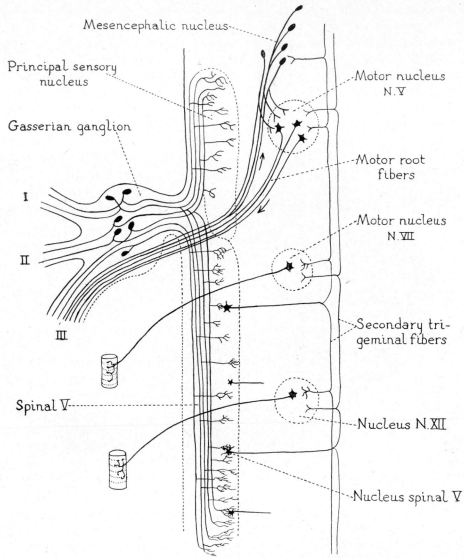

FIG. 215. Diagram of the trigeminal nuclei and some of the trigeminal reflex arcs. (Modified from Cajal.) *I*, ophthalmic nerve; *II*, maxillary nerve; *III*, mandibular nerve

scure but appear to be as follows:—From the nucleus of the spinal V, fibers mediating primarily pain and temperature cross to the opposite side and in the medulla ascend near the ventromedial portion of the medial main sensory nucleus and perhaps in part from the spinal nucleus, mediating touch and pressure, cross and ascend near the dorsomedial surface of the medial lemniscus. These are especially numerous at the level of entry of the fifth nerve, where they are sometimes known as the pontile lemniscus. All the trigeminothalamic fibers constitute the so-called trigeminal lemniscus and terminate in the posteromedial ventral nucleus of the thalamus, from which thalamocortical fibers (third neuron) are projected to the postcentral gyrus. The course of the secondary trigeminal tracts conveying proprioceptive impulses is not well understood.

The numerous secondary *reflex* fibers arising from the terminal nuclei of N.V ascend and descend in the dorsolateral part of the reticular formation giving off terminals or collaterals to various motor nuclei (Fig

absence of reflex eye closure on both sides when the involved cornea is stimulated, while in lesions of the facial nerve only the direct (ipsilateral) reflex will be lost since the arc for the consensual (contralateral) reflex is still intact. (2) The *lacrimal* or *tearing* reflex, to "lacrimal" nucleus of N.VII; (3) *sneezing*, to nucleus of N.XII, nucleus ambiguus and associated respiratory nuclei of the cord i.e. phrenic, intercostal and others; (4) *vomiting*, to dorsal motor nucleus of N.X, nucleus ambiguus and other nuclei including motor nucleus of N.V; (5) *salivary reflexes*, to salivary nuclei of Nn. VII and IX; (6) *oculocardiac* reflex (slowing

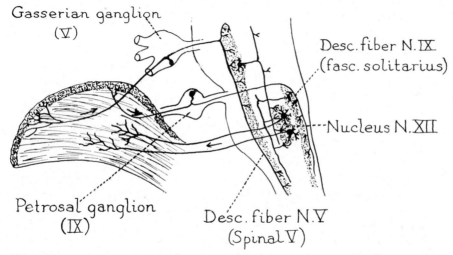

Fig. 216. Diagram of glossopharyngeal and trigeminal reflex arcs.   (After Cajal)

215). They are largely uncrossed. They supply the connections for the many reflexes initiated by stimulation of the skin of the face, the oral and nasal mucous membrane and the tendons and bones of jaw and face. Among the more important of these reflexes and the motor nuclei to which the secondary fibers go are (1) the *corneal reflex* to motor nucleus of N.VII. Impulses from the cornea connect with the facial nuclei of both sides through crossed and uncrossed secondary fibers, hence stimulation of one cornea will produce closure of both eyes (consensual reflex). In injury of the trigeminal nerve (ophthalmic branch) there will be an

of the heart elicited by pressure on the eyeball), to dorsal motor nucleus of N.X. Secondary fibers also go to the hypoglossal nucleus for reflex tongue movement following stimulation of the tongue and oral mucous membrane and possibly for reflex control of tongue movements during the act of eating. A few fibers probably enter the medial longitudinal fasciculus, and according to some authorities direct or secondary trigeminal fibers go to the cerebellum.

The locus caeruleus. The locus caeruleus or *nucleus pigmentosus pontis* is a considerable aggregation of closely packed pigmented cells appearing near the oral end of the main sensory trigeminal nucleus and extending some distance into the midbrain. It is composed of medium sized polygonal cells among which there often may be found some scattered large oval cells probably belonging to the mesencephalic nucleus which lies immediately dorsal to the locus caeruleus (Figs. 219, 220). In spite of its large size the significance of the nucleus is not clear. It is believed by many investigators to be intimately related to the fifth nerve, either receiving afferent trigeminal fibers or contributing fibers to the motor root, but the evidence is inconclusive and contradictory. It receives fibers from the intertrigeminal nucleus (de Nó) and most of its axons combine to form a tract, the *bundle of Probst*, which descends in the dorsolateral part of the reticular formation and has been traced as far as the nucleus intercalatus and dorsal motor vagus nucleus. As already stated, this bundle relates masticatory movements (chewing) with salivary secretion. Some consider the locus caeruleus as an upper pontile reflex center for respiratory regulation (Hess and Pollack).

Similar pigmented cells extend from the locus caeruleus into the roof of the fourth ventricle toward the cerebellum. Others are found scattered diffusely throughout the pontile tegmentum.

Sections through isthmus of hindbrain at level of exit of trochlear nerve (N.IV) (Figs. 217, 218)

The narrower portion of the hindbrain lying oral to the cerebellum and merging with the midbrain is often known as the *isthmus rhombencephali*, and the sections shown in Figs. 217, 218 represent the most cephalic level of this region i.e. the junction of isthmus and midbrain. As in previous sections three regions are distinguishable: roof, tegmentum and pons.

The cerebellum has disappeared, the roof consisting now of a thin white membrane, the *anterior medullary velum*. The neural cavity is greatly reduced and forms the transition between the fourth ventricle and the *Sylvian aqueduct* or *iter* of the midbrain. The cavity is bounded ventrally and laterally by a broad band of central gray matter. The root fibers of the *trochlear nerve* (*N.IV*) are seen in the anterior medullary velum. They originate from nuclei which lie more cephalad in the ventral part of the central gray. The fibers arch dorsally and somewhat caudally around the fourth ventricle or iter, then decussate in the roof and emerge. Only the decussation is seen in this level. The nerve innervates the superior oblique muscle of the eyeball.

The pons is considerably larger than the tegmentum. The pontile nuclei are extensive, the pyramidal and corticopontile tracts broken up into numerous bundles.

In the tegmentum the mesencephalic tract of N.V forms a slender sickle-shaped bundle in the lateral part of the central gray. Mingled with it may be seen the oval cells of the mesencephalic nucleus and ventral to this is the relatively large nucleus pigmentosus pontis or locus caeruleus characteristic of the uppermost pontile levels. The lateral lemniscus lies near the surface in the lateral part of the tegmentum, forming the major part of the external structure known as the *trigonum lemnisci*. Groups of cells among its fibers constitute the *nucleus of the lateral lemniscus*, one of several nuclei interpolated in the auditory pathway. The medial lemniscus is a flattened band extending transversely in the lateroventral part of the tegmentum, and the spinothalamic tract is in its usual position between the two lemnisci. Included in the medial lemniscus and spinothalamic tracts are most of the secondary trigeminal and vago-glossopharyngeal fibers, though according to some authorities secondary trigeminal fibers also ascend in the dorsal part of the reticular formation, lateral to the medial longitudinal fasciculus. All these secondary cranial nerve tracts carry tactile, proprioceptive, pain and temperature sensations from the head and mouth, and possibly also

visceral sensibility.   Thus at this level the
principal afferent suprasegmental paths
form a peripheral shell of fibers enclosing
the rest of the tegmentum and representing
general body and head sensibility and hearing.

The superior cerebellar peduncle or *brachium conjunctivum* has entered the tegmentum where it forms a large crescentic

goes a complete decussation.   Most of its
fibers end in the nucleus ruber, others continue directly to the lateral ventral nucleus
of the thalamus.   Some ascend and descend
in the reticular formation where they make
connections with the motor nuclei of the
midbrain, pontile tegmentum and medulla.
Many of the fibers are already decussating
at this level.

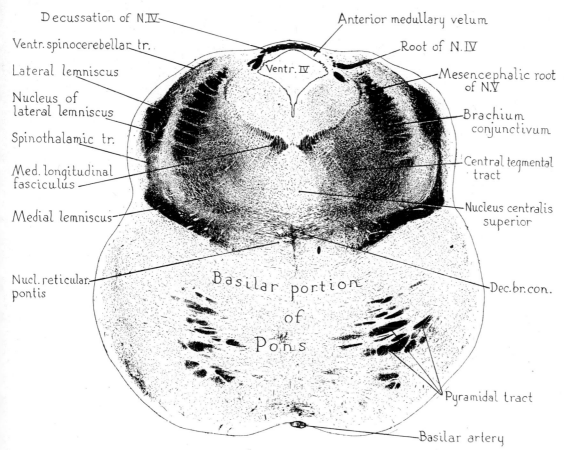

FIG. 217. Section of isthmus of one month infant, through exit of nerve IV.   Weigert's myelin stain.
Photograph, × 7

bundle in the lateral part of the reticular
formation.   The brachium conjunctivum
which arises from the dentate and emboliform nuclei forms the most important efferent fiber system of the cerebellum.   Emerging from the latter it first forms the
dorsolateral wall of the fourth ventricle,
then dips into the pontile tegmentum, and
in the caudal portion of the midbrain under-

The central tegmental tract is large and
occupies a truly central position.   The ventral spinocerebellar tract now lies on the
surface, external to the brachium conjunctivum, and its fibers appear to be cut longitudinally.   This tract has an aberrant
course to the cerebellum.   It ascends in the
lateral part of the reticular formation to
the uppermost limit of the pons, and at this

point turns caudally, forming a loop on the external surface of the brachium conjunctivum (Fig. 168). Then accompanying the latter but in a reverse direction, it descends in the anterior medullary velum to terminate in the vermis of the anterior lobe of the cerebellum. Only the turn or bend of the fibers is seen at this level (Fig. 217).

are most extensive near the raphé (Fig. 219). Most ventrally in this region is the *reticular tegmental nucleus* already described, considered by some as a tegmental extension of the pontile nuclei (Jacobsohn). Dorsal to this is the *superior central nucleus* characteristic of the upper pons, a large closely packed aggregation of small and medium

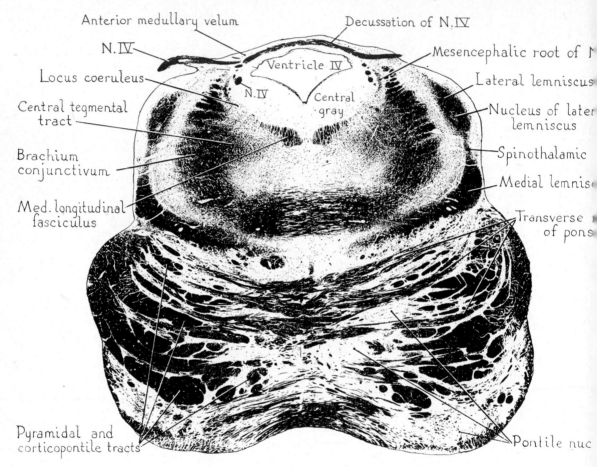

FIG. 218. Section of isthmus of adult through exit of nerve IV. Weigert's myelin stain. Photograph, × 7

The medial longitudinal and predorsal fasciculi are in their usual positions. The rubrospinal tract has shifted to a more medial position, lying dorsal to the medial lemniscus. It is more easily distinguishable as a definite tract in the caudal portions of the midbrain, near its origin from the nucleus ruber (Fig. 224).

The cell groups of the reticular formation

sized cells extending laterally into the reticular formation. On each side of the midline, dorsal to the medial longitudinal fasciculus, is the *dorsal nucleus of the raphé*, a narrow band of cells which merge orally with the larger and more complex *dorsal tegmental nucleus* of the midbrain (Fig. 225).

The main body of the reticular formation

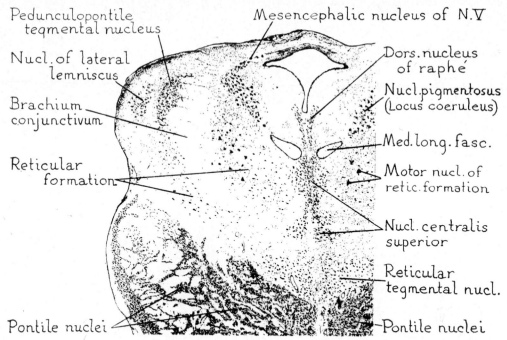

Pedunculopontile
teqmental nucleus

Mesencephalic nucleus of N.V

Nucl.of lateral
lemniscus

Dors.nucleus
of raphé

Nucl.pigmentosus
(Locus coeruleus)

Brachium
conjunctivum

Med. long. fasc.

Reticular
formation

Motor nucl. of
retic. formation

Nucl. centralis
superior

Reticular
tegmental nucl.

Pontile nuclei

Pontile nuclei

FIG. 219. Section through isthmus of three months infant. Cresylviolet. Photograph, with cell group
schematically blocked in

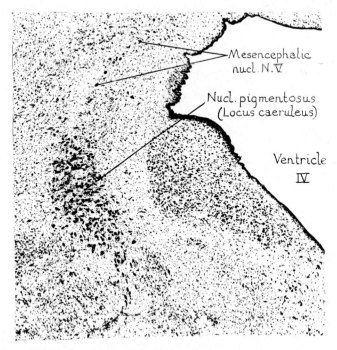

Mesencephalic
nucl. N.V

Nucl. pigmentosus
(Locus caeruleus)

Ventricle
IV

FIG. 220. Portion of pontile tegmentum in oral region of pons (isthmus). Twelve weeks baby. Nissl
stain. Photograph

is divided into a medial and a lateral portion by the superior cerebellar peduncle. In the lateral part a dense collection of medium sized cells constitutes the *pedunculopontile tegmental nucleus* closely applied to the external surface of the brachium conjunctivum

The blood supply of the medulla and pons

The medulla and pons receive their arterial blood supply from the *anterior* and *posterior spinal arteries*, the *vertebral*, the *basilar* and the *posterior inferior cerebellar arteries*. Minor contributions of a neg-

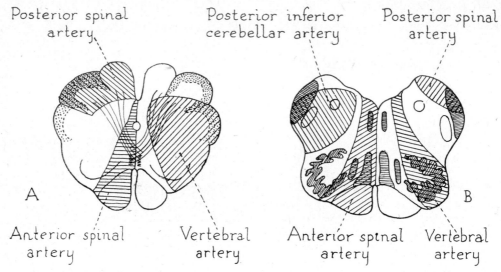

FIG. 221. Diagram showing arterial supply of medulla.   *A*, level of clava; *B*, midolivary level.   (From data by Stopford)

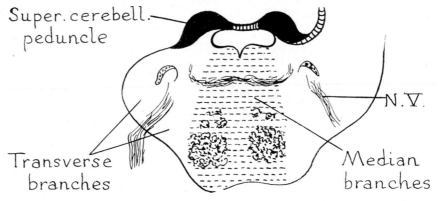

FIG. 222. Diagram of arterial supply of pons by the median and transverse pontile branches of the basilar artery. (After Stopford)

and extending into the caudal portion of the midbrain. Elsewhere the reticular formation is diffusely organized, and scattered within it, especially in its medial portion, are the large multipolar cells belonging to the *motor reticular nucleus.*

ligible character may also be made by the *superior* and the *anterior inferior cerebellar arteries.* There is great variation in the extent of the areas supplied by each vessel, as well as considerable overlapping of adjacent fields, hence the normal distribution of the individual arteries is often difficult to determine. These variations are due in part to the fluctuating level of origin of the anterior spinal arteries and to the equally varying level of fusion of the two vertebrals into the basilar artery. Not uncommonly one or another artery may be missing altogether and its place taken by the vessel supplying the adjacent territory. Thus the area of the posterior spinal may be taken over by the posterior inferior cerebellar artery, or the latter be replaced by the vertebral. Since the vascular supply of this region has a considerable clinical importance, the main structures normally supplied by the various arteries are briefly summarized (Figs. 221, 222).

The *anterior spinal* supplies the medial structures of the medulla including the pyramids and pyramidal decussation, medial lemniscus, medial longitudinal fasciculus, predorsal bundle, the hypoglossal nucleus except its most cephalic portion, the medial accessory olive and the most caudal portion of the nucleus and fasciculus solitarius and of the dorsal vagus nucleus. Towards the lower border of the pons the distribution of the artery is gradually reduced, to be replaced by branches of the vertebral and basilar arteries.

The bulbar branches of the *vertebral* normally supply the pyramids at the lower border of pons, the most cephalic part of the hypoglossal nucleus, most of the olive including the dorsal accessory olive, the olivocerebellar fibers traversing the reticular formation, and a portion of the dorsal vagus nucleus and the nucleus and fasciculus solitarius in the region of the calamus scriptorius. At the level of the pyramidal decussation the most caudal branches are distributed to practically the whole lateral region of the medulla lying between the ventral horn and fasciculus cuneatus.

The *posterior inferior cerebellar artery* supplies the retro-olivary region containing the spinothalamic and rubrospinal tracts, the nucleus and tract of the spinal V, nucleus ambiguus, dorsal vagoglossopharyngeal nu-

cleus and the emerging fibers of these nerves, and the ventral part of the restiform body. Descending central autonomic tracts are also found in this area.

The *posterior spinal* supplies the gracile and cuneate fascicles and their nuclei, and the caudal and more dorsal portion of the restiform body. When missing, its territory is taken over by the posterior inferior cerebellar artery.

The pons and pontile tegmentum are supplied by the *medial* and *transverse pontile* branches of the *basilar artery*. The former are minute vessels arising from the cerebral surface of the basilar and penetrating the pons along the basilar groove. They are distributed to the medial portion of the pons including the abducens and trochlear nuclei and the caudal part of the oculomotor, facial genu, medial longitudinal fasciculus, medial lemniscus, medial portion of the trapezoid body, and the greater part of the pyramidal, corticopontile and transverse fibers of the pons.

The transverse pontile branches, as a rule symmetrically arranged on both sides, extend laterally and divide into smaller branches which enter the pons at right angles. Usually a larger branch extends to the trigeminal nerve. The transverse rami appear to be arranged segmentally similar to the radicular arteries of the spinal cord. They supply the brachium pontis, lateral part of trapezoid body, superior olive, the nuclei of Nn.VII and VIII, and the pontile portions of the trigeminal nuclei including the motor nucleus of N.V.

The exact distribution of the veins of the medulla has not been fully ascertained. In general they run parallel to the arteries and drain the corresponding territories. They are gathered into larger branches on the surface and make connections caudally with the veins of the spinal cord. Orally they join the pontile veins. The latter are usually gathered into two larger trunks lying on either side of the basilar groove, which empty into the superior petrosal sinus.

CHAPTER XVI

THE MESENCEPHALON

The midbrain is the smallest and least differentiated of the five brain divisions, having a length of about 15–20 mm. Its caudal part is overlapped ventrally by the cephalic portion of the pons. Externally the dorsal surface extends from about the exit of the fourth nerve to the root of the pineal body, the ventral surface from the rostral border of the pons to the mammillary bodies (Figs. 166, 167).

the peduncle as distinguished from the tegmentum. Externally the tegmentum and basis are separated by two furrows, medially by the *oculomotor sulcus* from which the third nerve emerges, laterally by the *lateral mesencephalic sulcus*. The portion of the tegmentum which comes to the surface between the lateral mesencephalic sulcus and the inferior colliculi, is occupied mainly by the fibers of the lateral lemniscus and

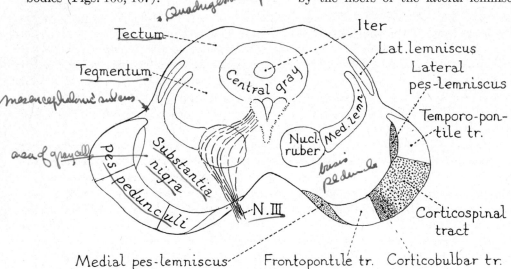

Fig. 223. Transverse section through upper portion of midbrain, schematic

The midbrain consists of a dorsal part, the *quadrigeminal plate* or *tectum*, and a more massive ventral portion known as the *cerebral peduncles* or *crura cerebri*. Its narrow channel or cavity extending from the fourth to the third ventricle, is the *Sylvian aqueduct* or *iter*. In section each cerebral peduncle or crus shows a division into a dorsal part, the *tegmentum*, continuous with that of the pons, and a ventral part, the pes *pedunculi*, separated from each other by a broad pigmented plate of gray matter, the *substantia nigra* (Fig. 223). Pes pedunculi and substantia nigra together constitute the basis of

forms a slight superficial bulge known as the *trigonum lemnisci*, (Fig. 167).

Viewed from the ventral surface the cerebral peduncles appear as two massive fiber bundles extending from the rostral border of the pons to the optic tracts where they disappear into the deep substance of the forebrain. On emerging from the pons the peduncles diverge laterally enclosing between them a deep triangular groove, the *interpeduncular* or *intercrural fossa*, bounded rostrally by the mammillary bodies. When freed from the pia the floor of this fossa shows a number of fine perforations serving

pons, medulla, cerebellum ⇒ telencephalon (cerebral tem.), diencephalon
= prosencephalon   no ventricle small.

for the passage of blood vessels and is hence known as the *posterior perforated substance*.

On the dorsal surface the quadrigeminal plate or roof shows two pairs of eminences, the *superior* and *inferior colliculi* (*corpora quadrigemina*), the latter somewhat smaller and more rounded than the former. The colliculi of the two sides are separated by a median longitudinal groove in the rostral portion of which lies the pineal body tucked in between the superior colliculi. A narrow band extending from the anterior medullary velum and known as the *frenulum veli* is attached to the caudal part of the sulcus.

Each colliculus is connected with the thalamus by a superficially placed fiber strand which arises from the lateral margin of the colliculus and constitutes its arm or *brachium*. The *inferior quadrigeminal brachium* is a short flat band which runs from the inferior colliculus to the medial geniculate body, one of the caudal thalamic nuclei lying closely apposed to the lateral surface of the midbrain (Figs. 167, 168). The *superior quadrigeminal brachium* is a longer narrower strand extending from the superior colliculus to the lateral geniculate body of the thalamus. A portion of this strand continues beyond the geniculate body and merges with the optic tract.

The midbrain contains the principal segmental mechanisms for the various ocular reflexes and other eye movements, and higher postural reflex centers related especially to the "righting reactions" from abnormal to normal positions. Besides this it contains various paths to and from the cerebellum, pallium, striatum and other forebrain structures, including certain gray masses forming their relay stations. The most conspicuous of these are the nucleus ruber and substantia nigra.

Section of midbrain through inferior colliculi (Figs. 224, 172)

Compared with sections of the isthmus the following are the most conspicuous changes: The roof has expanded into the inferior colliculi, a great part of the tegmentum is occupied by the decussating fibers of the superior cerebellar peduncle, the pyramidal and corticopontile fibers are being organized into the pes pedunculi, and dorsal to the pes a new gray mass has appeared, the substantia nigra.

The *nucleus of the trochlear nerve* (N.IV) which supplies the superior oblique muscle is located in the ventral part of the central gray, indenting the dorsal surface of the medial longitudinal fasciculus. It is a column of typical somatic motor cells and is practically a caudal appendage of the oculomotor nucleus with which it is orally continuous in the adult. The root fibers emerge from the nucleus, curve dorsally and caudally around the aqueduct in the outer part of the central gray and reach the superior medullary velum in which they decussate and make their exit (Fig. 163).

The mesencephalic tract and nucleus of N.V, locus caeruleus, medial lemniscus, spinothalamic and spinotectal tracts are in the same position as in the previous section. The fibers of the lateral lemniscus however have spread out and are apparently entering or enveloping the inferior colliculus whose capsule they form. Many of these fibers end in the colliculus, while others pass it by laterally to reach the medial geniculate body. From the inferior colliculus arise fibers which likewise go to the medial geniculate body, joining the fibers of the lateral lemniscus, and together with these constituting the *inferior quadrigeminal brachium* which thus represents a continuation of the auditory pathway to the thalamus. In higher sections the brachium may be seen lying on the lateral aspect of the midbrain tegmentum (Figs. 226, 227).

The brachia conjunctiva now occupy a large part of the reticular formation and many of their fibers are crossing to the opposite side in the *decussation of the brachia conjunctiva*. Immediately ventral to the decussation and not far from the midline are the rubrospinal tracts now definitely organized into two small and compact fiber bundles. The central tegmental tract lying in its usual position is difficult to distinguish from the decussating fibers of the superior cerebellar peduncle.

The narrow aqueduct, somewhat triangular in section, is surrounded by a broad layer of central gray substance poor in myelinated

Immediately ventral to the medial longitudinal fasciculus the cells near the raphé are sometimes known as the *ventral tegmental nucleus* which appears to be a continuation of the superior central nucleus of the pons. Near the medial ventral surface of the tegmentum in the floor of the interpeduncular fossa is the *interpeduncular nucleus* composed

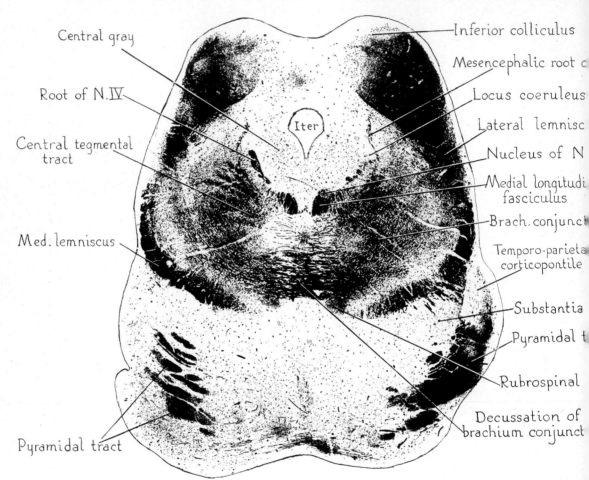

Central gray

Root of N. IV

Central tegmental tract

Med. lemniscus

Pyramidal tract

Inferior colliculus

Mesencephalic root c

Locus coeruleus

Lateral lemnisc

Nucleus of N

Medial longitudi fasciculus

Brach. conjunc

Temporo-parieta corticopontile

Substantia

Pyramidal t

Rubrospinal

Decussation of brachium conjunct

Iter

FIG. 224. Section of midbrain through inferior colliculi. One month infant. Weigert's myelin stain. Photograph, ×7. The lighter staining region ventral to the colliculus and lateral to the mesencephalic root is the parabigeminal area.

fibers and containing numerous diffusely grouped cells. In the raphéal region several new nuclei are present at this level (Fig. 225). The dorsal nucleus of the raphé has expanded into the *dorsal tegmental nucleus* composed of many small cells among which are scattered larger ones. It lies in the central gray dorsal to the trochlear nucleus.

of medium sized, multipolar, slightly pigmented cells. Prominent in most mammals it is greatly reduced in man. It receives fibers from the nucleus habenulae of the diencephalon (*habenulo-interpeduncular*) and sends fibers to the dorsal tegmental nucleus (Fig. 270). The latter also receives fibers from the mammillary bodies (*mammillo-*

tegmental) and participates in the formation of the tract in the central gray known as the dorsal longitudinal bundle of Schütz which descends as far as the dorsal motor nucleus of N.X. The interpeduncular and the dorsal tegmental nucleus are thus relay stations in descending pathways from olfactory and other visceral centers.

The pyramidal tract and a large mass of corticopontile fibers are now gathered to-

sized cells, the latter sending their axons into the inferior quadrigeminal brachium. It receives afferent fibers from the lateral lemniscus, from the colliculus of the opposite side, and from the medial geniculate body *via* the inferior brachium. Many fibers of the lateral lemniscus, coming mainly from the superior olive and the nucleus of the lateral lemniscus, terminate directly in the colliculus, some crossing to the collicu-

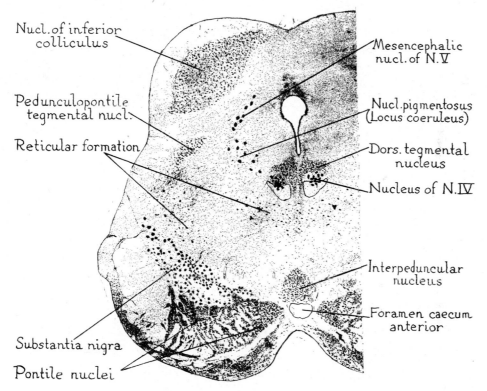

Nucl.of inferior colliculus
Pedunculopontile tegmental nucl.
Reticular formation
Substantia nigra
Pontile nuclei
Mesencephalic nucl. of N.V
Nucl.pigmentosus (Locus coeruleus)
Dors. tegmental nucleus
Nucleus of N.IV
Interpeduncular nucleus
Foramen caecum anterior

FIG. 225. Section through inferior colliculi of midbrain. Three months infant. Cresylviolet. Photograph, with schematic representation of main cell groups

gether to form the *pes pedunculi* separated from the tegmentum by a mass of gray matter, the *substantia nigra*. Both pes and substantia nigra are covered ventrally by the cephalic portion of the pons.

The inferior colliculi. Each inferior colliculus consists of an ovoid cellular mass, the *nucleus of the inferior colliculus*, and a thin cellular layer or cortex on the surface external and medial to the nucleus. The nucleus is composed of small and medium

lus of the opposite side. Other lemniscal fibers, probably from the dorsal cochlear nucleus, send collaterals to the colliculus, the fibers themselves continuing to the medial geniculate body.

The efferent fibers arising from collicular cells go in considerable part to the medial geniculate body *via* the inferior quadrigeminal brachium. Others pass to the opposite inferior colliculus and to the superior colliculi or enter the tegmentum to form descending tracts which terminate in the nucleus of the lateral lemniscus and other reticular nuclei. The exact location of these descending fibers is not fully ascertained. Some probably become incorporated in the predorsal bundle as tectobulbar and tectospinal fibers, though according to some authorities the latter fibers come entirely from the superior colliculi.

The inferior colliculi are thus both relay stations in the hearing pathway and reflex acoustic centers. They are newer parts of the brain related primarily to the cochlear apparatus and the projection of auditory stimuli upon the neopallial cortex.

Ventral to the caudal portion of the inferior colliculus is a fairly well defined zone known as the *parabigeminal area*. It is limited dorsally by the inferior colliculus, medially by the mesencephalic tract of N.V, ventrally by the reticular substance of the tegmentum, and laterally by the dorsal portion of the lateral lemniscus (see legend in Fig. 224). The area is composed mainly of obliquely or transversely running fibers among which are scattered cells or groups of cells constituting the *parabigeminal nucleus*. Its connections and significance are obscure, but apparently some fibers from the nucleus go to the lateral nuclei of the pons.

Sections of the midbrain through superior colliculi (Figs. 172, 226, 227, 230)

The sections through the rostral half of the midbrain show the following main features. The roof is formed by the *superior colliculi;* the tegmentum contains the *nucleus ruber (red nucleus)* and the nuclei and roots of the oculomotor nerve (N.III); and instead of the pons, the ventral part of the brain now consists of the *pes pedunculi*, composed of a mass of efferent pallial fibers, and the *substantia nigra* (Fig. 223).

The aqueduct is surrounded by a broad band of central gray, poor in myelinated fibers and having a gelatinous appearance in Weigert preparations. The nuclear complex of the *oculomotor nerve* is located in the ventral part of the central gray in a V-shaped trough formed by the diverging medial longitudinal fasciculi. The complex is composed of several nuclear groups which can not all be seen in any one section. In the most caudal level only the *lateral* or *chief* nuclei are seen (Fig. 226), but in the middle levels a medially placed cell group, the *central nucleus of Perlia*, is wedged in between the two lateral nuclei (Figs. 227, 228, 229). In the most oral portions the central nucleus disappears again, to be replaced by two small cell groups, the *nuclei of Edinger-Westphal*, lying dorsomedial to the lateral nuclei (Figs. 230, 231). The root fibers emerge ventrally from the nucleus, pass through and around the nucleus ruber, then converge again and make their exit on the ventral surface of the midbrain. The oculomotor nerve and its connections are discussed more fully below.

The brachia conjunctiva have completed their decussation and in the most caudal levels each brachium forms a large oval fiber bundle about to make contact with the red nucleus (Fig. 226). In higher levels some of these fibers may be seen within the red nucleus which is one of their terminal nuclei. Other fibers continue without interruption to the thalamus.

The lateral lemniscus which had partly terminated in the inferior colliculus is now replaced by the inferior quadrigeminal brachium lying on the lateral surface of the tegmentum. As already stated the brachium is composed in part of long lemniscal fibers, in part of fibers from the inferior colliculus, all of which terminate in the medial geniculate body (Fig. 168). Axons from cells of this body constitute the last relay of the cochlear path to the temporal cortex.

The medial lemniscus is now a curved bundle displaced laterally by the red nucleus and brachium conjunctivum. The lateral spinothalamic tract is plainly distinguishable as a small bundle close to the dorsal tip of the medial lemniscus with which

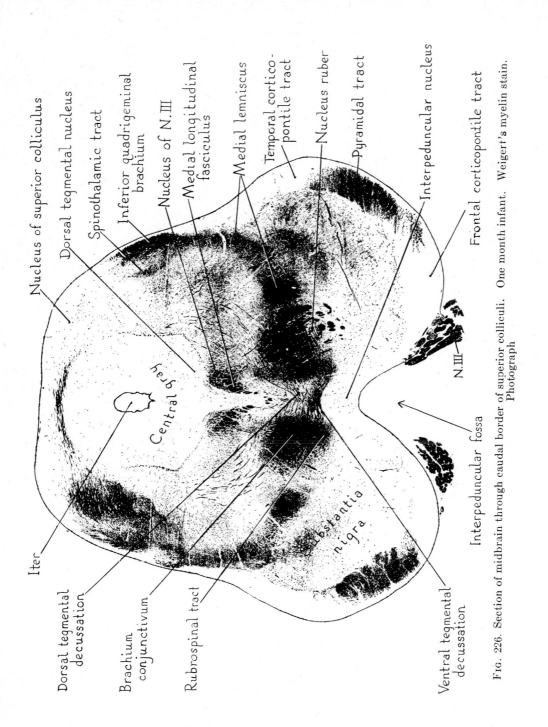

Nucleus of superior colliculus
Dorsal tegmental nucleus
Spinothalamic tract
Inferior quadrigeminal brachium
Nucleus of N. III
Medial longitudinal fasciculus
Medial lemniscus
Temporal cortico-pontile tract
Nucleus ruber
Pyramidal tract
Interpeduncular nucleus
Frontal corticopontile tract

Iter

Central gray

Substantia nigra

N. III

Interpeduncular fossa

Dorsal tegmental decussation
Brachium conjunctivum
Rubrospinal tract
Ventral tegmental decussation

Fig. 226. Section of midbrain through caudal border of superior colliculi. One month infant. Weigert's myelin stain. Photograph

it practically fuses. At this level therefore, the ascending sensory tracts from spinal cord and medulla are in close continuity. Spinocollicular fibers running in close vicinity of the spinothalamic tracts, detach themselves in this region and enter the superior colliculus (Fig. 168).

The medial longitudinal fasciculus is an elongated obliquely placed fiber bundle. In transverse sections the two fasciculi form a V-shaped trough in which the oculomotor nucleus is set. Progressing orally the bundle diminishes in size and peters out completely in the region of junction of superior colliculi and thalamus.

The rubrospinal and colliculospinal tracts arise from this region of the midbrain. The rubrospinal tract is emerging from the caudal portion of the nucleus ruber and is crossing as a compact bundle to the opposite side, forming the *ventral tegmental decussation of Forel* (Fig. 226). After crossing some of the descending fibers go to the motor nuclei of the pons and medulla (rubrobulbar), others reach the cord as rubrospinal fibers. The *dorsal tegmental decussation* or *fountain decussation of Meynert* is composed of more loosely arranged, obliquely crossing fibers (Figs. 226, 229). These arise from large cells of the superior colliculi, sweep fountain-like through the reticular formation, and after decussating in the dorsal part of the raphé, descend as colliculobulbar and colliculospinal fibers in the predorsal fasciculus. Other fibers from the superior colliculi probably descend uncrossed in the reticular formation, in or near the medial longitudinal fasciculus. While the rubrospinal decussation is limited to the caudal region of the nucleus ruber, the dorsal tegmental decussation is more extensive and some of its crossing fibers may be seen in practically all sections of the superior collicular levels.

The central tegmental tract is displaced dorsally by the nucleus ruber and becomes less and less conspicuous in the more cephalic sections. Most of its fibers are believed to originate from the nucleus ruber and other reticular cells of the upper midbrain tegmentum.

Reticular cells and nuclei of the tegmentum. The reticular formation contains many scattered cells and several important nuclear masses which may be regarded as special condensations of such cells. The most conspicuous of these is the *nucleus ruber*, other smaller ones are the *interstitial nucleus of Cajal* and the *nucleus of the posterior commissure* (nucleus of Darkschewitsch) located in the region of junction of midbrain and thalamus. In the raphéal area are still the dorsal tegmental and the interpeduncular nucleus which as already stated constitute relay stations in descending olfactory and other visceromotor pathways.

The diffuse cells may be roughly grouped into a lateral and a medial mesencephalic nucleus (Fig. 232). The cells are of large or medium size and generally belong to the so-called "motor reticular nucleus" whose cells, isolated or in groups, have been noted in practically all sections of the pontile tegmentum and reticular formation of the medulla. Their axons largely uncrossed usually bifurcate into ascending and descending arms of variable length. Some of these reach the motor nuclei of the brain stem and spinal cord as reticulobulbar or reticulospinal fibers, some go to the inferior olive as reticuloolivary fibers. The latter together with similar fibers from the nucleus ruber and possibly from the globus pallidus form a large part of the central tegmental tract. Other shorter fibers terminate in the reticular formation of lower levels (reticuloreticular) and reach the spinal cord by a series of short intercalated neurons. Within the cord these chains are probably continued downward by short spinospinal fibers of intersegmental neurons.

The reticular cells receive collaterals or terminals from secondary afferent neurons (medial lemniscus, secondary trigeminal, vestibular, cerebellar), from the nucleus

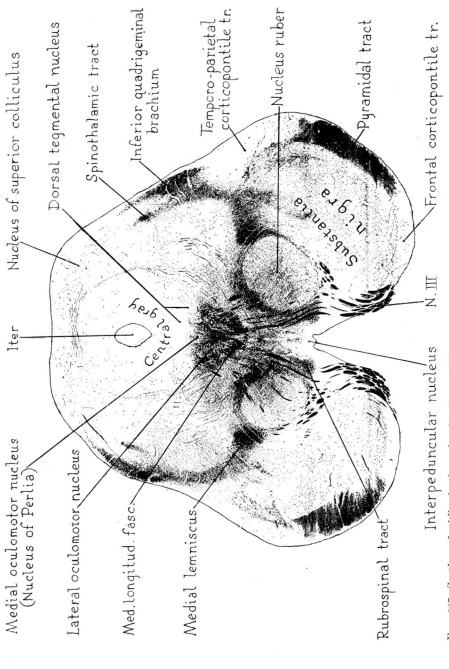

Medial oculomotor nucleus
(Nucleus of Perlia)

Lateral oculomotor nucleus

Med. longitud. fasc.

Medial lemniscus

Iter

Nucleus of superior colliculus

Dorsal tegmental nucleus

Spinothalamic tract

Inferior quadrigeminal brachium

Tempro-parietal corticopontile tr.

Nucleus ruber

Pyramidal tract

Frontal corticopontile tr.

Substantia nigra

Central gray

N. III

Rubrospinal tract

Interpeduncular nucleus

Fig. 227. Section of midbrain through exit of nerve III. One month infant. Weigert's myelin stain. Photograph, × 7

ruber and tectum of the midbrain, from the corpus striatum hence indirectly from the thalamus, and probably also from the cerebral cortex. Thus the reticular cells and their fibers constitute a diffuse but extensive system which constitutes the intrinsic associate mechanism of the brain stem, mediating and coordinating bulbar and spinal reflexes and forming important links in the descending extrapyramidal

prominent in man (Fig. 232). The magnocellular portion, extensive in lower mammals but greatly reduced in man, consists of large multipolar somatochrome cells which give rise to the rubrospinal and rubrobulbar fibers. The small-celled or parvocellular portion forms the bulk of the nucleus and is composed of smaller somatochrome cells rather sparsely distributed. Between the cells run numerous small bundles of

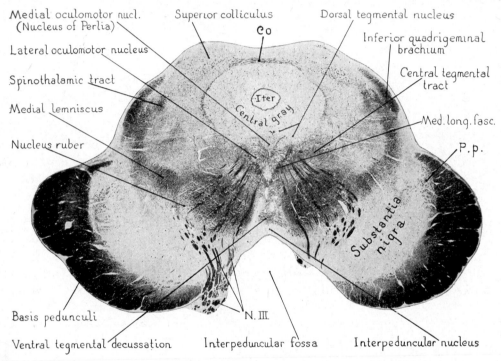

FIG. 228. Transverse section of adult midbrain through exit of nerve III. Weigert's myelin stain Photograph, × 6. *Co*, commissure of superior colliculi; *P.p.*, pallidopeduncular tract

pathways from cortex, thalamus and striatum.

The nucleus ruber. The red nucleus, which in the fresh condition has a pinkish-yellow color, is a large ovoid or cylindrical column of cells extending from the caudal margin of the superior colliculi into the diencephalon. In transverse sections it appears as a circular area occupying a considerable portion of the tegmentum. The nucleus is composed of a caudal large-celled part (paleoruber) and a more extensive smaller-celled part (neoruber) especially

myelinated fibers which give the nucleus a punctate appearance in transverse sections. These are primarily fibers from the superior cerebellar peduncle which terminate in the nucleus or traverse it on the way to the thalamus. The nucleus is surrounded by a capsule of fibers most abundant on the medial surface and representing afferent and efferent connections of the nucleus. In a general way the cephalic portion of the capsule represents connections with the thalamus, cortex and corpus striatum, while the caudal portion is related to the cerebellum and to the brain stem structures lying caudal to the red nucleus.

The fiber systems of the nucleus ruber are extensive. The afferent fibers include (a) a strong contingent from the cerebellum (dentatorubral) by way of the brachium conjunctivum, the largest part of which ends in the red nucleus. Most of these fibers go to the neoruber, only a small portion terminating in the magnocellular part and reticular formation; (2) some *vestibulorubral* fiber ascending in or near the medial longitudinal fasciculus; (3) *pallidorubral* fibers from the globus pallidus of the corpus striatum, either directly or through intercalated cells (nucleus of the field of Forel) lying immediately oral to the red nucleus; (4) *corticorubral* fibers from the centro-opercular cortex, perhaps also from the prefrontal cortex; (5) *colliculorubral* or *tectorubral* fibers from the superior colliculi by way of the dorsal tegmental decussation.

The efferent fibers include (1) the *rubrospinal* and *rubrobulbar* tracts arising from the magnocellular portion. Strongly developed in lower mammals where the magnocellular nucleus is large, it is greatly reduced in man, forming a small bundle which crosses completely in the ventral tegmental decussation and descends in the reticular formation. Some go to the motor nuclei of the cranial nerves, the rest enters the spinal cord where they continue downward in the lateral funiculus. (2) *Rubroreticular* and *rubro-olivary fibers*. This is a fairly extensive system and as repeatedly stated forms part of the complex central tegmental tract. Some go directly to the inferior olive, others end in the reticular formation whence new neurons send fibers to the olive (reticulo-olivary), to the motor nuclei of the cranial and spinal nerves (reticulobulbar and reticulospinal) and to other levels of the reticular formation (reticuloreticular). The rubro-olivary fibers are uncrossed, the rubro-reticular are in part composed of crossed fibers. (3) A considerable bundle of *rubrothalamic* fibers goes mainly to the lateral ventral nucleus of the thalamus whence they are projected to the motor and premotor cortex (Areas 4 and 6). With these there are probably also direct *rubro-cortical* fibers to the same areas and to the prefrontal cortex.

It is evident from the above that the red nucleus is a station interposed in many complex pathways. It relays cerebellar and vestibular impulses *via* the rubrospinal and rubroreticular tracts to the motor nuclei of the stem and cord, thus mediating postural reflex adjustments. This is perhaps more important in lower mammals than in man where many postural adjustments are to a large extent dominated by the cerebral cortex and the higher extrapyramidal centers. More significant is the great development of the small-celled portion (neoruber) as a link in the extensive and phylogenetically younger cerebello-pallial pathway connecting the cerebellar hemispheres with the motor and premotor areas of the cortex. Finally the nucleus ruber is one of the important relay stations through which extrapyramidal impulses from the cortex, thalamus and corpus striatum may be related to the motor neurons of the brain stem and cord.

There is considerable evidence that in lower mammals (cats and dogs) the midbrain contains a center for the integration of those complex postural reflexes which enable an animal to change from an abnormal to a normal position (righting reactions). This center is probably located in the caudal magnocellular portion of the red nucleus and in the adjacent reticular formation of the same level. Destruction of the superior colliculi or of the substantia nigra does not interfere with these reactions, but they are abolished when the ventral tegmental decussation is severed. It is doubtful if the same conditions obtain in man where the magnocellular nucleus is greatly reduced and the righting reactions and postural orientation as a whole is to a larger extent mediated by retinal impulses which are integrated in cortical centers. Clinically, large lesions of the nucleus ruber produce tremor and certain types of exaggerated involuntary movements known as choreo-athetoid movements. By some, these symptoms are believed to be due to the interruption of the pathway running from the cerebellum through the red nucleus and thalamus, which influences the activities of the corpus striatum. According to others, they are due to interruption of the

tively large cells resembling those of the red nucleus and reticular formation. It receives fibers from the vestibular nuclei, globus pallidus, superior colliculi and probably also from the substantia nigra. It contributes uncrossed descending interstitio-spinal fibers to the medial longitudinal fasciculus, which go primarily to the nuclei innervating the eye and neck muscles (Fig. 210). It is probable that the extrapyramidal control of the mimetic musculature is in

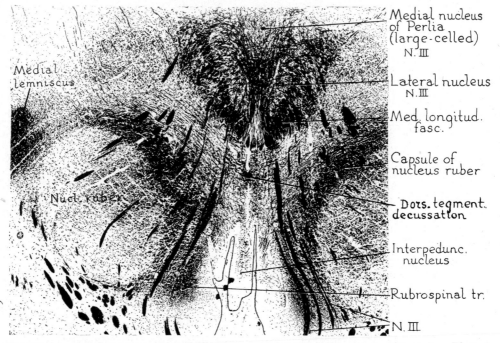

FIG. 229. Portion of midbrain tegmentum of one month infant. Weigert's myelin stain. Photograph

cerebellopallial pathway, the lack of cerebellar reinforcement producing defective or disorganized pyramidal movements. Since the brachium conjunctivum forms the initial outlet from the cerebellum for the two paths, it is quite possible that the activities of both cortex and striatum may be involved.

Other tegmental nuclei. The *interstitial nucleus of Cajal* is a small cell group located at the junction of iter and third ventricle in the dorsomedial part of the tegmentum immediately oral to the oculomotor nucleus (Figs. 235, 268). It is composed of rela-

part mediated by fibers from the interstitial nucleus and nucleus of Darkschewitsch.

Dorsal to the interstitial nucleus in the same region is another small cell group, the *nucleus of Darkschewitsch* or *nucleus of the posterior commissure*, set practically within the central gray substance. Its afferent connections are similar to those of the interstitial nucleus. Many of its efferent fibers cross through the posterior commissure and descend as commissurospinal fibers in the medial longitudinal fasciculus. Others descend uncrossed (Figs. 235, 210).

Substantia nigra. The substantia nigra

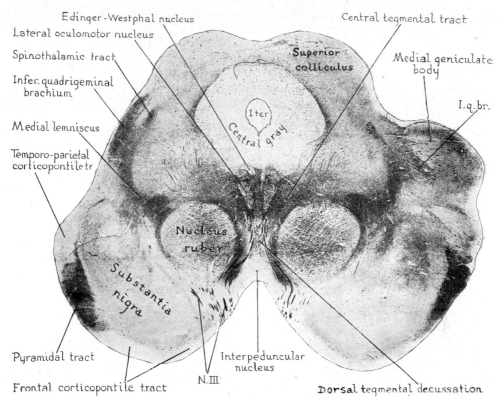

Edinger-Westphal nucleus

Lateral oculomotor nucleus

Spinothalamic tract

Infer. quadrigeminal brachium

Medial lemniscus

Temporo-parietal corticopontile tr

Pyramidal tract

Frontal corticopontile tract

N. III.

Central tegmental tract

Superior colliculus

Medial geniculate body

I.q.br.

Iter

Central gray

Nucleus ruber

Substantia nigra

Interpeduncular nucleus

Dorsal tegmental decussation

FIG. 230. Transverse section of midbrain through superior colliculi, somewhat higher than Fig. 227. One month infant. Weigert's myelin stain. Photograph, *I.q.br.*, inferior quadrigeminal brachium

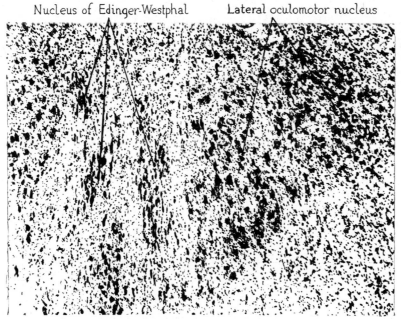

Nucleus of Edinger-Westphal

Lateral oculomotor nucleus

FIG. 231. Transverse section through upper portion of oculomotor nucleus. Three months infant Cresylviolet. Photograph

is the most voluminous nuclear mass of the human mesencephalon, extending the whole length of the midbrain and projecting into the diencephalon. It is rudimentary in lower vertebrates, making its definite appearance in mammals and reaching its greatest development in man. In sections two zones are distinguishable: a dorsal found only in man. The zone extends to the most caudal part of the midbrain where it is covered ventrally by the pontile nuclei. The reticular or red zone, also known as the stratum intermedium, lies close to the pes pedunculi and is composed of scattered cells of irregular shape, rich in iron content but containing no melanin pigment. Islands

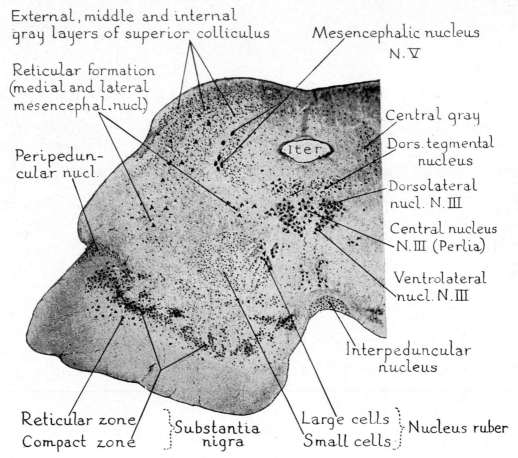

FIG. 232. Section through superior colliculi of midbrain. Three months infant. Cresylviolet. Photograph in which the main cell groups have been schematically blocked in

compact or black zone and a ventral reticular zone which has a reddish-brown color in the fresh condition, similar to that of the globus pallidus (Fig. 232). The compact zone appears as an irregular band of closely packed large polygonal or pyramidal cells containing granules of melanotic pigment. These pigmented cells do not appear until the fourth or fifth year and are apparently of such cells may be seen penetrating between the peduncular fibers. Within the stratum intermedium especially in its lateral portion are many bundles of descending myelinated fibers coming chiefly from the globus pallidus and subthalamic nucleus (pallidopeduncular and subthalamopeduncular fibers (Fig. 228). The zone extends orally into the diencephalon where it lies ventral to the subthalamic nucleus (Fig. 269).

Dorsal to the substantia nigra, between the latter and the nucleus ruber is a region containing scattered cells of various sizes and shapes among which are large cells with melanin pigment. It is not quite certain whether some of these belong to the substantia nigra or the tegmentum, but many authorities regard the whole region as a diffusely organized extension of the compact zone. Lateral to the substantia nigra a layer of small cells, the *peripeduncular nucleus*, caps the dorsal surface of the pes (Fig. 232).

In spite of its prominence the fiber connections of the substantia nigra are still poorly understood. The bulk of the afferent fibers comes from the corpus striatum, largely from the globus pallidus (pallidonigral) but also from the putamen and caudate nucleus (strionigral). Others come from the subthalamic nucleus (subthalamonigral) and from the caudal part of the frontal lobe (corticonigral). Fibers from the temporal and parietal cortex have also been described (Kodama, Levin, Mettler). The bundles of myelinated fibers seen in the stratum intermedium are largely composed of the above named descending tracts. Fewer fibers apparently reach the substantia nigra from the superior colliculi, medial lemniscus, lateral lemniscus and basal olfactory areas, representing practically all the sensory modalities but the number of such fibers is slight compared to that from the corpus striatum and cortex.

The efferent fibers from the substantia nigra are largely obscure. Many are believed to enter the pes pedunculi, descend for a short distance and terminate in the motor centers of the reticular formation. Others pass dorsally to the midbrain tegmentum, some going to the nucleus ruber, the course of most of them being still undetermined. A portion seems to cross in the posterior commissure and go to the interstitial and commissural nuclei. Some ascend to the corpus striatum and cortex, intermingled with the more extensive descending fibers from these areas.

The substantia nigra is undoubtedly an important center of the extrapyramidal motor pathway, influenced primarily by the corpus striatum and thalamus, and by the pallium. Extensive lesions of the nucleus give symptoms similar to those of the globus pallidus, and occasionally even more accentuated. There is muscular rigidity and tremor interfering with the ease and rapidity of volitional activities. There is impairment or loss of those semi-automatic associated movements normally accompanying voluntary movements or postural changes, such as swinging the arms when walking. The emotional play of the mimetic musculature is likewise reduced or absent, the face appearing immobile or mask-like.

Pes pedunculi. The most ventral part of the midbrain which constitutes the pes pedunculi is composed of a massive band of descending cortical fibers. The middle three fifths are occupied by the corticospinal and corticobulbar tracts coming from the motor cortex. Those for the legs are most laterally placed, the larger area for the arm is in the middle portion while those for the face are located most medially. Medial to the pyramidal tracts are the frontal corticopontile fibers from the frontal lobe, while lateral to the pyramids are corticopontile fibers from the temporal and superior parietal and probably also from the occipital cortex. Besides the above named tracts there are often found two fiber bundles, which descend partly within the pes and partly in the region of the medial lemniscus and are hence known as *pes-lemniscus* bundles. The *medial* or *superficial pes-lemniscus* detaches itself from the lateral portion of the peduncles, winds ventrally around the pes and forms a semilunar fiber bundle lying medial to the frontal corticopontile tract (Fig. 223). In lower levels the fibers leave the peduncle, pass dorsally through the substantia nigra and descend in or near the ventromedial portion of the medial lemniscus. The *lateral* or *deep pes-lemniscus* detaches itself from the dorsal surface of the pes, runs for some distance in the lateral portion of the substantia nigra, then turns dorsally and likewise descends in the region of the medial lemniscus (Fig. 223). The significance of these bundles is not clear. According to Déjérine they represent aberrant pyramidal (corticobulbar) fibers which go to the motor nuclei of the eye muscles, and hence they are also known as the medial and lateral corticobulbar tracts. There is considerable evidence however that this interpretation is incorrect at least for the medial bundle whose fibers do not degenerate after lesions of the motor area. They are probably aberrant corticopontile fibers which terminate in the reticular tegmental nucleus of the pons (Poppi).

The corticobulbar tract. The pyramidal fibers mediating volitional control of the muscles innervated by the cranial nerves constitute the corticobulbar or corticonuclear tract. The fibers destined for the muscles of the larynx, pharynx, palate, jaw, tongue, face and some of the neck muscles originate from cells in the ventral portion of the precentral and caudal part of the inferior frontal gyrus. Those for the eye muscles come from the caudal part of the middle frontal gyrus. The fibers descend through the corona radiata and genu of the internal capsule and enter the pes pedunculi where most of them lie medial to the corticospinal tract. During its further descent the tract gradually diminishes in size, constantly giving off fibers which pass to the tegmentum to reach the motor nuclei of the cranial nerves. The course of the fibers to the oculomotor nuclei is not well known. Some of them probably detach themselves in the most rostral part of the midbrain, perhaps even in the subthalamus and reach the oculomotor nucleus in some as yet unknown way. Others appear to leave through the lateral corticopontile tract (lateral pes-

lemniscus), descend in the region of the medial lemniscus to the upper pontile levels and join the medial longitudinal fasciculus through which they are distributed to the nuclei of N.VI, N.IV and N.III (Fig. 223).

In the most rostral part of the pons most of the corticobulbar fibers are still in contact with the pyramidal tract and form the most dorsal bundles of the latter. From about the level of the trochlear decussation and continuing downward, fibers constantly leave these dorsal bundles and enter the tegmentum. In the upper portion of the pons they appear as obliquely running fascicles (aberrant pyramidal bundles, Fig. 212), in the lower pons and medulla they leave as isolated fibers. Some fibers run dorsomedially and cross in the raphé to reach the contralateral motor nuclei, others terminate in the nuclei of the same side. Many of the fibers, especially the crossed ones, detach themselves some distance above the level of the nuclei supplied and hence have a short descending course in the region of the medial lemniscus, where they are easily recognized as lighter staining fiber bundles.

It is obvious from the above that the the cranial muscle groups receive a far more extensive bilateral pyramidal innervation than do those of the extremities. This bilateral control is most marked in those muscle groups which can not as a rule be voluntarily contracted on one side only. Unilateral electrical stimulation of the motor area for these groups causes bilateral movements of the vocal cords, pharynx, palate and upper facial muscles. The vertical and converging movements of the eyes and the vertical movements of the jaw are likewise bilaterally controlled. On the other hand, there is conjugate lateral movement of the eyes to the opposite side and contralateral contraction of the lower facial muscles when the respective cortical areas are unilaterally excited, indicating that the pyramidal innervation for the external rectus and lower facial muscles is mainly crossed. The head

VI put VII crossed.
all bilateral

is likewise deviated to the opposite side but here the reverse must be true. Since the sternocleidomastoid normally turns the head to the opposite side, it is assumed that the muscle is primarily controlled by ipsolateral pyramidal fibers.

Due to this bilateral control, the symptoms in unilateral lesions of the cortico-bulbar tract (upper motor neuron paralysis) are comparatively mild. There is marked voluntary weakness of the lower facial movements such as showing the teeth, pursing the lips or puffing out the cheek,

they are massive bodies whose complex laminated structure resembles that of the cerebral cortex. They receive the optic fibers and many fibers conveying general somatic sensibility and constitute a most important suprasegmental correlation center. Beginning with the reptiles their significance progressively diminishes. The optic fibers establish more and more extensive connections with the thalamus and cortex, as do also the fibers of general body sensibility. In man they have become greatly reduced optic reflex centers primarily

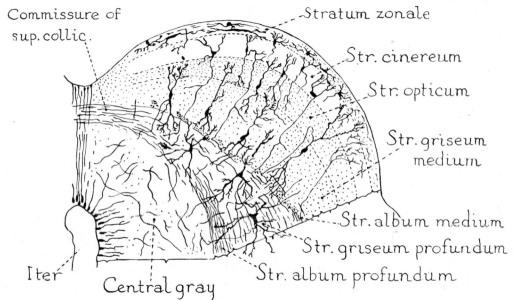

FIG. 233. Cells of superior colliculus reconstructed from Golgi preparations. Human foetus of eight months. (After Sterzi)

while movements of the upper face are little affected. There is usually also a slight weakness of the tongue (genioglossus) and jaw (pterygoid) movements on the opposite side, expressed by deviation of the tongue when protruded and of the jaw when the mouth is opened. Emotional facial movements such as spontaneous crying or laughing are not affected.

The superior colliculi and pretectal area. The superior colliculi are two flattened eminences which form the rostral half of the midbrain roof. In fishes and amphibians

concerned with the reflex adjustments of the eyes and head in response to optic stimuli.

Each colliculus still shows in a rudimentary form the complex laminated structure found in lower forms, consisting of several alternating layers of gray and white matter (Figs. 233, 234). These layers proceeding from the external surface inward are: (1) An outer mainly fibrous layer, the *stratum zonale*, composed of fine nerve fibers coming mainly from the occipital cortex and entering the colliculus through the superior quadrigeminal brachium. Among the fibers are small mostly horizontal cells with tangentially or centrally directed axons. (2) The *stratum cinereum* or superficial gray layer consists of radially arranged cells whose dendrites pass peripherally and their axons inward. The larger cells lie deepest. The corticotectal fibers mentioned above and most of the optic fibers terminate in this layer. (3) The *stratum opticum* or superficial white layer is composed of optic fibers from the retina and lateral geniculate body which enter through the superior brachium and terminate mainly in the

of the reticular formation (colliculoreticular) or cross to the opposite nucleus through the *commissure of the superior colliculi.* Among them are probably some colliculorubral and colliculonigral fibers. The axons of the large cells, which form the main part of the deep white layer, swing ventrally around the central gray and cross in the dorsal tegmental decussation. Some terminate in the oculomotor nucleus, the others descend as colliculobulbar and colliculospinal fibers in the predorsal bundle. Colliculobulbar fibers are also believed to

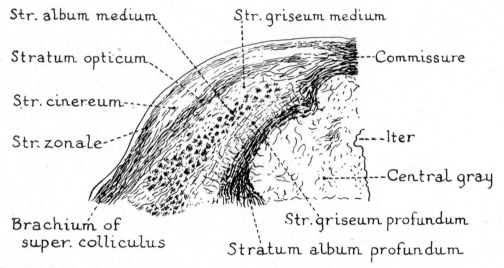

FIG. 234. Section through superior colliculus of adult. Weigert's myelin stain. (After Sterzi)

stratum cinereum, some however going to the deeper layers of the colliculus. Among the fibers are scattered cells whose axons pass into the next layer. (4) The remaining layers are often collectively termed the *stratum lemnisci* which may be subdivided into a middle gray and white layer, and a deep gray and white layer (Figs. 233, 234). The stratum lemnisci receives the spinocollicular fibers and probably also some fibers from the medial and the lateral lemniscus and from the inferior colliculus. It contains many medium sized and large stellate cells, the latter sometimes known as the "motor" cells of the tectum. The axons of the smaller cells pass to the lateral portion

descend uncrossed near the medial longitudinal fasciculus.

The superior colliculus thus receives afferent fibers from the pallium, lateral geniculate body and retina, these fibers entering the dorsal and oral portion through the superior brachium and terminating in the superficial layers of the colliculus. The spinocollicular and other secondary afferent fibers end in the deeper layers. The efferent fibers are collected in the deep white layers and their most important connections are with the muscles of the eyes, neck and face and possibly also with the body. Between the afferent fibers and the efferent neurons are the smaller association cells whose axons do not leave the colliculus. The older optic connections are reduced, the pallial connections are phylogenetically new. It is quite possible that some of the optic "reflexes", such as turning of eyes and head with a moving object, have a cerebral arc in which the optic stimuli first reach the occipital cortex and are then referred to the colliculi by corticocollicular fibers.

Immediately oral to the superior colliculus, in the region of junction of midbrain

light reflex. The pathway consists of the following neurons: (1) Fibers from retinal cells which pass through the optic nerve and tract and enter the superior brachium through which they reach the pretectal area; (2) axons of pretectal cells, partially crossing through the posterior commissure, sweep ventrally along the central gray matter and terminate in the Edinger-Westphal nucleus of the same and opposite side; (3) preganglionic fibers from the Edinger-West-

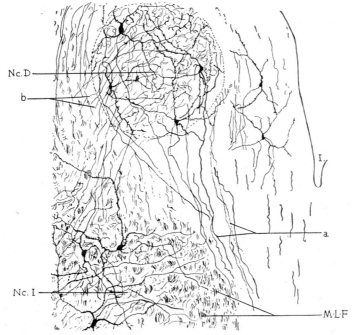

FIG. 235. Nucleus of Darkschewitsch (*NcD*) and portion of interstitial nucleus of Cajal (*NcI*) of cat several days old. Golgi impregnation. (After Cajal.) *I*, iter; *a*, axons entering the medial longitudinal fasciculus (MLF); *b*, collaterals terminating in Darkschewitsch' nucleus.

and thalamus is the *pretectal area*, usually considered a part of the mesencephalon (Fig. 268). The area which is composed of several indistinct groups of small and large cells, receives fibers from the optic tract, lateral geniculate body and the posterior parietal cortex (Le Gros Clark), and sends fibers to the mesencephalic tegmentum and the substantia nigra. Ranson and his collaborators have demonstrated that the pretectal area, and not the superior colliculus, is the midbrain center for the pupillary

phal nucleus go by way of N.III to the ciliary ganglion from which (4) postganglionic fibers pass to the sphincter of the iris.

In the zone of junction of iter and third ventricle (pretectal area), the roof contains a considerable bundle of crossing fibers, known as the *posterior commissure*. The origin and termination of its component fibers are not altogether clear. Included are (1) Fibers from the globus pallidus, some of which go to the tegmentum and red nucleus, either directly or through intercalated cells lying within the commissure itself. Others go to the interstitial nucleus and nucleus of Darkschewitsch, and through these to the medial longitudinal fasciculus. (2) Probably some fibers from the substantia nigra, but the course of these is undetermined. (3) Commissural fibers connecting the superior colliculi. (4) Corticocollicular fibers entering the stratum zonale of the superior colliculus. (5) Fibers from cells of pretectal area going to the contralateral Edinger-Westphal nucleus. These form part of the pupillary reflex pathway.

The oculomotor nerve (N.III). The third nerve is primarily efferent but also contains some afferent proprioceptive fibers from the muscles supplied by N.III. These fibers are derived in part at least from ganglion cells found along the root and orbital portion of the nerve (Tozer and Sherrington), in part perhaps from central ganglion cells of unknown location, possibly from the mesencephalic nucleus of N.V. The efferent portion contains (a) Somatic efferent fibers to the voluntary striped external muscles of the eyeball except the lateral rectus and superior oblique. These include the superior, inferior and internal recti, the inferior oblique and also the levator palpebrae superioris. (b) Visceral efferent preganglionic fibers to the ciliary ganglion whose postganglionic fibers, by way of the short ciliary nerves, supply the smooth internal muscles of the eye, including the ciliary body and the sphincter of the iris. The nerve thus elevates the eyelid, controls the vertical and converging movements of the eyeball, participates in the lateral movements, contracts the pupil and alters the convexity of the lens (accommodation).

The oculomotor nuclear complex is located in the ventral part of the central gray in a V-shaped trough formed by the diverging fibers of the medial longitudinal fasciculi (Figs. 227, 228), and extends from the trochlear nucleus to about the rostral limit of the superior colliculi. It is divided into large-celled and small-celled groups. The

former constitute the somatic motor nuclei of N.III, composed of typical large motor cells which innervate the striped muscles and comprise the paired *lateral* and the unpaired *central nucleus of Perlia*. The small-celled groups include the *nucleus of Edinger-Westphal* and the *anterior median nucleus*, composed of smaller spindle-shaped or ovoid cells resembling those of the lateral horn or dorsal motor vagus nucleus. These are the visceral motor nuclei of N.III, believed to send preganglionic fibers to the ciliary body and sphincter iridis. Each lateral nucleus is an obliquely placed plate of cells, extending practically the whole length of the complex, closely applied to the dorsomedial surface of the medial longitudinal fasciculus. The cells actually infiltrate the fasciculus and may even extend to the external surface of the bundle. The nucleus is indistinctly divided into a smaller dorsolateral and a larger ventrolateral portion. The lateral nuclei are fused along their middle third with the centrally placed nucleus of Perlia (Figs. 229, 236). The Edinger-Westphal nucleus is located in the cephalic part of the nuclear complex lying dorsomedial to the lateral nucleus. It begins in the region of the nucleus of Perlia and extends beyond the rostral tip of the lateral nucleus. In front of and ventral to the Edinger-Westphal nucleus is the vertical plate of cells constituting the anterior median nucleus, regarded by many as merely the rostral continuation of the Edinger-Westphal nucleus (Fig. 237).

Attempts to determine the cell groups within the oculomotor nucleus which innervate specific muscles of the eyeball, have yielded contradictory results. The most accepted view is that the lateral nucleus, beginning at its rostral end and proceeding caudally, supplies the extrinsic muscles in the following order (Bernheimer, Edinger, Brouwer): levator palpebrae, superior rectus, internal rectus, inferior oblique, inferior rectus. The fibers to the levator and superior rectus are uncrossed, those to the internal rectus and inferior oblique are both crossed and uncrossed, while those to the inferior rectus are entirely crossed. The nucleus of Perlia is probably concerned with movements of convergence and sends fibers to the internal rectus of both eyes (Fig. 236).

The specific innervation of the intrinsic eye muscles is likewise not fully determined. The accepted belief is that the Edinger-Westphal nucleus controls the pupillary contraction to light, while the anterior accommodation, which is most highly developed in man.

The root fibers arising from the oculomotor nucleus pass ventrally in a number of bundles, some coursing medial to, some traversing, and some passing lateral to the superior cerebellar peduncle and red nucleus. Ventral to these the fibers converge and emerge in the oculomotor sulcus on the ventral aspect of the midbrain. This spreading

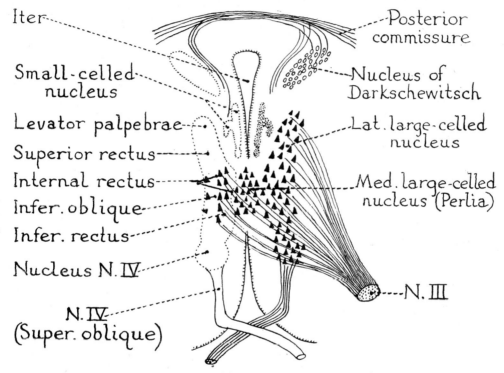

FIG. 236. The region of the Sylvian aqueduct viewed from above. Diagram showing the position of the nuclei of nerves III and IV and their subdivisions. The small-celled nucleus represented as one on each side, is subdivided into a lateral portion (Edinger-Westphal nucleus) and medial one (anterior-median nucleus). (Modified from Edinger.)

median nucleus sends fibers to the ciliary body for accommodation. Comparative anatomical studies suggest that the reverse may be true. Thus the Edinger-Westphal nucleus is variably developed in many mammals, reaching its greatest extent in primates and man, while the anterior median nucleus is a constant feature of all mammals. This is correlated with the relatively constant occurrence of the pupillary reflex and the rather variable capacity for of the root fibers through and around the nucleus ruber is an expression of the intra-radicular expansion of the red nucleus during embryological development.

The oculomotor nucleus receives terminals and collaterals from the medial longitudinal fasciculus, including ascending axons from the vestibular nuclei and from internuclear neurons lying near the nucleus VI and descending fibers from the interstitial and commissural nuclei; from the superior colliculi, superior cerebellar peduncle and reticular formation. The vestibular fibers reflexly correlate the positions of the eyes with those of the head; the internuclear fibers associate the abducens and oculomotor nuclei in the performance of lateral eye movements; the collicular fibers put the eye movements under control of the collicular optic reflex center and thereby indirectly under one of the pallial eye-movement centers which sends fibers to the superior colliculus. The fibers to the Edinger-Westphal nucleus believed to effect pupillary contraction do not come from the

ters" for the vertical and converging movements. The fact that the conjugate eye movements, lateral, vertical and converging, can not be dissociated voluntarily or reflexly suggests that the pyramidal and other fibers act on cells which in turn associate the various root neurons in these movements. This would certainly seem to be the case with the conjugate lateral movements which are performed by two widely separated nuclei, VI for external rectus and III for internal rectus. It is not so certain in the case of the other movements performed by the nuclei of nerves III and IV

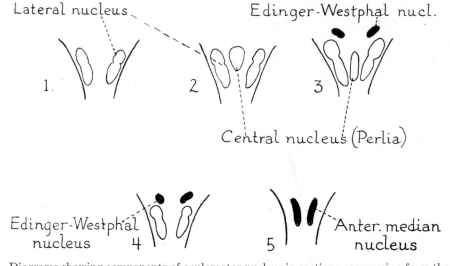

FIG. 237. Diagrams showing components of oculomotor nucleus in sections progressing from the caudal to the rostral end of the nucleus. (After Brouwer)

superior colliculi but from a region immediately oral to them, known as the pretectal area. The oculomotor nucleus also receives corticobulbar (pyramidal) fibers for voluntary movement, whose course is not fully understood. Some of them appear to detach themselves from the pes pedunculi in the caudal part of the midbrain and join the medial longitudinal fasciculus through which they are distributed to the motor nuclei of the eye nerves. The pyramidal fibers probably do not reach the nucleus directly but through the intermediation of intercalated cells in the adjacent reticular formation, which constitute intrinsic "cen-

which are close together and in which there are groups of cells with crossed and uncrossed axons. There is much that is still obscure about the central mechanisms of the vertical and converging movements.

Lesion of the third nerve produces an ipsilateral lower motor neuron paralysis of the muscles supplied by the nerve. There is an external strabismus (squint) due to the unopposed action of the external rectus, inability to move the eye vertically or inward, drooping of the eyelid (ptosis), dilation of the pupil (mydriasis), loss of pupillary reflex to light and convergence and loss of accommodation of the lens. The nearness of the emerging root fibers of N.III to the pyramidal tracts of the pes pedunculi may lead to the inclusion of both structures in a single lesion, causing an alternating hemiplegia similar to those already described for the sixth and twelfth nerves. In this case there would be an ipsilateral lower motor neuron paralysis of N.III showing the symptoms described above, combined with a contralateral spastic hemiplegia of the body and extremities. Since at this level the corticobulbar and corticospinal fibers are in close conjunction, there may also be contralateral paralysis or paresis (weakness) of the muscles innervated by the cranial nerves, especially those of the lower face. This constitutes the *superior* or *oculomotor alternating hemiplegia* ordinarily known as *Weber's syndrome*.

The pupillary reflexes. When a beam of light is thrown on the retina of one eye both pupils contract. The response of the eye stimulated is called the *direct reaction*, that of the opposite eye the *consensual reaction*. As already stated (p. 263), the pathway for this *pupillary* or *light reflex* is by retinal fibers which leave the optic tract to terminate in the pretectal area, whence crossed and uncrossed fibers reach the Edinger-Westphal nuclei.

When the gaze is suddenly shifted from a distant to a near object the accommodation-convergence reaction occurs. Contraction of the internal recti muscles causes convergence of the eyes, contraction of the ciliary muscle effects a thickening of the lens (*accommodation*) and the pupils likewise contract as an aid to the sharper definition of the image. In this case the pupillary contraction is an associated element of a larger movement complex directed from the cerebral cortex. The retinal impulses or perhaps proprioceptive impulses from the contracting ocular muscles reach the visual cortex from which descending impulses are then sent directly or by way of the frontal eye centers to the "convergence center" of

the oculomotor nuclei. Since the pupilloconstrictor pathways for light and accommodation are distinct, they may be involved separately in isolated lesions. This occurs in certain diseases such as tabes dorsalis, where there is loss of pupillary contraction to light but not to accommodation, a condition known as the *Argyll Robertson pupil*. The lesion affects the retinal fibers which have detached themselves from the optic tract to go to the pretectal area or the cells and fibers of the pretectal area itself. The fibers serving accommodation, which remain in the optic tract and go to the geniculate bodies and cortex are left intact.

In intense illumination contraction of the pupil may be accompanied by closure of the eyelids, lowering of the brows and general contraction of the face, designed to shut out the maximal amount of light. In so far as they are not volitional, these are reflex movements mediated through the superior colliculi and the colliculobulbar tracts.

The central pathway for pupillary dilation is not fully ascertained. Dilation occurs reflexly on shading the eye or scratching the side of the neck with a pin, and is a constant feature in severe pain and emotional states. Experimental evidence points to a path from the frontal cortex to the posterior region of the hypothalamus which is the highest autonomic center of the brain stem. From the hypothalamus fibers descend through the reticular formation (and periventricular region) of the midbrain, pons and medulla and terminate in the upper portion of the lateral sympathetic nucleus (intermediolateral column) of the spinal cord. The latter sends preganglionic fibers by way of the upper two or three rami communicantes and sympathetic trunk to the superior cervical ganglion, whence postganglionic fibers go to the dilator muscle of the iris. The descending pathway from the hypothalamus probably contains intercalated neurons, and the dilator fibers run close to those which control the tonic elevation of the upper eyelid through the superior tarsal muscle.   Hence central lesions usually affect both of these fibers and cause the diminished pupil (myosis) and slight drooping of the eyelid (ptosis) characteristic of Horner's syndrome.

Blood supply.   The arterial supply of the midbrain is derived principally from the basilar system, to a lesser degree from branches of the internal carotid.   The main vessels include the *posterior cerebral*, the *superior cerebellar*, the *posterior communicating*, and the *anterior chorioidal arteries* (Fig. 324).   The branches from these arteries which supply the midbrain may be grouped, as in the case of the pons, into (a) *paramedian* or *central* arteries which enter medially in the region of the interpeduncular fossa, and (2) *peripheral* or *circumferential* arteries which wind laterally around the peduncle and supply its lateral and dorsal portions.

The paramedian branches are derived from the posterior communicating artery and also from the basilar bifurcation and proximal portions of the posterior cerebral arteries.   They form an extensive plexus in the interpeduncular fossa and enter the posterior perforated substance to supply the floor of the fossa, the raphéal region including the oculomotor nucleus and medial longitudinal fasciculus, the red nucleus and the most medial part of the pes pedunculi.

Branches from the anterior chorioidal artery supply similar vessels to the most oral portion of the interpeduncular fossa, medial to the optic tract.

The circumferential branches may be short or long ones.   The short ones arise in part from the interpeduncular plexus, in part from the proximal portions of the posterior cerebral and superior cerebellar arteries and supply the middle and lateral parts of the pes, the substantia nigra and lateral part of the tegmentum.   In the oral portion, similar branches are contributed by the anterior chorioidal artery.   The long circumferential arteries arise primarily from the posterior cerebral.   The most important of these is the *quadrigeminal artery* which encircles the lateral periphery and furnishes the main blood supply to the superior and inferior colliculi.   Other long branches contributing to the supply of the roof are furnished by the inferior chorioidal and superior cerebellar arteries.

The numerous veins which arise from the capillaries generally run parallel to the arteries but not directly with them.   They form an extensive peripheral plexus in the pia and are collected by two larger channels, the basal veins, which drain into the great cerebral vein of Galen or into the internal cerebral veins.

CHAPTER XVII

THE CEREBELLUM

General anatomy. The cerebellum lies above the medulla oblongata beyond which it extends laterally for a considerable distance and is covered dorsally by the cerebral hemispheres. Two surfaces may be distinguished: a superior somewhat flattened surface covered by the tentorium, and a strongly convex inferior surface which fills the cerebellar fossae of the occipital bone. The frontal margin of the cerebellum is notched by the shallow *anterior cerebellar incisure* (Fig. 240), the caudal margin by the deeper and narrower *posterior cerebellar incisure* which contains a fold of the dura mater, the falx cerebelli.

The human cerebellum consists of a median portion, the *vermis*, connecting two lateral lobes or *hemispheres*. The superior portion of the vermis is only poorly delimited from the hemispheres, but on the inferior surface two deep sulci separate the vermis from the lateral portions. The convex inferior surface is divided into two halves by a deep median fossa continuous with the posterior incisure. This is the *vallecula cerebelli* whose floor is formed by the inferior vermis and in which is lodged the medulla oblongata.

Structurally the cerebellum consists of a superficial mantle of gray matter, the cerebellar cortex, enclosing an internal mass of white, the corpus medullare. Within the latter are found four pairs of nuclear masses: the fastigial, globose, emboliform and dentate nuclei (Fig. 254). The surface of the cerebellum receives its characteristic appearance from numerous transversely running sulci and fissures of varying depth, which separate a large number of narrow leaf-like lamina, the cerebellar *folia* or *gyri*. These lamina are in turn folded into secondary and tertiary folia, each composed of a medullary core capped by a superficial layer of cortex. In sagittal sections this complex branching of the corpus medullare and its cortical covering presents a tree-like appearance to which the name *arbor vitae* has been given (Fig. 238).

The more prominent transverse fissures, some of which nearly reach the roof of the fourth ventricle, divide the cerebellum into a number of lobules, each with a medial portion belonging to the vermis and two wing-like extensions belonging to the hemispheres (Figs. 239, 240, 241). These lobules are still cumbered with peculiar and morphologically meaningless names given to them by the older anatomists. Thus the superior vermis consists of the *lingula*, *lobulus centralis*, *monticulus* divided into *culmen* and *declive*, and *folium vermis*. On the under surface the inferior vermis includes the *tuber*, *pyramis*, *uvula* and *nodulus*. Each of these lobules has corresponding lateral continuations in the hemispheres. The central lobule is continued into the *alae lobuli centralis;* the monticulus into the *quadrangular lobule* whose anterior portion belongs to the culmen, the posterior portion to the declive. The folium vermis extends laterally into the *superior semilunar lobule* separated from the *inferior semilunar lobule* which belongs to the tuber by the horizontal cerebellar fissure which roughly marks the boundary between the superior and inferior surfaces. The remaining hemispheral portions are the *biventral lobules* for the pyramis, the *tonsils* for the uvula, and the *flocculi* for the nodulus. The flocculi lie on the under surface of the middle cerebellar peduncle and are connected with the nodule by the peduncles of the flocculi and the inferior medullary velum (Fig. 241).

A simpler and more fundamental plan

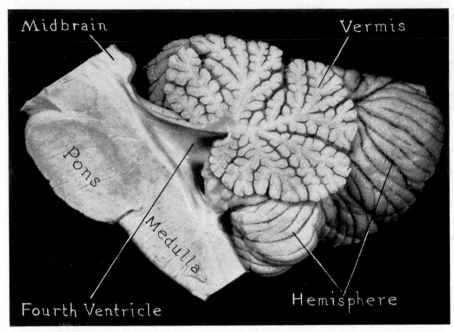

FIG. 238. Median longitudinal section through cerebellum. Photograph

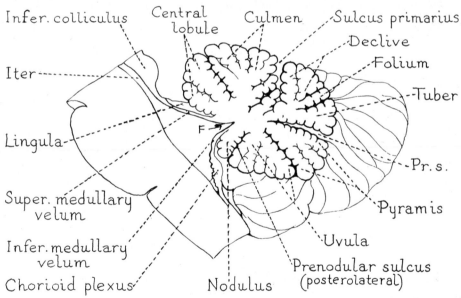

FIG. 239. Median section through cerebellum. *Pr.s.*, prepyramidal sulcus; *F*, fastigial recess of fourth ventricle

of mammalian cerebellar organization has been made possible by the comparative and ontogenetic investigations of Bolk, Ingvar, Jakob, Larsell and others. According to Ingvar, the cerebellum may be divided into three lobes: anterior, middle and posterior (Fig. 242). The middle lobe, phylogenetically the youngest, is bounded anteriorly

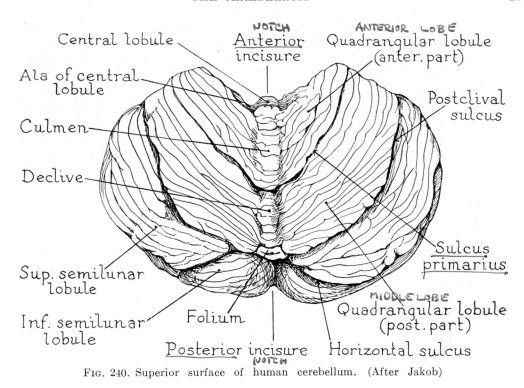

Central lobule

Ala of central lobule

Culmen

Declive

Sup. semilunar lobule

Inf. semilunar lobule

NOTCH
Anterior incisure

ANTERIOR LOBE
Quadrangular lobule (anter. part)

Postclival sulcus

Sulcus primarius

MIDDLE LOBE
Quadrangular lobule (post. part)

Folium

Posterior incisure
NOTCH

Horizontal sulcus

FIG. 240. Superior surface of human cerebellum. (After Jakob)

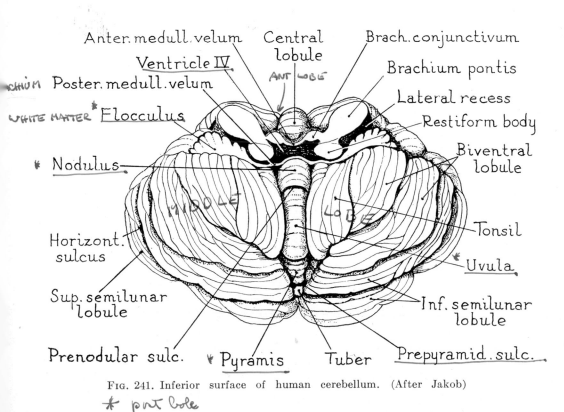

Anter. medull. velum

Ventricle IV

RCHIUM
Poster. medull. velum

WHITE MATTER * Flocculus

* Nodulus

Horizont. sulcus

Sup. semilunar lobule

Prenodular sulc.

* Pyramis

Central lobule
ANT LOBE

MIDDLE

LOBE

Tuber

Brach. conjunctivum

Brachium pontis

Lateral recess

Restiform body

Biventral lobule

Tonsil

* Uvula

Inf. semilunar lobule

Prepyramid. sulc.

FIG. 241. Inferior surface of human cerebellum. (After Jakob)

* post lobe

by the sulcus primarius, posteriorly by the prepyramidal sulcus, two fundamental sulci appearing in early stages of development (Figs. 243, 239). The anterior lobe lies in front of the sulcus primarius and in man is composed of three or four lobules comprising the lingula, central lobule and culmen and their lateral extensions. It is an unpaired structure with transverse folia running con-

the flocculi. They are phylogenetically newer structures found only in mammals. The ansiform portion of each lobule includes the semilunar and biventral lobules, the paramedian portion comprises the tonsil. In most mammals, the latter is of considerable size and is seen on the lateral surface of the cerebellum. In man, however, the tonsils have been pushed ventrally by the

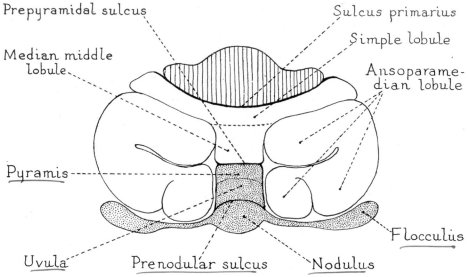

FIG. 242. Diagram of human cerebellum. Anterior lobe striped, middle lobe clear, posterior lobe stippled

tinuously through vermis and lateral portions. A distinction between vermis and hemispheres is difficult.

In the middle lobe the anterior portion, known as the simple lobule, resembles the anterior lobe in showing continuous transverse folia and in the lack of distinction between vermis and hemispheres. It includes the declive and the posterior portion of the quadrangular lobe. The rest of the middle lobe consists of a median and two lateral portions. The former, the lobulus medius medianus, is relatively small and comprises the folium and tuber of the vermis. The lateral portions are, however, tremendously enlarged to form the folded ansoparamedian lobules which practically constitute the whole of the cerebellar hemispheres except

enormously developed ansiform lobules and lie closely apposed to the uvula (Fig. 241).

The posterior lobe consists of a median portion composed of the pyramis, uvula and nodule and the paired flocculi which are connected to the nodulus by the peduncles of the flocculi and the inferior medullary velum (Fig. 241). In most mammals lateral extensions known as the paraflocculi are connected by narrow stalks with the uvula and pyramis, but in man these are rudimentary or entirely absent.

According to Larsell, the flocculonodular lobe (flocculi, nodule and their connections) should be distinguished as a separate entity from the rest of the cerebellum (corpus cerebelli). The paired flocculi (auricles of lower vertebrates) are the first cerebellar structures to appear phylogenetically as expansions of the vestibular portion of the rhombencephalon. Their function and that of the nodulus which appears much later in phylogeny is entirely vestibular. The corpus cerebelli arises somewhat later and primarily receives general proprioceptive impulses through the spinocerebellar (and trigeminocerebellar) fibers. The corpus cerebelli is separated from the flocculi by the posterolateral (prenodular) sulcus which, according to Larsell, is the first sulcus to appear both phylogenetically and in individual development (Fig. 243).

portion of the ansoparamedian lobules myelinating last. The topographical cellular differentiation of the cerebellar cortex is temporally similar to the myelinating areas.

The structure of the cerebellar cortex

The cerebellar cortex, which unlike the cortex cerebri has a relatively similar structure in all parts of the cerebellum, is composed of three layers: an outer *molecular* layer with relatively few cells and few myelinated fibers, an inner densely cellular *granular* layer, and between the two a single row of large flask-shaped cells, the *cells of*

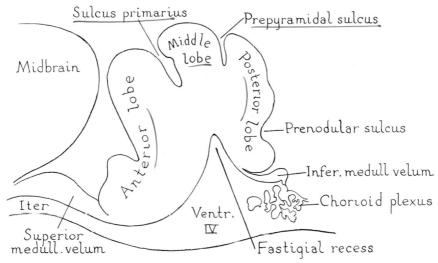

FIG. 243. Median longitudinal section through cerebellum of three months foetus, diagrammatic. (After Jakob)

The middle lobe, especially the large ansoparamedian lobule, represents the newer portion of the cerebellum (neocerebellum) and has extensive afferent and efferent connections with the cerebral cortex. The rest of the vermis and the flocculi which primarily receive vestibular and general proprioceptive impulses constitute the older portion or paleocerebellum. Myelinization begins first in the floccular formation and in the basal portions of the superior and inferior vermis, to be continued soon in the rest of the vermis except the middle lobe which matures later. The process then spreads into the hemispheres, the caudal

Purkinje (Figs. 244, 245, 246, 247). These cells have a clear vesicular nucleus with deeply staining nucleolus, and irregular Nissl bodies usually arranged concentrically. Each cell gives off two or three main dendrites which enter the molecular layer and form a remarkably rich arborization extending to the surface. The larger and medium sized branches are smooth, but the finer terminal ones are beset with numerous small excrescences or "gemmules". The dendritic arborization does not spread uniformly in all directions but is flattened fan-like in a plane at right angles to the long axis of the folium, hence its full extent can only be seen in transverse sections (Figs. 248, 249, 251). The axon arises from the end of the cell opposite to the dendrites, acquires a myelin sheath, passes through the granular layer and enters the underlying white matter to go to one of the deep cerebellar nuclei or to some other part of the cortex. Not far from its origin, each axon gives off a number of collaterals which run horizontally and terminate on the bodies of adjacent Purkinje cells (Fig. 249). Occasionally somewhat smaller aberrantly placed Purkinje cells

granule cells, about 4–8 micra in diameter. The cells have three or four rather short dendrites which arborize in peculiar clawlike endings within the "glomeruli". The unmyelinated axons ascend to the molecular layer where each bifurcates into two branches which run parallel to the long axis of the folium. These parallel fibers practically fill the whole depth of the molecular layer and run transversely to the dendritic expansions of the Purkinje cells. They traverse layer after layer of these expansions,

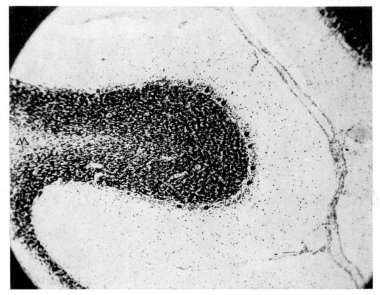

FIG. 244. Section through small folium of human cerebellum showing the dark staining granular layer with glomeruli (light spaces), the light staining molecular layer containing scattered nuclei, and between the two a single row of Purkinje cell nuclei. Cresylviolet. Photograph. *M*, medullary core.

may be found in the granular or molecular layer. Since the axons of the Purkinje cells are the only ones to enter the white, it is evident that all impulses entering the cerebellum must converge on these cells to reach the efferent cerebellar paths.

The *granular layer* in ordinary stains presents the appearance of closely packed chromatic nuclei, not unlike those of lymphocytes, with irregular light spaces here and there which constitute the so-called "islands" or "glomeruli" (Figs. 244, 246). In silver preparations these nuclei are seen to belong to small multipolar cells, the

appearing like telegraph wires strung along the branches of a tree, and extend the whole length of a folium, finally terminating in delicate button-shaped enlargements (Fig. 249).

Scattered through all parts of the granular layer are the *Golgi type II cells* or *cells of van Gehuchten*, with vesicular nuclei and definite chromofilic bodies (Figs. 246, 247). Many of their branching dendrites enter the molecular layer where they may extend to the surface. Their axon springs directly from the cell body and almost immediately splits into a complex arborization within the granular layer (Fig. 251), the terminal fibrils being mainly concentrated in the glomeruli entering the white, are believed to be aberrantly placed Purkinje cells (Cajal, Jakob).

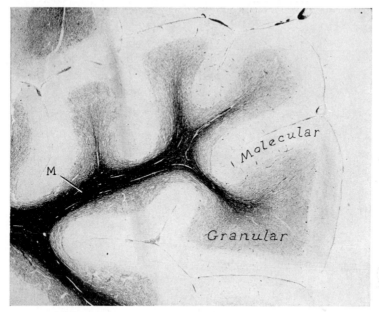

FIG. 245. Section through portion of adult cerebellum showing several secondary folia. Weigert's myelin stain. Photograph. *M*, medullary core

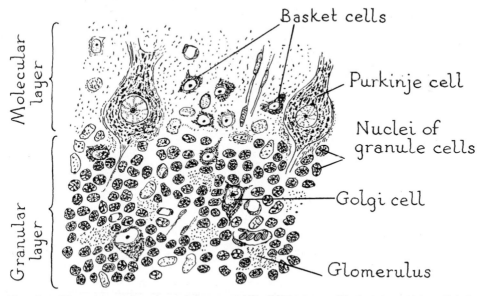

FIG. 246. Part of a section through human cerebellar cortex. Nissl stain. (After Cajal)

where they come in contact with the dendritic terminals of the granule cells. Larger cells found occasionally in the superficial portion of the granular layer, which have long axons

The *molecular layer* contains relatively few cells of a stellate or triangular shape. The superficial stellate cells are small, with short thin dendrites and fine unmyelinated often horizontally running axons. The larger deeper stellate cells situated in the vicinity of the Purkinje cell bodies are also known tal fibers transversely to the folium, i.e., in the same plane as the dendritic arborizations of the Purkinje cells. These horizontal

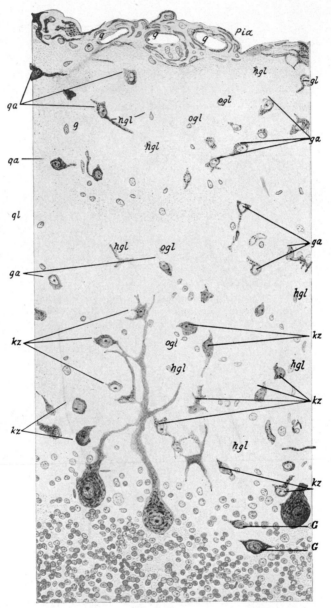

FIG. 247. Section of human cerebellar cortex. Toluidin blue. (Jakob.) *G*, Golgi type II cell; *g*, blood vessel; *ga*, stellate cell; *gl*, macroglia; *hgl*, microglia; *ogl*, oligodendroglia; *kz*, basket cells

as *basket cells*. Many of their numerous branching dendrites ascend in the molecular layer. The unmyelinated axons spring from one side of the cell body and run as horizon- axons pass a number of Purkinje cells, to each of which they give off one or more descending collaterals which form an intricate end arborization or "basket" around the

Purkinje cell bodies (Figs. 44, 251, 248). A single collateral may furnish terminals for two Purkinje cells or the latter may receive terminals from several basket cells. Thus a single basket cell may come in synaptic relations with many Purkinje cells situated in a transverse plane of the folium, its axon even extending to a neighboring folium. It is evident from the above that besides the relatively few cells the molecular layer nated fibers composed of collaterals from the axons of Purkinje cells (Fig. 249).

Nerve fibers. The efferent fibers of the cerebellar cortex are all axons of Purkinje cells which go mainly to the deep cerebellar nuclei, though a few may leave the cerebellum without relaying in those nuclei. Such fibers have been found in the flocculi and nodule and may also be present in other portions of the vermis. Some of the Pur-

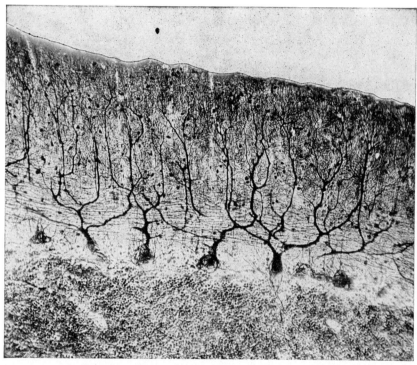

FIG. 248. Transverse section through portion of cerebellar cortex, showing the bodies and main dendritic processes of the Purkinje cells. The fine parallel fibers in the deep portion of the molecular layer are axons of basket cells. Cajal's silver stain. Photograph.

is composed primarily of unmyelinated dendritic and axonal processes which include the dendrites of the Purkinje cells, the longitudinally running axons of the granule cells, the transversely running axons of the basket cells, and also the dendrites of the basket and Golgi type II cells. Section of all these processes gives to the molecular layer its finely punctate appearance. Only in its deepest portion is there found a narrow horizontal plexus of myeli-

kinje cell axons are undoubtedly associative in character, connecting different parts of the cerebellum on the same side or crossing through the white of the vermis to terminate on the opposite side (Clarke and Horsley, Brouwer and Coenen, Saito). These association fibers are found in the most superficial portion of the medullary substance and as short, arcuate fibers may connect adjacent folia or lobules, or may extend a distance of two or three lobules.

The afferent fibers to the cerebellar cortex are furnished by the tracts entering the cerebellum through the inferior and middle peduncles, including the vestibulo-, spino-, olivo- and pontocerebellar fibers. To a smaller extent, there are the associative fibers coming from other parts of the cerebellum. Structurally two types of afferent terminals are found in the cerebellar cortex, *mossy fibers* and *climbing fibers*. The mossy fibers, so-called from the appearance of

of the mossy fibers, the dendritic endings of the granule cells and the axonal terminals of the Golgi type II cells.

The climbing fibers pass from the white matter through the granular layer and past the Purkinje cell bodies to reach the main dendrites of the latter. There they lose their myelin sheath and split into a number of terminal fibrils which climb ivy-like along the dendritic arborization whose branchings they closely imitate (Fig. 45).

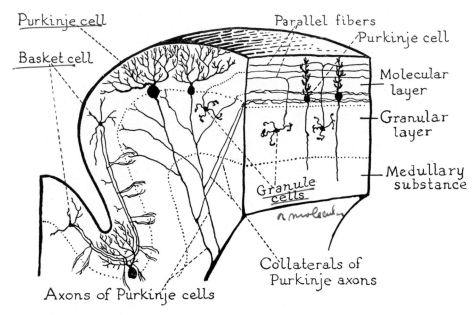

FIG. 249. Schematic representation of neuronal arrangement in a transverse and longitudinal section of a cerebellar folium. (Jakob, after Villiger)

their terminations in the embryo, are the coarsest fibers in the white matter. While still in the white they bifurcate repeatedly into numerous branches which then enter the granular layer, the branches of a single fiber often going to adjacent folia. They course through the granular layer and give off many fine collaterals, each of which enters a "glomerulus", loses its myelin sheath and forms an arborization related to the claw-like dendritic endings of the granule cells (Fig. 250). The fiber itself ends in a similar termination in the superficial portion of the granular layer. Thus the "islands" or "glomeruli" contain the endings

According to Cajal, each climbing fiber is related to only one Purkinje cell.

The respective sources of the climbing and mossy fibers are still obscure. Cajal suggested that the pontocerebellar and vestibulocerebellar tracts terminated in climbing fibers, while the spino- and olivocerebellar have mossy endings. This view has not been substantiated by the often contradictory findings of other investigators. According to Winkler, the older cerebellar paths, vestibulocerebellar and spinocerebellar, end in climbing fibers while the ponto- and olivocerebellar furnish the mossy ones. Mettler and Lubin have likewise found that destruction of both brachia pontis in the cat did not produce a degeneration of the climbing fibers. It has been suggested that the latter may not be afferent fibers at all, but terminals of recurrent Purkinje axons or their collaterals and thus form part of an intracerebellar association system (Saito, Lorente de Nó). It must be emphasized that both types of ending are found in all parts of the cerebellum though apparently more climbing fibers are found in the vermis and flocculi. Hence it is probable that each afferent system contributes both climbing and mossy fibers, but perhaps in different

would produce transverse diffusion along the axons of the basket cells. (d) Mossy fiber, granule cell, Golgi type II cell and back again to granule cell, an exceedingly involved pathway in which the impulse would pass to and from the granular and molecular layer, involving progressively new granule and Golgi cells. In addition, impulses may be transmitted directly from one Purkinje cell to adjacent ones by means of its axon collaterals. The cerebellar cortex thus constitutes a mechanism for tremendous radiation and reverberation of impulses which ultimately must be concentrated on the rela-

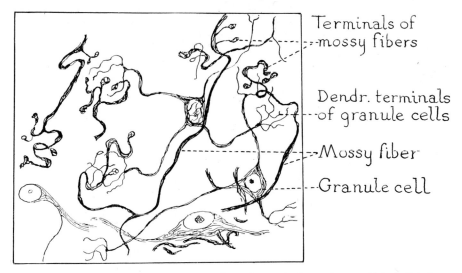

Terminals of mossy fibers

Dendr. terminals of granule cells

Mossy fiber

Granule cell

FIG. 250. Granule cells and mossy fibers in cerebellum of cat. (After Cajal)

proportions. However, a single fiber gives rise to only one type of ending and never to both.

The structural mechanism of the cerebellar cortex furnishes a number of intracortical paths for entering cerebellar impulses; some direct and limited, others intricate and diffuse. Thus impulses may pass through (a) Climbing fiber, Purkinje cell and out again by the axon of the latter, the shortest circuit possible. (b) Mossy fiber, granule cell and Purkinje cell, permitting extensive diffusion in the longitudinal axis of the folium. (c) Mossy fiber, granule cell, basket cell and Purkinje cell. Such circuit

tively few efferent Purkinje cells. Such mechanism and also the fact that all parts of the cerebellar cortex have a similar structure would argue against any precise localization of cerebellar function.

Neuroglia. While most of the neuroglia cells in the cerebellum are of the same general types seen elsewhere, there are found in the Purkinje layer modified astrocytes known as the epithelial cells of Cajal (cells of Bergmann). They are small rounded cells, lying in several rows between the Purkinje cell bodies, which give off a number of vertical processes beset with short leaf-like branches. These processes reach the surface and terminate in small end feet which fuse to form the external limiting glial membrane. They probably support the dendritic processes of the Purkinje cells. Related to these cells are the feathered cells of Fañanas, found in the deeper portion of the molecular layer, with fewer and shorter vertical processes (Fig. 252).

nuclei and lies in the white of the cerebellar hemisphere close to the vermis. It is a convoluted band of gray having the shape of a much-folded bag with the opening or hilus directed mesially and dorsally, giving in transverse section a characteristic denticulate appearance similar to that of the inferior olivary nucleus. It is found as a

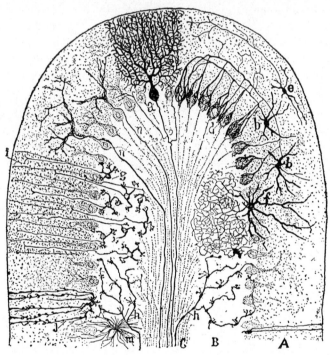

FIG. 251. Semi-diagrammatic transverse section through cerebellar folium, as shown by the Golgi method. (Cajal.) *A*, molecular layer; *B*, granular layer; *C*, white matter; *a*, Purkinje cell; *b*, basket cell, its terminal arborization enveloping the bodies of Purkinje cells; *e*, superficial stellate cell; *f*, Golgi cell; *g*, granule cells with axons ascending and bifurcating at *i*; *h*, mossy fibers; *j, m*, neuroglia cells; *n*, climbing fibers.

The deep cerebellar nuclei

Imbedded in the white matter of each half of the cerebellum are four nuclear masses (Figs. 253, 254). The most medial of these, and phylogenetically the oldest, is the nucleus fastigii placed near the midline in the roof of the fourth ventricle, close and ventral to the lingula and lobulus centralis. It consists of a lateral older portion containing large multipolar cells and a medial newer portion of smaller cells.

The *nucleus dentatus* is the largest of the

definite nucleus only in the mammals and becomes greatly enlarged in man and the anthropoid apes. A dorsomedial older portion may be distinguished from a newer larger ventrolateral portion. The nucleus is composed mainly of large multipolar cells with branching dendrites and high iron content, whose axons acquire a myelin sheath while still in the nucleus and pass out as fibers of the superior cerebellar peduncle. Between these cells are small stellate ones whose axons apparently arborize within the nucleus. Afferent fibers from the Purkinje

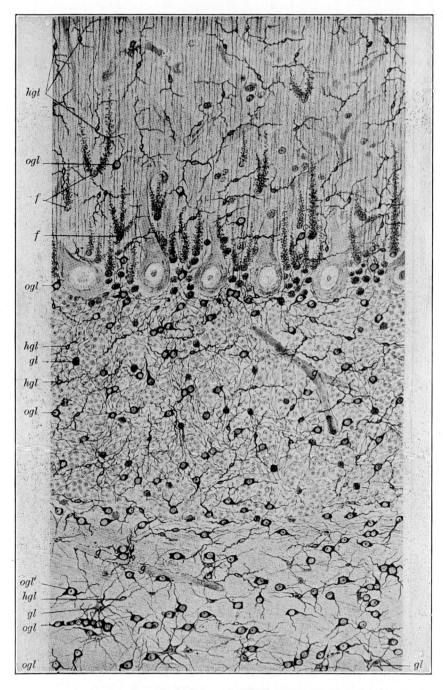

FIG. 252. Arrangement of neuroglia cells in human cerebellar cortex. (Jakob, after A. H. Schröder.)
f, cells of Fañanas; *gl*, astroglia; *hgl*, microglia; *ogl, ogl'*, oligodendroglia

cells enter on the lateral side and form a
dense fiber plexus, the amiculum, around
the nucleus.

The *nucleus emboliformis* is a wedge-
shaped gray mass placed close to the hilus
of the dentate nucleus and often difficult

to delimit from the latter. It is composed of clumps of cells resembling those of the dentate nucleus.

The *nucleus globosus* consists of one or several rounded gray masses lying between

pathways. They project to the vestibular nuclei and reticular formation of the medulla (fastigial, globose), to the large-celled portion of the red nucleus and to the tegmentum of midbrain and pons (globose,

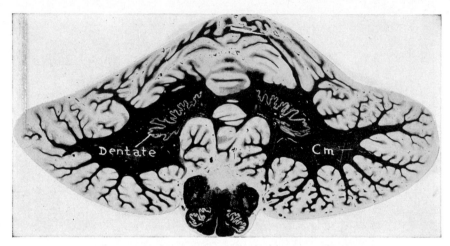

Fig. 253. Transverse section through adult cerebellum and medulla. Weigert's myelin stain. Photograph. *Cm*, corpus medullare

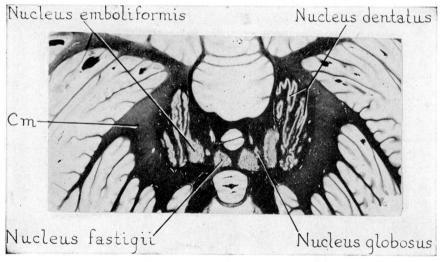

Fig. 254. Horizontal section through adult cerebellum showing corpus medullare and deep nuclei. Weigert's myelin stain. Photograph, slightly retouched. *Cm*, corpus medullare

the fastigial and emboliform nuclei. It likewise contains large and small multipolar cells.

The fastigial, globose and emboliform nuclei, and the dorsomedial part of the dentate nucleus, may be considered paleocerebellar, related to the older cerebellar

emboliform, dentate). The large ventrolateral neocerebellar portion of the dentate nucleus sends fibers to the small-celled part of the red nucleus and to the thalamus from which impulses are projected into the frontal cortex.

Corpus medullare and fiber connections

The corpus medullare is a compact mass of white matter continuous from hemisphere to hemisphere and covered everywhere by the cerebellar cortex. It consists of afferent projection fibers to the cerebellar cortex, efferent projection fibers from the cerebellar cortex and, to a lesser extent, of association fibers connecting the various portions of the cerebellum. Many fibers, afferent, efferent and associative, cross to the other side, the commissural fibers being concentrated in two cerebellar commissures: a posterior commissure in the region of the fastigial nuclei; and an anterior in front of the dentate nuclei.

The corpus medullare is continuous with the three peduncles which connect the cerebellum with the brain stem: the inferior cerebellar peduncle or *corpus restiforme* with the medulla; the middle peduncle or *brachium pontis* with the pons; and the superior cerebellar peduncle or *brachium conjunctivum* with the midbrain. Medially and ventrally, near the roof of the ventricle, the corpus medullare splits into two white lamina, inferior and superior, which separate at an acute angle to form the tent-like roof recess (fastigium) of the fourth ventricle. The inferior lamina is a thin white plate which passes backward over the nodulus as the *inferior* medullary velum and becomes continuous with the tela chorioidea and chorioid plexus of the fourth ventricle, with which it forms the roof of the lower half of that ventricle (Fig. 239). Laterally the inferior medullary velum extends to the flocculi and actually forms the narrow bridge connecting these structures with the nodulus (Fig. 241).

The largest part of the medullary substance is continued into the superior lamina which consists of the three cerebellar peduncles and the superior medullary velum (Fig. 241). The latter is a thin white plate joining the two brachia conjunctiva, and together these structures form the roof and dorsolateral walls of the upper part of the fourth ventricle.

Afferent fibers. The afferent fibers enter the cerebellum through the inferior and middle peduncles.  The former consists of a larger entirely afferent lateral portion, the restiform body, and a smaller medial juxta-restiform portion containing both afferent and efferent fibers primarily concerned with vestibulocerebellar and cerebellovestibular connections.

Entering through the restiform body are: (1) The dorsal spinocerebellar fibers to the cortex of the anterior and posterior vermis (lobulus centralis, culmen, pyramis and uvula) and in part to the simple lobule of the middle lobe. (2) Dorsal external arcuate fibers from the external cuneate nucleus of the same side to the anterior vermis (Mussen). (3) Ventral external arcuate fibers, mainly crossed, from the lateral reticular and arcuate nuclei, perhaps also from the gracile and cuneate nuclei, principally to the anterior vermis. (4) The olivocerebellar fibers which form the largest component of the restiform body. Fibers from the medial portion of the olive and from the accessory olives go to all portions of the vermis, a much stronger component from the larger lateral portion is distributed to the hemispheres. The dorsal part of the olive is related to the superior surface, the ventral to the inferior surface of the cerebellum (Holmes and Stuart). (5) The aberrant ventral spinocerebellar fibers, though not a part of the restiform body, may be included here (Fig. 168). They ascend to the isthmus, then bend around the brachium conjunctivum and enter the cerebellum to terminate in the culmen and lobulus centralis of the anterior vermis, more medially than the dorsal spinocerebellar tract.

All these tracts, except perhaps the olivocerebellar, may be considered as carrying proprioceptive impulses from the body. The function of the olives is not entirely clear. It receives a strong bundle of fibers, the central tegmental tract, from the nucleus ruber and tegmentum of the midbrain, and is connected to the upper cervical portion of the cord by the tract of Helweg. It is highly developed in man and the olivo-cerebellar tract may be part of a newer striato-rubro-cerebellar or cortico-rubro-cerebellar pathway or of both.

to the cortex of the anterior vermis and uvula. Some terminate in the nucleus emboliformis and nucleus dentatus (Winkler). (3) Arcuatofloccular fibers from the arcuate nuclei cross and pass dorsally in the raphé to reach the surface of the ventricle, where as striae cerebellares (striae medullares)

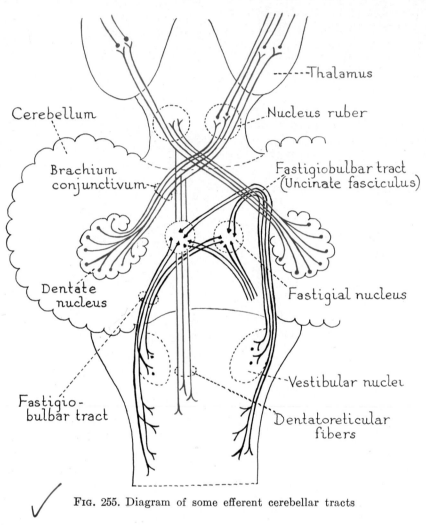

FIG. 255. Diagram of some efferent cerebellar tracts

The afferent fibers entering through the juxtarestiform body include: (1) Direct vestibular root fibers to the nodulus and flocculi, and probably also to the lingula and uvula. (2) Vestibulocerebellar fibers coming mainly from the lateral and superior vestibular nuclei. Most of them go to the nucleus fastigii and nucleus globosus, others

they enter the flocculi (Winkler, Brouwer). (4) Secondary trigeminal and vagal fibers are likewise believed to go to the cerebellum, but their course in man is obscure.

The brachium pontis consists almost entirely of crossed pontocerebellar fibers conveying to the cerebellum impulses from the cerebral cortex (Fig. 256). Corticopontile fibers from the temporal cortex terminate in the caudal, those from the frontal cortex in the oral portion of the pons. The ponto-cerebellar fibers terminate primarily in the ansoparamedian lobules (hemispheres) and probably also in the lobulus medius medi-

the cerebellar cortex are nearly all relayed in the deep nuclei, though a small phylo-genetically old bundle appears to go directly from the flocculi to the vestibular nuclei (flocculovestibular tract). Fibers from the vermis go principally to the fastigial and

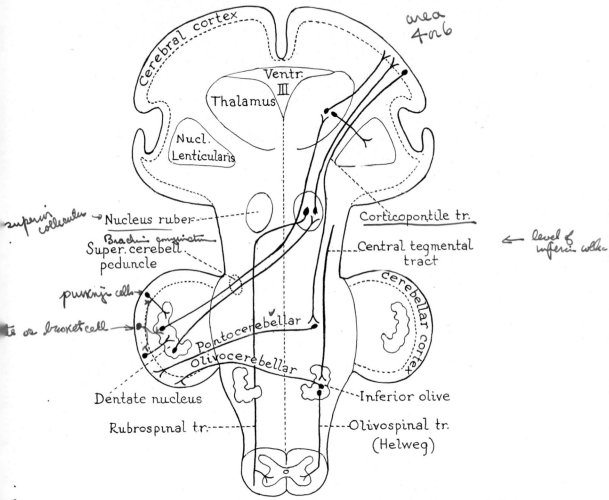

FIG. 256. Diagram of principal afferent and efferent cerebellar connections (largely neocerebellar) with midbrain and forebrain

anus of the middle lobe. The fibers from the oral pontile nuclei go to the inferior cerebellar surface, those from the caudal to the superior surface. According to Wink-ler, both crossed and uncrossed pontile fibers also pass to all parts of the vermis except the nodulus.

Efferent fibers. The efferent fibers from

globose nuclei, those from the hemispheres to the dentate, emboliform and perhaps also the globose nuclei. From the nucleus fas-tigii (and globosus) arise efferent fibers, many of them crossing in the roof, which go principally to the vestibular nuclei, espe-cially the lateral, and the reticular formation of the medulla. These *fastigiobulbar* fibers

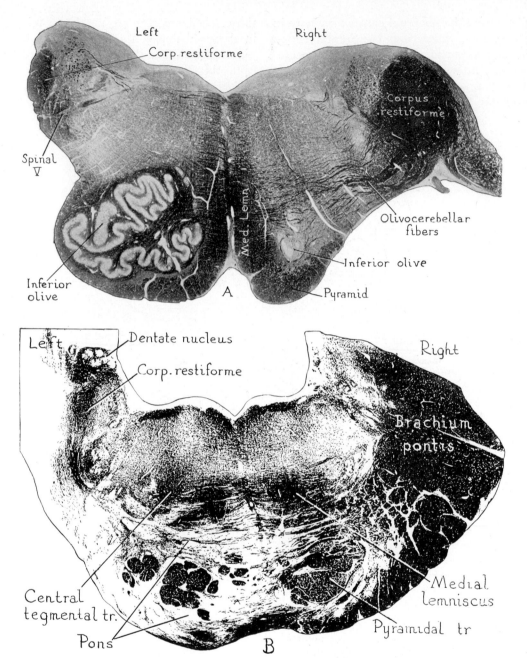

Fig. 257. Transverse section through medulla (*A*) and pons (*B*), from a case in which the left cerebellar hemisphere had failed to develop. Myelin stain. Photograph. See text for discussion

form part of the juxtarestiform body. Some of them pass close to the ventricle and mesial to the dentate nucleus. Others curve around the superior cerebellar peduncle as the *uncinate fasciculus* of Russell (Fig. 255).

The whole system carries cerebellar impulses by way of the vestibular pathways and reticular formation to the muscles especially of the eyes, neck and body.

The brachium conjunctivum which arises

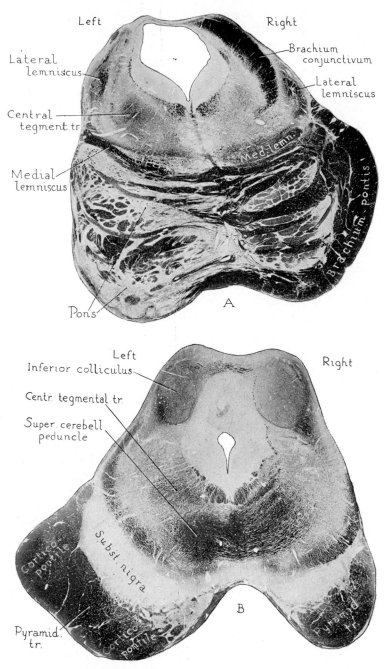

FIG. 258. Transverse section through isthmus (*A*) and midbrain (*B*), from same case as Fig. 257. Myelin stain. Photograph

from the dentate, emboliform and perhaps also the globose nuclei, constitutes the most important efferent fiber system of the cerebellum. Emerging from the hilus of the dentate nucleus, it forms the dorsolateral wall of the upper part of the fourth ventricle, then dips into the pontile tegmentum, and in the region of the inferior colliculi undergoes a practically complete decussation (Figs. 255, 256). The majority of the fibers terminate in the contralateral red nucleus (dentatorubral), related primarily to the small-celled newer portion of that nucleus and to a lesser extent with the large-celled older portion which gives origin to the rubrospinal tract. Another strong component continues upward to end in the lateral ventral nucleus of the thalamus (dentatothalamic). Fibers which go to the subthalamic nucleus (André-Thomas), and perhaps directly to the cerebral cortex have also been described.

Some fibers enter the tegmentum of the midbrain (dentatotegmental) to terminate in the contralateral oculomotor and trochlear nuclei and to contribute perhaps to the medial longitudinal fasciculus. Others detach themselves from the brachium conjunctivum just before and beyond the decussation and descend as crossed and uncrossed fibers in the reticular formation of the pons and medulla.

It is probable that the fibers to the large-celled portion of the red nucleus and to the reticular formation of the midbrain, pons and medulla have their origin in the emboliform and dorsomedial older portion of the dentate nucleus (paleodentatum). They represent an older pathway transmitting cerebellar impulses to the muscles of the head and body by way of the rubrospinal and reticulospinal tracts. The bulk of the superior peduncular fibers represents an extensive newer pathway linking the cerebellar hemispheres with the cerebral cortex and probably also with the striatum (Fig. 256). These fibers arise from the newer and larger ventrolateral part of the dentate nucleus (neodentatum) and are projected on the frontal cortex by way of the nucleus ruber and thalamic nuclei.

Some of the neocerebellar connections in man are especially brought out in Figs. 257, 258. These show sections through the medulla, pons, isthmus and midbrain from a case in which the left cerebellar hemi-

sphere, except the flocculus, had failed to develop (agenesia). With this there was a correlated agenesia of all the afferent and efferent pathways to and from the left cerebellar hemisphere. The spinocerebellar and the vestibular connections were normal, since the vermis and flocculi were intact. On the other hand, the left dentate nucleus was represented by a minute structure (paleodentatum), the right inferior olive greatly reduced (paleo-olive), the right nucleus ruber (not shown) and right pontile nuclei practically absent. As a result, the left restiform body was greatly reduced by absence of olivocerebellar fibers. The left brachium conjunctivum was represented by a few scattered fibers, and the left brachium pontis was entirely absent. Similarly lacking were the right central tegmental tract and the corticopontile tracts, the right pes pedunculi being composed only of pyramidal fibers. A survey of these preparations shows that in man the superior and middle peduncles and the olivocerebellar fibers are practically all crossed.

Blood supply

Each half of the cerebellum is supplied by two inferior and one superior cerebellar arteries going respectively to the inferior and superior surfaces (Fig. 259). The *posterior inferior cerebellar artery* springs from the vertebral artery, runs for a short distance along the medulla oblongata whose dorsolateral portion it supplies and goes to the inferior vermis, especially the uvula and nodulus, also giving branches to the chorioid plexus. The *anterior inferior* cerebellar artery arises from the basilar artery and supplies the pyramis, tuber, flocculi and hemispheral portions of the inferior surface. It also sends branches to the deep portion of the corpus medullare, and according to Shellshear (1922) the dentate nucleus is mainly supplied by this artery. In some cases, the flocculus and portions of the tonsil and biventral lobule may be supplied by an inconstant middle inferior cerebellar artery

(Jakob), (Fig. 259). The *superior cerebellar artery* emerges in back of the oculomotor nerve from the rostral end of the basilar artery. On reaching the cerebellum, it divides into two main branches, a median one for the superior vermis and adjacent lateral portions, and a lateral for the remaining hemispheral portions of the superior surface. From these arteries numerous branches extend deeply into the cerebellum to go to the superior medullary velum,

the hemispheres and flocculi to the lateral, and in part also to the superior petrosal sinuses.

Functional considerations

The cerebellum has been called the "head ganglion" of the proprioceptive system (Sherrington). However, the cerebellum is not concerned with sensation and even in severe cerebellar lesions there is no impairment of the sense of position and movement.

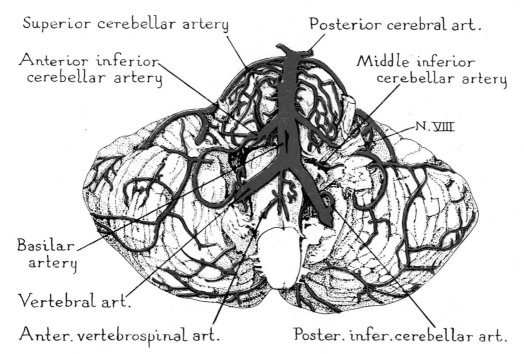

Superior cerebellar artery

Posterior cerebral art.

Anterior inferior cerebellar artery

Middle inferior cerebellar artery

N. VIII

Basilar artery

Vertebral art.

Anter. vertebrospinal art.

Poster. infer. cerebellar art.

FIG. 259. The arterial supply of the human cerebellum. (After Jakob)

middle and superior peduncles, deep portion of the corpus medullare and to the nuclei including probably part of the dentate nucleus. Twigs are also given to the chorioid plexus of the fourth ventricle.

The veins have a course generally similar to the arteries. A superior and an inferior median vein drain the respective portions of the vermis and adjacent regions and the deep cerebellar nuclei, the superior vein terminating in the *vein of Galen*, the inferior in the straight and lateral sinuses. Superior and inferior lateral veins bring blood from

Nor does it send motor impulses for the initiation of movements comparable to those of the motor cerebral cortex. The cerebellum is primarily a neural mechanism regulating and graduating muscular tension states for the proper maintenance of equilibrium and the smooth performance of voluntary movements. Each movement requires the coordinated action (synergy) of a group of muscles. There are the agonists which actually move the part and the antagonists which must give or relax to permit the movement. Associated with these are other synergic or fixating muscles which fix neighboring or even distant joints to the extent needed for the desired movement. The maintenance or changes of posture similarly involve the cooperation of synergically acting muscle groups.

Such synergic units must obviously have a complex reciprocal innervation, receiving both inhibitory and excitatory impulses which effect the alterations in muscular tension needed for any specific movement. While other neural centers are probably involved in this reciprocal innervation, the cerebellum may be regarded as the highest center for its finest automatic regulation. Its function is to furnish optimum tension states for all the muscles both during rest and during activity.

In man injury to the cerebellum or its fiber systems causes hypotonia and certain abnormalities of movement collectively termed *cerebellar asynergia* or *ataxia*. Sensation is normal. In unilateral lesions the symptoms appear on the same side as the injury.

Lesions involving only the vermis and flocculi (paleocerebellum) mainly affect the axial musculature and the bilaterally linked movements used for locomotion and for the maintenance of posture. The patient sways and is generally unsteady when standing, he walks staggeringly or "drunkenly" on a broad base and has a tendency to fall backward. The speech muscles may be affected, resulting in jerky and slurring articulation, the words often shot out with unnecessary force. Nystagmus and abnormal attitudes when present are usually ascribed to injury of the vestibular tracts. Muscle tone is only slightly affected and there is usually no tremor. (*shakes*)

Lesions of the hemispheres (neocerebellum) primarily affect the isolated finer movements of the extremities, i.e., pyramidal movements. The muscles are flabby (*hypotonia*) and tire easily. There are severe disorders of movement (asynergia) expressed in faulty range, direction and force of muscular contraction. Most striking is the inability to gauge distance properly (*dysmetria*), the movements overshooting or falling short of the mark, or erring in direction and passing it by (*past-pointing*). The cerebellar asynergia may be brought out in many tests. When the elbow of a normal man is made to flex against resistance and the arm is suddenly released, overflexion is arrested by the contraction of the triceps. In cerebellar disease this contraction is delayed with resulting uncontrolled flexion which may hit the patient in the face or chest (*rebound phenomenon*). There is inability to execute rapid alternating movements such as pronation and supination of the hand (*adiadochokinesis*), and movements which require simultaneous action at several joints may be broken up into series of successive movements each involving a single joint (*decomposition of movement*). Thus when asked to touch his nose with a finger raised above his head, the patient will first lower his arm and then flex the elbow to reach his nose.

The hypotonia and irregularities of muscular contraction are probably responsible for the coarse tremor in voluntary movements often demonstrable in cerebellar disease (Holmes). It is especially conspicuous and enduring when the dentate nucleus or the superior peduncle is destroyed. Nystagmus, occurring when the eyes are moved laterally, is likewise present in many cases and is similarly explained by the asynergy of the ocular muscles (Holmes).

Phylogenetically the cerebellum first arises as lateral expansions of the vestibular area of the hindbrain, and this vestibular portion still persists, comprising the flocculi and certain parts of the vermis (lingula, nodulus, uvula). Added to this were the centers for the reception of general proprioceptive stimuli from the muscles of the body and head forming the greater part of the cerebellum in lower forms and represented principally by the spinocerebellar portion of the cerebellum (lobulus centralis, culmen,

[margin notes: ataxic gate; projectal speech; middle lobe]

[bottom handwritten note: Tremor of intent → middle lobe damage.]

pyramis, uvula and simple lobule). These older portions (paleocerebellum) are primarily related to equilibrium and the grosser synergic movements of locomotion. The maintenance of equilibrium does not depend on vestibular impulses alone but also on general proprioceptive stimuli, and the vestibular and spinocerebellar components are closely interrelated and difficult to dissociate. On the efferent side the paleocerebellum exerts its influence through the fastigiobulbar (vestibular) fibers of the juxtarestiform body and the older portion of the brachium conjunctivum. The fibers of the latter originate in the globose, emboliform and dorsomedial parts of the dentate nuclei and go to the large-celled portion of the red nucleus and to the reticular formation and motor nuclei of the midbrain, pons and medulla. It has been shown experimentally that stimulation of the anterior lobe inhibits the extensor tonus of the antigravity muscles, and its removal increases the rigidity of decerebrate animals. The flocculi and nodulus are similarly believed to exert an inhibitory influence on vestibular tonus.

With the development of the pallium and the appearance of isolated pyramidal movements, the cerebellum increases in impor-tance, acquiring the massive cortico-ponto-cerebellar connections related to the larger part of the cerebellar hemispheres and the median portion of the middle lobe. Along with this there was the increased development of the dentate nuclei, superior peduncles and red nuclei representing new cerebello-cortical pathways. Thus the neo-cerebellum is characterized by its massive afferent and efferent cortical connections, and functionally is principally concerned with the regulation of pyramidal movements. Hence the dysmetric symptoms of cerebellar disease are well marked only when volitional movement is intact, and are greatly diminished or disappear altogether with destruction of the motor area or pyramidal tract.

How far there is topographical bodily representation in the cerebellum is still an open question. There is some evidence that the neck muscles may have their center in the simple lobule, the arm in the superior, and the leg in the inferior portions of the ansoparamedian lobules. Clinically there is no evidence of functional localization as far as the extremities are concerned, neo-cerebellar lesions producing ipsilateral symptoms in both arm and leg (Holmes).

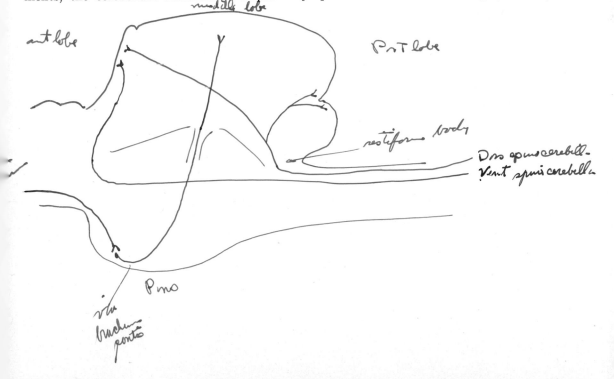

middle lobe
ant lobe
Post lobe
restiform body
Dos spinocerebell.
Vent spini cerebell
Pons
via
brachium
pontis

CHAPTER XVIII

THE DIENCEPHALON AND CORPUS STRIATUM

It has been noted in an earlier chapter that the primordial forebrain differentiates into a rostral portion, the endbrain or telencephalon, and a caudal portion, the interbrain or diencephalon. The endbrain arises as a hollow unpaired bud from the dorsal anterior wall of the forebrain, which then begins to bulge laterally and expands into the two hemispheric vesicles connected to each other by the lamina terminalis and the most rostral portion of the third ventricle which here communicates with the hemispheric cavities or lateral ventricles by the large interventricular foramina (Fig. 16). These two structures, lamina terminalis and the most rostral portion of the third ventricle, therefore belong to the end brain and constitute the median telencephalon as distinguished from the lateral telencephalon or cerebral hemispheres. All the forebrain structures caudal to the interventricular foramina belong to the diencephalon.

The hemispheric vesicles expand rapidly in all directions. Their medial surfaces at first extend backward along the lateral surfaces of the diencephalon (Figs. 16, 10), separated from the latter on each side by the hemispheric sulcus which progressively deepens with the growth of the hemisphere. Soon they expand dorsally and cover the roof of the diencephalon as well, so that the dorsal surface of the latter is now hidden from view and is separated from the overlying hemisphere by the *transverse cerebral fissure* formed by the folding back of the telencephalon. Into this fissure extends a double fold of pia mater, the *velum interpositum*, the dorsal layer of which is closely applied to the basal surface of the hemisphere, the ventral layer forming the pial investment of the diencephalic roof. The walls of the diencephalon become tremen-

dously thickened while the floor and especially the roof plate remain relatively thin. The dorsal portion especially of each wall through the development of numerous nuclear masses constituting the thalamus, becomes so massive that it now furnishes most of the dorsal surface of the diencephalon (Figs. 260, 264). The originally large cavity of the diencephalon becomes reduced to the cleft-like third ventricle whose thin roof is formed by a layer of ependymal cells invested by richly vascular pial tissue from the velum interpositum, the two together constituting the *tela chorioidea* of the third ventricle. From the tela a double row of vascular tufts, invaginated along the median plane, projects into the ventricle forming its *chorioid plexus*. The plexus extends from the most caudal portion of the roof to the interventricular foramen where it becomes continuous with the chorioid plexuses of the lateral ventricles.

The hemispheric vesicles give rise to all the main parts of the telencephalon: the *olfactory lobes* or *rhinencephalon*, the large *pallium* or *cerebral cortex*, and a number of deep lying gray masses or *basal ganglia* comprising the *corpus striatum*, *amygdaloid nucleus* and *claustrum* (Fig. 292). These ganglia, especially the corpus striatum are structurally so closely related to the diencephalon that it seems desirable to discuss them at this point, though actually they are parts of the endbrain. The corpus striatum develops as a thickening in that part of the hemispheric wall which lies adjacent to the lateral surface of the diencephalon i.e. the fundus region of the hemispheric sulcus where the endbrain originally evaginated from the primitive forebrain (Fig. 16). As the corpus striatum and diencephalic wall increase in thickness they gradually approach each other and finally fuse, the zone of junction marked by a longitudinal groove, the *terminal* or *semicircular sulcus*, in which there is an undivided cellular mass, but during further development it becomes perforated by fibers which pass to and from the cerebral

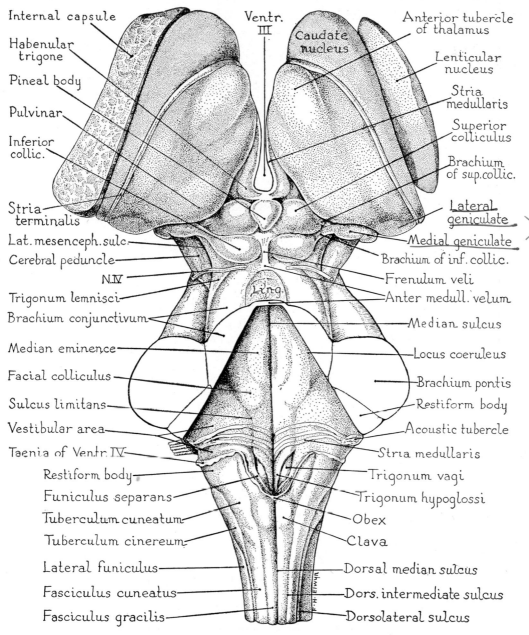

Internal capsule
Habenular trigone
Pineal body
Pulvinar
Inferior collic.
Ventr. III
Caudate nucleus
Anterior tubercle of thalamus
Lenticular nucleus
Stria medullaris
Superior colliculus
Brachium of sup. collic.

Stria terminalis
Lat. mesenceph. sulc.
Cerebral peduncle
N. IV
Trigonum lemnisci
Brachium conjunctivum
Median eminence
Facial colliculus
Sulcus limitans
Vestibular area
Taenia of Ventr. IV
Restiform body
Funiculus separans
Tuberculum cuneatum
Tuberculum cinereum
Lateral funiculus
Fasciculus cuneatus
Fasciculus gracilis

Ling.

Lateral geniculate
Medial geniculate
Brachium of inf. collic.
Frenulum veli
Anter medull. velum
Median sulcus
Locus coeruleus
Brachium pontis
Restiform body
Acoustic tubercle
Stria medullaris
Trigonum vagi
Trigonum hypoglossi
Obex
Clava
Dorsal median sulcus
Dors. intermediate sulcus
Dorsolateral sulcus

Meta Thalmus

Fig. 260. Dorsal view of the brain stem. *Ling.*, lingula

later found a fiber bundle known as the *stria terminalis* or *stria semicircularis* (Figs. 260, 15). At first the corpus striatum appears as cortex. These fibers increase in number and finally form a massive bundle, the *internal capsule*, containing all the projection fibers connecting the pallium with the brain stem and spinal cord. This capsule divides the corpus striatum into two nuclear masses, a medial *caudate nucleus* and a lateral *lenticular* nucleus (Fig. 260). The division is incom-

cle forming part of its lateral wall. Thus the internal capsule is flanked laterally by the lenticular nucleus, medially by the diencephalon and the caudate nucleus (Figs. 263, 264).

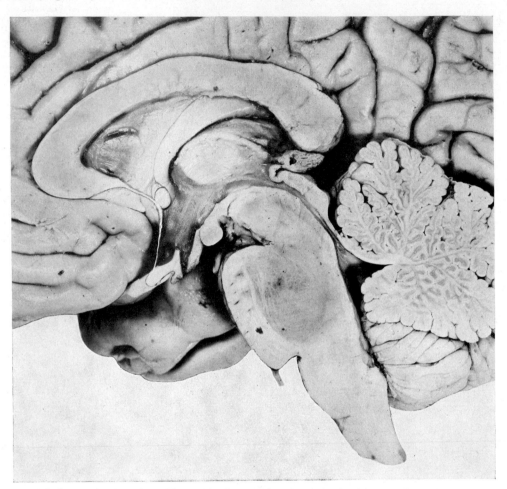

Fig. 261. Median sagittal section of human brain stem (portion of brain shown in Fig. 162). Photograph. For identification of structures see Fig. 262

plete since ventrally and anteriorly the caudate and lenticular nuclei retain their continuity (Fig. 293). The caudate nucleus is closely apposed to the thalamus, its expanded cephalic portion or *head* projecting rostrally beyond the latter, its attenuated caudal portion or tail extending along the entire dorsolateral border of the thalamus (Fig. 260). Throughout its length the caudate nucleus projects into the lateral ventri-

THE DIENCEPHALON

General structure. The diencephalon is composed of a larger dorsal and a smaller ventral portion, marked off from each other on the ventricular surface by a shallow longitudinal groove, the *hypothalamic sulcus*, extending from the interventricular foramen to the iter (Fig. 262). The dorsal portion comprises the massive *thalamus* and certain roof structures collectively known as the *epithalamus.* The ventral portion is composed of the medial *hypothalamus* lying close to the ventricle and a deeper lateral part, the *subthalamus or ventral thalamus*, which can only be seen in sections of the diencephalon (Fig. 264).

The thalamus which forms the great bulk of the interbrain is an elongated somewhat egg-shaped ganglionic mass set obliquely above the midbrain. The narrower cephalic

brachium, and lateral to this the shallower elongated swelling of the *lateral geniculate* body, also largely hidden by the overhanging pulvinar (Fig. 260). Medial and lateral geniculate bodies are often spoken of as the *metathalamus.*

The dorsal and medial surfaces of the thalamus are free, but ventrally and laterally it fuses with adjacent structures, ventrally with the subthalamus, laterally with

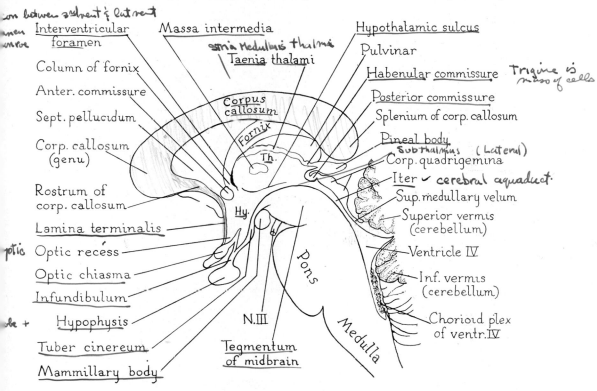

FIG. 262. Median sagittal section of brain stem. *Hy,* hypothalamus; *Th,* thalamus

portions of the two thalami lie close together near the midline, the stouter caudal portions lie laterally and are separated by a wide space containing the superior colliculi. Rostrally each thalamus shows an ovoid swelling, the *anterior tubercle,* caused by the subjacent anterior thalamic nucleus. Caudally a larger prominence, the *pulvinar,* projects over the dorsolateral surface of the midbrain. Springing from the ventral surface of the pulvinar is the *medial geniculate body* connected to the inferior quadrigeminal

the internal capsule and caudate nucleus (Fig. 264). The free dorsal surface is everywhere covered by a thin plate of fibers, the *stratum zonale,* which gives it a whitish appearance, and is laterally marked off from the caudate nucleus by the *terminal* or *semicircular* sulcus in which is lodged the terminal (thalamostriate) vein and a slender fiber bundle, the *stria terminalis* (*stria semicircularis*). A shallow diagonal groove, the chorioid sulcus, divides the surface into a medial and a lateral zone (Fig. 263). The larger medial area forms the floor of the transverse cerebral fissure, separated by a pial fold from the overlying corpus callosum and fornix of the hemispheres. The narrower lateral strip forms part of the floor of the lateral ventricle which has secondarily infringed on the dorsal surface of the thalamus. The ependymal epithelium covering this lateral portion is known as the *lamina affixa*, to the medial border of which is attached the

a triangular field, the *trigonum habenulae*, beneath which lies the habenular ganglion. The two trigones are connected by a white band, the habenular commissure, to the caudal border of which is attached the cone-shaped *pineal body* or *epiphysis* tucked in between the superior colliculi. Stretched out between the two striae medullares is the thin roof of the third ventricle from which vascular tufts covered by ependymal epithe-

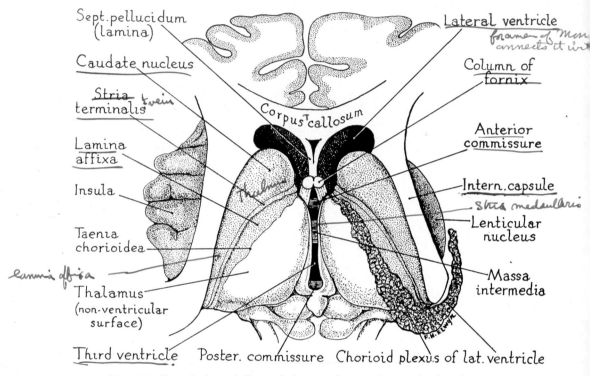

Sept. pellucidum (lamina)
Caudate nucleus
Stria terminalis (t. vein)
Lamina affixa
Insula
Taenia chorioidea
lamina affixa
Thalamus (non-ventricular surface)
Lateral ventricle
foramen of Mon connects it wi
Column of fornix
Corpus callosum
Thalamus
Anterior commissure
Intern. capsule
stria medullaris
Lenticular nucleus
Massa intermedia
Third ventricle   Poster. commissure   Chorioid plexus of lat. ventricle

FIG. 263. Dorsal view of diencephalon, caudate nucleus and related structures

chorioid plexus of the lateral ventricle (Figs. 263, 264).

The medial or ventricular surfaces of the thalami extend ventrally to the hypothalamic sulcus. In their middle regions the two surfaces approach each other closely and in most cases fuse to form a gray bridge of variable extent, the *massa intermedia* (Fig. 263). At the junction of the medial and dorsal surfaces a whitish fiber stripe, the *stria medullaris*, extends along the edge of the ventricular roof, and broadens caudally into

lium project into the ventricle as its chorioid plexus (Fig. 264). When the thin roof is removed the torn edge of attachment to the stout thalamic wall appears as a narrow seam, the *taenia thalami*, which in its lateral portion contains the stria medullaris. Caudally the taenia of each side continues over the habenular trigone and fuses with its mate on the dorsal surface of the pineal gland.

The cavity of the interbrain is the cleft-like third ventricle whose most cephalic portion extends into the endbrain. Caudally it empties into the cerebral aqueduct, rostrally it communicates on each side with the lateral ventricle of the hemisphere by a narrow oval opening, the *interventricular foramen*. The relations of the ventricle are best seen in a medial sagittal section (Figs. 261, 262). Laterally it is bounded by the thick diencephalic walls, divided into a dorsal thalamic and a ventral hypothalamic portion by the

newer parts of the pallium. A small portion of the rostral wall is also formed by the fornix, a large fiber bundle which curves ventrally over the anterior border of the thalamus and perforates the hypothalamic region (Fig. 265). It lies immediately in front of the interventricular foramen.

The thin roof, formed by the chorioid tela and plexus, extends to the dorsal surface of the pineal body into which projects a spur of

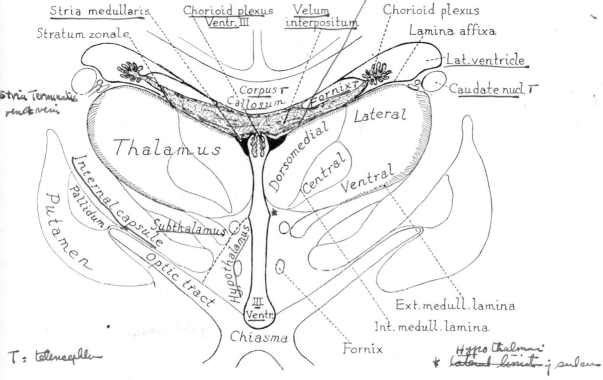

Fig. 264. Transverse section through diencephalon and adjacent structures, semischematic

hypothalamic sulcus which extends from the interventricular foramen to the iter. Rostrally it is bounded by the thin *lamina terminalis* which ascends dorsally to the *anterior commissure* where it becomes continuous with the rostral lamina of the corpus callosum. The anterior commissure is an ancient fiber bundle connecting the older olfactory regions of the two hemispheres. The corpus callosum is the massive commissure connecting the more extensive phylogenetically

the ventricle, the *pineal recess*. Below this recess the posterior commissure marks the junction of the third ventricle and cerebral aqueduct. The floor of the ventricle is formed by the basal structures of the hypothalamus, including the *optic chiasma* separated from the lamina terminalis by the *optic recess*, the *tuber cinereum* and the *mammillary bodies*. The most caudal part of the floor is bounded by the cephalic portion of the midbrain tegmentum. From the tuber

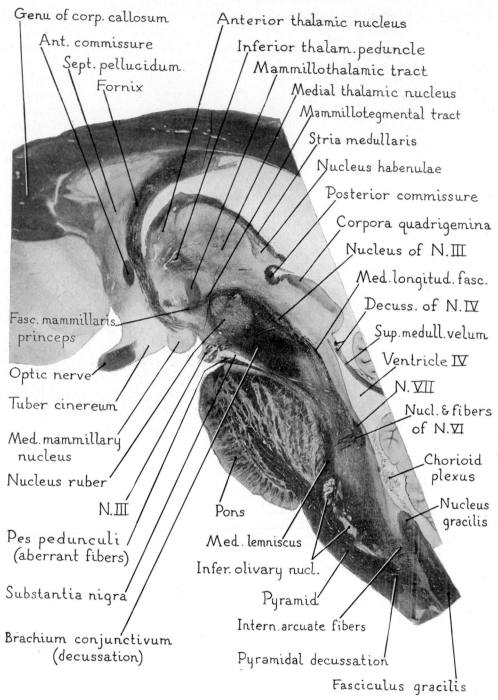

Genu of corp. callosum
Ant. commissure
Sept. pellucidum.
Fornix

Anterior thalamic nucleus
Inferior thalam. peduncle
Mammillothalamic tract
Medial thalamic nucleus
Mammillotegmental tract
Stria medullaris
Nucleus habenulae
Posterior commissure
Corpora quadrigemina
Nucleus of N.III
Med. longitud. fasc.
Decuss. of N.IV
Sup. medull. velum
Ventricle IV
N. VII
Nucl. & fibers of N.VI
Chorioid plexus
Nucleus gracilis

Fasc. mammillaris princeps
Optic nerve
Tuber cinereum
Med. mammillary nucleus
Nucleus ruber
N.III
Pes pedunculi (aberrant fibers)
Substantia nigra
Brachium conjunctivum (decussation)

Pons
Med. lemniscus
Infer. olivary nucl.
Pyramid
Intern. arcuate fibers
Pyramidal decussation
Fasciculus gracilis

FIG. 265. Sagittal section of brain stem through pillar of fornix and root of third nerve. Weigert's myelin stain. Photograph

cinereum a funnel-shaped stalk, the *infundib-ulum* extends to the posterior lobe of the *hypophysis* or *pituitary body*. Into it ex-tends a spur of the third ventricle, the *infundibular recess*.

Internal structure. The diencephalon,

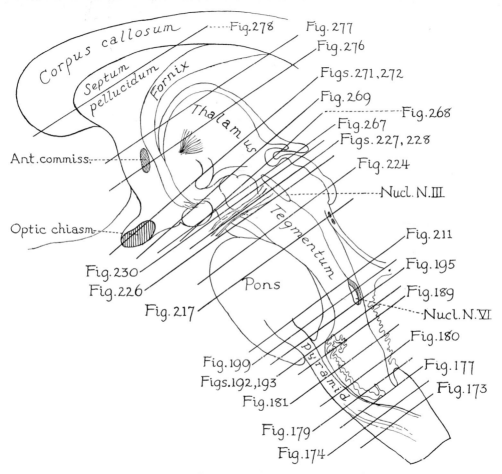

Corpus callosum
Septum pellucidum
Fornix
Thalamus
Ant. commiss.
Optic chiasm
Tegmentum
Pons
Pyramid

Fig. 278
Fig. 277
Fig. 276
Figs. 271, 272
Fig. 269
Fig. 268
Fig. 267
Figs. 227, 228
Fig. 224
Nucl. N. III
Fig. 211
Fig. 195
Fig. 189
Nucl. N. VI
Fig. 180
Fig. 177
Fig. 173
Fig. 230
Fig. 226
Fig. 217
Fig. 199
Figs. 192, 193
Fig. 181
Fig. 179
Fig. 174

NOTE: Refer to this figure for correct references to other figures in the book

especially its thalamic portion, is composed of numerous nuclei and fiber tracts disposed spatially in a very complex manner. Before attempting a significant discussion of these structures it is essential to become acquainted with their actual location, extent

Section through rostral portion of midbrain near its junction with the thalamus
(Figs. 267, 266)

To the midbrain structures are now added several nuclei of the thalamus including the *medial* and *lateral geniculate bodies* and the

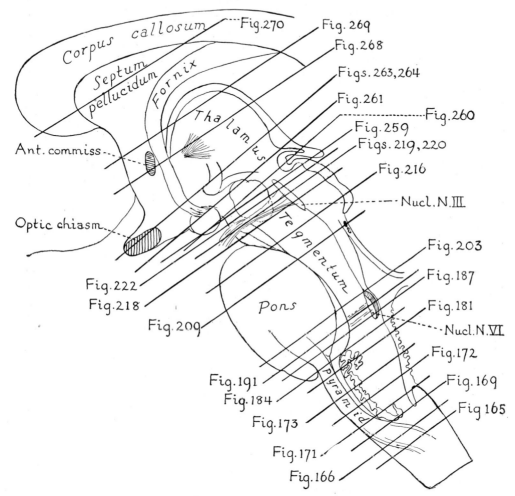

FIG. 266. Outline of paramedian sagittal section of brain stem, showing level and plane of the transverse sections of the figures indicated.   For identification of structures see Fig. 265

and relationship. This will be done by a number of microphotographs representing a graded series of transverse sections extending from the uppermost portion of the midbrain through the entire extent of the diencephalon and corpus striatum. The level and plane of each section are given in Fig. 266.

pulvinar, and the posterior (retrolenticular) portion of the *internal capsule*. The caudal tip of the pineal gland is lying between the superior colliculi, while in the interpeduncular space are seen the caudal portions of the mammillary bodies. From the thalamic nuclei fibers are passing laterally to the internal capsule through which they are dis-

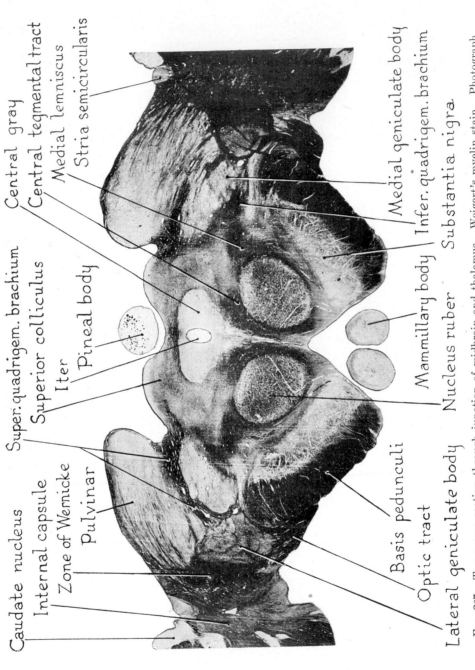

Central gray
Central tegmental tract
Medial lemniscus
Stria semicircularis

Super. quadrigem. brachium
Superior colliculus
Iter
Pineal body

Caudate nucleus
Internal capsule
Zone of Wernicke
Pulvinar

Medial geniculate body
Infer. quadrigem. brachium
Substantia nigra

Mammillary body
Nucleus ruber

Basis pedunculi
Optic tract
Lateral geniculate body

FIG. 267. Transverse section through junction of midbrain and thalamus. Weigert's myelin stain. Photograph

tributed to various portions of the pallium (cerebral cortex). Many of these arise in the thalamus and go to the cortex, others arise in the cortex and end in the thalamus. These thalamocortical and corticothalamic fibers constitute the *thalamic radiations*. Lateral to the pulvinar is the tail of the caudate nucleus separated from the former by the *semicircular sulcus* (terminal sulcus).

The fibers of the optic tract are entering the ventral surface of the lateral geniculate body, in which most of them terminate. Some optic fibers however continue beyond the lateral geniculate body to form the *superior quadrigeminal brachium* which terminates in the optic stratum of the superior colliculi and in the pretectal area, mediating reflex adjustment of eye, neck and perhaps body muscles to optic stimulation. From the lateral geniculate body fibers pass laterally into the internal capsule, representing the beginning of the geniculocalcarine tract (optic radiation) to the occipital cortex, thereby completing the visual pathway.

Internal to the lateral geniculate body is the medial geniculate body in which terminate the fibers of the inferior quadrigeminal brachium. From its lateral surface fibers gather to form the geniculotemporal tract (auditory radiation) which enters the internal capsule and is projected to the temporal cortex, thus completing the auditory pathway.

The pulvinar is a large nuclear mass lying dorsal to the medial geniculate body. Its dorsal surface is covered by a thin plate of fibers, the *stratum zonale*. Fibers passing laterally from the nucleus contribute to the retrolenticular portion of the internal capsule and are distributed to the posterior parietal and occipitotemporal cortex. The innermost portion of the internal capsule wedging in between the pulvinar and lateral geniculate body, forms a triangular area, the *field of Wernicke*, in which there is a mixture of transverse and longitudinal fibers (Fig. 267). The field is composed mainly of fibers of the optic radiation which after leaving the lat-

eral geniculate body run forward for a distance and then loop backward to reach the occipital cortex. Intermingled with these are fibers from the pulvinar and perhaps also from the medial geniculate bodies.

In the midbrain portion the fibers of the third nerve have practically disappeared, but the rostral portions of the oculomotor nucleus are still present, mainly the small celled Edinger-Westphal nucleus. The large nucleus ruber is surrounded by a fibrous capsule. Within the nucleus are seen fibers of the superior cerebellar peduncle, while the capsular fibers mainly represent connections of the nucleus ruber with the thalamus and pallium. Lateral to the nucleus ruber are the medial lemniscus and the spinothalamic tract, while the inferior quadrigeminal brachium is terminating in the medial geniculate body. The reticular formation is greatly reduced, as is also the central tegmental tract. The small medial longitudinal and predorsal fasciculi are difficult to distinguish from the medial capsule of the red nucleus.

The pes pedunculi occupies the same position and dorsal to it is the diminished substantia nigra containing many myelinated fiber bundles. These include pallidonigral and strionigral fibers from the corpus striatum, and subthalamonigral from the subthalamus. Others may be pallionigral fibers entering from the pes, and efferent fibers from the substantia nigra going to the tegmentum of the midbrain and pons.

Section through junction of midbrain and thalamus passing through posterior commissure (Fig. 268)

The plane of the section is such (Fig. 266) that ventrally the same structures are seen as in Fig. 267, while dorsally the section passes through a more rostral level. The iter is expanding into the deeper third ventricle whose roof is here formed by the posterior commissure which marks the boundary between midbrain and interbrain. Above the commissure is the stalk of the pineal body enclosing the pineal recess of the third ventricle. The superior colliculi have disappeared as have the oculomotor nuclei and fibers, though possibly the anterior median nucleus may still be present in the light staining area below the ventricle. In close

Lateral to the posterior commissure is the pretectal area, transitional between the superior colliculus and pulvinar of the thalamus. It is believed to be the center for the pupillary reflex, receiving fibers from the optic tract and lateral geniculate body, and sending fibers to the Edinger-Westphal

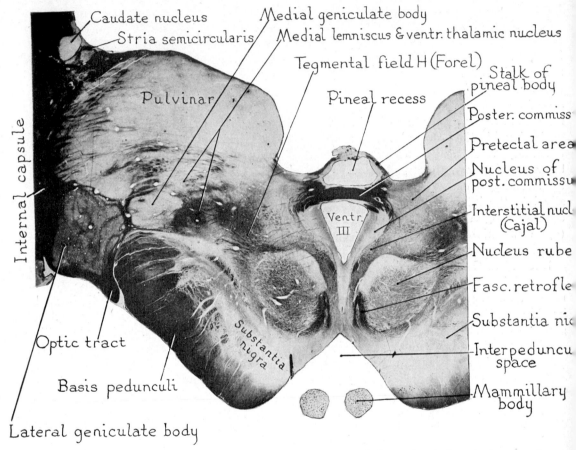

FIG. 268. Transverse section through caudal border of diencephalon at level of posterior commissure. Weigert's myelin stain. Photograph

contact with the dorsomedial surface of the red nucleus is the small *interstitial nucleus*, and dorsal to this the *nucleus of the posterior commissure* (nucleus of Darkschewitsch), practically placed within the central gray substance. Since these are the most rostral nuclei contributing to the medial longitudinal fasciculus, that already greatly diminished bundle will no longer be present above this level.

nucleus. The structure and connections of the pretectal area and posterior commissure have been discussed in a previous chapter (p. 263).

The medial portion of the nucleus ruber is traversed by a vertical fiber bundle known as the *fasciculus retroflexus* or *habenulopeduncular tract*. The fibers arise from the *habenular nucleus* situated at a somewhat more rostral level and pass backward and downward to end in the interpeduncular nucleus of the midbrain. The tract is a link in a reflex pathway connecting the olfactory areas of the brain with some of the motor nuclei of the brainstem (Fig. 270).

The medial lemniscus, spinothalamic and secondary trigeminal tracts are spreading out diffusely, about to terminate in the ventral thalamic nuclei from which they are projected to the cerebral cortex. The capsular fibers of the red nucleus are likewise changing from a longitudinal to a transverse direction and now form a radiating bundle extending from the dorsolateral surface of the nucleus ruber toward the ventral portion of the thalamus. This is the *tegmental field of Forel* (field H) mainly composed at this level of fibers connecting the red nucleus with the thalamus and pallium. Cells scattered among the fibers and especially along the dorsal surface of the field, constitute the *nucleus of the field of Forel* which may be regarded as a continuation of the mesencephalic reticular formation (Fig. 234)

The pulvinar is larger, the medial geniculate body somewhat reduced. From both of these nuclei and from the lateral geniculate as well, fibers stream as thalamic radiations into the internal capsule. In the groove between the ventricular surfaces of the caudate nucleus and the thalamus, lies a bundle of fibers known as the *stria semicircularis* (stria terminalis, stria cornea). It represents an olfactory connection to be discussed later.

Section of interbrain through habenular ganglion and infundibulum
(Figs. 269, 265)

The region of the interpeduncular space is now occupied by two rounded nuclear masses, the *mammillary bodies*, below which is seen the tuber cinereum, infundibular recess of the third ventricle and infundibulum. All these structures belong to the hypothalamus. Each mammillary body consists of a larger *medial nucleus* and a smaller lateral portion known as the *nucleus*

intercalatus (lateral nucleus of Le Gros Clark, intermediate nucleus). The mammillary body receives olfactomammillary fibers from the basal olfactory areas of the brain and corticomammillary fibers by way of the fornix from the hippocampal cortex (Figs. 270, 265). It also receives collaterals or terminals from the medial lemniscus and other sensory ascending tracts, these fibers forming the *peduncle* of the mammillary body (Fig. 270). From the mammillary body arises a considerable bundle of fibers, the *fasciculus mammillaris princeps*, which splits into two tracts. The larger *mammillothalamic tract* or *bundle of Vicq d'Azyr* passes diagonally upward and forward to terminate in the anterior nucleus of the thalamus. The smaller *mammillotegmental tract* curves caudally and goes to the tegmental nuclei of the midbrain (Fig. 270).

The third ventricle has deepened. The habenular ganglia or nuclei are two small gray masses forming triangular eminences on the medial surface of the thalamus. The thin roof of the ventricle extending between the habenulae has been removed, its torn margin of attachment on each side constituting the *taenia thalami* within which may be seen a transversely cut fiber bundle, the *stria medullaris*. The habenular ganglion receives fibers from the basal olfactory nuclei and from the hippocampal cortex by way of this bundle, some fibers crossing to the opposite ganglion in the slender *habenular commissure* (not shown in the section). The axons of the habenular cells form the fasciculus retroflexus which passes ventrally and caudally, perforates the medial portion of the red nucleus, and as already stated, terminates in the interpeduncular nucleus.

The diminished substantia nigra is diffusely infiltrating the medial portion of the pes pedunculi, its former area now occupied by an elliptic or lens-shaped gray mass, the *subthalamic nucleus (corpus subthalamicum)*, closely applied to the inner surface of the pes. Many fibers are in relation with this nucleus. They arise primarily from the

globus pallidus of the corpus striatum situated at a somewhat higher level, traverse the
pes pedunculi as perforating fibers and in
part terminate directly in the subthalamic
nucleus (pallidosubthalamic). Others continue over the nucleus, forming its dorsal
capsule, and together with fibers arising
within the nucleus itself pass medially to

dorsolaterally by the tegmental field of
Forel. Between the dorsal capsule of the
subthalamic nucleus and the tegmental field
is a narrow band of gray matter known as
the *zona incerta*. Like the nucleus of the
field of Forel it may be regarded as a continuation of the reticular formation (Figs.
271, 272).

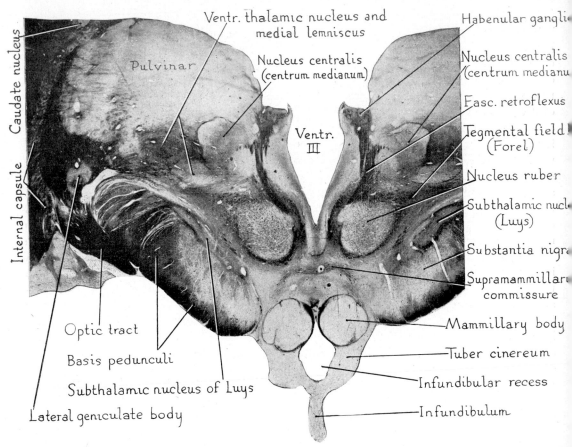

FIG. 269. Transverse section of diencephalon through habenular ganglion and infundibulum. Weigert's
myelin stain. Photograph

terminate in the substantia nigra, nucleus
ruber and reticular formation of the midbrain. Some cross to the opposite side
through the slender *supramammillary* or
posterior hypothalamic decussation and end
in the contralateral subthalamic nucleus or
reach the substantia nigra and red nucleus
of the opposite side.

The nucleus ruber is smaller and flanked

The thalamus is large. The pulvinar has
reached its greatest extent and may perhaps
already represent the lateral thalamic nucleus with which the pulvinar is rostrally
continuous. Ventral to this are the ventral
thalamic nuclei and the round *central* or
centromedian nucleus, the latter sharply delimited by a thin fibrous capsule. Within
the ventral nuclei are terminating the fibers

of the medial lemniscus, spinothalamic and secondary trigeminal tracts. The medial geniculate body has disappeared and the lateral geniculate is greatly reduced. From the now isolated optic tract a detached slender bundle, the transverse peduncular tract, is curving around the lateral margin of the pes to become lost in the subthalamic area.

laterally by the large lenticular nucleus. The latter shows an outer lighter staining portion, the *putamen*, in which there are few myelinated fibers, and an inner hemispherical portion rich in myelinated fibers and known as the *globus pallidus*. The two are separated by a sheath of fibers constituting the external medullary lamina, and the globus pallidus is itself broken up into several

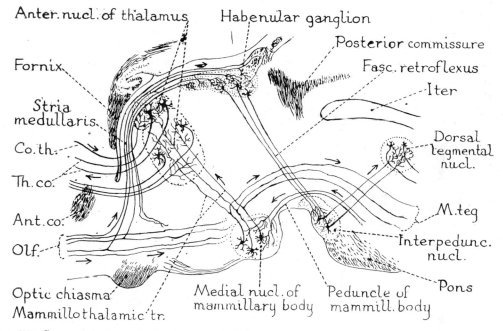

Fig. 270. Some of the important afferent and efferent connections of the mammillary body, habenular ganglion and anterior nucleus of the thalamus. (After Cajal.) *Ant.co.*, anterior commissure; *Co.th.*, corticothalamic fiber; *M.teg.*, mammillotegmental tract (tegmental tract of Gudden); *Olf.*, fibers from basal olfactory area (olfactohabenular, olfactohypothalamic).

Sections through interbrain and basal ganglia at level of optic chiasma
(Figs. 271, 272, 266)

These sections pass through the deepest part of the diencephalon, showing all its main portions: thalamus, hypothalamus and subthalamus. The third ventricle cuts into the optic chiasma, forming its optic recess (Fig. 272), and on each side a groove on the ventricular surface, the *hypothalamic sulcus*, separates the dorsal thalamus from the hypothalamus. The internal capsule is now represented by its lenticulothalamic portion, being flanked medially by the thalamus, and

segments by the internal medullary laminae (Fig. 271). From the dorsal surface of the putamen incomplete gray bridges extend across the internal capsule toward the caudate nucleus and in more rostral sections the two actually become continuous with each other (Figs. 276, 277). The putamen and caudate nucleus are similar in structure and represent the phylogenetically newer part or *neostriatum*, the globus pallidus is the *paleostriatum* more nearly equivalent to the structure found in lower vertebrates. There is a tendency to call the globus pallidus the *pallidum* and reserve the term *striatum* to

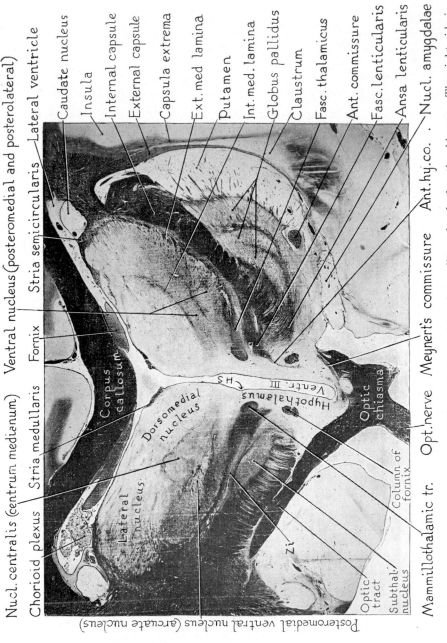

Nucl. centralis (centrum medianum)   Ventral nucleus (posteromedial and posterolateral)

Chorioid plexus   Stria medullaris   Fornix   Stria semicircularis   Lateral ventricle

Caudate nucleus

Insula

Internal capsule

External capsule

Capsula extrema

Ext. med. lamina

Putamen

Int. med. lamina

Globus pallidus

Claustrum

Fasc. thalamicus

Ant. commissure

Fasc. lenticularis

Ansa lenticularis

Nucl. amygdalae

Ant. hy. co.

Meynert's commissure

Opt. nerve

Mammillothalamic tr.

Corpus callosum

Dorsomedial nucleus

Lateral nucleus

Optic tract

Subthal. nucleus

Column of fornix

Zi

Hypothalamus   Ventr. III   HS

Optic chiasma

Posteromedial ventral nucleus (arcuate nucleus)

Fig. 271. Transverse section through diencephalon and basal ganglia at level of optic chiasma. The right side is higher than the left. Weigert's myelin stain. Photograph. *Ant.hy.co.*, anterior hypothalamic commissure; *Hs*, hypothalamic sulcus; *Zi*, zona incerta.

the putamen and caudate nucleus. The latter is composed mainly of small spindle-shaped or rounded cells among which are scattered relatively few larger multipolar ones. The axons of the small cells terminate within the striatum itself, those of the larger ones probably end in the pallidum. The globus pallidus is composed almost entirely of large multipolar cells of the "motor" type whose axons form the efferent fiber systems of the corpus striatum.

The fibers of the optic nerve are partially decussating in the optic chiasma beyond which the continuation of the optic fibers is known as the optic tract. Dorsal to the optic chiasma are usually seen several fine bundles of crossing fibers constituting the hypothalamic decussations. The stoutest of these is the *dorsal supraoptic decussation* or *commissure of Meynert* composed mainly of fibers from the globus pallidus to the sub-thalamic nucleus and zona incerta. Dorsal to this and somewhat more rostrally is the slender *anterior hypothalamic decussation* (Ganser's commissure) whose composition is not fully known (Fig. 273). In part it consists of pallidohypothalamic fibers to several hypothalamic nuclei, in part it prob-ably connects the hypothalamic regions of the two sides. A third bundle, insignificant in man, is the *ventral supraoptic decussation* or *Gudden's commissure* which lies closely applied to the dorsal surface of the optic chiasma and optic tract and is difficult to distinguish from these structures. Some maintain that this bundle is absent in man. It apparently belongs to the auditory path-way since it can be traced on each side to the medial geniculate body. Some of the fibers are believed to connect the geniculate body with the inferior colliculus and nucleus of the lateral lemniscus.

The thalamus is large, its dorsal surface covered by the stratum zonale, and at the junction of the dorsal and medial thalamic surfaces are the transversely cut striae me-dullares (taeniae thalami) which terminate caudally in the habenular ganglia. The thalamus is now divided into a medial and a lateral portion by a delicate band of obliquely cut fibers, the *internal medullary lamina* (Figs. 271, 264). In the lateral por-tion may be distinguished a ventral and a lateral (dorsal) nuclear mass. The ventral nuclear mass extends the whole length of the thalamus and is usually subdivided into three nuclei: a caudal or *posterior ventral*, an intermediate or *lateral ventral*, and a rostral or *anterior ventral*. The posterior ventral which is cut in these sections shows an ex-ternal segment, the *posterolateral ventral nucleus*, and an internal one, the *posterome-dial ventral nucleus*, also known as the *arcuate* or *semilunar nucleus* (Fig. 271). These two portions of the posterior ventral nucleus form the thalamic end station for the medial lemniscus, spinothalamic and secondary trigeminal tracts. The central (centrome-dian) nucleus if still present lies wedged between the medial and ventral nuclei.

Along the outer border of the thalamus fibers accumulate to form the *external medul-lary lamina* which separates the thalamus from the internal capsule. Cells lying between and external to these fibers form a gray stripe, the *reticular nucleus*, which may be regarded as the detached outer rim of the lateral nuclear mass. Most of these fibers represent thalamic radiations which enter the internal capsule and are distributed to the cortex. Some however go to the caudate nucleus or traverse the internal capsule to terminate in the putamen of the lenticular nucleus, representing thalamostriate connec-tions. From the caudate nucleus also fibers cross the internal capsule in a dorsoventral direction and enter the lenticular nucleus, most of them passing medial to the putamen in the outer medullary lamina to terminate in the globus pallidus. The latter likewise receives numerous fibers directly from the putamen. The external medullary layer of the lenticular nucleus thus represents essen-tially striopallidal connections. It is prob-able that the striatum, and perhaps the pallidum as well, also receive fibers from the frontal cortex by direct frontostriate tracts and possibly also by collaterals from the pyramidal tract (Cajal). From the preced-

With the disappearance of the lateral geniculate body the pes pedunculi has become incorporated in the internal capsule,

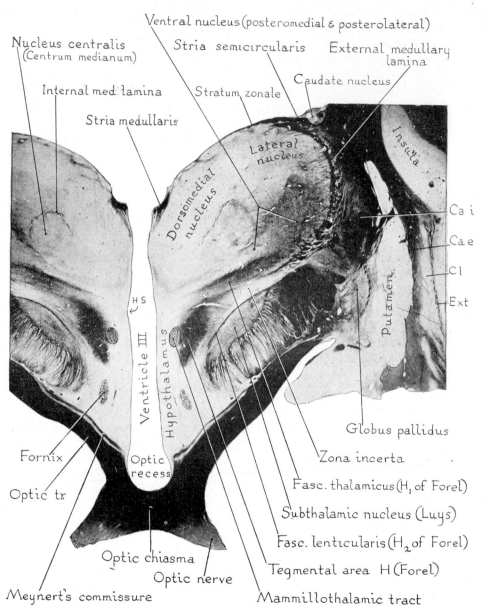

FIG. 272. Transverse section through diencephalon and basal ganglia at level of optic chiasma. Weigert's myelin stain. Photograph. *Ca e*, external capsule; *Ca i.* internal capsule; *Cl*, claustrum; *Ext*, capsula extrema; *Hs*, hypothalamic sulcus.

ing it is evident that the afferent connections of the striatum are from the thalamus and cortex, while its efferent fibers go mainly to the globus pallidus (Fig. 275).

forming its peduncular or subthalamic portion. The red nucleus has disappeared and in its place is seen the tegmental field of Forel, composed as already mentioned of fiber connections between the nucleus ruber and the thalamus and pallium i.e. rubrothalamic, dentatothalamic, rubrocortical and corticorubral fibers. Lateral to the tegmental field are two transversely running fiber bundles enclosing between them a strip of gray matter, the *zona incerta* (Fig. 272). The dorsal bundle or *thalamic fasciculus* (Field H1) is closely applied to the ventral surface of the thalamus; the *lenticular fasciculus* (H2) is in contact with the subthalamic nucleus or with the internal capsules in levels above that nucleus. The composition of these bundles is best understood by an

dum, sweep around the medial border of the internal capsule, forming a looped bundle, the *ansa lenticularis*, which curves dorsally to join the lenticular fasciculus (Fig. 274). These two bundles, ansa lenticularis and fasciculus lenticularis, constitute the whole system of efferent fibers from the globus pallidus, terminating in numerous and widely distributed nuclei which are relay or end stations in the extrapyramidal outflow from the corpus striatum (Fig. 275). Many of the fibers make homolateral connections, others cross in the several hypothalamic decussations previously discussed. Included are: (1)

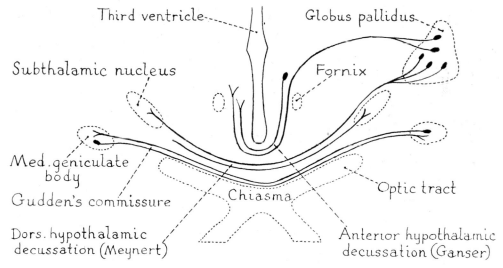

FIG. 273. Diagram of hypothalamic decussations, showing origin and termination of some of their fibers

analysis of the efferent pallidal connections. Subthalamic nucleus, tegmental field, zona incerta, lenticular and thalamic fasciculi, and peduncular portion of internal capsule together constitute the *subthalamus*.

The efferent fibers of the corpus striatum arise almost entirely from the globus pallidus. Many of these fibers perforate the peduncular portion of the internal capsule and on reaching the inner surface of the latter, are gathered into a bundle which runs medially and constitutes the lenticular fasciculus mentioned above. Other fibers, especially from the ventral part of the palli-

Pallidothalamic fibers to the anterior ventral nucleus and perhaps also to some of the medial thalamic nuclei. (2) Pallidohypothalamic fibers to the tuber cinereum and other hypothalamic regions. (3) Fibers to the subthalamic nucleus and zona incerta. (4) Pallidorubral fibers to the nucleus ruber, either directly or after a relay in the nucleus of the tegmental field or zona incerta. (4) Pallidonigral fibers. The substantia nigra also receives direct fibers from the large cells of the putamen and caudate nucleus (strionigral) and possibly sends nigrostrial fibers to these nuclei (Ranson). (5) Fibers to the interstitial nucleus and nucleus of Darksche-witsch by way of the posterior commissure. (6) Pallidoreticular fibers to the reticular formation of the midbrain, pons and me-dulla. It appears also that some of the pal-lidal fibers may go directly to the motor nuclei innervating the ocular, facial, mastica-tory and other muscles of the head (Mor-gan). From the above it is evident that efferent impulses from the globus pallidus do not reach the lower motor neurons by long fibers as is the case with the pyramidal tract, but are interrupted in many nuclei widely scattered throughout the brain stem. The

through which they reach the anterior por-tion of the ventral thalamic nucleus (Fig. 274). Thus the ventral nucleus receives sensory fibers in its posterior segment (poste-rior ventral nucleus), cerebellar fibers in its intermediate portion (lateral ventral nu-cleus), and pallidal fibers in its anterior por-tion (anterior ventral nucleus). Intermin-gled with these fibers are thalamopallidal and thalamostriate fibers from the ventro-medial thalamic nuclei to the corpus striatum.

External to the putamen is a band of mainly longitudinally running fibers, the

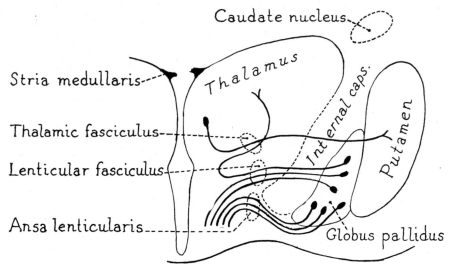

FIG. 274. Diagram showing composition of the ansa lenticularis and the lenticular and thalamic fasciculi. In the thalamic bundle only the connections of the thalamus with the corpus striatum are shown

further connections of many of these nuclei have been discussed in previous chapters.

The thalamic fasciculus has several com-ponents. In large part it is a continuation of the tegmental field connecting the red nucleus and cerebellum with the pallium and cortex. The rubrothalamic and dentato-thalamic fibers terminate in the intermediate portion of the ventral thalamic nucleus ros-tral to the termination of the medial lemnis-cus and spinothalamic tracts. Other fibers are from the globus pallidus, which emerge with the lenticular fasciculus, then loop laterally and enter the thalamic bundle

external capsule, flanked laterally by a plate of gray matter, the claustrum, whose func-tion and connections are not fully under-stood. It is regarded by some as a detached portion of the putamen, by others as belong-ing to the cortex of the insula (island of Reil). The latter is separated from the claustrum by a layer of subcortical white matter known as the capsula extrema. A transversely cut fiber bundle indenting the ventral surface of the lenticular nucleus is the beginning of the anterior commissure which will be described at a higher level (Fig. 271).

In the hypothalamic region which lies below the hypothalamic sulcus and merges laterally with the subthalamus, are seen two campal cortex of the temporal lobe, passes dorsally over the thalamus to reach the rostral surface of the latter. Then it curves

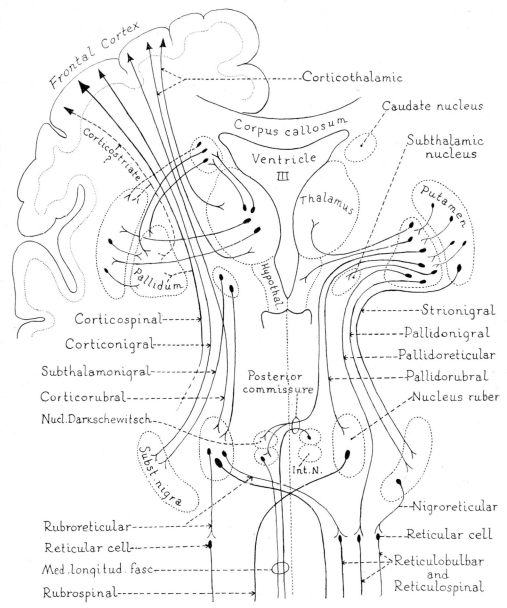

FIG. 275. The principal connections of the corpus striatum. Afferent fibers are shown on the left, efferent pallidal fibers on the right. The contralateral fibers from the globus pallidus crossing in the hypothalamic decussations are not shown. Int. N., interstitial nucleus.

conspicuous transversely cut fiber bundles: the *fornix* and the *mammillothalamic tract.* The former, to be studied more fully with the olfactory system arises in the hippo- ventrally, enters the hypothalamus and runs caudally to end in the mammillary body (Fig. 265). The mammillothalamic tract originates in the mammillary body and runs diagonally upward and forward to terminate in the anterior thalamic nucleus (Fig. 270).

Section through thalamus and corpus striatum at level of anterior commissure
(Figs. 276, 266)

The section passes rostral to the hypothalamus. The somewhat smaller thalamus shows clearly a division into an inner and an outer portion, the two separated by the internal medullary lamina. In the inner portion are the large *dorsomedial nucleus* and the central (ventricular) gray substance in which there are a number of poorly defined cell clusters known as the *midline nuclei*. The outer portion comprises the lateral nucleus and the *lateral ventral nucleus* which receives the cerebellar fibers from the red and the dentate nucleus. The medial lemniscus and other sensory tracts have already terminated at a lower level in the posterior ventral nucleus. Dorsally another gray mass, the *anterior thalamic nucleus*, has made its appearance spread out equally above the medial and lateral nucleus and separated from these by a fork of the internal medullary lamina. The striae medullares are still present and in the ventricular floor are seen the anterior commissure and dorsal to it the columns of the fornix. The commissure which can be followed on each side to the interior of the lenticular nucleus, in reality belongs to the rhinencephalons. It connects the olfactory portions of the two temporal lobes and to a lesser extent the two olfactory bulbs.

Fibers from the lateral nuclei and apparently from the anterior as well, gather along the outer border of the thalamus into the external medullary lamina and enter the internal capsule, forming a part of the superior or middle thalamic radiation related to the central and parietal cortex. In the medial nuclei are also seen longitudinally or obliquely cut fibers which run ventrally toward the most medial portion of the internal capsule. This bundle, known as the *ansa peduncularis*, is composed in part of fibers which connect the thalamus with the basal temporal cortex and the insula, in part of fibers of the ansa lenticularis connecting the globus pallidus with the medial thalamic nucleus. At the boundary between the medial and lateral nucleus is the mammillothalamic tract.

The lenticular nucleus is large, especially the putamen which now is medially continuous with the head of the caudate nucleus whose caudal portion is cut at this level. The boundary zone between the two is marked by a bundle of longitudinally cut fibers which represent the beginning of the anterior limb of the internal capsule (caudatolenticular portion). The tail of the caudate nucleus is still present and occupies its previous position, immediately lateral to the stria semicircularis.

Section through corpus striatum and rostral portion of thalamus
(Figs. 277, 266)

The medial thalamic nucleus has disappeared and the much diminished thalamus now consists of the anterior nucleus and the most rostral portion of the lateral nuclear mass, the two separated by the internal medullary lamina. The lateral mass is mainly made up of the anterior ventral nucleus, the most dorsal portion perhaps still belonging to the lateral nucleus. The mammillothalamic tract is about to enter the anterior nucleus in which its fibers terminate.

The putamen is large, the globus pallidus considerably smaller. Ventrally the putamen practically fuses with the head of the caudate nucleus which has increased in size, the junctional zone between the two perforated by fibers of the internal capsule (anterior limb) related to the frontal cortex. The internal capsule has the form of a shallow V whose apex is directed medially. The dorsal stouter portion between thalamus and lenticular nucleus still belongs to the posterior limb, the ventral portion between caudate and lenticular nuclei constitutes the anterior limb or lenticulo-caudate portion.

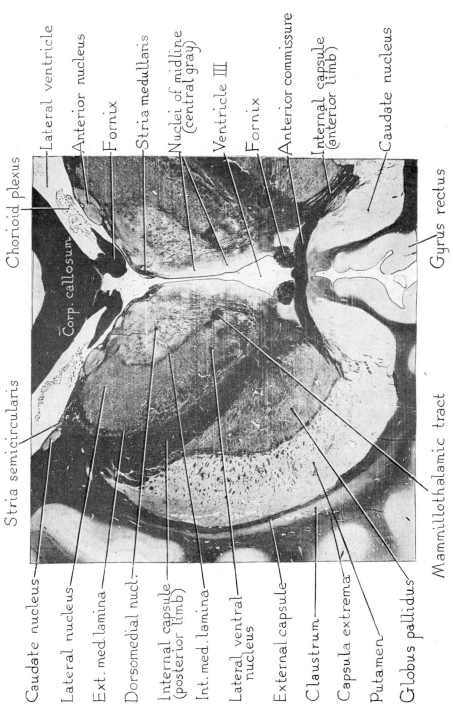

Fig. 276. Transverse section through diencephalon and basal ganglia at level of anterior commissure. Weigert's myelin stain. Photograph

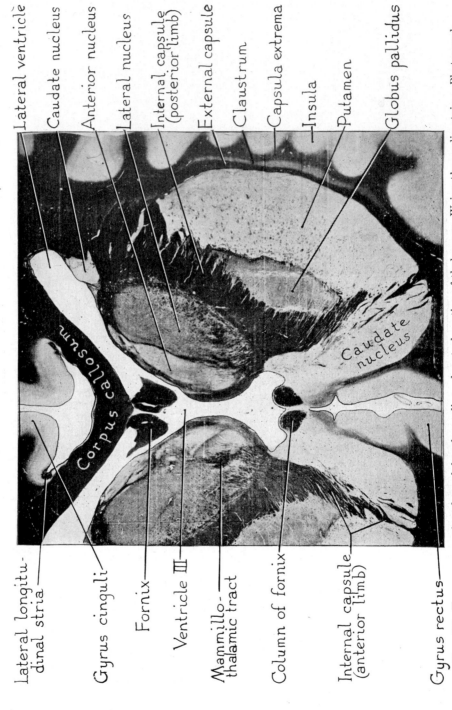

FIG. 277. Transverse section through basal ganglia and rostral portion of thalamus. Weigert's myelin stain. Photograph

External capsule, claustrum and extreme capsule are in the same position.

Section through septum pellucidum and head of caudate nucleus
(Figs. 278, 266)

The section passes rostral to the thalamus. The anterior limb of the internal capsule is bounded medially by the large head of the

frontal horns. The lateral wall of each ventricle is formed by the caudate nucleus, the roof and floor respectively by the body and rostrum of the corpus callosum. The thin medial wall separating the two ventricles is the *septum pellucidum* composed of two thin plates of neural tissue, the *laminae of the septum pellucidum*, between which there is a space of variable extent, the *cavum of the*

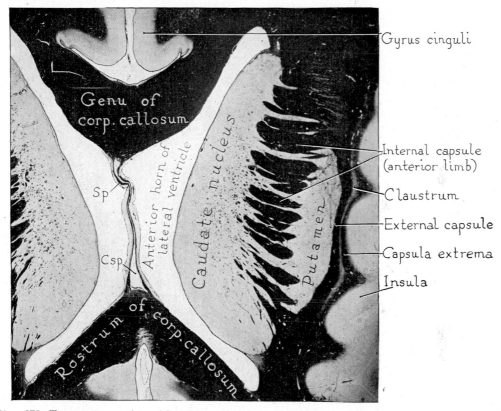

Gyrus cinguli

Genu of corp. callosum

Anterior horn of lateral ventricle

Caudate nucleus

Sp

Csp

Putamen

Internal capsule (anterior limb)

Claustrum

External capsule

Capsula extrema

Insula

Rostrum of corp. callosum

FIG. 278. Transverse section of basal ganglia, through head of caudate nucleus and anterior limb of internal capsule. Weigert's myelin stain. Photograph. *Sp*, septum pellucidum; *Csp*, cavum of septum pellucidum.

caudate nucleus, laterally by the much diminished putamen. The globus pallidus has disappeared. Putamen and caudate nucleus are connected by numerous gray bridges which extend across the internal capsule and produce the striped appearance responsible for the term corpus striatum.

The third ventricle has disappeared and the lateral ventricles are now represented by their most rostral portions, the anterior or

septum pellucidum. Each lamina consists of fibers covered superficially by a layer of gray matter.

The thalamic radiations and internal capsule. The fibers which connect the thalamus and cortex in both directions constitute the thalamic radiations. These thalamocortical and corticothalamic fibers form a continuous fan emerging along the whole lateral extent of the caudate nucleus, whose fibers radiate forward, upward, backward and downward, and pass obliquely through the various portions of the internal capsule of which they form a large part (Figs. 279, 283). Though the radiations connect with practically all parts of the cortex, the richness of connections varies considerably for specific cortical areas. Most abundant are the projections to the frontal granular cortex, the precentral and postcentral gyri, the calcarine area and the gyrus of Heschl. The lateral nuclei. The *superior* or *centroparietal peduncle* connects the Rolandie area and adjacent portions of the frontal and parietal lobes with the lateral and ventral thalamic nuclei. The fibers carrying general sensory impulses from the body and head form part of this radiation and terminate in the postcentral gyrus. The *posterior* or *occipital peduncle* connects the occipital and posterior parietal convolutions with the caudal portions of the thalamus especially the pulvinar,

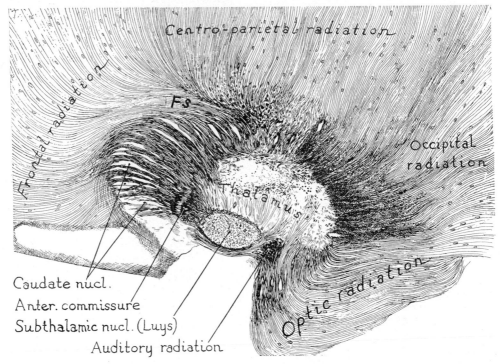

FIG. 279. The thalamic radiations. Composite picture drawn from photographs of serial sections and dissections. (After J. Rosett.) *Fs*, fasciculus subcallosus of frontal radiation

posterior parietal region and adjacent portions of the temporal lobe have likewise rich thalamic connections, but relatively scanty radiations go to other cortical areas, especially the temporal lobe (Walker).

The thalamic radiations are usually grouped into four subradiations, often known as the thalamic *peduncles* or *stalks* (Figs. 279, 283). The *anterior* or *frontal peduncle* connects the frontal lobe with the medial and anterior thalamic nuclei, and possibly with the anterior portion of the and also includes the optic radiation (geniculocalcarine) from the lateral geniculate body to the calcarine occipital cortex (striate area). The *inferior* or *temporal* peduncle is relatively small and includes the scanty connections of the thalamus with the temporal lobe and the insula. In this may be included also the stronger auditory radiation (geniculotemporal) from the medial geniculate body to the temporal gyrus of Heschl.

The cerebral hemisphere is connected with the brain stem and spinal cord by an extensive system of projection fibers, some afferent, others efferent. They arise from the whole extent of the cortex and enter the white substance of the hemisphere where they appear as a radiating mass of fibers, the *corona radiata*, converging toward the brain stem (Fig. 301). On reaching the latter they form a broad compact fiber band, the *internal capsule*, flanked medially by the thalamus and caudate nucleus, laterally by the lenticular nucleus. The internal capsule is thus composed of all the fibers, afferent and efferent which go to or come from the cerebral cortex. A large part of the capsule is obviously composed of the thalamic radiations described above. The rest is mainly composed of efferent cortical fiber systems which descend to lower portions of the brain stem and to the spinal cord, and includes the corticospinal, corticobulbar and corticopontile tracts, and the smaller bundles to the substantia nigra, nucleus ruber, subthalamic nucleus and to certain other gray masses of the brain stem. Below the level of the thalamus these descending systems constitute the pes pedunculi of the midbrain.

The internal capsule, as seen in a horizontal section, is composed of a shorter *anterior* and a longer *posterior limb* which meet at an obtuse angle, the junctional zone being known as the *genu* or geniculate portion (Fig. 280). The anterior or *lenticulocaudate portion* lies between the lenticular and caudate nuclei. The posterior limb consists of the large *lenticulothalamic* portion lying between the lenticular nucleus and the thalamus, and a caudal *retrolenticular portion* extending a short distance behind the lenticular nucleus. In this caudal region a number of fibers pass beneath the lenticular nucleus to reach the temporal lobe and collectively form the *sublenticular* portion of the internal capsule.

(1) The *lenticulocaudate portion* contains the anterior thalamic radiation or peduncle, the frontal corticopontile tract and the fibers connecting the prefrontal region with the nucleus ruber, probably both corticorubral

and rubrocortical fibers. (2) The *genu* contains the corticobulbar fibers to the motor cranial nuclei, those for the eye muscles being placed most anteriorly, those for the tongue and face extending a short distance into the posterior limb. (3) The *lenticulothalamic portion* includes the corticospinal tract, the superior thalamic radiation, the corticorubral fibers from the operculocentral area, the corticonigral and corticosubthalamic fibers. In the pyramidal tract the fibers for the neck are closest to the genu, followed respectively by those of the upper extremity, trunk and lower extremity. The fibers of the superior thalamic radiation which project general body sense to the postcentral gyrus are located in the caudal portion, immediately behind the pyramidal tract. (4) The *retrolenticular portion* contains the posterior thalamic radiation including among others the geniculocalcarine (optic) and geniculotemporal (auditory) radiations, and descending fibers from the occipital cortex to the superior colliculi and pretectal region. The *sublenticular portion*, difficult to separate from the retrolenticular, contains the inferior thalamic peduncle and the corticopontile fibers from the temporal and parieto-occipital areas. Many include the auditory radiation in the sublenticular portion.

THE VISUAL PATHWAY

The *retina* arises as an evaginated portion of the brain, the optic pouch, which secondarily is invaginated to form the two-layered optic cup. The outer layer gives rise to pigmented epithelium, the inner layer forms the neural portion of the retina in which are differentiated the bipolar rod and cone cells, the bipolar and horizontal neurons confined within the retina itself, and the multipolar ganglionic neurons whose axons form the optic nerve (Fig. 281). The latter thus really constitutes a fiber tract connecting two parts of the brain. Its fibers possess no neurilemma sheaths, its connective tissue investments represent continuations of the

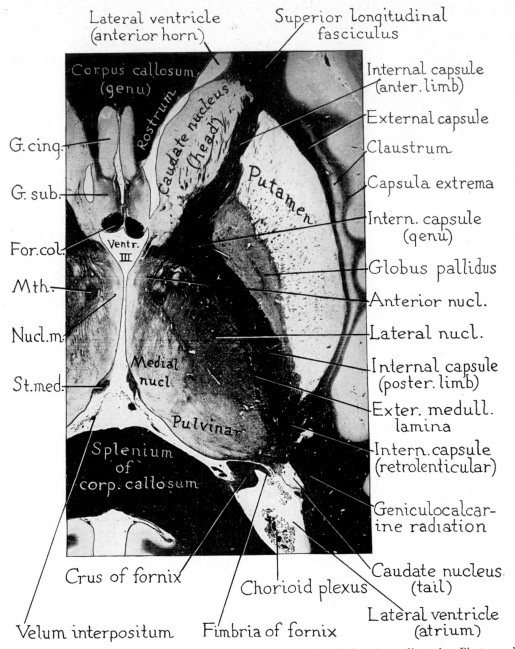

Lateral ventricle (anterior horn)
Superior longitudinal fasciculus
Corpus callosum (genu)
Rostrum
Caudate nucleus (head)
Putamen
Internal capsule (anter. limb)
External capsule
Claustrum
Capsula extrema
Intern. capsule (genu)
Globus pallidus
Anterior nucl.
Lateral nucl.
Internal capsule (poster. limb)
Exter. medull. lamina
Intern. capsule (retrolenticular)
Geniculocalcarine radiation
Caudate nucleus (tail)
Lateral ventricle (atrium)
G. cing.
G. sub.
For. col.
Ventr. III
Mth.
Nucl. m.
St. med.
Medial nucl.
Pulvinar
Splenium of corp. callosum
Crus of fornix
Velum interpositum
Fimbria of fornix
Chorioid plexus

FIG. 280. Horizontal section through thalamus and basal ganglia. Weigert's myelin stain. Photograph: *For.col.*, column of fornix; *G.cing.*, gyrus cinguli; *G.sub.*, gyrus subcallosus; *Mth.*, mammillothalamic tract; *Nucl.m.*, nuclei of the midline; *St.med.*, stria medullaris.

meningeal sheaths of the brain: pial, arachnoid and dural.

The rod and cone cells are the visual receptors which react specifically to physical light. The cones, numbering some 7,000,000 in the human eye, have a higher threshold of excitability and are stimulated by light of relatively high intensity. They are responsible for sharp vision and for color discrimination in adequate illumination. The rods whose number has been estimated at over 100,000,000 react to low intensities of illumination and subserve twilight and night vision. Close to the posterior pole of the eye, the retina shows a small circular yellowish area, the *macula lutea*, in direct line with the visual axis. The macula represents the retinal area for central vision, and the eyes are fixed in such a manner that the image of any object looked at is always focused on the macula. The rest of the retina is concerned

ranged in fine radiating bundles which run parallel to the retinal surface and converge at the optic disc to form the optic nerve. On emerging from the eyeball the fibers at once acquire a myelin sheath with consequent increase in the size of the optic nerve.

The optic nerves enter the cranial cavity through the optic foramen and unite to form the optic chiasma beyond which they are continued as the optic tracts. Within the chiasma a partial decussation occurs, the fibers from the nasal halves of the retina crossing to the opposite side, those from the

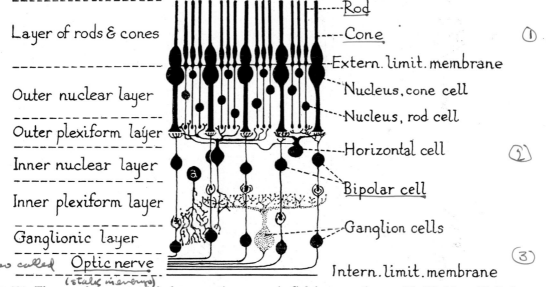

Layer of rods & cones — Rod — Cone ①

— Extern. limit. membrane
Outer nuclear layer — Nucleus, cone cell
— Nucleus, rod cell
Outer plexiform layer
Inner nuclear layer — Horizontal cell ②
Inner plexiform layer — Bipolar cell
Ganglionic layer — Ganglion cells
Optic nerve — Intern. limit. membrane ③

FIG 281. The neural elements of the human retina as seen in Golgi preparations. (Modified from Walls.) *a*, amacrine cell.

with pericentral (paracentral) and peripheral vision. In the macular region the inner layers of the retina are pushed apart, forming a small central pit, the *fovea centralis*, which constitutes the place of sharpest vision and most acute color discrimination. Here the retina is composed entirely of closely packed slender cones.

The nerve impulses "generated" in the rod and cone cells are transmitted to the bipolar neurons which in turn establish synaptic relations with the dendrites or bodies of the multipolar ganglionic cells. The axons of the latter, at first unmyelinated, are ar-

temporal halves remaining uncrossed (Fig. 282). It must be remembered that each visual field, right and left, is not represented by the retina of the corresponding side, but by portions of both retinae. Thus the images of objects in the right field of vision are projected on the right nasal and the left temporal half of the retina. In the chiasma the fibers from these two retinal portions are combined to form the left optic tract which now represents the complete right field of vision. The light rays to the temporal retina already come from the opposite side i.e. they cross in the air, the fibers from the nasal portion receiving light rays from the same side cross in the chiasma. By this arrangement the whole right field is projected upon the left hemisphere, and the left field upon the right hemisphere.

to the superior colliculi and pretectal area. Some of the optic fibers also enter the hypothalamus and terminate in the supraoptic nucleus and in the medial nuclei of the tuber cinereum (Marburg). Of all these terminal

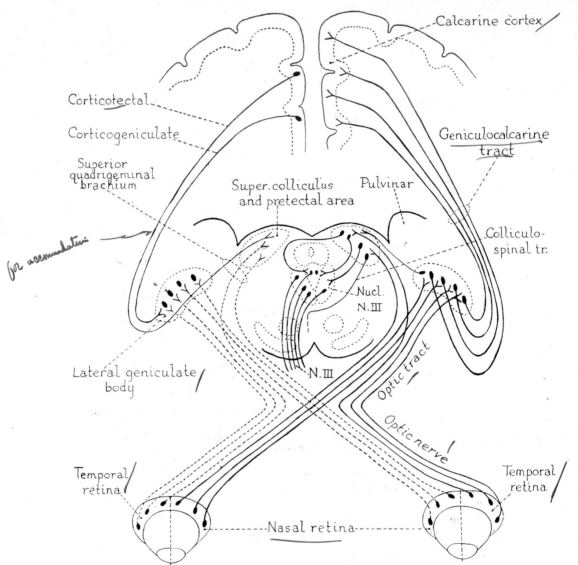

FIG. 282. Diagram of the visual pathway and some of the optic reflex connections

Each optic tract sweeps outward and backward encircling the hypothalamus and rostral portion of the pes pedunculi, and most of its fibers terminate in the lateral geniculate body, a smaller portion continuing as the superior quadrigeminal brachium

nuclei only the lateral geniculate body appears to receive fibers of visual perception and gives rise to the geniculocalcarine tract which forms the last relay of the visual path. The other nuclei subserve various optic reflexes. The pretectal area as already stated is concerned with the light reflex (p. 263), the superior colliculi with reflex movement of the eyes and head in response to optic stimuli. The retinohypothalamic fibers probably mediate the retinal reflex control of the hypophysis, since the latter receives fibers from the supraoptic hypothalamic nucleus. In lower vertebrates this may possibly regulate the distribution of pigment in the melanophores (pigment cells) of the skin in response to different light intensities. In

ward to the striate area. Those placed more ventrally first turn forward and downward into the temporal lobe, spread out over the tip of the inferior horn, then loop backward and running close to the outer wall of the lateral ventricle (external sagittal stratum) reach the occipital cortex. The more ventral the fiber, the longer is the loop, the most ventral ones extending to the uncus region of the temporal lobe before turning back.

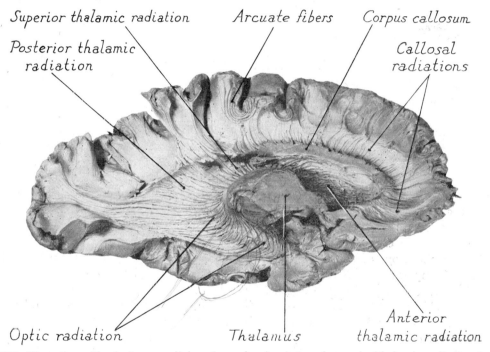

Superior thalamic radiation   Arcuate fibers   Corpus callosum
Posterior thalamic radiation   Callosal radiations
Optic radiation   Thalamus   Anterior thalamic radiation

Fig. 283. Dissection of brain from medial surface, showing internal capsule (thalamic radiations) and portion of callosal radiation. Photograph.

man the significance of these fibers is obscure.

The *geniculocalcarine* tract arises from the lateral geniculate body, passes through the retrolenticular portion of the internal capsule and forms the optic radiation which ends in the striate area (area 17) located on the medial surface of the occipital lobe on either side of the calcarine fissure. The fibers of this radiation do not all reach the cortex by the shortest route (Figs. 279, 283). The most dorsal fibers pass almost directly back-

The retinal areas have a precise point-to-point relationship with those of the external geniculate body, each retinal portion projecting on a specific and topographically limited portion of the geniculate. The fibers from the upper retinal quadrants representing the lower visual field, terminate in the medial half, those from the lower quadrants in the lateral half of the geniculate body. The macular fibers occupy the central portion, flanked medially and laterally by fibers from the paracentral and peripheral retinal areas.

A similar point-to-point relation exists between the geniculate body and the striate cortex. The medial half of the geniculate body representing the upper quadrants (lower visual field) projects to the dorsal lip of the calcarine fissure, the fibers forming the dorsal portion of the optic radiation. The lateral half representing the lower retinal quadrants (upper visual field) projects to the ventral lip of the calcarine fissure, the fibers occupying the ventral portion of the optic radiation. The macular fibers which constitute the intermediate half of the optic radiation, terminate in the caudal third of the calcarine cortex, those from the paracentral and peripheral retinal areas end in respectively more rostral portions.

Clinical considerations. Injury to any part of the optic pathway produces visual defects whose nature depends on the location and extent of the injury. These defects are *homonymous* when restricted to a single visual field, right or left; *heteronymous* when parts of both fields are involved. It is evident that homonymous defects will be caused by lesions on one side placed anywhere above the chiasma, i.e. optic tract, geniculate body, optic radiation and visual cortex. Complete destruction of any of these structures results in a loss of the whole opposite field of vision (*homonymous hemianopsia*), partial injury produces *quadrantic homonymous* defects. Lesions of the temporal lobe by compressing or destroying the looping fibers of the optic radiation are likely to produce such quadrantic defects in the upper visual field, while injury to the parietal lobe may involve the more dorsally lying fibers of the radiation and cause similar defects in the lower field of vision.

Lesion of the chiasma may cause several kinds of heteronymous defects. Most commonly the crossing fibers from the nasal portions of the retina are involved, with consequent loss of the two temporal fields of vision (*bitemporal hemianopsia*). In rare cases both lateral angles of the chiasma may be compressed, affecting the non-decussating fibers from the temporal retinae and resulting in a loss of the nasal visual fields (*binasal hemianopsia*). Injury of one optic nerve naturally produces blindness in the corresponding eye with loss of the pupillary reflex to light entering that eye. The pupil will however contract consensually to light entering the other eye, since the reflex pretectal center is related to both Edinger-Westphal nuclei. The pupillary reflex will not be affected by lesions of the visual pathway placed above the superior quadrigemina[1] brachium.

THE THALAMUS

The thalamic nuclei and their connections. The thalamus is divided by a vertical plate of fibers, the internal medullary lamina, into a medial and a lateral portion each containing several nuclear masses. The medial portion comprises the *anterior* and the *dorsomedial* (*medial*) *thalamic nucleus*. The lateral portion, lying between the internal and external medullary lamina, is divided into two tiers or étages, the ventral tier composed of the *ventral nucleus*, the dorsal tier comprising the *lateral nucleus* which does not extend rostrally as far as the ventral one. Caudally these become continuous with the *pulvinar* and the *geniculate bodies* which form the hindmost nuclei of the lateral portion, the pulvinar belonging to the dorsal tier, the geniculates to the ventral tier.

The anterior nucleus lies beneath the dorsal surface of the most rostral part of the thalamus where it forms a distinct swelling, the anterior tubercle. It consists of a large main nucleus (anteroventral) and several clumps of cells constituting the accessory anterior nucleus (anterodorsal). The rounded or polygonal cells composing the nucleus are of medium or small size, with little chromophilic substance and a moderate amount of yellow pigment. The anterior nucleus receives the stout mammillothalamic tract and sends fibers to the mammillary body by the same bundle (thalamomammillary). It is reciprocally connected with the gyrus cinguli and inferior surface of the frontal lobe, and sends some fibers to the habenular ganglion *via* the stria medullaris. Fibers to the caudate nucleus have likewise been described by some investigators.

The dorsomedial (medial) nucleus occupies most of the space between the internal medullary lamina and the periventricular gray substance (Figs. 264, 284). It is composed of a large dorsolateral portion containing relatively small cells, and a small median magnocellular portion. The nucleus re-

nucleus; and a caudal portion, the *posterior ventral nucleus*. The anterior ventral nucleus has no projection to the cortex but receives fibers from the globus pallidus. Its other connections are not fully understood.

The *lateral ventral nucleus* receives the fibers from the cerebellum i.e. the dentatothalamic and rubrothalamic fibers, and is connected with the motor area (area 4) of the cortex and to a lesser extent with the premotor (area 6). There appears to be a definite topographical representation within

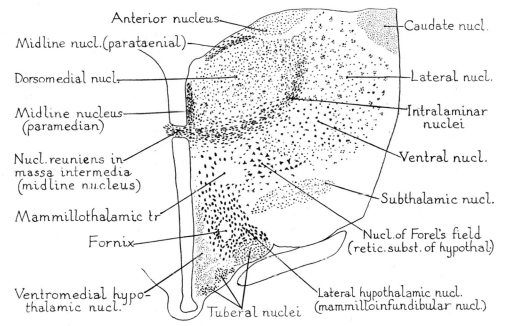

FIG 284. Transverse section through interbrain at level of tuber cinereum, showing some of the diencephalic nuclei. (Modified from Malone.)

ceives many fibers from other thalamic nuclei and possibly also a few terminals of the ascending sensory tracts. The small celled portion is connected by a considerable projection with the prefrontal cortex. The magnocellular portion has no cortical connection but is related to the periventricular gray and the hypothalamus. The dorsomedial nucleus also sends fibers to the corpus striatum.

The *ventral nuclear mass* consists of a most rostral portion, the *anterior ventral nucleus*; a larger middle portion, the *lateral ventral*

the nucleus, the most medial portion projecting to the cortical face area, the next to the arm area, and the most lateral part to the foot area.

The *posterior ventral nucleus* whose cells are among the largest in the thalamus is composed of two portions, *posteromedial* and *posterolateral* (Fig. 235). The former also known as the arcuate or semilunar nucleus receives the secondary trigeminal tracts. The posterolateral is the end station for the medial lemniscus and spinothalamic tract. These nuclei project to the postcentral gyrus (areas 3, 2, 1), here again the face area receiving fibers from the posteromedial nucleus, the arm area from the medial portion and the leg area from the lateral portion of the posterolateral nucleus.

The medial and lateral geniculate body may be considered as the caudal continuations of the ventral nuclear mass and like the latter receive terminals of sensory tracts. The *medial geniculate body* consists of a ventral nucleus of large closely packed polygonal cells and a dorsal nucleus of more loosely

late and perhaps to lower portions of the brain stem (Rioch).

The lateral geniculate body intimately associated with the optic tract consists in most mammals of a dorsal and a ventral nucleus, the former connected with the ventral thalamic nucleus, pulvinar and area striata of the cortex, the latter apparently representing a subthalamic structure related to the zona incerta. In man the "ventral" nucleus is practically indistinguishable and is represented by scattered cells lying medial

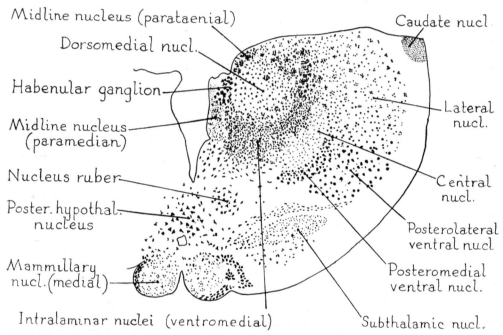

FIG. 285. Transverse section through interbrain at level of habenulae and mammillary bodies. Nissl stain. (Modified from Malone.)

arranged smaller cells (Malone). It receives the auditory fibers from the cochlear nuclei and inferior colliculus and its main connection (reciprocal) is with the superior temporal convolution (transverse gyrus of Heschl) by the geniculotemporal or auditory radiation. It also appears to be related by fibers to the ventral and lateral thalamic nuclei and to the pulvinar. The ventral portion of the nucleus sends fibers to the subthalamic region and by way of Gudden's commissure to the opposite medial geniculate to the main nucleus among the entering fibers of the optic tract. The principal nucleus is a lamellated mass having in section the shape of a horseshoe whose hilus is directed ventromedially (Fig. 286). It is composed of six concentrically arranged cell layers separated by intervening fiber bands. The four outer layers consist of small and medium sized cells; in the two narrower innermost layers the cells are large and more loosely arranged (magnocellular nucleus of Malone). Phylogenetically, the nucleus first differentiates into three cell layers, and becomes six-layered in forms where the optic tracts show only a partial decussation, the uncrossed and crossed portions each using three alternate lamina (Minkowski, Le Gros Clark).

The lateral geniculate nucleus is the main end station of the optic tract and sends a strong projection to the calcarine cortex (area 17) by the geniculocalcarine or visual radiation, also receiving corticogeniculate fibers from the same area. Its internuclear connections are with the pulvinar and with the ventral and lateral thalamic nuclei. It also sends fibers to the superior colliculi and

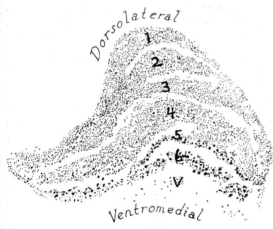

FIG. 286. The cellular laminae of the lateral geniculate body. (After Rose.) *v*, scattered cells ("ventral" nucleus) in basal medullary layer.

pretectal area by way of the superior quadrigeminal brachium, and according to Balado and Franke (1937) that brachium consists almost entirely of fibers from the magnocellular portion of the lateral geniculate, few if any optic fibers reaching the superior colliculus directly.

The lateral nucleus begins as a narrow strip some distance from the anterior limit of the thalamus, enlarges posteriorly and merges caudally with the pulvinar. It consists of a dorsal and a posterior portion whose boundaries are indistinct. The nucleus receives few ascending sensory fibers, possibly some from the medial lemniscus, but is connected reciprocally with a rather extensive cortical

area, especially with the superior parietal lobule (areas 5 and 7). Fewer fibers go to the postcentral and precentral region. Its internuclear connection are primarily with the ventral nucleus.

The pulvinar is a large nuclear mass forming the posterior portion of the thalamus. Caudally it overhangs the geniculate bodies and dorsolateral surface of the midbrain. It is usually divided into a narrower lateral portion lying above the lateral geniculate body and containing clumps of rather large deeply staining cells, and a larger medial portion composed of more compactly arranged smaller polygonal cells. The pulvinar does not receive any ascending sensory fibers but has internuclear relations with other thalamic nuclei, especially the medial and lateral geniculate bodies. It is connected in both directions with the supramarginal and angular convolutions, with the superior parietal lobule and with the occipital and posterior temporal portions of the cortex.

Besides the principal nuclei the thalamus contains smaller and diffusely organized cell groups which constitute the *nuclei of the midline* and the *intralaminar nuclei* (Figs. 284, 285).

The midline nuclei are more or less distinct cell clusters which lie in the periventricular gray of the dorsal half of the ventricular wall and in the massa intermedia. They are small and difficult to delimit in man but in the lower vertebrates they, together with some of the intralaminar nuclei, form the largest part of the thalamus (paleothalamus). They consist of small fusiform, rather darkly staining cells resembling preganglionic autonomic neurons (Malone), and hence are believed to be concerned with visceral activities. Their scanty connections are mainly with the hypothalamic region by finely myelinated and unmyelinated fibers which run in the periventricular gray substance. They are also related to the magnocellular portion of the dorsomedial nucleus and to the intralaminar nuclei. The more distinct of the midline cell groups include the *parataenial nucleus* near the stria medullaris, the *paramedian nucleus* in the ventricular wall, and the *nucleus reuniens* (median central nucleus) in the massa intermedia (Figs. 284, 285).

The intralaminar nuclei are diffuse cell groups infiltrating the internal medullary lamina which separates the medial from the lateral thalamic mass. Their cells are small and fusiform like those of the midline nuclei, their fiber connections diffuse and difficult to work out. In part they may represent the peripheral layers of the adjacent main nuclei, separated from the latter by fibers which pass through them. Included in this group, however, is the large and sharply defined *central* or *centromedian* nucleus found in the middle third of the thalamus between the dorsomedial nucleus above and the ventral nucleus below (Figs. 264, 285). Its cells are small and resemble those of the other intralaminar nuclei. The connections of the nucleus are not fully worked out. It apparently receives some sensory fibers from the secondary trigeminal tracts and from the medial lemniscus (Wallenberg, Vogt) and sends fibers to the globus pallidus (Walker). Its main connections are however with the adjacent thalamic nuclei. It is regarded as an expanded intralaminar nucleus prominent in primates and in man, constituting a more complex intrathalamic integrating mechanism.

Another "intralaminar" cell group, the *reticular nucleus*, is a narrow plate of rather dark staining polygonal cells lying between the external medullary lamina and the internal capsule along the lateral periphery of the thalamus. It largely represents the detached peripheral layer of the lateral nuclear mass.

In a general way the lateral half of the thalamus is related to exteroceptive somatic functions, the medial half to interoceptive visceral activities. The lateral half is connected primarily with the cerebral cortex and sends few fibers to subcortical structures.

The medial portion likewise projects to the cortex but in addition has strong efferent connections with the hypothalamus and corpus striatum. There has recently been a tendency to classify the thalamic nuclei on the basis of their fiber connections into three groups: (1) *Nuclei with subcortical connections* which include the midline and intralaminar nuclei. The former are connected with the hypothalamus and perhaps with lower portions of the brain stem, the latter have primarily intrathalamic connections. None of them are directly related to the cerebral cortex. The anterior ventral nucleus likewise belongs to this group. (2) *Cortical relay nuclei* which receive the sensory and cerebellar tracts and project to the primary sensory and motor areas of the cortex. These include the lateral and posterior ventral nuclei, the geniculate bodies and the anterior nucleus. Gustatory fibers probably also terminate in the thalamus but their terminal nuclei and further projection are not definitely known. (3) *Association nuclei* which receive few direct sensory fibers but have extensive relations with other thalamic nuclei and are connected reciprocally with the association areas of the frontal, parietal and occipitotemporal cortex. They comprise the dorso—medial and lateral nuclei and the pulvinar. To these may be added the anterior nucleus included in group 2 since olfactory impulses first reach the olfactory cortex and are then switched indirectly into the thalamus.

Functional considerations. All sensory impulses, with the sole exception of the olfactory ones, terminate in the gray masses of the thalamus from which they are projected to specific cortical areas by the thalamocortical radiations. Even the olfactory impulses which go directly to the older olfactory cortex are secondarily brought in relation with the anterior thalamic nuclei. Yet a consideration of its structure and connections strongly suggests that the thalamus is far more than a mere relay station for the various sensory paths to the pallium. Such stations appear to be adequately provided for by the ventral thalamic nuclei and by the geniculate bodies. There still remain the bulk of the thalamic nuclei, a large part of the thalamocortical fibers, all the corticothalamic fibers and the intrathalamic association fibers. It seems certain therefore that the thalamus is itself a sensory integrating organ of great complexity. The relatively simple impulses from the periphery do not pass through it unchanged, but are associated and synthesized on a "thalamic" level of greater or lesser complexity before being projected to the pallium. It has been pointed out by Head and Holmes, Foerster and others that while crude sensory modalities, such as touch, temperature and pain, may be separately injured below the thalamic level, above that level they become intimately fused and can no longer be individually segregated. If this is true, the sensory cortex has no direct association with the peripheral sense organs and must depend for its activities on sensory material already modified and integrated in the thalamus. In animals which have no pallium or but a poorly developed one, the thalamus undoubtedly constitutes the highest sensory correlation center in which somatic and visceral impulses are blended and integrated into more complex entities and then referred to visceral and somatic effectors by way of the hypothalamus and the basal forebrain ganglia.

There is moreover considerable clinical evidence verified by post mortem studies (Head and others) that the activities of the thalamus are related to consciousness, that the thalamus represents the neurological substratum of a crude sort of awareness such as the recognition of touch (mere contact), temperature and pain, and of the affect quality of sensation i.e. its pleasantness or unpleasantness. In certain lesions of the thalamus or of the thalamocortical connections, after a brief initial stage of complete contralateral anesthesia, pain, crude touch and much of temperature sense

return, while tactile localization, two-point discrimination and the sense of position and movement are lost or severely impaired. The sensations recovered are poorly localized and are accompanied by a great increase in "feeling tone", most commonly of an unpleasant character. Though the threshold of excitability is raised on the affected side, tactile and thermal stimuli previously not unpleasant, now evoke the most disagreeable sensations (dysesthesias) not always easily characterized by the patient. He can not endure innocuous cutaneous stimulation, yet can not tell the nature of the exciting stimulus. Occasionally the reverse occurs, a previously indifferent stimulus evoking a most pleasant feeling. These feeling states may even be induced by other sensations as for instance auditory ones (Head). Thus one patient could not go to church because listening to the hymns produced the most disagreeable sensations on his affected side. The dysesthesias may become intensified into spontaneous intractable pains which appear spasmodically, often without any apparent peripheral irritation, are difficult to localize and do not respond even to powerful narcotic drugs.

It has already been stated that there are two aspects to sensation: the discriminative and the affective. In the former, stimuli are compared as to intensity, locality and relative position in space and time, i.e. they are localized, discriminated and integrated into perceptions of form, size and texture; movements are judged as to extent, direction and sequence. It is this aspect which is primarily related to cortical function and is affected by cortical lesions and by lesions of certain sensory paths and their particular thalamic nuclei. On the other hand there is the "affective" side of sensation: pain, agreeableness and disagreeableness. Pain is naturally nearly all "affect" except perhaps its localization and intensity, temperature and many tactile sensations have likewise a marked affective tone, and this is especially true for all visceral sensations in which the discriminative element is practically absent. This affective quality which forms the basis of general bodily well being or of *malaise* and of the more intense emotional states is believed to be "appreciated" by the thalamus rather than the cortex, though profoundly modified and controlled by the latter. The appreciation of pain, crude touch and much of temperature is retained even after complete destruction of the sensory cortical areas of both sides.

The thalamus is played upon by two great streams of afferent fibers: the peripheral and the cortical. The former bring sensory impulses from all parts of the body informing the thalamus of any changes in the external and internal environment of the individual. The cortical connections link the thalamus to the associative memory mechanism of the pallium and bring it under the control of the latter. The thalamus has also efferent subcortical connections with the hypothalamus and corpus striatum through which thalamic influence may be referred to visceral and somatic effectors. The reactions mediated by this efferent thalamic pathway are primarily affective ones, characterized by immediate and excessive movements, secretory, vasomotor and other visceral changes, in contrast to discriminative ones which are precise, not excessive and often delayed. It is evident that this pathway like the thalamus itself is under the control of the cerebral cortex.

The significance of the corticothalamic fibers has been variously interpreted. They are considered as inhibiting thalamic activity and their interruption causes a thalamic release evidenced by the dysesthesias described above (Head and Holmes). According to Foerster the whole thalamostriate mechanism is involved in this release from cortical inhibition. It would seem however that in addition a more positive function should be assigned to the corticothalamic fibers. For example the perception of emotion-arousing objects exerts a strong

influence on visceral structures and it is very probable that the efferent pathway for this involves corticothalamic neurons. Some believe that the sensory changes are due to injury of the thalamus itself, either by irritation of the thalamic cells or interference with the intrathalamic associations. Brouwer and others have suggested that the corticothalamic fibers constitute a mechanism for the selective regulation of thalamic sensibility, permitting the more efficient functioning of one center while inhibiting the activity of others.

The significance of the individual thalamic nuclei can only be surmised from a consideration of their fiber connections. It has already been stated that in a general way the lateral part of the thalamus is related to somatic, the medial part to visceral functions. In the lateral mass the ventral nucleus and the geniculate bodies which receive the ascending sensory fibers probably send crude integrations to the primary sensory and motor areas. The lateral nuclei which receive fibers from the ventral one are apparently concerned with more complex somesthetic associations relating the various parts of the body, which are then projected to the parietal association areas. The pulvinar which receives geniculate fibers as well, integrates body sense with the special senses of vision and hearing and projects to the posterior parietal and occipitotemporal region. Thus the lateral thalamic mass is primarily concerned with simple or more complex integrations of somatic sensory impulses, to be used for the discriminative activities of the pallium.

In the medial half, the midline and some of the intralaminar nuclei are phylogenetically the oldest nuclei which practically make up the thalamus of the lower vertebrates. Some of them receive fibers from the spinothalamic tract and probably also from the medial lemniscus, either directly or through the hypothalamus and subthalamus. The impulses are primarily from visceral structures, representing the more elementary and affective forms of sensation. Other nuclei are concerned with intrathalamic associations. The whole group has no cortical connections, but is related on the efferent side to the hypothalamus and corpus striatum. It is believed that these are the nuclei which are concerned with the appreciation of the more primitive and affective forms of sensibility.

There has been much conjecture regarding the significance of the dorsomedial nucleus, the most prominent gray mass of the medial thalamus, which is highly developed in primates and especially in man. It is connected with the lateral thalamus, the hypothalamus and the corpus striatum, and has moreover a strong reciprocal connection with the frontal granular cortex. Head and Holmes believe that through its connections with the lateral thalamus, the nucleus abstracts and is able to appreciate the affect qualities of somatic sensations and to integrate them with the visceral. It would thus constitute an essential structure concerned with the consciousness of affect quality. It has been suggested (Le Gros Clark) that in this nucleus the somatic impulses forming the basis for discriminative cortical sensibility are blended with the feeling tone engendered by visceral activities, and these somatovisceral entities are then projected to the prefrontal cortex. The latter constitutes a large phylogenetically new cortical area highly developed only in man. While its significance is not fully understood, it may be regarded as the place where the discriminative cortical activities attain their highest elaboration and are blended with the activities of the hypothalamus and medial thalamus representing the more primitive affective components of consciousness. Large injuries to the frontal lobe of the dominant hemisphere are likely to cause defects in complex association as well as certain changes in behavior expressed by loss of acquired inhibitions and more direct and excessive emotional responses. There is evidence that similar alterations in emotional behavior are produced when the pathways between medial thalamus and frontal cortex are severed.

THE EPITHALAMUS

The epithalamus comprises the pineal body, the habenular trigones, the striae medullares and the epithelial roof of the third ventricle. The habenular ganglion consists in man of a smaller medial and a larger lateral nucleus. The medial nucleus consists of small closely packed deeply staining round cells; in the lateral the cells are larger, paler and more loosely arranged. The ganglion receives the terminals of the stria medullaris and gives origin to the habenulopeduncular tract or fasciculus retroflexus which terminates in the interpeduncular nucleus. The stria medullaris is a complex bundle composed of (1) fibers from the septal and basal olfactory nuclei which receive impulses from the olfactory bulb. (2) Fibers from the hippocampal formation which constitutes a higher cortical olfactory center. These fibers detach themselves from the fornix and join the stria medullaris. (3) Fibers from the anterior thalamic nucleus and perhaps also from the globus pallidus (Ranson). Some of the strial fibers cross to the opposite side in the habenular commissure. Thus the stria medullaris, habenula and fasciculus retroflexus form segments of efferent olfactory pathways, both reflex and cortical (Fig. 270).

The pineal body or epiphysis is a small cone-shaped body attached to the roof in the region of the posterior commissure. It appears to be a rudimentary gland whose function in the adult is not fully ascertained. It consists of a network of richly vascular connective tissue trabeculae in the meshes of which are found glia cells and cells of a peculiar type, the *pineal* or *epiphysial cells*. These are cells of variable size with pale nucleus, granular argentophile cytoplasm and relatively few branching processes. They may possibly represent modified nerve cells since they are not stained by glia stains. True nerve cells do not appear to be present though occasional cells with typical Nissl bodies have been observed by some investigators. The gland is said to receive fibers from the stria medullaris, habenular ganglion and posterior commissure, the fibers terminating in a plexus between the epiphysial cells.

is similarly continuous with the central gray matter and tegmentum of the midbrain. It may be conveniently described as extending from the region of the optic chiasma to the caudal tip of the mammillary body (Fig. 287). The region immediately in front of the chiasma, extending to the lamina terminalis and anterior commis-

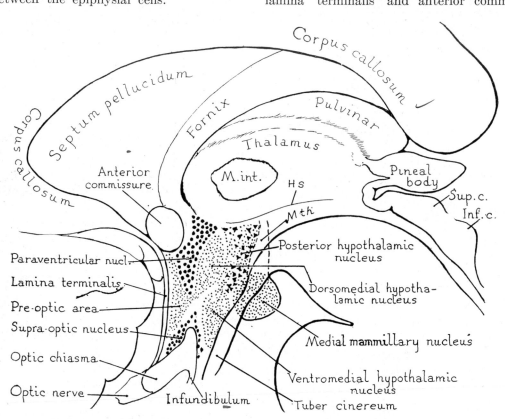

FIG. 287. Diagram of the ventricular surface of the human diencephalon (compare with Fig. 253). The position and extent of a number of hypothalamic nuclei are indicated as given by Le Gros Clark. *Hs*, hypothalamic sulcus; *Inf.c.*, inferior colliculus; *Mth*, mammillothalamic tract; *Sup.c.*, superior colliculus.

THE HYPOTHALAMUS

The hypothalamus comprises the ventral wall of the third ventricle below the hypothalamic sulcus and the structures of the ventricular floor including the optic chiasma, tuber cinereum with infundibulum, and the mammillary bodies. Anteriorly it passes without any definite demarcation into the basal olfactory area (diagonal gyrus of the anterior perforated substance), caudally it

sure, is known as the *preoptic area* and though belonging to the endbrain is usually included with the hypothalamic structures. Dorsally the hypothalamus is covered by the thalamus, laterally it is directly continuous with the subthalamic region (Fig. 264).

The hypothalamic nuclei. Pervading the whole area is a diffuse matrix of cells constituting the central gray substance in which are found a number of more or less definitely

shivering, sleeping & waking (post hypothalm.)
mammi (ant

organized nuclear masses. A sagittal plane passing through the anterior pillar of the fornix roughly separates a medial from a lateral hypothalamic area. The lateral area which abuts upon the subthalamus and pes pedunculi is narrow in its rostral and caudal portion, but in the region of the tuber it expands considerably (Fig. 288) It contains scattered groups of large darkly staining cells, the *lateral hypothalamic nucleus* and two or three sharply delimited circular cell groups known as the *nuclei tuberis* which often produce small visible eminences on the basal surface of the hypothalamus. They consist of small pale multipolar cells surrounded by a delicate fiber capsule about which are found the large cells of the lateral hypothalamic nucleus (Figs. 288, 289). The greater condensation of the large cells around the fornix has been called by some the *perifornical nucleus*.

In a cephalocaudal direction three hypothalamic regions may be conveniently recognized: (1) an anterior or *supraoptic*, lying above the chiasma and continuous in front with the preoptic area, (2) a middle or *tuberal*, and (3) a caudal or *mammillary* region, continuous behind with the central gray of the iter. The preoptic area is poorly differentiated and forms the central gray of the most rostral part of the ventricle. Le Gros Clark distinguishes a medial preoptic nucleus of rather densely grouped small cells, and a lateral nucleus in which the the medium sized cells are more diffusely arranged.

The supraoptic region contains two of the most striking and sharply defined hypothalamic nuclei, the *paraventricular* and the *supraoptic nucleus*, which have certain common features as to cell structure and fiber connections (Figs. 287, 288). They are both composed of large often bipolar deeply staining cells frequently possessing several nuclei. The Nissl substance is peripherally distributed and in the cytoplasm are found inclusion of colloidal material which have been regarded as evidence of secretory activity. Both nuclei send fibers to the posterior lobe of the hypophysis. The paraventricular nucleus is a fairly broad but flat vertical plate of densely packed cells occupying a considerable portion of the dorsal hypothalamic wall. Ventrally it extends almost to the optic chiasma, dorsally to the hypothalamic sulcus where it comes in relation with the midline nuclei of the thalamus. The supraoptic nucleus is ventrally placed and straddles the lateral portion of the optic chiasma. Scattered isolated cells or small cell groups appear to form an incomplete bridge between the two nuclei. The less differentiated central gray of this region is also known as the *anterior hypothalamic nucleus* which merges imperceptibly with the preoptic area.

In the tuberal region the hypothalamus reaches its widest extent, the fornix separating a medial from the lateral hypothalamic area already described. The medial portion forms the central gray substance of the ventricular wall in which there may be distinguished a *ventromedial* and a *dorsomedial nucleus* poorly delimited from each other (Le Gros Clark, Fig. 287). They are composed of uniformly small ovoid cells. In the caudal part of this region however there are found many large oval or rounded cells scattered in a matrix of smaller ones, which constitute the *posterior hypothalamic nucleus*. The large cells are especially numerous in man, and extend caudally over the mammillary body to become continuous with the ventricular gray and tegmentum of the midbrain. The cells resemble those of the lateral hypothalamic area, and are often included with the latter in a single and more extensive nuclear mass, the *mammilloinfundibular nucleus* (Malone). These large cells are believed to furnish most of the efferent hypothalamic fibers to the lower portions of the brain stem.

The mammillary portion consists of the mammillary bodies covered dorsally by the caudal cells of the posterior hypothalamic nucleus. In man the mammillary body

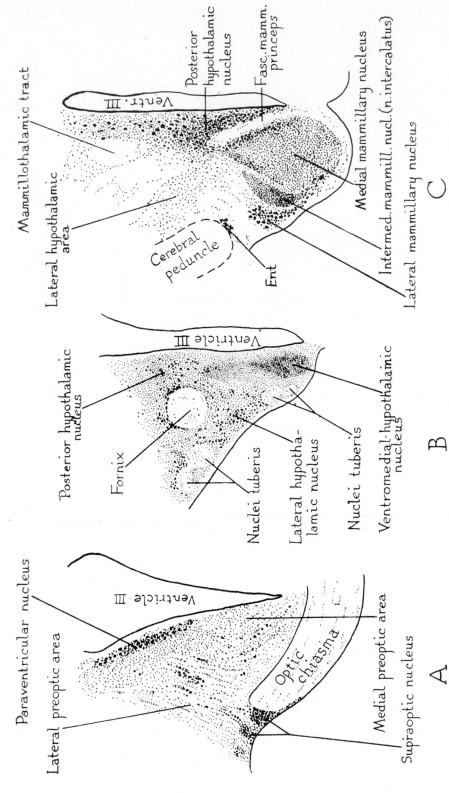

FIG. 288. Transverse sections through supraoptic (A), infundibular (B), and mammillary (C) portions of human hypothalamus. (After Le Gros Clark.) *Ent*, entopeduncular nucleus.

consists almost entirely of the large spherical *medial mammillary nucleus* composed of relatively small cells invested by a medullary laterally by a well defined group of large cells, the *lateral mammillary nucleus* (intercalated nucleus of Le Gros Clark), which

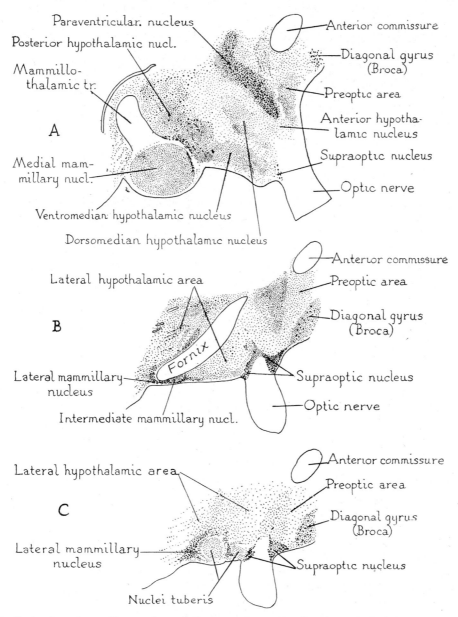

Paraventricular. nucleus
Posterior hypothalamic nucl.
Mammillo-thalamic tr.
A
Medial mammillary nucl.
Ventromedian hypothalamic nucleus
Dorsomedian hypothalamic nucleus
Anterior commissure
Diagonal gyrus (Broca)
Preoptic area
Anterior hypothalamic nucleus
Supraoptic nucleus
Optic nerve

Lateral hypothalamic area
B
Lateral mammillary nucleus
Intermediate mammillary nucl.
Fornix
Anterior commissure
Preoptic area
Diagonal gyrus (Broca)
Supraoptic nucleus
Optic nerve

Lateral hypothalamic area
C
Lateral mammillary nucleus
Nuclei tuberis
Anterior commissure
Preoptic area
Diagonal gyrus (Broca)
Supraoptic nucleus

Fig. 289. Sagittal sections of human hypothalamus. *A*, near median (ventricular) surface; *B*, through anterior column of fornix; *C*, near lateral border of hypothalamus. (After Le Gros Clark.)

capsule. Lateral to this is the small intermediate or *intercalated mammillary nucleus* (lateral nucleus of Le Gros Clark) composed of even smaller cells, flanked ventrally and probably represents a condensation of cells from the posterior hypothalamic nucleus (Fig. 288c).

The most characteristic features of the

human hypothalamus are the sharply circumscribed tuberal nuclei, the large size of
the medial mammillary nuclei, and the
extensive distribution of the large cells in
the posterior and lateral hypothalamic
areas.

Connections of the hypothalamus. The
hypothalamus in spite of its small size, has
remarkably extensive and complex fiber connections, some organized into definite and
conspicuous bundles, others diffuse and
difficult to trace. It receives fibers from the
secondary olfactory and general sensory
tracts, from the hippocampal cortex, from
the globus pallidus and subthalamic nucleus,
from the thalamus and directly or indirectly
from the frontal cortex. It sends fibers to
the preganglionic autonomic centers of the
brain stem and cord, to the posterior lobe of
the hypophysis, and an especially strong
fiber bundle to the anterior thalamic nucleus.

The afferent systems include (1) *Olfactohypothalamic fibers* from the basal olfactory regions including among others the
area olfactoria, amygdaloid nucleus and the
gray masses of the septum pellucidum.
These nuclei receive impulses from the
olfactory bulb and give rise in lower vertebrates to the medial forebrain bundle, a
tract of considerable size whose fibers terminate in part in the hypothalamus, in part
continue to the tegmentum of the midbrain
(Fig. 270). In man the tract is considerably reduced and inconspicuous, the diffusely
spread fibers passing through the lateral
hypothalamic area in which most of the
hypothalamic contingent of this bundle
apparently terminate. (2) *Corticomammillary fibers* from the hippocampal cortex and
dentate gyrus forming the conspicuous tract
known as the fornix. This tract goes mainly
to the hypothalamus, most of the fibers terminating in the mammillary nuclei. Some
however appear to end in the tuberal and
perhaps other hypothalamic nuclei and in
the preoptic area. (3) *Fibers from the
medial thalamic nuclei*, chiefly from the
magnocellular portion of the dorsomedial

nucleus and from the midline nuclei. These
form part of the periventricular fiber system
to be described below. (4) Fibers from the
globus pallidus, subthalamic nucleus and
zona incerta, some of the fibers crossing in the
anterior hypothalamic commissure. (5)
Ascending sensory fibers which detach themselves from the medial lemniscus in the midbrain region and as the *peduncle of the mammillary body* terminate mainly in the lateral
portion of that nuclear mass (Papez, Tello).
They are believed to conduct gustatory and
other visceral sensory impulses, and perhaps
also sensory impulses from the oral and nasal
mucous membranes. (6) The hypothalamus also receives fibers from the retina which
detach themselves from the optic tract and
terminate in the supraoptic and the ventromedial hypothalamic nucleus (Marburg).
Since both of these nuclei send fibers to the
posterior lobe of the hypophysis, the latter
is brought under retinal control by a two-
neuron pathway i.e. retinosupraoptic and
supraopticohypophysial.

The efferent hypothalamic fibers comprise
the conspicuous fiber bundles emerging from
the mammillary bodies, the periventricular
fibers, and the hypophysial connections.
From the medial mammillary nucleus and
perhaps from the lateral and intercalated as
well, arises a well defined fiber bundle, the
fasciculus mammillaris princeps, which passes dorsally for a short distance and then
separates into two bundles: the *mammillothalamic* and the *mammillotegmental tract*
(Fig. 270). The former passes upward and
forward and terminates in the anterior
thalamic nucleus. Some fibers of the tract
apparently run in the reverse direction i.e.
from the anterior nucleus to the mammillary
body. Since the anterior nucleus is reciprocally connected with the gyrus cinguli, the
mammillary body is brought indirectly
under the control of that cortical area.
The mammillotegmental tract curves in a
caudal direction and is believed to terminate
in some of the tegmental nuclei of the
midbrain.

The periventricular fibers arise primarily from the large cells of the posterior hypothalamic nucleus, to some extent also from the nuclei of the tuberal and supraoptic regions. These finely myelinated and unmyelinated fibers at first pass dorsally in the periventricular gray. Some terminate in the dorsomedial thalamic nucleus and in some of the midline nuclei, intermingled with fibers which pass from these thalamic nuclei to the hypothalamus (Fig. 290). This two-way connection brings the hypothalamus in relation with the granular cortex since the

spread out over considerable areas (Magoun). Those which reach the cord descend in the ventrolateral white and are believed to terminate in the intermediolateral column. The fibers appear to be largely uncrossed.

The connections of the hypothalamus with the posterior lobe of the hypophysis have been well established for man (Pines, Greving, Stengel). They are unmyelinated fibers which arise principally from the supraoptic and paraventricular nuclei and form a well defined bundle, the *supraopticohypophysial tract* (Fig. 290). A smaller bundle,

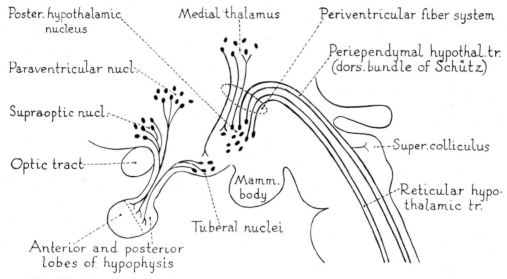

FIG. 290. Diagram showing some of the efferent fiber tracts from the hypothalamus

latter is reciprocally connected with the dorsomedial thalamic nucleus.

The majority of the periventricular fibers however turn caudally and descend to lower portions of the brain stem. Their exact course is not fully understood. A few run dorsal to the iter and terminate in the midbrain tectum. A larger number descends ventral to the iter in the subependymal portion of the central gray and forms the dorsal bundle of Schütz (periependymal tract) which has been traced as far as the vestibular nuclei and dorsal nucleus of the vagus. Other fibers, perhaps the greater part apparently descend in the reticular formation of the midbrain and medulla,

the *tuberohypophysial tract*, is contributed by the medial cells of the tuber cinereum.

It is evident from the above that the efferent descending hypothalamic fibers represent essentially connections with lower autonomic centers innervating visceral structures. In turn, the hypothalamus itself is under the control of the thalamic and pallial associative mechanisms. It is as yet uncertain whether there are direct corticohypothalamic tracts, but there are several indirect avenues of communication through which the pallium can influence the hypothalamus. Some of them have already been discussed, such as the connection with the frontal granular cortex through the dorsomedial thalamic nucleus, and with the cingular gyrus through the anterior nucleus. Other connections are through the zona incerta and gray matter of the septum pellucidum, both of which apparently receive fibers from the frontal cortex (Wallenberg, Mettler) and send fibers to the hypothalamus. Possibly the globus pallidus and subthalamic nucleus also represent links in palliohypothalamic pathways. It has been suggested that in monkeys at least the main cortical centers controlling hypothalamic i.e. visceral activities are located in the premotor frontal area (Fulton, Kennard and Watts).

Functional considerations. A large accumulation of experimental evidence and clinical observations have demonstrated beyond doubt that the hypothalamus and immediately adjoining region are intimately related to all kinds of visceral activities. The most diverse disturbances of autonomic functions such as water balance, internal secretion, sugar and fat metabolism, temperature regulation, can all be produced by stimulation or destruction of hypothalamic areas, and even the mechanism for normal sleep may be profoundly altered by such lesions. It is now definitely established that the hypothalamus is the chief subcortical center for the regulation of both sympathetic and parasympathetic activities and for the integration of these dual activites into coordinated responses having as their effect the maintenance of a constant internal environment of the body. Whether each of the autonomic activities has its own discrete center as many investigators assume, is highly improbable in view of the small size of the hypothalamus and the complex nature of these activities, though a specific and limited function has apparently been established for the supraoptic nucleus. There is however a fairly definite topographical orientation as regards the two main divisions of the autonomic system. The control of parasympathetic activities is related to the anterior and medial hypothalamic regions comprising the supraoptic and pre-

optic areas and the ventricular portion of the tuber cinereum. Stimulation of this region results in increased vagal and sacral autonomic activities characterized by reduced heart rate, peripheral vasodilation, and increased tonus and motility of the alimentary and vesical walls. Of the several nuclei found in this region, the supraoptic nucleus is definitely concerned with the maintenance of a proper water balance in the body. Destruction of the two supraoptic nuclei or their hypophysial connections is invariably followed by the condition known as *diabetes insipidus* in which there is increased secretion of urine (polyuria) without increase in the sugar content of the urine. It is believed that the nuclei stimulate the production of an antidiuretic hormone in the posterior lobe of the hypophysis, and their destruction causes the degeneration of the cells secreting the hormone. The significance of the other nuclei is not clear, though there is evidence that the ventromedial hypothalamic nucleus and probably also the paraventricular are related to sugar metabolism.

The lateral and posterior hypothalamic regions are concerned with the control of sympathetic responses. Stimulation of this area, especially of the posterior portion from which most of the descending efferent fibers arise, activates the thoracicolumbar outflow and results in the heightened metabolic and somatic activities characteristic of states of emotional stress, of combat or of flight. They are expressed in dilation of the pupil, erection of the hair, acceleration of the heart, elevation of blood pressure, increase in the rate and amplitude of respiration and somatic struggling movements, with concomitant inhibition of the gut and bladder. All these signs of emotional excitement are also readily elicited when the hypothalamus is released from cortical control ("sham rage") by removal of the cortex or by interruption of the cortical connections with the hypothalamus (Bard; Fulton and Ingraham). On the other hand destruction of the posterior hypothalamus produces emotional lethargy, abnormal sleepiness and a fall in temperature due to the reduction of general visceral (and somatic) activities.

The coordination of sympathetic and parasympathetic responses is strikingly shown in the regulation of body temperature. This complex function involving widely spread physical and chemical processes is apparently mediated by two hypothalamic mechanisms, one concerned with the dissipation of heat, the other with its production and conservation. There is considerable experimental evidence to the effect that the anterior hypothalamus, especially the preoptic area, is sensitive to increases in temperature and sets in motion the machinery for getting rid of the excess heat. In man this consists mainly in profuse sweating and vasodilation of the cutaneous blood vessels, permitting the rapid elimination of heat by convection and radiation from the surface of the engorged blood vessels and by the evaporation of sweat. In animals with fur this is supplemented to a considerable degree by rapid respiratory movements of shallow amplitude (panting), the heat loss being effected mainly by the warming of rapidly successive streams of inspired air.

The posterior hypothalamus, on the other hand, is sensitive to conditions of decreased body temperature and institutes measures for the conservation and increased production of heat. The cutaneous blood vessels are constricted and sweat secretion shut off, reducing to a minimum the heat loss through radiation and evaporation. Simultaneously there is augmentation of visceral activities and the somatic muscles stiffen and are thrown into the involuntary movements of shivering, all these activities tremendously increasing the processes of oxidation with consequent production of heat.

These two intrinsically antagonistic mechanisms do not function independently but are continually interrelated and balanced against each other to meet the changing needs of the body, the coordinated responses always directed to the maintenance of a constant optimum temperature.

THE BASAL GANGLIA

In close relation to the diencephalon are a number of gray masses belonging to the endbrain, more or less completely buried in the medullary substance of the hemisphere. These *basal ganglia* comprise the *lenticular* and *caudate nuclei,* the *amygdaloid nucleus* and possibly also the *claustrum*. The caudate and lenticular nuclei together with the internal capsule which separates them, constitute the *corpus striatum*.

The **amygdaloid nucleus** is a complex gray mass situated in the dorsomedial portion of the temporal lobe, in front and partly above the tip of the inferior horn. It is covered by a layer of rudimentary cortex and is caudally continuous with the uncus of the hypocampal gyrus (Figs. 291, 292). It is related medially to the area olfactoria, laterally to the claustrum, while dorsally it is hidden in part by the lenticular nucleus. The connections of the amygdaloid nucleus, mainly olfactory ones, have not been fully worked out. It receives fibers from the lateral olfactory stria, and gives rise to a fiber bundle known as the *stria terminalis* or *stria semicircularis* (Figs. 260, 263) which arches along the entire medial border of the caudate nucleus and terminates mainly in the area olfactoria, septal region and anterior portion of the hypothalamus. Some of the fibers cross in the anterior commissure, connecting the two amygdalae, and it is probable that many fibers of the stria terminalis run in a reverse direction, i.e. from the basal olfactory regions to the amygdaloid nucleus. The nucleus is also believed to receive fibers from the thalamus and from the anterior portion of the gyrus cinguli and to send fibers to the habenular ganglion by way of the stria medullaris, and to the uncus and hippocampal formation. The amygdaloid complex is found in all mammals and has been homologized with the olfactory stria-

Striatum = Caudate & Putamen
Pallidum = N. Pallidus

tum (archistriatum) of submammalian forms.

The **claustrum** is a thin plate of gray matter lying in the medullary substance of the hemisphere between the lenticular nucleus and the cortex of the insula, separated from these structures by two white lamina: the external capsule medially, and the extreme capsule laterally (Figs. 291, 292). Some consider it as a part of the striatum, but there is considerable evidence that it origi-

however is not complete. In its most rostral portion the head of the caudate is ventrally continuous with the lenticular nucleus, and more dorsally the two nuclei are connected by a number of slender gray bridges extending across the internal capsule (Figs. 293, 291, 278). These bridges give the striped appearance which has led to the designation of corpus striatum.

The *caudate nucleus* is an elongated arched gray mass related throughout its extent to

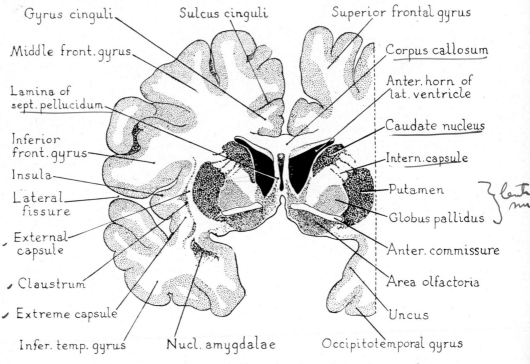

Gyrus cinguli   Sulcus cinguli   Superior frontal gyrus

Middle front. gyrus   Corpus callosum

Lamina of sept. pellucidum   Anter. horn of lat. ventricle

Inferior front. gyrus   Caudate nucleus

Insula   Intern. capsule

Lateral fissure   Putamen

External capsule   Globus pallidus

Claustrum   Anter. commissure

Extreme capsule   Area olfactoria

Uncus

Infer. temp. gyrus   Nucl. amygdalae   Occipitotemporal gyrus

FIG. 291. Frontal section of brain passing through anterior commissure

nates from the deep layers of the insular cortex from which it secondarily splits off. Its functions and connections are obscure.

The corpus striatum. The structure and connections of the corpus striatum have been discussed in an earlier part of this chapter (pp. 305–310) and will only be briefly summarized. Arising as a single gray mass during early development it becomes secondarily divided by the fibers of the internal capsule into two cellular masses, the *lenticular* and the *caudate nucleus*. This separation

the ventricular surface of the lateral ventricle (Figs. 253, 264). Its enlarged anterior portion or *head* lies rostral to the thalamus and bulges into the anterior horn. Its long attenuated caudal portion or *tail* extends along the dorsolateral border of the thalamus, separated from the latter by the terminal sulcus in which are lodged the stria terminalis and terminal vein. On reaching the caudal limit of the thalamus the tail arches ventrally and runs forward in the roof of the inferior horn to reach the amygdaloid nucleus (Fig. 293).

The lenticular nucleus has the form of a Brazil nut or of a stout wedge whose broad somewhat convex base is directed laterally and its blade medially. It has no ventricular surface but lies deeply buried in the white matter of the hemisphere closely applied to the lateral surface of the internal capsule which separates it from the caudate nucleus and the thalamus (Figs. 292, 293). A vertical plate of white matter, the external

tute the phylogenetically newer part of the striate complex (*neostriatum*) and are often designated as just the *striatum*. They are composed of small and medium sized cells with a sprinkling of larger ones, and represent primarily the receptive portion of the corpus striatum. The phylogenetically older globus pallidus (*paleostriatum* or *pallidum*) is composed almost entirely of large cells of a "motor" character whose axons form the efferent fiber systems.

The connections of the corpus striatum,

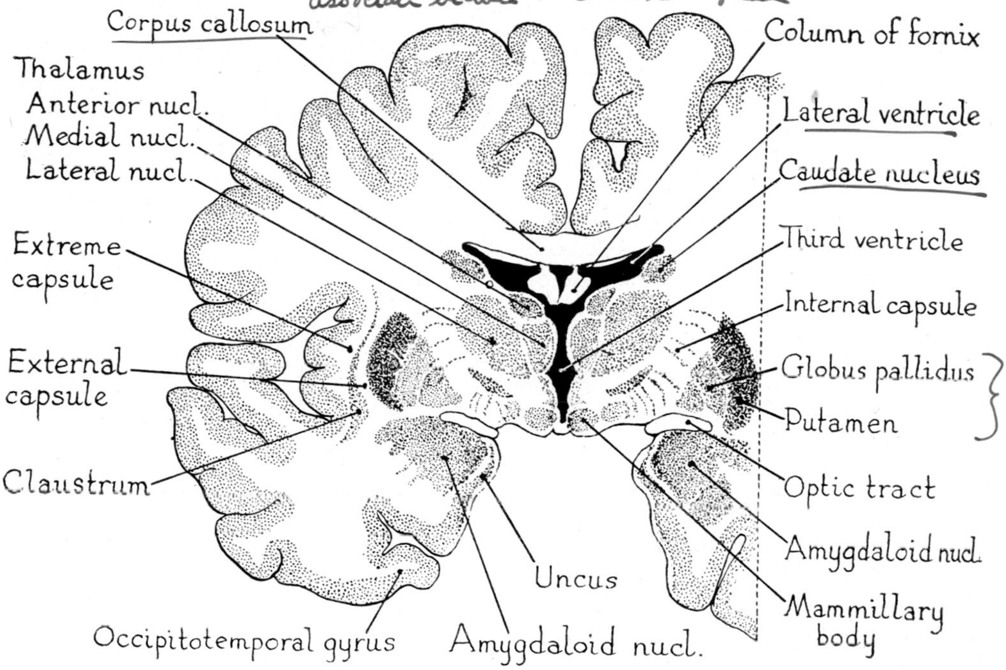

FIG. 292: Frontal section of brain passing through mammillary bodies

medullary lamina divides the nucleus into an outer larger portion, the *putamen*, and an inner portion known as the *globus pallidus* which is broken up into several segments by the internal medullary laminae (Figs. 292, 271). The globus pallidus is traversed by many myelinated fibers, hence in the fresh condition appears paler than the putamen or caudate nucleus in which such fibers are relatively scarce. Only the putamen is continuous with the caudate nucleus by the gray bridges mentioned above.

The putamen and caudate nucleus consti-

more fully discussed on pp. 307 and 309, may be briefly summarized. The afferent fibers which terminate principally in the putamen and caudate nucleus come mainly from the thalamus and probably also from the cortex, either directly or after a relay in the thalamus. The efferent fibers arising from the globus pallidus project on a number of nuclei (Fig. 275). They go to the thalamus, subthalamus and hypothalamus; to the substantia nigra, nucleus ruber, interstitial and commissural nuclei, and to the more diffuse cell groups of the reticular formation. Some may perhaps go directly to the motor nuclei of certain cranial nerves. It is evident that on the whole, the efferent pallidal impulses do not reach the lower motor neurons by long fibers as is the case with the pyramidal tract, but are first interrupted in many gray masses widely scattered throughout the brain stem.

The extrapyramidal motor system. It is now generally accepted that movements of a volitional or semivolitional character may be mediated through other than pyramidal

clinical evidence to suggest that the corpus striatum and associated nuclei, such as the substantia nigra, nucleus ruber and subthalamic nucleus, play an important part in this extrapyramidal motor control, and all these nuclei have been linked together as constituting an older or *extrapyramidal motor system,* in existence long before the advent of the motor cortex and pyramidal tract.

This older system is however under the dominance of the cerebral cortex. It has been demonstrated that stimulation of the

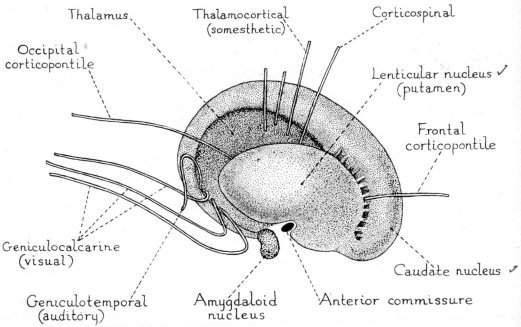

FIG. 293. Lateral view of corpus striatum, thalamus and amygdaloid nucleus, semischematic (Modified from Elze.) Some of the fibers in the anterior, superior, posterior and retrolentricular portions of the internal capsule are indicated.

channels. In lesions of the motor area or pyramidal tract, it is primarily the finer isolated movements of the distal parts of the extremities which are severely and permanently affected. Gross synergic movements of locomotion, expression and postural adjustment, and those semiautomatic movements which are normally associated with voluntary activities, such as swinging the arms in walking, persist to a considerable extent or reappear shortly after an initial period of paralysis. There is considerable

premotor cortex (area 6) and certain other cortical areas in the parietal and temporal lobes produce complex synergic movements on the opposite side even after complete destruction of the motor area (area 4). Such areas have been designated as extrapyramidal ones whose impulses do not pass uninterruptedly to the lower motor neurons but are relayed in the corpus striatum or other nuclei of the old motor system. Whether the cortex is directly connected with the basal ganglia is still a disputed question, but seems probable. Corticostriate fibers especially from the frontal lobe have been reported for the monkey by a number of investigators (Hirasawa and Kato, Poliak, Mettler and others), and according to Cajal collaterals from the pyramidal tract terminate in the striatum. But even if the existence of such fibers is denied (Wilson), there is an extensive route from cortex to striatum by way of the thalamus, and this cortico-thalamo-striate pathway is probably the most important channel through which cortical influence is transmitted to the basal ganglia. Through the thalamus the corpus striatum may also receive impulses from the ascending sensory tracts and the cerebellum.

The neopallium is phylogenetically a late acquisition, appearing first in the higher reptiles, but in both reptiles and birds it remains on a rudimentary plane and the descending fibers from the cortex are few in number. It is only in the mammals that the motor area and its massive pyramidal projection become a constant and striking feature of the nervous system. The corpus striatum on the other hand is an old part of the endbrain, found in all vertebrates. The paleostriatum comparable to the globus pallidus is already well developed in fishes. It receives mainly olfactory impulses and gives rise to the "basal forebrain bundle" which discharges into the thalamus, hypothalamus and midbrain, whence impulses are ultimately relayed to the motor nuclei of the cranial and spinal nerves. This bundle is probably homologous in mammals with the ansa lenticularis of the globus pallidus. In reptiles and birds a neostriatum is added, the caudato-putamen of higher vertebrates, now receiving impulses mainly from the thalamus, and especially in birds the whole striatal complex becomes highly differentiated and enlarged to form the most massive portion of the cerebrum. It seems certain that in animals without a cortex or with a poorly developed one, the corpus striatum is the most important center on whose integrity depend the normal largely instinctive

activities of these forms, such as locomotion, defense, feeding, courting, etc. In birds these activities are practically unaffected after ablation of the primitive cortex, but they are severely impaired in lesions of the corpus striatum (Rogers). Thus in sub-mammalian forms the diencephalon and corpus striatum together constitute the highest sensory-motor integrating mechanism of the forebrain, the thalamus representing the receptive center, the corpus striatum and hypothalamus related to motor control. The corpus striatum discharges through intercalated nuclei to the somatic muscles, the hypothalamus is similarly connected with the visceral effectors. These reactions are determined on the afferent side by sensory stimuli of an affective rather than discriminative nature, and are expressed in movements which are gross, postural and stereotyped.

With the evolution of the neopallium in mammals the functions of the corpus striatum become subordinated to those of the cerebral cortex and are brought in balance with the activities of the motor area. Dominated now by extrapyramidal cortical centers the old motor system is still however utilized for the production of many of the more or less automatic movements concerned with postural adjustments, reactions of defense, feeding, etc., and most mammals are able to perform their normal activities after destruction of both pyramidal tracts. Even chimpanzees recover sufficiently to feed themselves and execute movements of walking and climbing. Whether the human striatum has similar if reduced functions is still a disputed question, and it is possible that in man the basal ganglia have a different significance than in lower mammals. Destruction of the pyramidal tract causes a far more complete and lasting paralysis, but even in man the grosser movements are less severely affected and recover to a considerable extent. According to Kinnier Wilson the corpus striatum maintains a postural background for voluntary activities, reinforcing and steadying movements and postures of cortical origin, but is incapable of initiating such movements. Others however maintain that even in man the grosser more automatic volitional movements as well as postural adjustments are mediated through the extrapyramidal system, and that these kinds of movement are most severely affected in diseases of the corpus striatum.

The pallium thus projects to the lower motor centers through two main channels. The motor area discharging in part at least through the long fibers of the pyramidal tract is primarily concerned with the finer nonpostural isolated and modifiable movements which form the basis for the acquisition of skill. The extrapyramidal centers of the premotor, motor, and perhaps other cortical areas, are largely concerned with postural adjustments and the grosser volitional movement patterns, and through their hypothalamic connections, probably also with the regulation of autonomic functions. These areas do not discharge directly to the lower motor neurons but utilize the existing though modified machinery of the old motor system which was charged with similar functions in precortical days. The two systems do not function independently but are in constant balance with each other, the smooth execution of nonpostural pyramidal movements implying a concomitant regulation and modification of the postural mechanisms.

Clinically, the chief manifestations of striatal disease are muscular rigidity and involuntary movements such as tremor, chorea and athetosis. *Chorea* is expressed in spontaneous abrupt and rapidly successive movements of considerable complexity, resembling aimless fragments of voluntary or emotional activities. They involve the extremities and face, resulting in constant gesticulation and facial grimacing, and the tongue, pharynx and larynx may likewise be affected. Muscle tone is as a rule reduced. In *athetosis* there are slow writhing

or twisting movements of the extremities, especially of the fingers and hand, the movements blending with each other to give the appearance of a continuous mobile spasm. Similar more rarely occuring spasms may involve large portions of the body and lead to severe torsion of the neck, hip and shoulder girdle (torsion spasms). Between the spasms the muscles are apparently hypotonic.

Many clinicians recognize two symptom complexes of striatal disease, one hypokinetic, the other hyperkinetic. The former is best exemplified in the condition known as paralysis agitans (Parkinsonism). It is characterized by muscular rigidity and tremor resulting in disturbances of posture and the ease and rapidity of voluntary movements. The augmentation of muscle tone is not selective as in hemiplegia, but is present to the same extent in anatagonistic muscle groups, i.e. in both flexors and extensors of the same joint. With this there is impairment or loss of associated movements such as extension of the wrist on flexing the fingers or swinging the arms in walking, and of normal emotional expression, the face appearing immobile or mask-like. The poverty of associated movements and facial expression is ascribed to a loss of pallidal function, the rigidity and tremor to the release of medullary and spinal centers from pallidal control. The site of the destructive lesion is believed to be in the globus pallidus or substantia nigra.

The hyperkinetic manifestations of chorea and athetosis are more difficult to explain. These symptoms are the reverse of those present in paralysis agitans. Moreover choreoathetoid movements may appear in lesions of the superior cerebellar peduncle, nucleus ruber, thalamus and extrapyramidal cortex. When present in striatal disease the lesion is said to involve the neostriatum (caudato-putamen) which is believed to inhibit the activities of the globus pallidus. The exaggerated movements are hence ascribed to a release of the pallidum from

pill-rolling tremor in hand from extrapyramidal tract
& parkinsonism - cog wheel spasticity

striatal inhibition. Since the neostriatum is influenced by impulses from the extrapyramidal cortex and cerebellum, both reaching the striatum by way of the thalamus, it is assumed that lesions of the cortico-thalamo-striate and cerebello-rubro-thalamo-striate pathways will likewise effect a loss or impairment of striatal inhibition with consequent release of pallidal function.

Kinnier Wilson maintains that the influence of the corpus striatum is in the control of tone and steadiness of innervation and not in the initiation of movement. He believes that the poverty of movement in paralysis agitans may be fully explained by the rigidity which makes all movements difficult and requires a greater effort on the part of the patient. On the other hand, chorea and athetosis are regarded as being primarily due to lesions of the afferent pathway going from the cerebellum by way of the nucleus ruber and thalamus to the motor and premotor cortex. These cortical areas, especially the premotor area which is considered as a higher center of volitional control, suffer an impairment of function with the result that normal voluntary movements are displaced by disordered involuntary ones. Chorea and athetosis are thus considered as involuntary cortical activities mediated through the pyramidal tract, and disappear when the latter is destroyed by disease or surgical section. The loss of cerebellar impulses may also account for the hypotonia and incoordination of choreic movements.

4·5 suppressor strip area

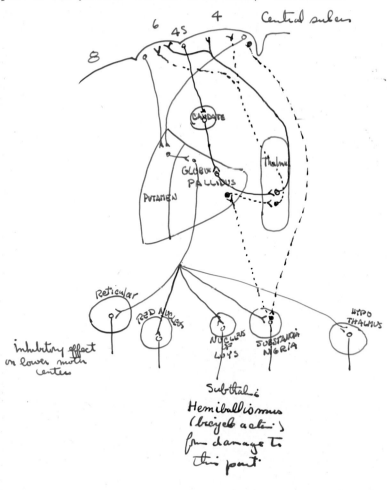

6 4·5 4 Central sulcus
8
CAUDATE
Thalamus
GLOBUS PALLIDUS
PUTAMEN
Reticular
RED NUCLEUS
NUCLEUS of LUYS
SUBSTANTIA NIGRA
HYPO THALAMUS
inhibitory effect on lower motor centers
Subthal:
Hemiballismus
(bicycle action)
from damage to
this part.

CHAPTER XIX

THE CEREBRAL HEMISPHERES

DEVELOPMENT AND GENERAL CONSIDERATIONS

The *telencephalon* or endbrain arises as a hollow bud from the dorsal anterior wall of the primary forebrain, then bulges laterally and expands into the two hemispheric vesicles which begin to overlap the diencephalon (Fig. 16). These vesicles are now connected to each other by the median portion of the endbrain (telencephalon medium) which undergoes relatively little growth and is composed of the lamina terminalis and the most rostral portion of the third ventricle. The lateral extensions of the cavity into the hemispheric vesicles constitute the future lateral ventricles which at this stage communicate with the third ventricle by large interventricular foramina (Fig. 16).

The hemispheric vesicles grow rapidly in all directions. At first their ventral surfaces fold back over the sides and roof of the diencephalon, thus forming the *transverse cerebral fissure* in which is lodged a double fold of pia mater, the *velum interpositum* or *tela chorioidea* of the third ventricle. Soon they expand dorsally to such extent that the hemispheric vesicles now tower steeply above the roof of the thalamus, their medial surfaces separated from each other by a deep sagittal cleft, the *interhemispheric* or *longitudinal fissure*, into which extends a dural fold, the *falx cerebri*. As expansion continues the midbrain and ultimately the cerebellum become likewise covered by the cerebral hemispheres.

From the hemispheric vesicles develop the three fundamental structures of the endbrain: *basal ganglia, olfactory lobe* and *pallium*. The basal ganglia arise as a thickening in the ventromedial part of the hemispheric wall which lies adjacent to the lateral surface of the diencephalon, and their further development has already been discussed (p. 292). The *olfactory lobe* makes its appearance in the second month as a narrow longitudinal bulge on the basal surface of the hemisphere, ventral and medial to the basal ganglia (Figs. 10, 12). It is distinctly demarcated from the lateral surface of the pallium by the *external rhinal fissure*, and soon differentiates into an anterior and posterior portion. The former at first containing an extension of the lateral ventricle elongates into a tubular stalk which becomes solid by the end of the third month and forms the rudiment of the olfactory tract and bulb. The posterior portion differentiates into the olfactory area (anterior perforated substance) and certain other olfactory structures closely related to the anteromedial portion of the temporal lobe and collectively known as the *piriform area*. These structures will be discussed more fully below.

The rest of the hemispheric wall at first remaining relatively thin, develops into the *pallium* or cerebral mantle which becomes tremendously expanded and forms by far the largest part of the hemisphere. The pallium grows forward and somewhat downward to form the frontal lobe carrying with it an extension of the lateral ventricle, the *anterior* or *frontal horn*. Posteriorly it curves ventrally and forward to form temporal lobe into which extends the *inferior* or *temporal horn* of the ventricle, while somewhat later the occipital lobe is produced by the backward growth of the pallium, likewise receiving a short prolongation of the lateral ventricle, the *posterior* or *occipital horn*. The portion of the pallium lying between the frontal and occipital lobe and containing the *body of the ventricle*, constitutes the parietal lobe. During the second month a shallow depression, the *lateral* or *Sylvian fossa*, appears on the lateral surface of each hemisphere in the region overlying the corpus striatum (Fig. 12). This is not produced by invagination, but is due to the more rapid growth of the adjacent portions, frontal, parietal and temporal. Gradually the latter completely overgrow the fossa whose external opening becomes reduced to a deep cleft, the *Sylvian* or *lateral fissure* (Fig. 18). The now submerged floor of the fissure develops into the *insula* or *island of Reil*. Those portions of the frontal, parietal and temporal lobes which form the lips of the fissure constitute the *opercula* or covers of the insula.

During the second month, a longitudinal thickening, the *hippocampal ridge*, appears on the medial wall of the hemisphere, a short distance from the dorsal margin (Fig. 17). This ridge soon folds into the hemisphere producing the *hippocampal fissure* on the medial surface and a corresponding elevation in the ventricular wall. When the pallium curves ventrally and forward to form the temporal lobe the hippocampal fissure and associated structures likewise increase in length and finally extend from the region of the interventricular foramen to the tip of the inferior horn. The hippocampal ridge develops into the *hippocampal formation* whose detailed structure will be given later. It is the most ancient olfactory portion of the pallium already present in amphibians and is hence known as the *archipallium* in distinction to the phylogenetically more recently acquired non-olfactory *neopallium* which is highly developed only in mammals. Olfactory lobe (paleopallium or paleocortex) and hippocampal formation (archipallium) together constitute the *rhinencephalon* concerned with the reception and integration of olfactory impulses. In lower vertebrates the rhinencephalon and its pathways form practically all of the endbrain, a rudimentary neopallium appearing first in the

reptiles. In mammals the neopallium becomes dominant, but even among them there is considerable variation as to the size and importance of the rhinencephalon. Some are *macrosmatic* i.e., possess a well developed rhinencephalon which in the case of some rodents may constitute the larger part of the hemisphere. In man, who is *microsmatic*, the olfactory lobe and portions of the archipallium have become greatly reduced, and the whole rhinencephalic complex has been pushed to the basal and medial surfaces of the hemisphere and is in part overgrown by the tremendously enlarged neopallium. In man, the rhinencephalon occupies only one twelfth of the entire hemispheric surface (Economo).

Ventral to the hippocampal ridge the medial wall is directly continuous with the roof of the third ventricle and forms the dorsal wall of the interventricular foramen (Fig. 17). During the second month, this portion of the wall which remains very thin, becomes invaginated into the lateral ventricle in the form of a longitudinal fold, the *plica chorioidea*. Externally the line of invagination is marked by the *chorioidal fissure* which extends from the interventricular foramen to the caudal end of the hemispheric vesicle, lying parallel and ventral to the hippocampal fissure. The chorioidal fold lined by a layer of ependymal epithelium, is soon invaded by richly vascular connective tissue from the pia, the two together constituting the chorioid tela which by proliferation gives rise to the chorioid plexus of the lateral ventricle. As the posterior end of the hemispheric vesicle grows downward and forward to form the temporal lobe, the chorioid plexus finally extends from the interventricular foramen to the tip of the inferior horn. At the interventricular foramen it becomes continuous with the chorioid plexus of the third ventricle.

The early stages in the histogenesis of the pallium resemble those of other parts of the neural tube. During the first two months the wall of the pallium remains relatively thin and is composed of an ependymal, a mantle and a marginal layer. At the end of the second month, however, cells begin to wander from the mantle layer into the marginal zone where they form a superficial gray layer, the *cerebral cortex*. As the cerebral cortex gradually thickens by the addition and differentiation of the migrating cells, it assumes a laminated appearance, the cells becoming organized into a number of horizontal layers, and sometimes between the sixth and eighth month six such layers may be distinguished (Brodmann). This sesquilaminated condition is characteristic of the whole neopallium, even in those portions where it subsequently becomes obscured, hence the neopallial cortex has been called the *isocortex* (Vogt) or *homogenetic cortex* (Brodmann). The rhinencephalon alone seems to be built on a different plan, either showing no lamination at all or only an incomplete one, and is hence known as the *allocortex* or *heterogenetic cortex*.

With the development of the cortex, nerve fibers begin to accumulate beneath its deep surface to form the *medullary* or *white substance* of the hemisphere. The latter is obviously composed of (1) fibers from the thalamus and other brain stem ganglia which terminate in the cortex; (2) fibers from cortical cells which go to other portions of the nervous system such as the brain stem and spinal cord; (3) association fibers which connect the various parts of a single hemisphere, and (4) commissural fibers connecting the two hemispheres. The crossing fibers become organized into three commissures: the *anterior* and *hippocampal commissures* connecting primarily the older olfactory portions, and the much larger *corpus callosum* or neopallial commissure. All of the commissural fibers cross through the lamina terminalis whose dorsal portion thickens at an early stage to form the commissural plate (Fig. 14). The anterior commissure is placed in the ventral portion of the plate, the fibers of the hippocampal

commissure cross more dorsally. The first fibers of the corpus callosum likewise appear in the dorsal portion above and in front of the hippocampal commissure. With the expansion of the hemispheres the corpus callosum grows backward, finally forming a broad band of fibers overlapping the thalamus and midbrain. Since the callosal fibers emerge from each hemisphere through the hippocampal fissure, the hippocampal formation is split throughout the region of the commissure into a dorsal portion lying above the corpus callosum and a ventral portion lying below it (Fig. 309). A small membranous portion of the lamina terminalis which is not invaded by commissural fibers, is stretched backward by the growth of the corpus callosum into a thin vertical plate, the *septum pellucidum*, which forms the medial wall separating the two ventricles (Figs. 291, 278). As a result of the stretching the septum usually splits into two lamina enclosing between them a cleft-like cavity (Fig. 291).

In human foetuses of the fifth month the surface of the hemisphere is still smooth and only the future lateral fissure is indicated by the still open Sylvian fossa. But from that time on the cortex begins to exhibit a number of folds, the gyri or convolutions, separated by sulci or fissures of varying depth, and by the end of the seventh month the convolutional pattern is almost fully established. The sulci do not arise by a linear invagination of the cortical surface but owe their existence to the convolutions themselves which are the primary structures to be formed. The cerebral wall does not increase in thickness uniformly, but rather in the form of stripes or bands which thicken rapidly and become raised above the surface as narrow ridges. The intervening strips which grow more slowly constitute the floor of the furrows thus formed. This unequal growth is reflected in the adult structure of the brain, the cerebral cortex being thickest on the crown of a convolution and gradually thinning out towards the floor of the sulcus.

While the basic convolutional pattern is the same in all human brains, the configuration and extent of the individual gyri vary considerably in different brains and even in the individual hemispheres of a single brain. Some of the furrows are very deep and involve the entire thickness of the cerebral wall, producing corresponding elevations on the ventricular surface. These complete furrows, often designated as fissures, include the hippocampal and chorioidal fissures already described, and the *calcarine* and *collateral fissures* (Fig. 298). The latter two give rise to ventricular prominences known respectively as the *calcar avis* and *collateral eminence* (Figs. 303, 310). The rest of the sulci merely indent the medullary substance without affecting the ventricular cavity.

By means of the sulci and fissures the brain is subdivided into a number of main territories or lobes, named in accordance with their topographical relations to the skull. This subdivision is largely a convenient one, and some of the lobar boundaries have to be arbitrarily determined. Furthermore each lobe consists of several histologically and functionally distinct cortical areas some of which may overlap the anatomical boundaries of the lobe. In general, five lobes are usually recognized: *frontal, parietal, occipital, temporal,* and *insular* or *central*. The olfactory portions are not included in the above named lobes, but are regarded as constituting a separate anatomical entity, the *rhinencephalon*.

THE EXTERNAL FEATURES OF THE CEREBRAL HEMISPHERES

Each hemisphere consists of the pallium and the deep-lying basal ganglia whose structure and connections have been discussed in chapter XVIII. The pallium or cerebral mantle is composed of an internal fibrous mass, the white or medullary sub-

stance, everywhere covered superficially by a layer of gray matter, the cerebral cortex. The paired cavities of the hemispheres are known as the lateral ventricles. The cerebral hemispheres are separated from each other by the deep vertical *interhemispheric* or *longitudinal fissure* containing the falx cerebri. In front and behind, the separation is complete, but in the middle portion the fissure extends only to the corpus callosum, a broad band of commissural fibers uniting the two hemisphres. Posteriorly the hemispheres overlap the thalamus, midbrain and cerebellum, separated from these structures by the transverse fissure which is occupied posteriorly by the tentorium cerebelli, anteriorly by the tela chorioidea of the third ventricle. In each hemisphere three surfaces may be distinguished: dorsolateral, medial and basal. A rounded dorsal border intervenes between the convex dorsolateral and the flat vertical medial surface, and similarly a lateral border separates the convex from the basal surface. The latter surface is more complex in shape, closely modeled in front to the base of the skull. Its anterior portion occupies the anterior and middle cranial fossa, its posterior portion rests on the tentorium cerebelli. A basal border separates the medial and basal surfaces.

The dorsolateral surface (Figs. 294, 295). The most striking furrows on the convex surface are the *lateral cerebral fissure (Sylvian fissure)* and the *central sulcus.* The *lateral fissure* starts on the basal surface as a deep cleft, the Sylvian fossa, separating the frontal and temporal lobes, then extends as the trunk of the fissure to the dorsolateral surface where it divides into three branches. The short anterior horizontal and anterior ascending branches incise the ventral surface of the frontal lobe. The long posterior branch which appears as a direct continuation of the trunk, passes backward almost horizontally and then curves upward to terminate in the parietal lobe (Fig. 295).

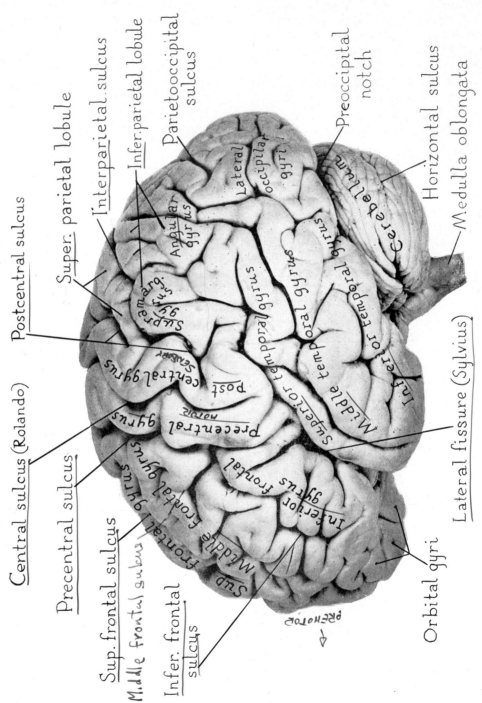

Central sulcus (Rolando)

Precentral sulcus

Postcentral sulcus

Super. parietal lobule

Interparietal sulcus

Inferparietal lobule

Parietooccipital sulcus

Preoccipital notch

Horizontal sulcus

Medulla oblongata

Lateral occipital gyri

Cerebellum

Angular gyrus

Supramarg. gyrus

Sensory

Post. central gyrus

Superior temporal gyrus

Middle temporal gyrus

Inferior temporal gyrus

Precentral gyrus

motor

Sup. frontal sulcus

Middle frontal sulcus

Infer. frontal sulcus

Sup. frontal gyrus

Middle frontal gyrus

Inferior frontal gyrus

Lateral fissure (Sylvius)

Orbital gyri

PREFRONTAL →

FIG. 294. Lateral view of human brain. Photograph

The central sulcus of Rolando is a deep and usually continuous furrow running downward and slightly forward from about the middle of the dorsal border to the Sylvian fissure without quite reaching the latter. The sulcus shows two knee-like bends and often incises the dorsal border to reach the medial surface.

The **frontal lobe** which comprises about one third of the hemispheric surface extends from the frontal pole to the central

gyri, separated from each other by the *superior* and *inferior frontal sulci*. Often a shallower middle frontal sulcus divides the stout middle gyrus into an upper lower tier. The inferior frontal gyrus which forms the frontal operculum of the insula, is subdivided by the anterior branches of the lateral fissure into an orbital, a triangular and an opercular portion (Fig. 295). In the left or dominant hemisphere the triangular and opercular portions are known as

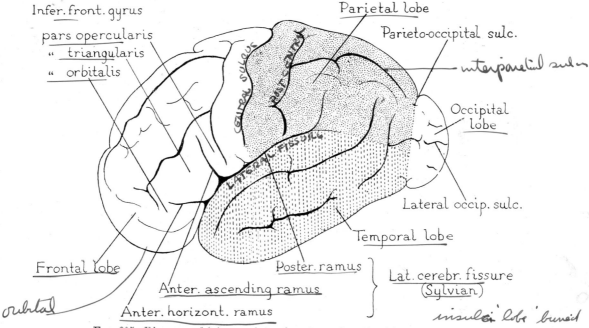

Fig. 295. Diagram of lobes on lateral surface of cerebral hemisphere

sulcus and is limited below by the trunk and posterior branch of the lateral fissure. On the convex surface four main convolutions may be distinguished. The vertical *precentral gyrus* runs parallel to the central sulcus, bounded in front by the *precentral sulcus* which is sometimes broken up into a superior and inferior segment. This gyrus comprises the motor and a considerable part of the premotor area, and is the site of origin of the corticospinal and corticobulbar tracts. The rest of the frontal lobe is composed of three horizontal convolutions, the *superior, middle* and *inferior frontal*

Broca's area, regarded as the cortical center for the motor formulation of speech.

The smaller **parietal lobe** is more difficult to delimit on the convex surface. Bounded sharply in front by the central sulcus, its posterior part merges imperceptibly with the occipital lobe behind and the temporal lobe below. Its occipital boundary is arbitrarily established by a vertical line drawn from the upper end of the parieto-occipital fissure to a shallow depression on the ventral hemispheric surface about 4 cm. from the occipital pole, and hence known as the preoccipital notch. Its temporal boundary is similarly established by an imaginary line extending the horizontal portion of the lateral fissure to the occipito-parietal line determined above (Fig. 295).

The sulci on the convex surface of the parietal lobe vary considerably in different individuals. As a rule two main sulci are distinguished though these may be continuous with each other and form a single sulcus of complicated form. The *postcentral sulcus* usually broken up into a superior and inferior segment runs parallel with the central sulcus and forms the caudal boundary of the vertical *postcentral gyrus* which represents the somesthetic sensory area of the cerebral cortex. The *intraparietal* or *interparietal sulcus* which is usually a direct continuation of the inferior postcentral, arches backward to the occipital lobe where it often ends as the transverse occipital sulcus beneath the dorsal margin of the parietoöccipital fissure. The sulcus divides the rest of the parietal lobe into a *superior parietal lobule* lying above it and an *inferior parietal lobule* below. The inferior lobule is primarily represented by the *supramarginal gyrus* which curves around the terminal ascending portion of the lateral fissure, and the *angular gyrus* which similarly surrounds the ascending terminal part of the superior temporal sulcus. The most caudal part of the inferior lobule which receives the terminal extension of the middle temporal sulcus is the poorly defined *posterior parietal gyrus*. The ventral portions of the precentral, postcentral and supramarginal gyri constitute the centroparietal operculum of the insula.

The large **temporal lobe** whose anterior tip is known as the temporal pole, shows three horizontal convolutions, the *superior, middle* and *inferior temporal gyri*, separated by similarly named sulci. The deep and constant superior temporal sulcus begins at the temporal pole and runs parallel to the Sylvian fissure, its ascending terminal portion ending in the angular gyrus. The posterior portion of the irregular and seg-mented middle temporal sulcus is related to the posterior parietal gyrus. The inferior temporal sulcus can only be seen on the basal surface. The superior temporal gyrus forms the temporal operculum, and its broad dorsal surface which faces the lateral fissure is marked in its caudal portion by several short obliquely running convolutions, the *transverse gyri of Heschl*, the most anterior of which represents the auditory projection area of the cortex (Fig. 296).

The small **occipital lobe** whose rounded apex constitutes the occipital pole, occupies only a restricted portion on the convex surface of the hemisphere. It is composed of a number of irregular and variable *lateral occipital gyri*, usually separated into a superior and an inferior group by the more definite and constant *lateral occipital sulcus* (Figs. 294, 295).

The **insula** or **island of Reil** lies buried in the lateral fissure and can only be seen when the lips of that fissure are drawn apart or the opercular portions removed (Fig. 296). It then appears as a large conical or triangular elevation, the apex of the triangle directed forward and downward to the floor of the Sylvian fossa. At this point, known as the *limen* or threshold of the insula, the surface of the island curves over to the basal surface of the hemisphere and comes into relation with the olfactory area. The base of the insula is surrounded by the *circular* sulcus, really triangular in shape, which separates it from the frontal, parietal and temporal opercula. Except for the limen, the surface of the insula is covered by sulci and gyri. A deep oblique furrow, the *central* or *longitudinal* sulcus, running parallel to the central sulcus of Rolando, divides the insula into a larger anterior and a smaller posterior part. The former is composed of a number of short convolutions, the *gyri breves*. The posterior part consists of a single long convolution, the *gyrus longus*, which often shows an incomplete bifurcation.

The medial and basal surfaces. These surfaces are exposed in their entirety only after the brain has been divided in the midsagittal plane and the brain stem removed posterior to the thalamus (Fig. 297). The cut surface of the corpus callosum appears as a white broad arched band whose thickened caudal end or *splenium* overhangs the pineal body and midbrain. The rostral margin turns abruptly downward to form the *genu* or bend and then

callosum is occupied by the membranous septum pellucidum.

The convolutions on the medial and basal surfaces are somewhat flatter than on the convex surface, and here it is even more difficult to determine the boundaries of individual lobes, many convolutions continuing uninterruptedly from one lobe to another. Only the dorsal half of the occipital lobe is sharply separated from the parietal by the deep parietoöccipital sulcus.

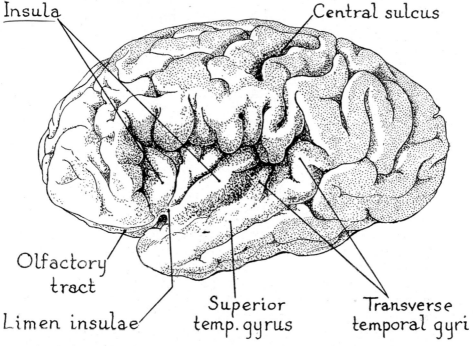

Insula   Central sulcus

Olfactory tract

Limen insulae   Superior temp. gyrus   Transverse temporal gyri

FIG. 296. Lateral surface of hemisphere. The lips (opercula) of the lateral fissure have been drawn apart to expose the insula. (After Henle.)

tapers downward and backward as the *rostrum* of the corpus callosum. The rostrum becomes attenuated into a thin membrane, the *rostral lamina*, which extends to the anterior commissure and there becomes continuous with the lamina terminalis (Figs. 297, 262). Another white band, the *fornix*, emerges from the under side of the splenium, arches forward over the thalamus and enters the substance of the hypothalamus immediately in front of the interventricular foramen (Fig. 262). The triangular area between fornix and corpus

A survey of the principal sulci will facilitate an understanding of the convolutional pattern and the allocation of the various parts to the respective lobes.

The corpus callosum is separated from the gyrus overlying it by the *callosal sulcus*. Beginning at the rostrum the sulcus follows the dorsal surface of the corpus callosum and curving ventrally around the splenium is continued as the *hippocampal fissure* which extends to the anterior portion of the temporal lobe (Figs. 297, 298). The *sulcus cinguli* or *callosomarginal sulcus* likewise

frontal, temporal, & occipital pole

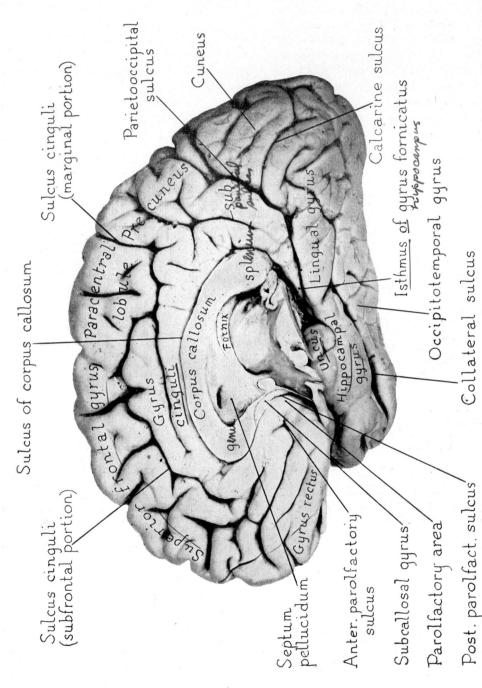

FIG. 297. Medial surface of right hemisphere. Hindbrain and larger part of midbrain have been removed. Photograph. g, spl, genu and splenium of corpus callosum; sub, subparietal sulcus.

starts some distance ventral to the rostrum and runs parallel with the callosal sulcus to about the region of the splenium where it turns upward as the *marginal sulcus* and reaches the dorsal border a short distance behind the central sulcus. Another furrow, the *subparietal sulcus*, which is usually regarded as a direct prolongation of the sulcus cinguli though often discontinuous with the latter, passes backward around the splenium. The sulcus cinguli gives off a number of dorsal branches, one of which, the

marginal sulci is notched by the central sulcus, hence represents the medial continuation of both precentral and postcentral gyri which here become continuous. The larger anterior portion belongs to the frontal, the small posterior portion to the parietal lobe. Behind the marginal sulcus is the *precuneus* or *quadrate lobule* belonging entirely to the parietal lobe and sharply marked off behind from the occipital lobe by the deep parietoöccipital sulcus. In close relation with the rostrum of the corpus

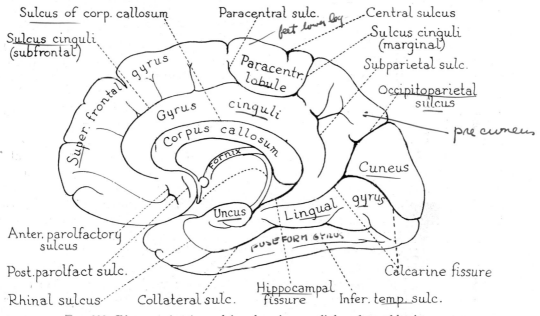

FIG. 298. Diagram showing sulci and gyri on medial surface of brain

paracentral sulcus, may reach the dorsal border at a point corresponding roughly to the position of the precentral sulcus. Thus the whole medial surface in front of and above the corpus callosum is divided by the cingular (and subparietal) sulcus into two tiers, an outer or marginal tier and an inner one, the *gyrus cinguli*, encircling the corpus callosum. The whole anterior portion of the outer tier up to the paracentral sulcus belongs to the frontal lobe and is the medial extension of the superior frontal gyrus, also known as the *marginal gyrus*. The paracentral lobule between the paracentral and

callosum are two small cortical fields belonging to the rhinencephalon. The *subcallosal gyrus* is closely applied to the rostral lamina and is limited in front by the *posterior parolfactory sulcus*, anterior to which is the *parolfactory area* (Broca). The latter is continuous in front with the superior frontal gyrus and above with the gyrus cinguli, from both of which it is separated incompletely by the *anterior parolfactory sulcus* (Figs. 297, 298). Subcallosal gyrus and parolfactory area collectively constitute the *paraterminal body* also known as the *septal* or *precommissural area*.

The *calcarine fissure* is a deep arched cleft extending from the mid-temporal region to the occipital pole, its anterior portion producing an elevation the *calcar avis*, in the wall of the lateral ventricle (Fig. 310). Beginning near the hippocampal fissure it runs horizontally backward and near its middle course is joined at acute angles by the *parietoöccipital sulcus* which extends obliquely downward and forward from the dorsal border. Then the calcarine fissure arches ventrally and usually terminates near the occipital pole, occasionally rounding the pole and extending a short distance on the lateral surface. Ventral to the calcarine fissure is the deep horizontal *collateral fissure* which likewise produces an impression in the ventricular wall known as the *collateral eminence* (Fig. 303). It runs forward from the region of the occipital pole and in the anterior portion of the temporal lobe usually becomes continuous with the shallow *rhinal fissure*, a phylogenetically old furrow separating the terminal archipallial portion of the hippocampal gyrus from the rest of the temporal lobe (Rh, Figs. 299, 300). Below and parallel to the collateral fissure is the inferior temporal sulcus, practically at the margin of transition between the basal and lateral surfaces.

The above named sulci enclose the following convolutions of the occipital and temporal lobes. The occipital lobe is divided by the calcarine fissure into the dorsal wedge-shaped *cuneus* limited above by the parietoöccipital sulcus, and the ventral tongue-shaped *lingual gyrus* bounded below by the collateral fissure. The cuneus belongs entirely to the occipital lobe, but the lingual gyrus extends into the temporal lobe. The lips of the calcarine fissure and immediately adjacent regions constitute the visual projection area of the cortex. Anteriorly the lingual gyrus overlaps the caudal part of the *hippocampal gyrus*, the most medial convolution of the temporal lobe, bounded ventrally by the rhinal and collateral fissures, and dorsally by the hip-

pocampal fissure. The rostral portion of the hippocampal gyrus hooks around the front end of the hippocampal fissure to form a short recurrent convolution, the *uncus* or *uncinate gyrus*. The hippocampal gyrus is directly continuous with the gyrus cinguli by a narrow strip of cortex known as the *isthmus cf the gyrus fornicatus*. Ventral to the hippocampal and lingual gyri and forming part of the basal surface is the long *occipitotemporal* or *fusiform* gyrus, bounded dorsally by the collateral fissure and ventrally by the inferior temporal sulcus.

The gyrus cinguli, isthmus, hippocampal gyrus and uncus together form a continuous ring-like convolution which has been designated as the *gyrus fornicatus* or *limbic lobe* (Broca) in the belief that all these structures were related to the rhinencephalon. It seems certain however that the larger portion of the gyrus cinguli and a considerable part of the hippocampal gyrus have other than olfactory functions, and moreover they are neopallial formations of isocortical structure. There has been a tendency therefore to allocate the various parts of the fornicate gyrus to the lobes in which these parts are situated. Thus the larger anterior part of the gyrus cinguli to the region of the central sulcus belongs to the frontal lobe, the smaller posterior portion to the parietal, while the hippocampal gyrus and uncus are included in the temporal lobe.

The **basal** surface is divided by the Sylvian fossa into two parts. The larger posterior portion belonging to the temporal and occipital lobes rests on the tentorium cerebelli and middle cranial fossa. Its gyri and sulci, visible on the medial surface have been described in the preceding paragraphs. The smaller anterior part forms the orbital surface of the frontal lobe. It is divided by the deep straight *olfactory sulcus* into a narrow medial convolution, the *gyrus rectus*, and a larger lateral area composed of a number of irregular and variable *orbital gyri* (Figs. 299, 300). The straight gyrus is continuous on the medial surface with the marginal convolution, of which it forms the most ventral part. The irregular sulci which separate the orbital convolutions, form patterns of various shapes. Some-

factory lobe. The *olfactory bulb*, resting on the cribriform plate of the ethmoid bone, is a flattened ovoid body, continuous caudally with a slender band, the *olfactory tract*. Both these structures are lodged in the olfactory sulcus. Posteriorly the olfactory

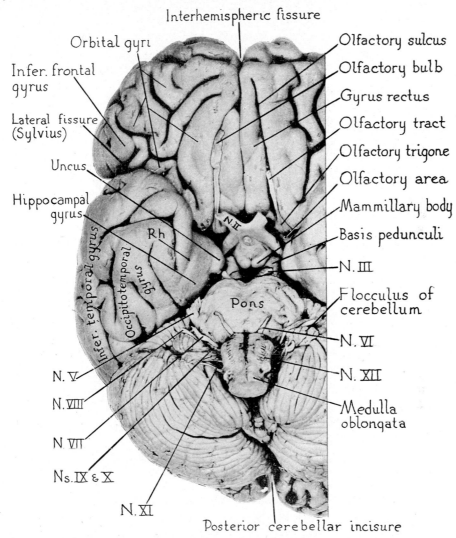

FIG. 299. Basal surface of human brain. Photograph. *Rh*, rhinal sulcus

times they have the form of a Maltese cross or an H, dividing the orbital area into four portions: lateral, medial, anterior and posterior. Laterally the orbital area is continuous with the inferior frontal gyrus.

On the orbital surface are also seen a number of structures belonging to the ol-

tract bifurcates into the *lateral* and *medial olfactory gyri* or *striae*, the bifurcation enclosing a triangular area, the *olfactory trigone*. Immediately behind the trigone is an irregular rhomboid area, the *olfactory area*, bounded caudally by the optic tract. This area especially in its anterior portion is studded with numerous apertures which serve for the passage of blood vessels, hence it is also known as *anterior perforated substance.* As already stated all these structures belong to the olfactory lobe and will be discussed more fully with the rhinencephalon.

system; (2) *association fibers* connecting the various cortical areas of the same hemisphere; and (3) *commissural fibers* which establish connections between the two hemispheres. Whether such commissural fibers always unite identical parts of both hemispheres, has not been fully ascertained.

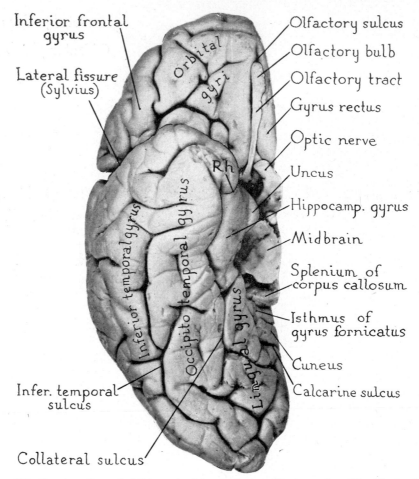

FIG. 300. Basal surface of right cerebral hemisphere. Photograph. *Rh,* rhinal sulcus

THE MEDULLARY SUBSTANCE

The white substance, especially in man, forms a volumetrically large portion of the hemisphere, filling in all the space between cortex, ventricle and basal ganglia, and furnishing medullary cores to the various convolutions. It is composed of three types of fibers: (1) *projection fibers* connecting the cortex with other parts of the nervous

Longitudinally running fibers have been observed in the corpus callosum and have been interpreted as commissural fibers connecting the occipital region of one side with the frontal region of the other.

Projection fibers. Afferent and efferent projection fibers arise from the whole extent of the cortex and enter the white substance where they form a radiating mass of fibers, the *corona radiata,* converging toward the brain stem (Fig. 301). On reaching the latter they form a broad compact fiber band, the internal capsule, flanked medially by the thalamus and caudate nucleus, and laterally by the lenticular nucleus. The composition of the thalamic radiations and other fiber systems of the internal capsule and hence of the corona radiata, has been fully discussed in an earlier chapter and need only be summarized briefly. The afferent fibers comprise the thalamocortical radiations

Smaller efferent bundles arising especially from the precentral region (areas 4 and 6) go to the nucleus ruber, substantia nigra and subthalamic nucleus, and the occipital lobe sends projection fibers to the superior colliculus and lateral geniculate body (Fig. 282). A small corticotegmental tract is believed to arise in the prefrontal cortex and descend to the reticular formation of the tegmentum, and corticostriate and cortico-hypothalamic fibers have likewise been

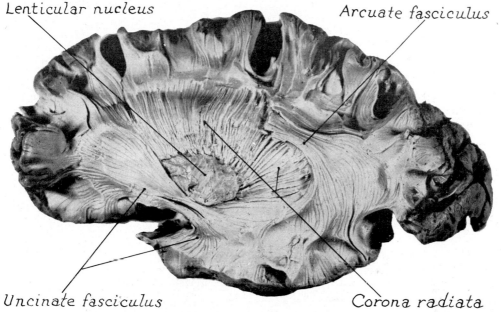

Lenticular nucleus

Arcuate fasciculus

Uncinate fasciculus

Corona radiata

FIG. 301. Dissection of the lateral wall of the hemisphere to show the corona radiata and some of the long association bundles. Photograph. The anterior portion of the arcuate fasciculus has been removed.

and some rubrocortical fibers to the frontal and centroöpercular cortex. The larger efferent bundles include (1) the corticospinal and corticobulbar tracts from the precentral cortex. (2) The frontopontile tract (Arnold's bundle) from the prefrontal and precentral cortex. (3) The temporo-parietopontile tract (Türck's bundle) from the superior and middle temporal gyri and superior parietal lobule. Some fibers probably also come from the occipital lobe. (4) Corticothalamic fibers from most parts of the cortex, usually distributed with the corresponding thalamocortical fibers.

described, though the origin and course of such fibers are still uncertain (p. 341). It is obvious that the cerebral cortex is directly connected with all the important nuclei of the brain stem.

Association fibers. The association fibers which are tremendously developed in man, may either run within the cortex itself or in the medullary substance, and are hence designated as *intracortical* and *subcortical*. The latter which are discussed here, may be grouped into short and long association fibers. The short ones known as arcuate fibers curve around the floor of each sulcus, thus connecting adjacent convolutions (Fig. 283). Such fibers are found in every part of the neopallium and always run transversely to the long axis of the sulcus. Short subcortical fibers which run lengthwise are unknown, hence diffusion of neural impulses along a single convolution must be mediated entirely by intracortical fibers. Besides the short arcuate fibers there are longer ones which may bridge two or even three sulci.

The long association fibers which interconnect parts of different lobes lie more deeply in the medullary substance. The majority are organized into more or less distinct longitudinally running bundles which have an arched course conforming to the shape of the hemisphere. The most prominent of these are the uncinate fasciculus, arcuate fasciculus and cingulum. The *uncinate fasciculus* lying immediately below the limen insulae is a compact bundle in its middle portion but spreads out fanlike at either end (Fig. 301). The most basal fibers loop sharply around the Sylvian fossa, connecting the posterior orbital gyri with the tip of the hippocampal gyrus. Proceeding dorsally the looping fibers gradually flatten out and finally become straight or even slightly concave, running obliquely downward from the frontal to the temporal lobe. The bundle connects the orbital gyri and rostral portions of the middle and inferior frontal convolutions with the anterior portion of the temporal lobe. The most dorsal part of the fascicle is designated by some as the *inferior occipitofrontal fasciculus*, believed to connect the frontal and occipital lobes.

Lying more dorsally is a similar bundle, the *arcuate fasciculus*, which sweeps around the insula parallel to the circular sulcus. It likewise has a compact middle portion with radiating fan-shaped ends (Fig. 301). In its ventral portion the fibers are strongly arched and connect the superior and middle frontal convolutions with the temporal lobe, some fibers reaching the temporal pole. The dorsal part, also known as the

superior longitudinal fasciculus connects the upper and caudal portions of the frontal lobe including the precentral gyrus with the occipital, parietal and adjacent portions of the temporal lobe.

The medial surfaces of the frontal, parietal and temporal lobes are likewise interconnected by a system of long association fibers which run longitudinally in the underlying medullary substance. Many of these fibers are diffusely organized, but the basal portion of this system forms a well-marked arched bundle, the *cingulum*, placed in the medullary substance of the gyrus cinguli

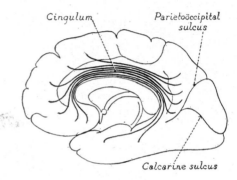

FIG. 302. Diagram showing some of the association fibers on the medial surface of the hemisphere.

immediately above the corpus callosum (Fig. 302). The bundle follows the contour of the gyrus cinguli, extending from beneath the rostrum of the corpus callosum (parolfactory area) to the splenium where it is continued as a greatly diminished strand into the hippocampal gyrus and uncus. The cingulum contains fibers of varying length, the longest and most curved ones connecting the frontal lobe with the hippocampal and adjacent temporal regions.

Running along the lateral walls of the posterior and inferior horns of the lateral ventricle is a longitudinal band of fibers which extends from the occipital to the temporal pole and was formerly thought to be an occipitotemporal association tract. It has been designated by some as the *inferior longitudinal fasciculus*, by others as the *external sagittal stratum* (Sachs). When however the bundle is exposed from the medial surface, it becomes obvious that it consists mainly of fibers from the geniculo-calcarine tract (optic radiation), which run forward into the temporal lobe and then loop backward to go to the calcarine region (Fig. 283). Afferent projection fibers from the pulvinar to the occipital cortex and efferent temporopontile fibers likewise contribute to the bundle, and it seems certain that the external sagittal stratum constitutes primarily a mixed projection system of which the geniculocalcarine tract forms

Commissural fibers. The crossed association fibers are primarily represented by the massive *corpus callosum* which reciprocally interconnects the neopallial cortex of the two hemispheres. In its middle portions the commissure is a broad thick plate of densely packed transverse fibers placed in the floor of the interhemispheric fissure and forming most of the roof of the lateral ventricles (Fig. 304). Laterally it spreads out on either side into a mass of radiating fibers, the callosal radiations, which are distributed to practically all parts of the cortex. Since the rostral and

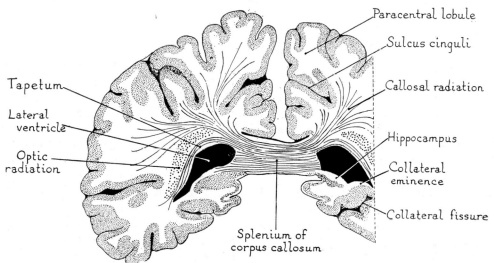

FIG. 303. Frontal section of cerebral hemispheres passing through splenium of corpus callosum. Semischematic.

by far the largest component. It is probable that the most externally placed fibers may be associative in character and connect the occipital with the temporal lobe.

Vertical association fibers running in the medullary substance of the convex surface are also found, but in relatively few numbers. The *vertical occipital fasciculus* runs in the front part of the occipital lobe and apparently connects the inferior parietal lobule with the more caudal portions of the inferior temporal and fusiform gyri. Other vertical fibers have been described as connecting the dorsal regions of the frontal lobe with the orbital gyri.

caudal ends of the corpus callosum are placed at a considerable distance from the frontal and occipital poles respectively, the fibers distributed to these regions of the two hemispheres form U-shaped bundles known as the *anterior* and the *posterior forceps*. The former loops forward from the genu toward the frontal pole, the larger posterior forceps loops backward toward the occipital pole. The genu supplies the larger anterior part of the frontal lobe; the whole parietal and caudal portion of the frontal lobe receive fibers from the body or trunk of the commissure. The fibers which supply the temporal and occipital lobes come from the splenium and posterior part of the trunk, and are split into a dorsal and a ventral component by the external sagittal stratum (optic radiations) which runs its longitudinal course through this portion of the medullary substance (Fig. 303). The dorsal fibers sweep over and lateral to the stratum and supply the dorsal and lateral portions of the temporal and occipital lobes. The ventral fibers pass medially to the stratum and form a thin medullary plate, the *tapetum*, which sweeps around the ependymal lining of the roof and lateral walls of the inferior and posterior horns (Fig. 303). The tapetum is distributed to the medial and basal surfaces of the temporal and occipital lobes.

The exact distribution of the callosal fibers has not been fully ascertained. For the most part they connect identical portions of the two hemispheres, but fibers connecting morphologically dissimilar areas are also present (Déjérine). The fibers are difficult to follow beyond the lateral ventricles where they become intermingled with association and projection fibers.

The *anterior* and *hippocampal* commissures are primarily olfactory commissures and will be discussed with the rhinencephalon.

THE LATERAL VENTRICLES

The lateral ventricles are ependyma-lined cavities of irregular arched shape corresponding to the arched form of the hemispheres, and communicate with the rostral part of the third ventricle by two narrow and short channels, the *interventricular foramina*. They vary considerably in extent especially as regards their width, in some cases being narrow and cleft-like, in other cases constituting relatively wide spaces. Normally they are always filled with cerebrospinal fluid. When the ventricles become pathologically enlarged with a corresponding increase in fluid, the condition is known as internal hydrocephalus.

Each ventricle consists of a *central portion* or *body* from which three prolongations or horns extend respectively into the frontal, temporal and occipital lobes (Figs. 304, 305). The **anterior** or **frontal horn** extends forward from the interventricular foramen and in transverse section has a triangular shape (Fig. 291). Its roof and rostral wall are formed by the corpus callosum, while medially it is separated from the horn of the opposite side by the thin vertical laminae of the septum pellucidum. Floor and lateral wall are combined into the sloping hypotenuse of the triangle, formed by the head of the caudate nucleus whose surface bulges convexly into the cavity of the horn (Fig. 291).

The **central portion** is a relatively shallow cavity extending from the interventricular foramen to the splenium where it enlarges into the *collateral trigone* formed by the junction of posterior and inferior horns. Its roof is formed by the corpus callosum which curves ventrally at either end and becomes continuous with the dorsally slanting floor, so that a true medial and lateral wall are not present. The floor is formed by a number of structures (Figs. 264, 263). Most laterally is the caudate nucleus forming a bulge in the ventricular cavity. Proceeding medially are the stria terminalis, a part of the dorsal thalamic surface (lamina affixa), the chorioid plexus and the fornix.

The **posterior** or **occipital horn** extends a variable distance into the occipital lobe. It may be quite short and taper rapidly to a point, or it may form a longer more tubular prolongation. Its dorsal and lateral walls are formed by the tapetal fibers of the corpus callosum, its floor by the medullary substance of the occipital lobe. The medial wall shows a longitudinal prominence, the *calcar avis*, produced by the deep penetration of the calcarine fissure (Fig. 310).

The **inferior** or **temporal horn** begins at the collateral trigone, curves ventrally around the posterior portion of the thalamus and extends rostrally into the medial part of the temporal lobe, ending about one inch from the temporal pole (Fig. 304). Its floor, directly continuous with that of the posterior horn, is marked by a more or less distinct prominence, the *collateral eminence*, medial region of the roof a small part is furnished by the tail of the caudate nucleus and the accompanying stria terminalis.

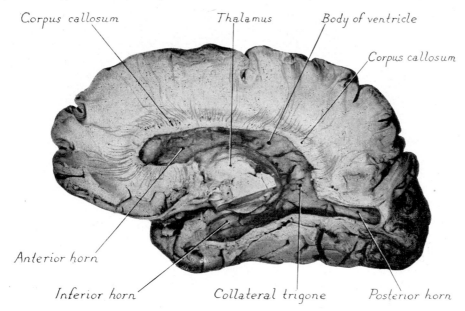

Corpus callosum   Thalamus   Body of ventricle

Corpus callosum

Anterior horn

Inferior horn   Collateral trigone   Posterior horn

FIG. 304. Dissection of medial surface of cerebral hemisphere, showing lateral ventricle and callosal radiations. The usually shallow body of the ventricle is here abnormally enlarged. Photograph.

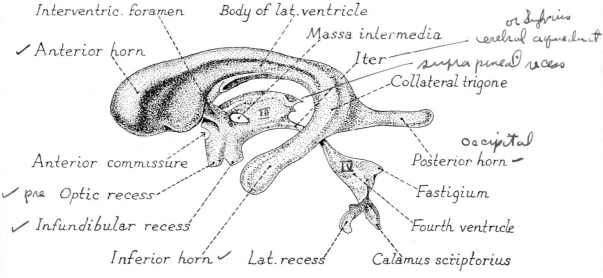

Interventric. foramen   Body of lat. ventricle

✓ Anterior horn   Massa intermedia   or Sylvius
cerebral aqueduct

Iter   supra pineal recess

Collateral trigone

Anterior commissure   occipital

✓ pre Optic recess   Posterior horn —

✓ Infundibular recess   Fastigium

Fourth ventricle

Inferior horn ✓   Lat. recess   Calamus scriptorius

FIG. 305. Cast of the brain ventricles, viewed from the side. Only the left lateral ventricle is represented. (After Rauber-Kopsch.)

caused by the deep collateral fissure (Figs. 303, 310). The roof and lateral walls are largely formed by the tapetum, but in the

The most remarkable feature of the inferior horn is the *hippocampus* or *horn of Ammon*, produced by the infolding of the pallium along the hippocampal fissure (Fig. 310). The hippocampus is a prominent sickle-shaped ridge on the medial wall of the horn, extending from the region of the splenium to the temporal tip of the ventricle where it is continuous with the ventricular surface of the uncus. Its broader anterior portion known as the *pes hippocami*, shows a number of slight fingerlike elevations, the hippocampal digitations, separated by shallow radial furrows. Running along the dorso-medial surface of the hippocampus is a

motor activities in response to such stimuli. As already stated it consists of the basally placed *olfactory lobe* sometimes designated as the paleocortex, and the *archipallium* represented by the hippocampal formation. Large and conspicuous in lower vertebrates and even in many macrosmatic mammals, the human rhinencephalon is considerably reduced in size, and its archipallial portion has become pushed to the medial surface and is largely hidden from view by the tremendous expansion of the neopallium.

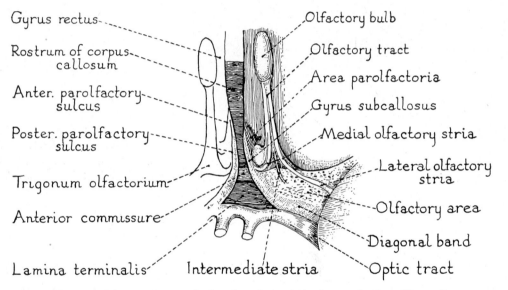

Gyrus rectus
Rostrum of corpus callosum
Anter. parolfactory sulcus
Poster. parolfactory sulcus
Trigonum olfactorium
Anterior commissure
Lamina terminalis
Intermediate stria
Olfactory bulb
Olfactory tract
Area parolfactoria
Gyrus subcallosus
Medial olfactory stria
Lateral olfactory stria
Olfactory area
Diagonal band
Optic tract

FIG. 306. Olfactory lobe as seen on the basal surface of the human brain. The optic nerves and chiasma have been folded backward. (Modified from His.)

flattened white band, the *fimbria*, which extends from the uncus toward the splenium and is directly continued into the crus of the fornix. Hippocampus and fimbria are in part overlapped by the inferior portion of the chorioid plexus which extends to the tip of the inferior horn (Fig. 263).

THE RHINENCEPHALON AND OLFACTORY PATHWAYS

The rhinencephalon comprises all those portions of the brain primarily concerned with the reception and integration of olfactory impulses and with the regulation of

The structures of the olfactory lobe are practically limited to the basal surface. The *olfactory bulb* is a flattened ovoid body resting on the cribriform plate of the ethmoid bone, its dorsal surface pressed into the anterior portion of the olfactory sulcus (Figs. 299, 306). Delicate fascicles of fine unmyelinated fibers, the *fila olfactoria*, pass from the nasal fossa through the apertures of the cribriform plate and enter the ventral surface of the bulb. These fila are the central processes of the bipolar receptor cells in the olfactory mucous membrane, and collectively they constitute the *olfactory nerve* (N.I). The olfactory bulb is thus the terminal "nucleus" of the olfactory nerve.

The olfactory tract is a narrow white band lying in the olfactory sulcus. It extends from the olfactory bulb to the anterior perforated substance where it enlarges to form the *olfactory trigone* and divides into two roots, the *lateral* and *medial olfactory striae* (Fig. 306). Often also a less definite intermediate stria dips directly into the anterior perforated substance. The olfactory tract consists principally of second-

to the medial hemispheric surface and there becomes continuous with a small field known as the *parolfactory area* placed beneath the rostrum of the corpus callosum (Figs. 306, 309). This area is limited in front by the anterior parolfactory sulcus, while behind it is separated by the posterior parolfactory sulcus from another strip of cortex, the *subcallosal gyrus*, closely applied to the rostral lamina of the corpus callosum. Parolfactory area and subcallosal gyrus together constitute the *paraterminal body* or *septal*

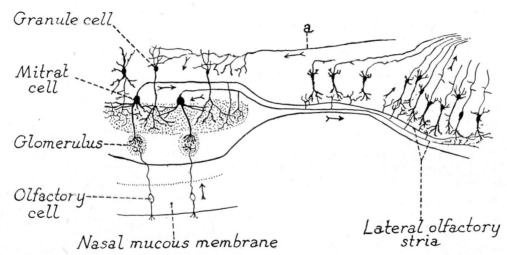

FIG. 307. Diagram showing structure of olfactory bulb and olfactory tract. (After Cajal.) *a*, fiber to bulb from opposite olfactory tract.

ary olfactory fibers from cells of the bulb, covered dorsally by a layer of primitive cortex greatly reduced in man. The cells of this gray layer receive collaterals from the secondary olfactory fibers and in turn contribute fibers to the olfactory tract (Fig. 307). The latter thus contains both secondary and tertiary myelinated fibers which are continued into the olfactory striae mentioned above. The olfactory striae are likewise covered by a thin coating of gray substance greatly reduced in man, and are hence also known as the *lateral* and *medial olfactory gyri*.

The medial olfactory gyrus is prolonged

area. The parolfactory area connects the medial olfactory gyrus with the gyrus cinguli.

The lateral olfactory gyrus passes outward across the anterior perforated substance towards the Sylvian fossa and reaches the inferior apex of the insula (Fig. 296). There it loops sharply backward, the loop forming the limen of the insula, and passes medially in the floor of the fossa to terminate in the uncus and anterior portion of the hippocampal gyrus. Some fibers also end in the amygdaloid nucleus which lies buried beneath the uncus, above and in front of the tip of the inferior horn. Lateral olfactory gyrus, uncus and anterior part of the hippocampal gyrus constitute the so-called *piriform area* which is more highly developed in macrosmatic mammals. In man the caudal limits of this area are indistinct, and it is uncertain how much of the hippocampal area should be included.

The *area olfactoria* or *anterior perforated substance* is a quadrilateral or rhomboid region bounded rostrally by the olfactory trigone and caudally by the optic tract. Its surface especially in the anterior region is studded with numerous apertures serving for the passage of blood vessels. The posterior region which borders on the optic tract is however smoother in appearance and forms an oblique band, the *diagonal band* or *gyrus* extending from the region of the uncus to the medial surface where it becomes continuous with the subcallosal gyrus previously described (Fig. 306). The functions of the olfactory area are not wholly olfactory ones. In macrosmatic animals, especially in those with well developed snouts or muzzles, the rostral portion of the area is marked by a prominent elevation, the *olfactory* tubercle, of which only rudiments are present in man. This tubercle receives not only olfactory fibers, but also a strong ascending bundle of secondary trigeminal fibers from the oral and nasal mucous membranes and adjacent portions of the skin (Edinger). It has been suggested that the olfactory tubercle constitutes a center for "oral sense" concerned with the feeding reflexes of the snout (Edinger). Olfactory area, diagonal band and subcallosal gyrus constitute the posterior portion of the olfactory lobe, the anterior portion comprising the olfactory bulb, trigone, lateral and medial olfactory gyri and the parolfactory area.

The *hippocampal formation* which represents the cortical part of the olfactory system is laid down in the embryo on the medial wall of the hemisphere along the hippocampal fissure, immediately above and parallel to the chorioidal fissure which marks the invagination into the ventricle of the chorioid plexus (p. 345). With the formation of the temporal lobe both these fissures are carried downward and forward, each now forming an arch extending from the region of the interventricular foramen to the tip of the inferior horn. The various parts of the hippocampal arch do no develop to the same extent. The upper or anterior portion of the hippocampal fissure becomes invaded by the crossing fibers of the corpus callosum and ultimately becomes the callosal fissure separating the massive commissure from the overlying pallium. The corresponding part of the hippocampal formation which now lies above the corpus callosum differentiates but little, forming in the adult a vestigial convolution, the supracallosal gyrus or indusium griseum (Fig. 309). The lower temporal portion of the arch which is not affected by the corpus callosum differentiates into the main structures of the hippocampal formation. The hippocampal fissure deepens, the invaginated portion which bulges deeply into the inferior horn becomes the *hippocampus*, while the lips of the fissure give rise to the *dentate* and the *hippocampal gyrus*. The relation of these structures are best illustrated in a frontal section through this area (Fig. 308). Proceeding from the collateral sulcus, the *hippocampal gyrus* extends to the hippocampal fissure whose dorsal lip it forms, and there dips into the ventricle to form the *hippocampus*. The latter curves dorsally and medially and on reaching the medial surface curves inward again and forms a semilunar convolution, the *dentate gyurs* or *fascia dentata* which closely applied to the hippocampal gyrus reaches the surface as the ventral lip of the hippocampal fissure. The whole ventricular surface of the hippocampus is covered by a layer of white substance, the *alveus*, composed primarily of axons from cells of the hippocampus and dentate gyrus. These fibers converge on the medial surface of the hippocampus to form a flattened band, the *fimbria*, lying between the hippocampus and the dentate gyrus and constituting the beginning of the fornix system (Figs. 309, 310). The free thin border of the fimbria is directly continuous with the epithelium of the chorioidal fissure which lies immediately above it. The chorioid plexus invaginated into the ventricle along this fissure partly covers the hippocampus (Fig. 308). The dorsal portion of the hippocampal gyrus adjoining the hippocampal fissure is known as the

(Fig. 309). Traced backward the gyrus accompanies the fimbria almost to the splenium. Then it separates from the fimbria, loses its notched appearance and as the delicate *fasciolar gyrus* (fasciola cinerea) passes to the dorsal surface of the corpus callosum, where it spreads out into a thin gray sheet representing a vestigial convolution, the *supracallosal gyrus* or *indusium griseum* (Fig. 309). Imbedded in the indusium are two slender bands of myelinated

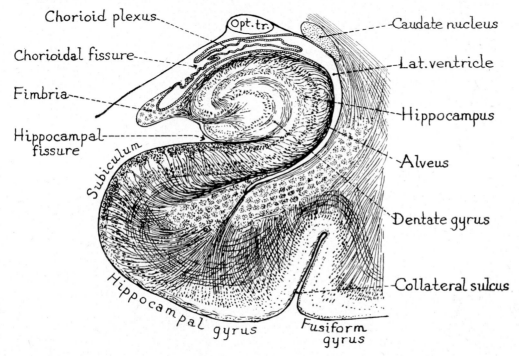

FIG. 308. Transverse section through human hippocampus and hippocampal gyrus. (After Edinger.)

subiculum, and the area of transition between it and the hippocampus proper as the *presubiculum.* Subiculum, presubiculum, hippocampus and dentate gyrus, all belong to the archipallium which has an allocortical structure. The larger ventral portion of the hippocampal gyrus bounded by the collateral fissure is neopallial and has the general structure of the isocortex.

When the hippocampal fissure is opened up the *dentate gyrus* is seen as a narrow notched band of cortex between the hippocampal fissure below and the fimbria above

fibers which appear as narrow longitudinal ridges on the dorsal surface of the corpus callosum. These are known as the *medial* and *lateral longitudinal striae* or *striae Lancisii* and constitute the white matter of the vestigial convolution. Indusium griseum and longitudinal striae extend the whole length of the callosum, pass over the genu and become continuous with the subcallosal gyrus which in turn is prolonged into the diagonal band of Broca (Fig. 306). Traced forward the dentate gyrus extends into the notch between the uncus and hippocampal gyrus where after making a sharp dorsal bend it passes as a smooth band across the inferior surface of the uncus. This terminal portion is known as the *band of Giacomini*, and the part of the uncus lying posterior to it is often designated as the *intralimbic gyrus*.

On the dorsal surface of the fasciolar gyrus there are usually found several small strips of cortex known as the *callosal gyri* or *gyri*

as the *alveus* and then converge to form the *fimbria*, a flattened longitudinal fiber band running from the uncus along the medial edge of the hippocampus. Proceeding backward the fimbriae of the two sides increase in thickness and on reaching the posterior end of the hippocampus, leave the latter and arch under the splenium as the *crura* or *posterior columns* of the fornix, at the same time converging toward each other. In this

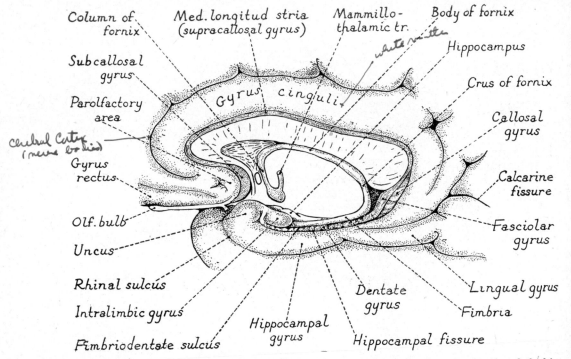

FIG. 309. Portion of medial surface of hemisphere. The thalamus has been removed and the hippocampal gyrus pulled downward to expose the structures related to the hippocampal fissure.

of Andreas Retzius. Their significance is not known (Fig. 309).

The general configuration of the *hippocampus* has already been given in connection with the lateral ventricles and is illustrated in Fig. 310.

The *fornix* constitutes the main efferent fiber system of the hippocampal formation, including both projection and commissural fibers (Figs. 310, 309). As already stated it is composed of axons from the large cells of the hippocampus and dentate gyrus, which spread over the ventricular surface

region a number of fibers pass to the opposite side, forming a thin sheet of crossing fibers, the *hippocampal commissure* or *psalterium*, rather poorly developed in man. The bundles then join to form the *body of the fornix* which runs under and close to the corpus callosum to the rostral margin of the thalamus. Here the bundles separate again and as the *anterior columns of the fornix*, arch ventrally in front of the interventricular foramina and enter the substance of the hypothalamus to reach the mammillary bodies.

The *anterior commissure* crosses the median plane as a compact fiber bundle placed in the lamina terminalis, immediately in front of the columns of the fornix (Fig. 310). Proceeding laterally it splits into two portions. The small anterior or olfactory portion, greatly reduced in man, loops rostrally and connects the gray substance of the olfactory tract with the olfactory bulb of the opposite side. The larger posterior or

The olfactory pathways. The olfactory receptors are spindle-shaped bipolar cells situated in the epithelium of the nasal mucous membrane. Their short peripheral processes extend to the nasal surface, their long fine central processes form the unmyelinated fibers of the olfactory nerve. Arranged in delicate bundles, the *fila olfactoria*, they pass through the apertures of the cribriform plate and enter the olfactory bulb

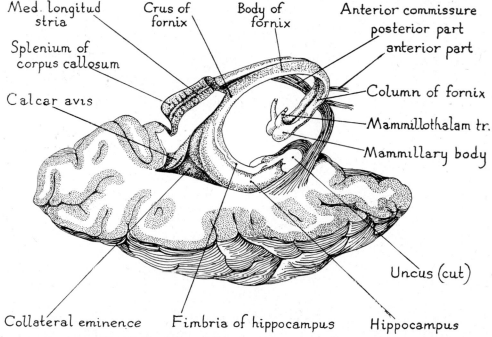

FIG. 310. Dissection of right hemisphere showing inferior and posterior horns of the lateral ventricle, hippocampus, fornix and anterior commissure. (After Rauber-Kopsch.)

temporal portion which forms the bulk of the commissure, passes laterally beneath the lenticular nucleus, arches backward and downward and streams into the anterior portion of the hippocampal gyrus and adjacent area of the temporal lobe. The archipallial portions of the two hemispheres are thus interrelated by two commissural systems. The reduced hippocampal commissure connects the two hippocampi and dentate gyri, the larger part of the anterior commissure connects the hippocampal gyri and probably also adjacent neopallial portions of the temporal lobe.

where they form synaptic relations with certain cells of the latter (Fig. 307). The olfactory bulb is thus the terminal "nucleus" of the olfactory nerve. Within the gray matter of the bulb are several types of nerve cells, the most striking of which are the large triangular or pyramidal *mitral cells*, so named because of their resemblance to a bishop's mitre (Fig. 307). Each of these cells gives off a number of peripherally directed dendrites, one of which passes vertically toward the layer of olfactory nerve fibers and suddenly breaks up into a brush-like mass of short terminals which interlace with similar terminals from one or more olfactory fibers, the two together forming circumscribed spherical structures, the *olfactory glomeruli.* Smaller cells of the olfactory bulb, known as *tufted cells,* similarly have a number of dendrites one of which participates in the formation of a glomerulus. The axons of the mitral and tufted cells enter the olfactory tract as secondary olfactory fibers.

The secondary olfactory pathways are numerous and complicated and many of them have become greatly reduced in man.

which constitute the basal olfactory nuclei, arises a diffuse system of fibers, often known as the medial or *basal olfactory bundle* (Edinger-Wallenberg), which represents part of an old olfactosomatic reflex pathway greatly reduced in man (Fig. 311). The fibers pass beneath the head of the caudate nucleus through the hypothalamic region giving terminals or collaterals to the tuber cinereum and mammillary body (*olfactohypothalamic*) and continuing to the tegmentum of the midbrain (*olfactotegmental*), some possibly reaching the medulla and

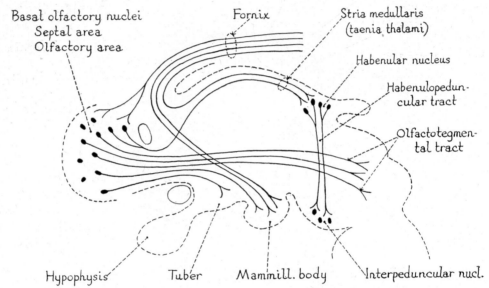

FIG 311. Diagram showing some of the olfactory connections

As in the case of other sensory systems they may be grouped into *reflex* and *cortical paths.* The former reach the lower motor neurons, especially the motor nuclei of the cranial nerves, through a series of intercalated subcortical centers. The cortical connections involve the hippocampal formation.

Reflex connections. The secondary fibers from the mitral and tufted cells of the olfactory bulb end directly or by collaterals in the gray substance of the olfactory tract, the olfactory trigone, the olfactory area and the septal region (subcallosal gyrus and parolfactory area). From these centers

even the spinal cord. Other fibers curve dorsally and entering the medullary stria of the thalamus go to the habenular nucleus of the same and opposite side (*olfactohabenular*). The further course of this pathway has already been discussed in connection with the diencephalon and may be briefly summarized. The habenular nucleus gives origin to the *habenulopeduncular tract* (fasciculus retroflexus) which goes to the interpeduncular nucleus and is thence relayed to the dorsal tegmental nucleus of the midbrain (Fig. 312). From this nucleus fibers descend to the pons and medulla forming part at least of the *dorsal longitudi-*

nal bundle of Schütz which also contains direct fibers from the hypothalamus (periependymal hypothalamic tract). This bundle has been traced downward as far as the dorsal vagus nucleus.

The hypothalamus likewise gives origin to a number of descending fiber tracts. The *periventricular fiber system* arising from the posterior and tuberal hypothalamic regions, descends through the entire length of the brain stem, many of its fibers entering

tion of the olfactory bulb with the cortical centers is through the lateral olfactory stria. These arise from the mitral cells and pass directly to the uncus and adjacent anterior portions of the hippocampal gyrus. These regions may therefore be regarded as the olfactory projection areas of the archipallium, just as the calcarine region represents the visual projection area of the neopallium. From the uncus a diffuse system of fibers reaches the hippocampus and dentate gyrus

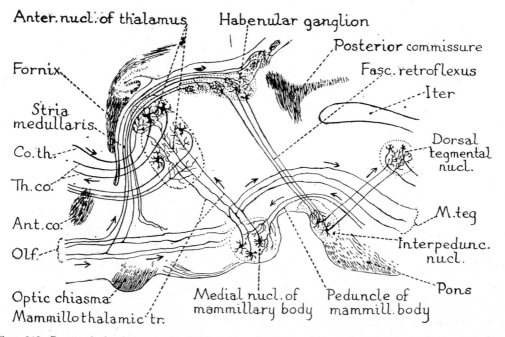

FIG. 312. Some of the important olfactory connections. (After Cajal.) *Ant.co.*, anterior commissure; *Co.th.*, corticothalamic fiber; *M.teg.*, mammillotegmental tract; *Olf.*, fibers from basal olfactory nuclei (olfactohabenular, olfactohypothalamic); *Th.co.*, thalamocortical fibers.

the spinal cord (p. 334). Some run with the dorsal longitudinal bundle, others run more diffusely through the reticular formation. From the mammillary body also a *mammillotegmental tract* reaches the midbrain tegmentum and is thence relayed to the lower motor neurons. Thus by this extensive if diffuse system involving a number of intercalated nuclei, the somatic and visceral effectors of the body and especially of the head are brought under reflex olfactory and hypothalamic control.

Cortical connections. The main connec-

which represent higher olfactory cortical centers, including also the dorsal (subicular) portion of the hippocampal gyrus. To a much smaller extent the hippocampal formation receives afferent fibers through the medial olfactory striae and diagonal band. The former arise from the gray substance of the olfactory tract and trigone, and go to the subcallosal gyrus and parolfactory area. The fibers of the diagonal band originate from the olfactory area and the uncus and likewise reach the subcallosal gyrus. Some of these fibers, probably joined by others from the subcallosal gyrus itself, are continued into the medial and lateral longitudinal striae which run on the dorsal surface of the corpus callosum and reach the dentate gyrus and hippocampus. According to Cajal few if any fibers reach the hippocampus by this route.

The *amygdaloid nucleus* likewise receives fibers from the lateral olfactory stria and gives rise to a fiber bundle known as the *stria terminalis*. This bundle arches along the entire medial border of the caudate nucleus (Fig. 263) and terminates mainly in the olfactory area, septal region and anterior portion of the hypothalamus. Some of its fibers cross in the anterior commissure, connecting the two amygdalae, and it is probable that many fibers of the stria terminalis run in a reverse direction i.e. from basal olfactory regions to the amygdaloid nucleus. It is also believed to have connections with the thalamus, habenular nucleus, uncus and hippocampus, but these have not been fully worked out. The functions of the amygdaloid nucleus are obscure. Believed by some to be a cortical olfactory center (Déjérine), it is now regarded as belonging to the basal ganglia and is usually homologized with the olfactory striatum (archistriatum) of submammalian forms.

The main efferent system from the hippocampal formation is the *fornix* whose anatomical relations have been previously described (Figs. 310, 309). The majority of the fibers form the large *corticomammillary tract* which terminates in the mammillary body. However some fibers go to the septal and preoptic areas, while others pass through the medullary stria of the thalamus to end in the habenular nucleus (*corticohabenular*, Fig. 311). A few efferent fibers from the dentate gyrus and hippocampus are continued over the splenium into the longitudinal striae where they run a variable distance and then perforate the corpus callosum to join the fornix. Some of these perforating fibers are believed to come from the gyrus cinguli. The further course of the efferent cortical impulses to the motor nuclei of the cranial and spinal nerves is the same as that described for the reflex pathways.

Besides its connections with lower brain stem nuclei, the mammillary body sends a strong bundle of fibers, the *mammillothalamic* tract to the anterior nucleus of the thalamus. This tract is of especial interest since the anterior thalamic nucleus is reciprocally connected with practically all parts of the gyrus cinguli. The significance of the gyrus cinguli is largely obscure, but this connection suggests that in part at least it may represent a higher newer neopallial center related to olfactory and hypothalamic activities.

CHAPTER XX

THE CEREBRAL CORTEX

The cerebral cortex is the external layer of gray matter covering the convolutions and sulci of the cerebral hemispheres. It has an area of some 2200 square centimeters or nearly $2\frac{1}{2}$ square feet, of which only about one third is found on the free surface of the cortex, the other two thirds lining the walls and floors of the fissures. The average thickness of the cortex is 2.5 mm. but varies considerably in different regions, from a maximal thickness of about 4.5 mm. in the motor area of the precentral gyrus to a minimal one of 1.5 mm. in the floor of the calcarine fissure. In any portion of the hemisphere the cortex is always thickest on the crown of a convolution and gradually attenuates towards the floor of the sulcus. It has been estimated that besides nerve fibers, neuroglia and blood vessels, the cerebral cortex contains the cell bodies of nearly fourteen billion neurons (Economo).

The cerebral cortex obviously contains (1) the endings of afferent fibers from other parts of the nervous system, such as the thalamocortical fibers; (2) association neurons whose axons interrelate near and distant parts of the same hemisphere, or as commissural fibers pass to the cortex of the opposite side; and (3) projection neurons whose axons conduct the integrated cortical impulses to other portions of the nervous system. These latter axons pass through the corona radiata and form the corticospinal, corticopontile, corticothalamic and other descending cortical tracts previously studied. Which neurons furnish the projection fibers is still largely an unsettled question except in the case of the precentral motor cortex where it has been definitely determined that the pyramidal tract arises in part at least from the giant pyramidal cells of Betz. There is however considerable evidence for the belief that most of the projection fibers arise from the deeper layers of the cortex, while the association fibers come mainly though not exclusively from the more superficial ones. A striking feature of pallial structure is the relatively small number of efferent projection fibers as compared with the enormous number of cortical neurons, indicating that by far the great majority of the latter are concerned with associative functions.

The cortical cells and fibers. The principal types of cells found in the cortex are the pyramidal, stellate and fusiform (Figs. 313, 314). The *pyramidal cells*, most characteristic of the cortex, have the form of a pyramid or isosceles triangle whose upper pointed end is continued toward the surface of the brain as the *apical dendrite* or main shaft. Besides the main shaft a number of more or less horizontally running *basal dendrites* spring from the cell body and arborize in the vicinity of the cell. The axon emerges from the base of the cell and descends toward the medullary substance, either terminating in the deeper layers of the cortex or entering the white matter as a projection or association fiber. The pyramidal cells have a large vesicular nucleus and well marked Nissl bodies. They are usually classified as small, medium and large, the height of the cell body varying from 10 or 12 micra for the smaller to 45 or 50 micra fro the larger ones. Unusually large pyramidal cells, the giant pyramidal cells of Betz, whose body may be more than 100 micra in height, are found in the motor area of the precentral gyrus.

The *stellate cells* also known as *granule cells* are as a rule small polygonal or triangular cells with dark-staining nuclei and scanty cytoplasm, varying in size from 4–8 micra.

They have a number of dendrites passing in all directions and a short axon which ramifies close to the cell body (Golgi type II). Other larger stellate cells have longer axons which may enter the medullary substance, and there are some which resemble pyramidal cells by having an apical dendrite which extends to the surface and are hence

dendrites, the lower one arborizing within the layer, the upper ascending toward the surface and often reaching the superficial layer. The axon arises from the middle or lower part of the cell body and enters the white as a projection or association fiber.

Other cell types found in the cortex are the *horizontal cells of Cajal* and the *cells with*

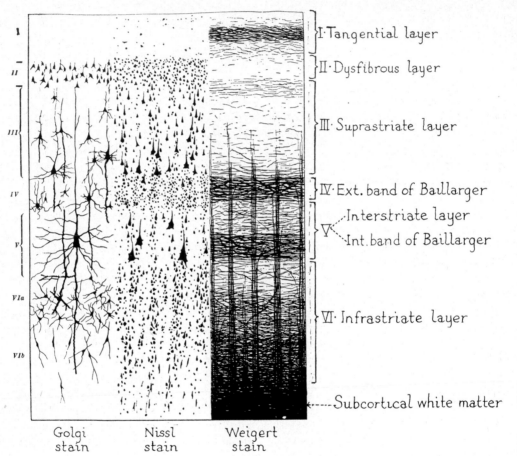

Golgi stain   Nissl stain   Weigert stain

I·Tangential layer
II·Dysfibrous layer
III·Suprastriate layer
IV·Ext. band of Baillarger
Interstriate layer
V Int. band of Baillarger
VI·Infrastriate layer
Subcortical white matter

FIG. 313. The cell layers and fiber arrangement of the human cerebral cortex. Semischematic. (After Brodmann.)

known as *stellate pyramidal cells* or *star pyramids* (Lorente de Nó). Stellate cells are found throughout the whole depth of the cortex but are especially numerous in layer IV.

The *fusiform* or *spindle cells* are mainly found in the deepest layer, their long axis usually placed vertical to the surface. The two poles of the cell are continued into

ascending axons also known as the *cells of Martinotti* (Fig. 315). The former are small fusiform or pear-shaped cells found in the most peripheral layer, their long axons running horizontally for considerable distances and arborizing within that layer. The Martinotti cells, present in practically all the layers, are small triangular or polygonal cells whose axons are directed toward the surface and extend a variable distance, some arborizing in the same layer, others sending collaterals to a number of layers. It is evident from the above that the projection and subcortical association fibers are continuations of descending axons from the pyramidal, fusiform and larger stellate cells. The Golgi type II granule cells, the horizontal and Martinotti cells are wholly concerned with intracortical connections.

The *fibers* of the cortex, as far as their direction is concerned are disposed either radially or tangentially. The former are arranged in delicate radiating bundles running vertically from the medullary substance toward the cortical periphery (Fig. 313). They obviously include the axons of pyramidal, fusiform and stellate cells which leave the cortex as projection or association fibers, and the entering afferent projection and association fibers which terminate within the cortex. The ascending axons of the Martinotti cell likewise have a vertical course. The tangential fibers run horizontal to the surface and are composed principally of the terminal branches of the afferent projection and association fibers, the axons of the horizontal and granule cells, and the terminal branches of collaterals from the pyramidal and fusiform cells. It is evident that the horizontal fibers represent in large part the terminal portions of the radial fibers, which bend horizontally to come in synaptic relation with cortical cells. The tangential fibers are not distributed evenly throughout the thickness of the cortex but are concentrated at varying depths into denser horizontal bands or plexuses, separated by layers in which such fibers are relatively few (Fig. 313). The two most prominent bands are known as the *bands of Baillarger*, visible even to the naked eye as delicate white stripes in sections of the fresh cortex.

The cortical layers. A striking feature of cortical structure is its laminated character. In sections stained by the Nissl method it is seen that the cell bodies are not uniformly distributed, but are arranged in horizontal superimposed layers, each layer distinguished by the types and density of arrangement of its cells. In preparations stained for myelin, a similar lamination is visible, in this case determined primarily by the disposition of the horizontal fibers which differ in amount and density for each corresponding cellular layer (Fig. 313). In the neopallial cortex or isocortex which forms over 90% of the hemispheric surface, six fundamental layers are usually recognized (Brodmann), some of them being subdivided into two or more sub-layers. Proceeding from the surface of the cortex toward the medullary substance these layers include (I) the molecular layer, (II) the external granular layer, (II) the layer of pyramidal cells, (IV) the internal granular layer, (V) the ganglionic layer, and (VI) the multiform layer.

I. The *molecular* or *plexiform layer* contains relatively few cells of two kinds, cells with horizontal axons and Golgi type II cells. Within it are found the terminal dendritic ramifications of the pyramidal and fusiform cells from the deeper layers and the axonal endings of Martinotti cells. All these dendritic and axonal branches form a fairly dense tangential fiber plexus, hence the name of plexiform layer.

II. The *external granular layer* or *layer of small pyramids* consists of numerous closely packed small cells of triangular or pyramidal shape, whose apical dendrites terminate in the molecular layer. Their axons descend to the deeper layers, many terminating in the cortex, some entering the white as association fibers. The layer is rather poor in myelinated fibers, containing the basal dendrites of its own cells and the terminals of axon collaterals from more deeply lying cells. The dendritic shafts of pyramidal and fusiform cells naturally pass through it to reach the molecular layer.

III. The *layer of pyramidal cells* (external pyramidal layer) is composed mainly of typical well formed pyramids. Two sublayers are usually recognized: a superficial layer of medium pyramids and a deeper layer of larger ones. Their apical dendrites go to the first layer, while most of their axons enter the white matter, chiefly as association or commissural fibers. Some may end within the cortex. Intermingled with the pyramids are many granule cells and cells of Martinotti. In the most superficial part of the layer there is a greater

(granules). Many of these are very small, with short axons ramifying within the layer. Others are larger and have descending axons which terminate in the deeper layers or may enter the white substance. The whole layer is permeated by a dense horizontal plexus of myelinated fibers forming the external band of Baillarger, composed in considerable part of the terminal ramifica-

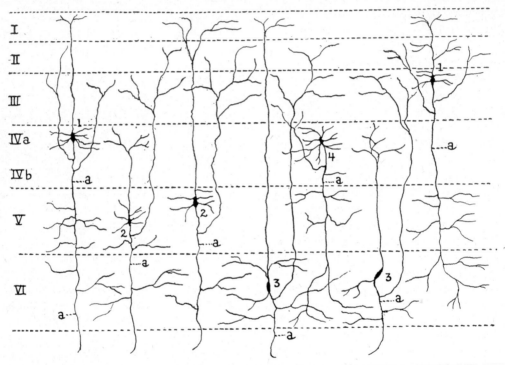

FIG. 314. The dendritic and axonal branchings of several types of cortical neurons with descending axons. Semischematic. Based on data by Cajal and de Nó. *1*, pyramidal cells of superficial layers; *2*, pyramidal cells from ganglionic layer; *3*, spindle cells; *4*, stellate cells; *a*, axon.

number of horizontal myelinated fibers constituting the band of Kaes-Bechterew.

Lorente de Nó places the larger deeper pyramids into layer IV where they are designated as the sublayer of stellate pyramids. According to him these cells, in addition to their numerous shorter dendrites which give them a stellate appearance, possess an apical dendrite which gives off collaterals to layer IV and then ascends unbranched to the molecular layer.

IV. The *internal granular layer* is composed chiefly of closely packed stellate cells

tions of thalamocortical and other afferent fibers. According to de Nó the large stellate pyramids of layer III should be included in this layer.

V. The *ganglionic* or *internal pyramidal layer* consists principally of medium-sized and large pyramids intermingled with granule and Martinotti cells. The apical dendrites of the larger pyramids ascend to the molecular layer, those of the smaller ones ascend only to layer IV or may even arborize within the ganglionic layer (de Nó). The axons enter the white matter chiefly as projection fibers and to a lesser extent as association fibers. According to de Nó a considerable number of callosal fibers are furnished by the smaller pyramids. The rich horizontal fiber plexus in the deeper portion of this layer constitutes the internal band of Baillarger.

VI. The *multiform layer* or *layer of fusiform cells* contains predominantly spindle-shaped cells whose long axis is perpendicular to the cortical surface, and also granule, Martinotti and stellate cells. Like the pyramids of layer V, the spindle cells also vary in size, the larger ones sending a dendrite to the molecular layer. The dendrites of the smaller ones ascend only to layer IV or arborize within the fusiform layer itself. Thus the dendrites of many pyramidal and spindle cells from layers V and VI come in direct relation with the endings of sensory thalamocortical fibers which ramify chiefly in the internal granular layer. The axons of the spindle cells enter the white substance both as projection and association fibers, and it is maintained that many of the short arcuate association fibers connecting adjacent convolutions are furnished by the deep stellate cells of this layer (de Nó). The multiform layer may be subdivided into an upper sublayer of more densely packed larger cells, and a lower one in which the smaller cells are more loosely arranged. The whole layer is pervaded by fiber bundles which enter or leave the medullary substance.

Besides the horizontal cellular lamination the cortex also exhibits a vertical radiate arrangement of the cells, giving the appearance of slender vertical cell columns passing through the whole thickness of the cortex (Fig. 320). This vertical lamination is quite distinct in the parietal, occipital and temporal lobes, but is practically absent in the frontal lobe. The arrangement into vertical cell columns is produced by the radial fibers of the cortex just as the horizontal lamination is largely determined by the distribution of the tangential fibers.

Many authorities believe that a distinction should be made between the *supragranular* and *infragranular layers* of the cortex. The former which include layers II and III are the latest to arise and are most highly differentiated and most extensive in man. The fibers which they receive or send out are chiefly associative in character, hence they are believed to be concerned with the more purely cortical associative mnemonic functions. The infragranular layers, composed of layers V and VI, are well developed in other mammals and are directly connected with subcortical structures by descending projection systems. It has been shown by Nissl that when the cortex of newborn rabbits is isolated from the rest of the nervous system, the infragranular layers fail to increase during subsequent development while the growth of the supragranular cortex remains unaffected. Those older layers appear to be concerned with the more fundamental cortical activities primarily of a motor character. The internal granular layer which intervenes between the supragranular and infragranular cortex, chiefly receives the afferent projection fibers. The supragranular layers are lacking in the archipallium.

The interrelation of cortical neurons. The pictures of cortical structure seen in preparations treated with the Nissl or myelin methods, are of necessity incomplete. They show only the types and arrangement of the cell bodies or the course and distribution of the myelinated fibers, but give no information regarding the dendritic and axonal end arborizations which constitute the synaptic junctions through which nerve impulses are transmitted. An understanding of the neuronal relationships and hence of the intracortical conduction circuits can only be obtained by impregnation methods which give a total picture of the cell body and all its processes. By the use of such methods, the distribution of the dendritic and axonal terminals has been worked out by a number of investigators, notably by Cajal, and more recently Lorente de Nó has given a detailed account of the elementary pattern of cortical organization applicable for the parietal, temporal and occipital isocortex. According to this investigator the arrangement of the axonal and dendritic branchings forms the most constant feature of cortical structure and is fundamentally

association fibers from other cortical areas of the same and opposite side. The thalamocortical fibers, especially the specific afferent ones from the ventral thalamic nuclei and the geniculate bodies which form the last relays of the ascending sensory systems, pass unbranched to layer IV where

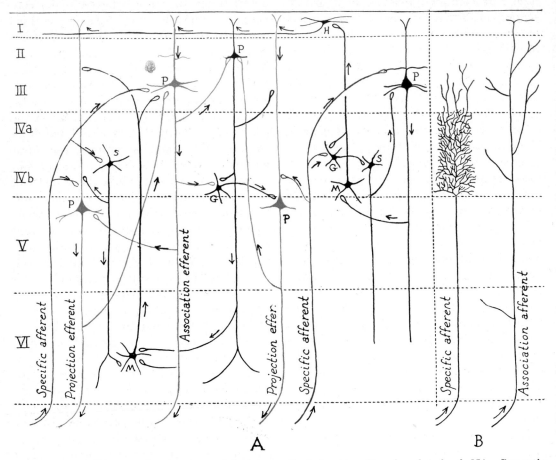

FIG. 315. *A*, Diagram showing some of the intracortical circuits. Based on data by de Nó. Synaptic junctions are indicated by loops. *Red*, afferent thalamocortical fibers; *blue*, efferent cortical neurons; *black*, intracortical neurons. *G*, granule cell; *H*, horizontal cell; *M*, Martinotti cell; *P*, pyramidal cell; *S*, stellate cell. *B*, mode of termination of afferent cortical fibers.

the same in different mammals and in man for comparable cortical areas which otherwise may show considerable variations in the type and size of their cell bodies. The following paragraphs are largely based on de Nó's account.

The afferent fibers to the cortex include projection fibers from the thalamus and

they arborize into a dense terminal plexus, some of the fibers however extending to layer III and arborizing there (Fig. 315B). The association and callosal fibers on the other hand, give off some collaterals to layers V and VI and ramify mainly in layers II and III and to a lesser extent in layer IV. The further course of the entering impulses will naturally depend on the axonal branching of the cells which have synaptic relations with the afferent fibers.

The cortical neurons, as regards the direction and extent of their fiber processes, may be grouped into cells with descending, ascending, horizontal and short axons. The last three types serve wholly for intracortical connections. The cells with descending axons, represented by the pyramidal, fusiform and larger stellate cells, furnish all the efferent projection and association fibers, but in addition their axonal collaterals form an extensive system of intracortical connections. Naturally, the descending axons which do not reach the medullary substance have only the intracortical branches.

The pyramidal cells of layers II, III and IV have a similar pattern of dendritic and axonal branchings (Fig. 314). They have a number of basilar dendrites which arborize in the same layer and an apical dendrite which ends in the molecular layer. Their descending axons in part terminate in the deeper layers of the cortex, in part are continued as association or callosal fibers. During their descent they give off a few recurrent collaterals to their own layers, chiefly II and III, few if any to layer IV, but numerous horizontal collaterals to V and VI where they contribute to the horizontal plexuses of these layers. These axonal ramifications thus chiefly connect layers II and III with V and VI.

The pyramidal and fusiform cells of layers V and VI have a very characteristic pattern of dendritic and axonal branchings. All the pyramidal cells of V give off basilar dendrites to their own layer and an apical dendrite which in most cases extends to the molecular layer. There are however medium pyramids whose apical dendrites terminate in IV, and short pyramids whose dendrites all ramify in V (Fig. 314). The spindles of layer VI have a similar dendritic branching and may likewise be grouped

into long, medium and short ones, whose ascending dendritic shafts terminate respectively in I, IV and VI, and whose other dendrites arborize in VI. The dendritic terminals of the medium pyramids and spindles thus come in direct contact with the endings of specific afferent fibers in layer IV. The axons of the pyramids and spindles and of many deep stellate cells are continued as projection, association or callosal fibers, and have collateral branchings of a definite character. All these axons send horizontal collaterals to V and VI, contributing largely to the horizontal plexuses of these layers especially V (internal band of Baillarger). Many however have in addition one or more recurrent collaterals which ascend unbranched through layer IV and arborize in II and III, some even extending to the molecular layer (Fig. 314). The horizontal plexus of III and II is in considerable part formed by these recurrent collaterals. Thus the impulses reaching the efferent cells of the deeper layers may spread horizontally within these layers or be returned by the recurrent collaterals to the superficial layers, and especially II and III.

Added to this extensive system of intracortical connections furnished by the cells with descending axons, are the still more intricate arborizations of the cells with short, ascending and horizontal axons. These small cells, less numerous in lower mammals, have become tremendously increased in man where their number has been estimated at six billion (Economo), most of them short axon granule cells. These latter are small stellate or polygonal cells with numerous short dendrites, whose axon breaks up close to the cell body into a dense end arborization synaptically related to the bodies of many pyramidal or other cells with descending axons. The cell and all its processes are confined to one layer, though the axon may extend horizontally for a short distance before ramifying. The short axon cells are most concentrated in layer IV but are found in large numbers in all the layers. The cells with horizontal axons are chiefly found in the molecular layer, their long axons present in every layer except the most superficial one. Their dendrites are usually but not always confined to a single layer, their

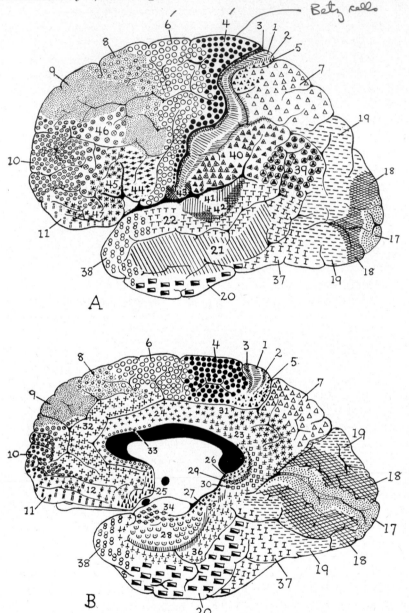

FIG. 316. Cytoarchitectural map of human cortex. (After Brodmann.) *A*, convex surface; *B*, medial surface.

often running for considerable distances and making contact with the dendritic terminals of many pyramidal and fusiform cells (Fig. 315). The cells of Martinotti are also ascending axons have a variable length and distribution. Some from layers V and VI arborize chiefly in III and II. Others extend to the surface and may send collaterals to all the layers through which they pass. Thus while the horizontal and short axon cells have intralaminar connections, the Martinotti cells interconnect the various lamina, so that impulses reaching the cells of the deeper layers can be returned again and again to the more superficial ones.

From the arrangement of the cell processes described above it is evident that any vertical strip of cortex may be regarded as

involving a progressively larger number of synaptic junctions. The character of the axonal branchings definitely indicates that in such complex circuits the entering impulses are repeatedly switched from the more peripheral to the deeper layers and vice versa, the impulses returning again and again to the same cells and ultimately leaving the cortex through efferent fibers. All these vertical chains are however intercon-

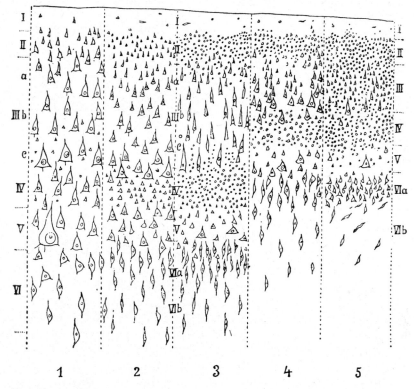

Fig. 317. The five fundamental types of cortical structure.   (Economo.)   *1*, agranular; *2*, frontal; *3*, parietal; *4*, polar; *5*, granulous (koniocortex).

an elementary functional unit or aggregation of such units in which are present all the necessary elements, afferent, internuncial and efferent, for the formation of complete cortical circuits.   The simplest vertical chain of such a unit involves a single synapse only, such as the synaptic junction of an afferent fiber with the apical dendrite of an efferent pyramidal cell (Fig. 315).   Superimposed upon this fundamental cortical arc, are vertical chains of varying complexity

nected by short neuronal links represented primarily by the short axon granule cells whose processes arborize within a single layer.   Through these short links cortical excitation may spread along the horizontal plane and involve a progressively larger number of vertical chains.   Thus a specific afferent fiber may not only fire off the vertical chains in its immediate vicinity but also reach more distant chains through the shorter communicating links of the Golgi type II cells. While therefore in architectonic pictures (Nissl pictures) the primary organization of the cortex appears in the form of a horizontal lamination, the intracortical connections are disposed both vertically and horizontally. The vertical chains are composed of long links which connect the various cortical layers, the horizontal ones consist of short links which spread horizontally within a single layer. The vertical chains are fundamentally similar in all mammals, but the chains with short links increase in complexity in the higher forms and especially in man whose brain contains enormous numbers of short axon cells. According to Cajal, the intricacy and delicacy of functioning of the human brain is anatomically expressed by the large number of its small cells.

THE CORTICAL AREAS

The cerebral cortex does not have a uniform structure throughout its extent but may be mapped out into a number of areas which differ from each other in the thickness of the cortex as a whole, the thickness and density of the individual layers and the arrangement and amount of their cells and fibers. In certain areas the structural deviations are so extreme that the basic sesquilaminated pattern is practically obscured and individual cortical layers can no longer be made out, or only with great difficulty. Such areas are termed *heterotypical* as opposed to the *homotypical* cortex in which the six layers are easily distinguished (Brodmann). Histological surveys based on differences in the arrangement and types of the cells and in the pattern of the myelinated fibers, have furnished several fundamentally similar cortical maps in which however the number of areas has been variously estimated. Thus Campbell (1905) described some 20 cortical fields which were increased by Brodmann (1909) to 47 and by von Economo (1929) to 109, while the Vogts (1919) parcelled the human brain into more than 200 areas. Even this number is apparently insufficient, since recent investigators have found a number of cytoarchitectural fields in regions previously considered homogeneous (Rose, Beck). Brodmann's chart which is most widely used for purposes of reference, is shown in Fig. 316.

According to von Economo all cortical structure is reducible to five fundamental types, based primarily on the relative development of the granule and pyramidal cells. Types 2, 3 and 4, known respectively as the frontal, parietal and polar types are homotypical and constitute by far the largest part of the cortex. The agranular (1) and granulous (5) types are heterotypical and are limited to relatively small regions (Fig. 317).

The *frontal type* is thick and shows the six layers distinctly (Fig. 319C). The pyramidal cells of layers III and V are large and well formed, as are the spindles of layer VI. The granular layers though distinct are rather narrow and composed chiefly of loosely arranged small triangular cells. In the *parietal type* the layers are even more distinct due to the greater depth and density of the granular layers (Fig. 320, A, B). The pyramidal layers are however thinner, and their cells smaller and more irregularly arranged. The *polar type* found near the frontal and occipital poles, is characterized by its thinness and its comparative wealth of cells which are especially numerous in the narrow but well defined granular layers. At the frontal pole the ganglionic layer contains many large pyramidal cells, while at the occipital pole these are as a rule smaller and fewer. The *agranular type* is distinguished by its great thickness and the practical absence of granule cells (Fig. 319, A, B). The pyramidal cells of layers III and V are well formed and large, but even the smaller cells of layers II and IV are mostly pyramidal in shape, hence the individual layers are difficult to distinguish. This type is best represented by the cortex of the precentral gyrus. The *granulous type* or *koniocortex* is the reverse of type I. It is even thinner than the polar cortex and is composed mainly of densely packed granule cells. These are not only found in layers

there is even a duplication of the internal granular layer (Fig. 320, C).

The general distribution of these five structural types is shown in Fig. 318. The

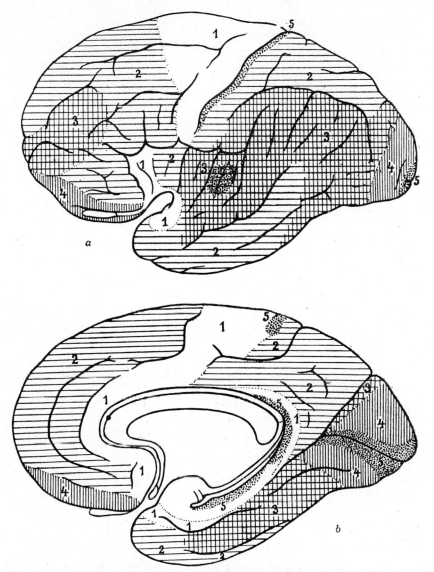

FIG. 318. Distribution of the five fundamental types of cortex over the convex (*a*) and the medial (*b*) surface of the hemisphere. (Economo.) *1*, agranular; *2*, frontal; *3*, parietal; *4*, polar; *5*, granulous (koniocortex).

II and IV, but the other layers also, especially III, show large numbers of such small cells with a consequent reduction of the pyramidal cells. The most striking example of this type is the calcarine cortex, in which

agranular cortex covers the caudal part of the frontal lobe in front of the central sulcus, the anterior half of the gyrus cinguli and the anterior portion of the insula. A narrow strip is also found in the retrosplenial region of the gyrus cinguli, and is continued along the hippocampal gyrus and uncus, the latter regions belonging to the allocortex. Since the chief efferent fiber systems arise from the anterior wall of the postcentral gyrus, the walls and lips of the calcarine fissure and the transverse temporal gyrus of Heschl. Again there is a narrow strip in the retrosplenial

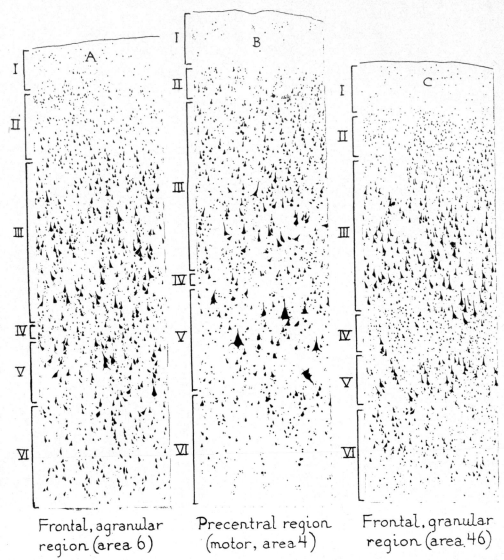

Frontal, agranular region (area 6)

Precentral region (motor, area 4)

Frontal, granular region (area 46)

Fig. 319. Cytoarchitectural pictures of several representative cortical areas. (After Campbell.)

these regions, especially from the precentral gyrus, this may be considered as the efferent or motor type of cortex. Similarly the koniocortex may be regarded as primarily sensory in character since it is found only in the areas receiving the specific sensory thalamocortical projections. These include region and along the dorsal wall of the hippocampal fissure.

By far the largest part of the hemispheric surface is covered by homotypical cortex. The frontal type is spread over the larger anterior part of the frontal lobe, the superior parietal lobule, precuneus, and most of the middle and inferior temporal gyri. The parietal type chiefly includes the inferior parietal lobule, the superior temporal gyrus, the fusiform gyrus and the anterior convex parts of the occipital lobe. The polar type as already stated covers the areas near the frontal and occipital poles. These extensive lamic level. The areas lying behind the central sulcus are primarily related to receptive or psychosensory activities, segregating and recombining the primary afferent impulses into more complex unisensory and multisensory entities. Similarly the frontal areas may form the substratum of the more

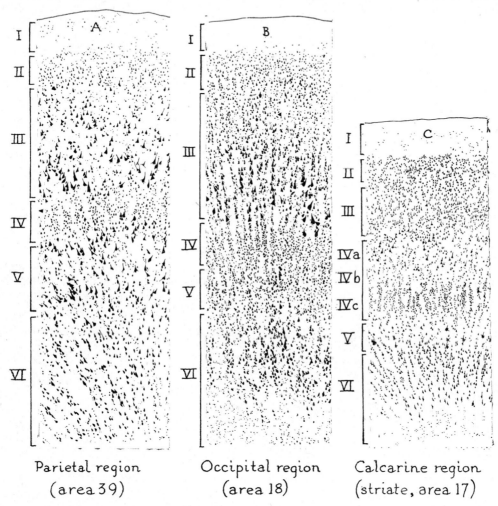

Parietal region
(area 39)

Occipital region
(area 18)

Calcarine region
(striate, area 17)

FIG. 320. Cytoarchitectural picture of several cortical areas. (After Campbell)

cortical areas are probably concerned with the higher mnemonic associative functions, and their thalamic connections are chiefly with the association nuclei, such as the medial and lateral thalamic nuclei and the pulvinar, from which they receive more diffuse and complex afferent impulses already combined and integrated at a tha-

complex psychomotor activities ultimately expressed through the efferent projection systems of the agranular cortex, especially the pyramidal tract.

Practically every part of the cerebral cortex is connected with subcortical centers by afferent and efferent projection fibers, hence strictly speaking there are no circumscribed cortical areas which are purely associative or projective in character. In a general way however, there are regions from which arise the more important descending tracts which directly or through intercalated centers reach the lower motor neurons for the initiation and control of both somatic and visceral activities. These primarily efferent or motor areas from which muscular movements can be elicited by electrical stimulation, are chiefly concentrated in the precentral part of the frontal lobe, but to a lesser extent are also found in widely distributed areas of the parietal, occipital and temporal lobes. Similarly those more specific regions which receive the direct thalamocortical sensory fibers from the ventral thalamic nuclei and from the geniculate bodies, represent the primary receptive or sensory areas which constitute the terminus of the long ascending sensory pathways of the spinal cord and brain stem. The remaining portions of the cortex are less directly related to the sensory and motor periphery. They receive their afferent impulses from the association nuclei of the thalamus and more especially from the primary receptive cortical areas, and discharge in turn into the efferent centers of the precentral and other regions of the cortex. These "association areas" characterized by the wealth of their intracortical connections constitute by far the largest part of the cerebral cortex.

THE EFFERENT CORTICAL AREAS

The motor area. Area 4 of Brodmann, commonly designated as the motor area, is located on the anterior wall of the central sulcus and adjacent portions of the precentral gyrus (Fig. 316). Broad at the dorsal border of the hemisphere, where it spreads over a considerable part of the precentral gyrus, it constantly narrows in a ventral direction, and at the level of the inferior frontal gyrus is practically limited to the anterior wall of the Rolandic fissure. On the medial surface it comprises the anterior portion of the paracentral lobule, extending as far as the sulcus cinguli. The unusually thick cortex of the motor area (3.5–4.5 mm.) is agranular in structure and its ganglionic layer contains the giant pyramidal cells of Betz whose cell bodies may reach a height of 60–120 micra (Fig. 319B). They are largest in the paracentral lobule and near the dorsal border, and smallest in the ventral opercular portion.

The pyramidal tract which transmits impulses for volitional movements from the cortex to the lower motor neurons arises principally from this area. The larger corticobulbar and corticospinal fibers are undoubtedly axons of the giant pyramidal cells, the more numerous finer fibers probably come from other cells of this region, from the premotor area (area 6) and possibly also from other cortical areas. Due to the crossing of the pyramidal fibers the motor cortex of one side controls the muscular activities of the opposite side, but this crossing is incomplete and all muscles are represented to some extent in the ipsolateral motor area. In muscles which as a rule can not be voluntarily contracted on one side alone, such as the vocal cords, pharynx, upper face and trunk, the bilateral pyramidal control is most marked and unilateral lesions of the motor cortex produce negligible symptoms.

Electrical stimulation of the motor area evokes discrete isolated movements on the opposite side of the body. Usually the contractions involve the functional muscle groups concerned with a specific movement, but individual muscles, even a single interosseus, may be separately contracted. While the pattern of excitable foci is the same for all mammals, the number of such foci and hence the number of discrete movements is greatly increased in man. Thus flexion or extension at a single finger joint, twitchings at the corners of the mouth, elevation of the palate, protrusion of the tongue and even vocalization expressed in involuntary cries or exclamations, may all be evoked by careful stimulation of the proper areas. Charts of motor representation, which are in substantial agreement, have been furnished by a number of investigators, notably by Foerster (1936) and by Penfield and Boldrey (1937) who stimulated a large number of human brains under local anesthesia. The location of centers for specific movements may vary from individual to individual, but the sequence of motor representation appears to be constant, e.g., the point which on stimulation produces a movement of the pharynx will always lie nearer to the Sylvian fissure than that producing a movement of

ated at the medial border and extending into the paracentral lobule which also contains the centers for the anal and vesical sphincters.

There is still considerable controversy regarding the location of the centers for the lower extremity, due in part to the difficulty of stimulating the medial surface. The paracentral lobule undoubtedly "contains the foci of the foot, of the toes, of the bladder and of the rectum" (Foerster). Yet there must be a wide overlapping of motor foci, since Penfield and Boldrey obtained leg movements in twenty-three cases by stimu-

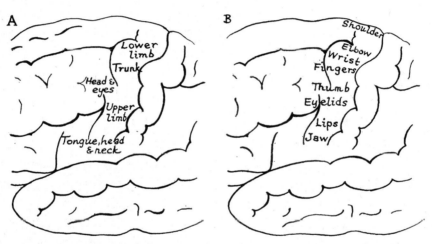

FIG. 321. The representation of the body in the motor area of the human brain (A) according to a diagram from Gray's Anatomy and (B) according to the observations of J. E. Scarff. (Scarff.)

the lips, and so on. Ipsilateral movemnets have not been observed in man, but bilateral responses occur in the eyes, face, tongue, jaw, larynx and pharynx. According to Penfield and Boldrey, the center for the pharynx (swallowing) lies in the most ventral opercular portion of the precentral gyrus, followed above by those for the tongue, jaw, lips, larynx (vocalization), eyelid and brow in the order named. Next come the extensive areas for finger movements, the thumb being lowest and the little finger highest, and this is followed by the hand, wrist, elbow and shoulder. Finally in the most dorsal part are the centers for the hip, knee, ankle and toes, the last named situ-

lating the dorsal portion of the precentral gyrus. More recently however, Scarff (1940) was unable to elicit any leg movements by stimulating the lateral surface of the hemisphere in fourteen patients, though he did get such movements in one case when the medial surface was stimulated (Fig. 321). He concludes "that the primary motor area for the upper extremity commonly extends upward on the lateral surface to the superior mesial border, while the leg as a rule is represented only on the mesial surface" i.e. in the paracentral lobule. He believes that this upward shift of the motor area, unique in man, is due to the release of the upper extremity from the burden of locomotion and

its consequent elaboration into a more complex motor organ and to the acquisition of
speech and other forms of symbolic expression. These new acquisitions have led to an
expansion of the motor areas representing
the tongue, mouth, lips and upper extremity, so that the leg areas have been crowded
upward and finally pushed over to the
medial surface. Focal contractions of the
rectal sphincter by stimulating the paracentral lobule, were likewise reported for the
first time by this investigator.

Lesions of the motor cortex produce a
contralateral paralysis of volitional move-

spasticity only appeared when the premotor
area (area 6) was involved. Fulton believes
that the same is applicable to man, and
several clinical cases supporting this view
have recently been reported (Shmidt, 1946).
In extensive lesions of the pyramidal tract
below the cortical level, spasticity is a common feature, but the pyramidal tract receives contributions from both the motor
and premotor areas. A full discussion of the
structure and significance of the motor area
may be found in the "*Precentral Motor
Cortex*" edited by P. C. Bucy (1944).

Extrapyramidal motor areas. The pre-

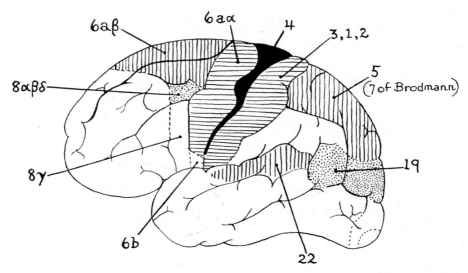

FIG. 322. The areas of electrically excitable cortex on the lateral surface of the human brain. (After
Foerster.) The motor area is shown in black, the extrapyramidal areas are hatched except for the eye
fields which are stippled.

ments, of the type already described in
previous chapters (pp. 140–142). Since the
pyramidal tract is widely spread out in this
region, cortical lesions are likely to involve
only part of the fibers and produce a paralysis of a single limb (monoplegia) or of the
face. In time there may be considerable
restitution especially for the grosser movements, while the finer isolated movements
are permanently lost.

Fulton and his co-workers (Kennard,
Jacobsen, Viets) found that ablation of the
motor area (area 4) in primates produced a
paralysis of the flaccid type, and that

motor area (area 6) lies immediately in front
of the motor area. It likewise runs dorso-
ventrally along the whole lateral aspect of
the frontal lobe and is continued on the
medial surface to the sulcus cinguli (Fig.
316). Near the dorsal border it is quite
broad and includes the caudal portion of the
superior frontal gyrus. Proceeding ventrally it narrows rapidly and at the operculum is completely limited to the precentral
gyrus. Its histological structure resembles
that of the motor area, being principally
composed of large well-formed pyramidal
cells, but the giant cells of Betz are alto-

gether lacking (Fig. 319A). This region likewise responds to electrical stimulation but stronger currents are required to evoke movements than are necessary in the case of area 4. Area 6 is usually divided into a larger upper portion (6a) lying in front of the leg and arm area of the motor cortex, and a smaller narrower portion (6b) in front of the face area (Fig. 322).

Foerster and others have shown that faradic stimulation of area 6 gives rise to two kinds of contralateral movements: isolated movements of individual muscles resembling those of the motor area, and more complex synergic movements such as flexion of the contralateral extremities or turning of head and eyes to the opposite side. Similar complex movements involving the facial, masticatory, laryngeal and pharyngeal muscles are evoked by stimulating the lower portion of this area (6b). The isolated movements are apparently due to a transmission of the stimulation to area 4, for they are no longer elicitable when area 6 is isolated from the motor area by a cortical incision or when the motor area or pyramidal tract are destroyed. The more complex mass movements however remain. These therefore must be mediated by extrapyramidal fibers which pass by way of the thalamus, basal ganglia and other subcortical centers to the lower motor neurons. Thus the premotor area both relays cortical impulses to area 4 for the execution of the finer isolated movements, and is itself capable of mediating grosser volitional synergies related perhaps to postural adjustments and the more instinctive activities of locomotion and defense.

Immediately in front of the premotor area is a narrow strip of cortex which is likewise motor in function and responds to strong faradic stimulation. This area 8 differs cytoarchitecturally from the motor and premotor cortex by having distinct if narrow granular layers, and thus belongs to the sesquilaminated frontal type. Its dorsal portion is usually included as part of the premotor area. Its middle segment which forms the caudal portion of the middle frontal gyrus constitutes the frontal eye field designated in Foerster's map as 8 $\alpha\beta\delta$ (Fig. 322). Stimulation of this area causes strong conjugate deviation of the eyes, and occasional vertical movements have likewise been described (Foerster). It is believed to be the cortical center for the voluntary scanning and spying movements of the eyes. The lower part of area 8 and adjacent portion of area 6 which together form the opercular part of the inferior frontal gyrus, have become considerably modified in man and form the area of Broca, believed to be concerned with the motor formulation of speech (areas 44 and 45 of Brodmann).

The extrapyramidal areas are not limited to the frontal lobe, but are also found behind the central fissure in regions which otherwise must be considered as receptive or sensory in character (Fig. 322). Strong faradic stimulation of the postcentral gyrus (Areas 3, 1, 2) likewise produces both isolated and complex movements, the former again depending on the integrity of the motor area. Similar mass movements are elicited by stimulation of the superior parietal lobule (area 7 of Brodmann) and the superior temporal gyrus, while conjugate deviation of the eyes to the opposite side may be evoked from area 19 of the occipital lobe (occipital eye field).

Summarizing the results of stimulating the various cortical areas it may be said that the motor cortex represents the specific area for the production of isolated movements, and any such movements evoked from other regions depend on the integrity of the motor area. There are however a number of areas capable of responding with complex synergic movements of the head, eyes, trunk and extremities, even when the motor area and the pyramidal tract are destroyed. These extrapyramidal areas (Foerster), especially those of the frontal lobe, constitute the cortical centers of the extrapyramidal motor pathway whose fibers are relayed in the thalamus and other subcortical nuclei before reaching the motor cells of the cranial and spinal nerves. Their significance in the control of postural adjustments and of the grosser volitional movements of instinctive behavior has been discussed in connection with the corpus striatum and diencephalon (p. 340).

It is a fact of every day experience that the cortex exerts a strong influence on autonomic activies, both sympathetic and parasympathetic, as shown in the cardiovascular, digestive and other visceral changes occurring in mental states of all types. The anatomical pathways have not been fully worked out, but there is considerable experimental evidence that this influence is in large part mediated through extrapyramidal fibers from the motor and premotor areas, and perhaps through the pyramidal tract as well (Spiegel and Hunsicker). An equally important channel is undoubtedly furnished by the corticothalamic fibers from the prefrontal cortex to the medial thalamic nucleus from which impulses may be relayed to the hypothalamus by the periventricular fiber system.

Another important system of efferent cortical fibers is represented by the extensive corticopontile tracts which arise from the frontal, precentral and temporal regions and to a lesser extent from the superior parietal lobule and anterior portion of the occipital lobe. Through these tracts the cerebral cortex is brought into intimate association with the synergic regulating mechanism of the cerebellum which is concerned with the adjustment and appropriate distribution of tone in synergic muscle groups for the proper execution of precise voluntary movements and for the maintenance of posture. The ataxia and hypotonia sometimes observed in frontal and temporal lesions may be due to injury of these corticocerebellar connections.

A survey of the various descending fibers described above suggests that at least three main streams of efferent impulses emerge from the cerebral cortex. One is primarily concerned with the finer nonpostural discrete movements of skilled activity. Another regulates the somatic and visceral reactions of affective or instinctive behavior, while the third acts on the synergic regulating cerebellar mechanism. The first is mediated largely through the pyramidal tract, the second through the corticothalamic and other extrapyramidal fibers, the third through the cortico-ponto-cerebellar system. The coöperation of all three is probably necessary for the production of properly balanced and properly executed pallial reactions.

THE PRIMARY RECEPTIVE AREAS

The **somesthetic sensory area** which subserves general somatic sensibility, superficial as well as deep, is principally located on the postcentral gyrus and its medial extension in the paracentral lobule (Fig. 316). Histologically the gyrus is composed of three narrow strips of cortex (3, 1, 2) which differ in their architectural structure. The most anterior strip (area 3) facing the central sulcus is very thin (2 mm. or less) and is composed principally of granular elements, hence belongs to the granulous type of Economo. Areas 1 and 2, forming respectively the crown and posterior wall of the postcentral gyrus, have the sesquilaminated structure of the frontal type (type 2).

The postcentral gyrus receives the thalamic projections from the posterior ventral nuclei which relay impulses from the medial lemniscus and secondary trigeminal tracts. The various regions of the body are represented in specific portions of the postcentral gyrus, the pattern corresponding to that of the motor area. Thus the face area lies in the most ventral part, while above this are placed the sensory areas for the hand, arm, trunk, leg and foot in the order named, the lower extremity probably extending into the paracentral lobule. There are many observations which suggest that the somesthetic area is not limited to the postcentral gyrus, but may extend caudally into the superior and inferior parietal lobule, and frontally into the precentral gyrus (de Barenne, Head). Dusser de Barenne has found also that application of strychnine to the postcentral gyrus in monkeys induced cutaneous sensory hyperesthesias most marked on the opposite side but present to some extent on the same side also. Deep sensibility appeared to have a contralateral representation only. Whether the discriminative aspects of tactile sensibility are bilaterally represented in the human cortex spatial relations; (b) a graduated response to stimuli of different intensity; (c) appreciation of similarity and difference in external objects brought into contact with the surface of the body" (Head). Hence in lesions of the sensory area there is loss of appreciation of passive movement, of two point discrimination and of ability to differentiate various intensities of stimuli. These faculties have a definite spatial orientation in the sensory area and may correspondingly be disturbed to an unequal degree, depending on the location and extent of the

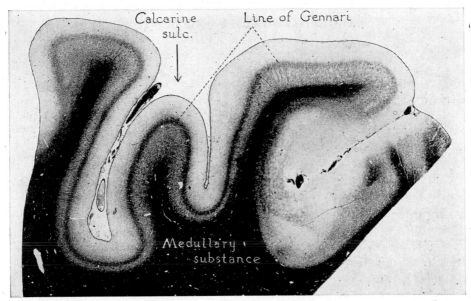

FIG. 323. Frontal section through calcarine cortex (area striata) showing extent of stripe of Gennari. Weigert's myelin stain. Photograph.

is not definitely known. Clinically the sensory defects caused by cortical lesions of this area are noticeable only on the opposite side.

The sensory cortex is not primarily concerned with the recognition of crude sensory modalities, such as pain, temperature and mere contact. These apparently enter consciousness at the level of the thalamus, and their appreciation is retained even after complete destruction of the sensory area. "The sensory activity of the cortex ... endows sensation with three discriminative faculties. These are: (a) recognition of injury. Spatial relationship is most severely affected when the lesion is in the most anterior portion of the postcentral gyrus. The appreciation of similarities and differences are related to the middle portion, while lesions of the posterior wall of the gyrus and adjacent portions of the supramarginal convolution and superior parietal lobule disturb the faculty of discriminating between stimuli of different intensities. In severe lesions the patient though aware of the stimulus and its sensory modality is unable to locate accurately the point touched; to gauge the direction and extent of passive movement; to distinguish between different weights, textures or degrees of temperature; and as a result is unable to identify objects by merely feeling them (astereognosis). The more complicated the test, the more evident becomes the sensory defect. With all this there is a variability of response so that a definite threshold for a given sensation can not be established.

The **visual receptive area** (area 17) is located in the walls of the calcarine fissure and adjacent portion of the cuneus and lingual gyrus, occasionally extending around the occipital pole to the lateral surface of the hemisphere (Fig. 316). The exceedingly thin cortex of this area (1.5–2.5 mm.) is the most striking example of the heterotypical granulous cortex (type 5). Layers II and III are narrow and contain numerous small pyramidal cells, hardly larger than the typical granule cells (Fig. 320C). Layer IV is very thick and subdivided by a light band into three sublayers. The upper and lower sublayers are packed with small granule cells. In the middle lighter layer, the small cells are fewer, and scattered between them are large stellate cells, the so-called giant stellate cells of Meynert. The light layer is occupied by the greatly thickened outer band of Baillarger, here known as the band of Gennari, which is visible to the naked eye in sections of the fresh cortex and has given this region the name of *area striata* (Fig. 323). Layer V is relatively narrow and poor in cells, but scattered among them are isolated large pyramidal cells which may reach a height of 60 micra (Fig. 320C).

The visual cortex receives the geniculocalcarine tract whose course and exact projection have been discussed in an earlier chapter (p. 321). The macular fibers terminate in the caudal third of the calcarine area, those from the paracentral and peripheral retinal areas end in respectively more rostral portions. In man, complete destruction of the visual cortex on one side produces a crossed homonymous hemianopia i.e. loss of the contralateral half of the visual field. Destruction of both striate areas causes total blindness. Other mammals, such as dogs or even monkeys, are still able to distinguish between light intensities after ablation of the visual cortex.

The **auditory receptive area** (areas 41, 42) is located on the two transverse gyri of Heschl which lie on the dorsal surface of the superior temporal convolution, buried in the floor of the Sylvian fissure (Figs. 316, 296). Area 41 occupies the middle of the anterior transverse gyrus and a portion of the posterior, and is surrounded by area 42 which extends somewhat on the lateral surface in the middle region of the superior temporal convolution. The two areas are cytoarchitecturally different. Area 41, though relatively thick (3 mm.), is composed of koniocortex resembling that of areas 3 and 17. Area 42 has the sesquilaminated cortex of the parietal type (type 3). A distinctive feature of the latter is the presence of a number of large pyramidal cells in layer III.

The auditory area receives the geniculotemporal fibers (auditory radiation) from the medial geniculate body. Since these fibers conduct impulses from both ears, the area is bilaterally represented, hence unilateral lesions cause only partial deafness. According to Penfield and Evans, removal of one temporal lobe produces an impairment of sound localization on the opposite side, especially as regards judgment of the distance from which the sounds are coming. While the integration and interpretation of auditory impulses is highly elaborated and wholly corticalized in man, it is still uncertain whether the fundamental auditory sensations, such as the pitch and quality of sound, may not also be appreciated to some extent by subcortical structures. In animals, ablation of both temporal lobes does not apparently cause total deafness.

The temporal cortex probably also contains a primary receptive center for vestibular impulses, though its exact location has not been fully ascertained. When the temporal convolutions are sensitized with strychnine, stimulation of the labyrinth produces convulsive movements (Spiegel), but these movements fail to appear when the eighth nerve is destroyed. In man, sensations of dizziness or vertigo often occur in vestibular disease or in irritative lesions of the temporal lobes. The work of Winkler (p. 225) suggests that vestibular fibers in part terminate in the cochlear nuclei and reach the cortex by way of the lateral lemniscus and auditory radiation. If this is the case, areas 41 and 42 would constitute receptive centers for both auditory and vestibular impulses.

The **gustatory** and **olfactory receptive areas** have not been determined with certainty. The work of Börnstein suggests that taste is located in the most ventral (opercular) portion of the postcentral gyrus, and this view has been strengthened by more recent experimental work (Patton, Ruch and Walker). The primary centers for smell are probably located in the uncus and anterior portion of the hippocampal gyrus, since the lateral olfactory stria terminates in these areas.

THE GENERAL NATURE OF CORTICAL FUNCTIONING

One of the most striking features of the human brain is the tremendous extent of its neural mechanism for the more complex correlation and discrimination of sensory impulses, and the greater utilization in various neural reactions of traces of former reactions. The principal function of this mechanism may be termed *associative memory* and such reactions *mnemonic* (memory) reactions. Memory i.e. the modification of structure by external influences, is a property displayed by other than neural tissues and by other parts of the nervous system than the pallium. Whether cortical plasticity is due simply to a summation of the modifiability possessed by all neurons, or to some specially evolved qualities is not known. Whatever its nature, the acquired changes of the pallium, due to its plasticity and consequent capacity of "learning," alter the action of subsequent stimuli reaching the cortex and furnish the basis of conscious and unconscious memory, of personal experience and of individually acquired neural mechanisms. Moreover, the transmission of this acquired and ever varying experience, by means of complex symbols, to the plastic brains of other individuals, constitutes an abbreviated *neopallial* evolution as contrasted with the slow process of *germinal* evolution. Other animals utilize individual experience and thus "learn", but it is very doubtful if any other animal than man summates experience by transmitting it to other individuals and generations in ever varying amounts. The symbolization necessary for this summation undoubtedly requires a great complexity of the pallial mechanism for associative memory. It has been estimated that the cerebral cortex contains nearly 14 billion nerve cells, and by far the greater number of these are utilized for the above activities.

In a general way, the central sulcus of Rolando divides the brain into a posterior receptive portion and an anterior portion related more closely to efferent or motor functions. In the posterior part are located all the primary receptive areas which receive specific sensory impulses from the lower centers of the brain, and hence indirectly from the sensory periphery. The stimuli entering these primary areas produce sensations of a sharply defined character such as distinct vision and hearing, sharply localized touch and accurate sensations of position and movements. These sensations have however not yet attained the perceptual level necessary for the recognition of an object. This requires the association of primary stimuli into progressively more complicated sensory entities, and is mediated by the extensive cortical fields which lie between the receptive centers and constitute the so-called "associative areas" of the brain. The regions in immediate contact with the receptive centers, often known as parasensory areas, serve for the combination and elaboration of the primary impulses into more complex unisensory perceptions capable of recall under appropriate conditions. In the more distant associative areas where the various sensory fields are overlapping, such as the inferior parietal lobule and adjacent portions of the occipital and temporal lobes, the combinations are still more complicated and are expressed as multisensory perceptions of a progressively higher order. Thus tactile and kinesthetic stimuli are built up into perceptions of form, size and texture (stereognosis), and visual impulses are similarly compounded into perceptions of visual object recognition. Hence any object comes to be ultimately represented by a constellation of memories compounded from several sensory channels as a result of previous experience. When the tactile or visual impulses initiated by feeling or seeing an object are capable of exciting these memory constellations, the object is "recognized" i.e. is remembered as having been seen or felt before. This arousal of the associative mnemonic complexes by afferent cortical impulses may be termed "Gnosis" and forms the basis of understanding and knowledge. Disorders of this mechanism caused by lesions in the associative areas are usually known as gnostic disturbances or *agnosias*. The tactile, visual or auditory stimuli evoked by an object no longer arouse the appropriate memories, hence the object and its uses appear unfamiliar and strange. When such gnostic disturbances involve the far more complicated associative mechanisms underlying the comprehension of language, they are known as *aphasias* or *dysphasias*. The symbolic meanings of spoken or written words and of their interrelationships in phrases and sentences are no longer understood and as a result there is also impairment of appropriate and purposeful behavior. In extensive lesions of certain asso-

ciative areas, such as the inferior parietal lobule and adjacent regions, the gnostic disturbances may have the character of a severe intellectual deterioration in which the understanding of the importance and the relationships of things in the external world is wholly disrupted, a condition which Head has designated as *semantic aphasia*.

In the frontal lobe there is a similar superimposition of more complex associative areas upon the primary ones, but here they are more closely related to the expressive phases of cortical activity. Immediately in front of the Rolandic sulcus are the primary motor centers of the precentral gyrus, concerned with the contraction of individual muscles or muscle groups for specific movements of the limbs or face. Destruction of these centers produces a motor paralysis, just as destruction of the primary sensory areas causes blindness, deafness or loss of touch and movement sensations. In front of the motor area lie the centers for progressively higher types of motor expression. The premotor or paramotor area is concerned with the more complex purposive skilled movements related to locomotion, manual manipulation, mastication and swallowing, and the more complicated acts of motor speech formulation. The execution of these pallial acts may be termed "*Praxis*" and is based on memory constellations of similar acts previously performed. Lesions of this area do not cause paralysis of muscular movement, but there is inability to carry out complex purposive movements. When such *apraxic* disturbances affect the motor formulation of speech, they are again known as aphasias, but in this case it is the expressive phases of speech which are most severely affected. The patient has difficulty in forming words both in speaking and writing, and his memory for the proper sequence of letters in a word or of words in a sentence is likewise impaired. Yet the misspelled and mispronounced words are used in the correct sense, and his appreciation of the meaning of words in complex relations is apparently unimpaired. It is the formulation rather than the comprehension of speech which is primarily disturbed.

Still more forward are the extensive prefrontal areas, of relatively late acquisition, which are strongly developed only in man. The complex memory patterns formed in the post-Rolandic part of the brain are transmitted to these areas, to be synthesized into mnemonic constellations of a still more complex type, which form the basis of abstract thinking and of the higher creative activities. In the prefrontal regions these highly discriminative cortical activities are blended with the activities of the hypothalamus and medial thalamus representing the more primitive affective components of consciousness. Large lesions in the prefrontal lobe of the dominant hemisphere not only cause defects in complex association, but produce disturbances of judgment, of the will and of emotional behavior with resulting regressive changes in character. All these belong to the expressive part of the personality and may be regarded as motor defects of a high psychic order.

The above discussion of cortical function does not imply that there are two distinct divisions for intelligence. On the contrary, every mnemonic reaction is a continuous process which requires the cooperation of the entire brain. A lesion in any part of the mnemonic apparatus will cause an impairment of cortical functioning as a whole, the severity of the symptoms corresponding to the amount of brain substance destroyed. However, the organization of the cortex and its relation to the sensory and motor periphery are such that disturbances of understanding will be more marked in lesions of the caudal half, while in those of the frontal lobe the expressive functions will be most severely affected.

It is an interesting but unexplained fact that in man the higher cortical functions are vested principally in one cerebral hemisphere, the left one in right-handed individuals, a phenomenon known as *"cerebral dominance"*. The various agnosias and apraxias discussed above, occur only when the dominant hemisphere is damaged, lesions of the other hemisphere producing as a rule no recognizable disturbances. The causes of this unilateral dominance are not fully understood.

CHAPTER XXI

THE BLOOD SUPPLY OF THE BRAIN

THE CEREBRAL ARTERIES

The whole brain is supplied by two pairs of arterial trunks, the two *carotid* and the two *vertebral arteries.* In a general way the branches derived from the vertebral arteries supply the caudal half of the brain including the hindbrain, midbrain, caudal half of the thalamus, occipital lobes and basal portions of the temporal lobes. The anterior half of the thalamus, the corpus striatum, practically all of the internal capsule, the frontal, parietal and lateral portions of the temporal lobes, are fed by branches of the internal carotids.

On the basal surface of the brain the four main arterial trunks form an anastomosing system known as the *arterial circle of Willis* (Fig. 324). The two vertebral arteries entering through the foramen magnum run obliquely forward on the ventral surface of the medulla and near the caudal border of the pons fuse to form the unpaired *basilar artery*. At the rostral border of the pons this artery bifurcates into the two *posterior cerebral arteries* which run laterally in front of the oculomotor nerves and encircle the cerebral peduncles. The internal carotid artery enters the cranial cavity through the carotid foramen and reaches the base of the brain just lateral to the optic chiasma. Here it divides into its two terminal branches: the smaller *anterior cerebral artery* and the larger *middle cerebral artery* which may be regarded as the direct continuation of the carotid. At or immediately before its division the carotid gives off the *posterior communicating artery* which runs backward and anastomoses with the proximal portion of the posterior cerebral. The *anterior cerebral artery* runs medially and rostrally toward the interhemispheric fissure and in front of the optic chiasma is joined to its mate by a short connecting channel, the *anterior communicating artery*. In this manner there is formed a circular or rather heptagonal arterial wreath, the *circle of Willis*, surrounding the optic chiasma, tuber and interpeduncular fossa, composed of the posterior and anterior communicating arteries and the proximal portions of the anterior and poasterior cerebrals. This anastomosis serves to equalize the blood flow to various parts of the brain and furnishes collateral circulation in cases of occlusion of one or more of the arteries contributing to the circle.

From the circle of Willis and the main cerebral arteries (anterior, middle and posterior) arise two types of branches: the *paramedian* or *central* also known as the *ganglionic*, and the *circumferential* or *cortical*. The central and cortical arteries are not connected with each other but form two distinct systems. The *central* arteries arise from the circle of Willis and the proximal portions of the three cerebral arteries, dip perpendicularly into the brain substance and irrigate the diencephalon, corpus striatum and internal capsule. They are terminal arteries, i.e. the branches of one artery do not anastomose with those of others, hence occlusion of these vessels will produce a softening of the area deprived of its blood supply. The anterior and posterior chorioidal arteries, respectively branches of the middle and posterior cerebral arteries, may be included in this group.

The larger *cortical* branches of each cerebral artery enter the pia mater where they form a superficial plexus of more or less freely anastomosing vessels, in some places continuous with the plexuses derived from the other main arteries. From these plexuses arise the smaller terminal arteries which enter the brain substance at right angles and run a variable distance, the shorter ones arborizing in the cortex, the longer ones supplying the medullary substance of the hemispheres. Due to the anastomosis of the larger cortical branches, the occlusion of one of these vessels is compensated to a variable extent by the blood supply from neighboring branches, though such col-

curving over the genu of the corpus callosum and continuing along the dorsal surface of that commissure. Its branches supply the olfactory lobe, gyrus rectus and medial portion of the orbital gyri, the gyrus cinguli and the whole medial surface of the frontal and parietal lobes to the parieto-occipital sulcus where they anastomose with branches of the posterior cerebral (Fig. 325). Some of the

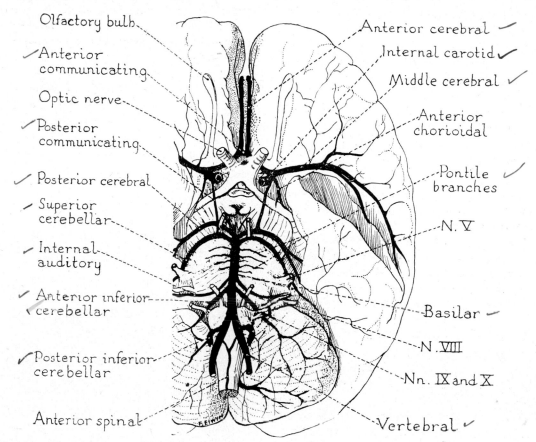

FIG. 324. The basal surface of the brain showing the main cerebral arteries and some of their branches

lateral circulation is rarely sufficient for the full nutritional maintenance of the deprived area.

The cortical branches. The *anterior cerebral artery* passes medially and forward to the interhemispheric fissure, approaching the corresponding artery of the opposite side with which it is connected by the anterior communicating artery (Fig. 324). It then runs on the medial surface of the hemisphere,

branches curve over to the lateral surface to supply the superior frontal gyrus, while numerous small branches are distributed to the corpus callosum. Thus the territory irrigated by the anterior cerebral includes the somesthetic and motor leg area of the paracentral lobule. One of the basal branches of the anterior cerebral is peculiar in having both a cortical and central distribution. This *medial striate artery* or *recur-*

rent artery of Heubner arises near the level of the anterior communicating artery, runs backward, and after giving off a few branches to the orbital cortex, dips into the anterior perforated space and supplies the anteroventral portion of the head of the caudate nucleus and adjacent portions of the putamen and internal capsule (Fig. 328). Occlusion of this vessel produces a softening of the rostral part of the internal capsule with a consequent supranuclear paralysis of the face, tongue and shoulder.

The *middle cerebral artery* passes laterally

territory of the middle cerebral artery is extended caudally to take in most of the lateral gyri of the occipital lobe. Thus the extensive and important territory irrigated by this artery includes the motor and premotor areas, the somesthetic and auditory projection areas and the higher receptive association areas. Occlusion of the middle cerebral artery near the origin of its cortical branches, when not fatal, produces a contralateral hemiplegia most marked in the upper extremity and face, and a contralateral sensory loss of the cortical type, such

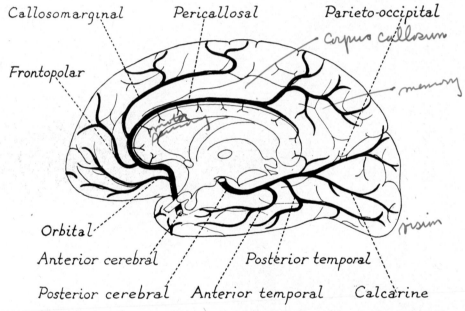

Callosomarginal Pericallosal Parieto-occipital Corpus callosum

Frontopolar memory

Orbital

Anterior cerebral Posterior temporal

Posterior cerebral Anterior temporal Calcarine

FIG. 325. The main arteries on the medial surface of the hemisphere. Semischematic

over the anterior perforated substance into the Sylvian fossa and there divides into a number of cortical branches which curve outward over the opercular margins of the lateral fissure and spread over the convex surface of the brain (Fig. 326). Besides the insula these branches supply the lateral parts of the orbital gyri, the inferior and middle frontal gyri, the portions of the precentral and postcentral gyri seen on the lateral surface of the brain, the superior and inferior parietal lobules, and the superior and middle temporal gyri including the temporal pole. In many instances the

as astereognosis and the inability to distinguish between different intensities of stimuli. When the left or dominant hemisphere is involved there are also severe aphasic disturbances both as to the motor formulation of speech (verbal asphasia) and the comprehension of spoken or written words.

Each of the *posterior cerebral arteries* formed by the bifurcation of the basilar, passes laterally and backward over the cerebral peduncles. After receiving the posterior communicating artery it continues to the inferior surface of the hemisphere, where it divides into four cortical branches (Fig. 325). These supply the medial and inferior surfaces of the occipital lobe and the inferior surface of the temporal lobe exclusive of the temporal pole. Especially important is the calcarine branch which is distributed to the visual area. The branches also extend to the lateral surface, supplying the inferior temporal gyrus and a variable portion of the lateral occipital region, and may invade a considerable part of the superior parietal lobule. In all these regions the branches come in contact and anasto-

capsule are arranged in four general groups: anteromedial, anterolateral, posteromedial and posterolateral (Fig. 327). The *anteromedial* arise from the domain of the anterior cerebral and anterior communicating arteries, some twigs coming directly from the carotid at its place of bifurcation (Fig. 328). They enter the most medial portion of the anterior perforated space and are distributed to the anterior hypothalamus including the preoptic and suprachiasmatic regions.

The numerous *posteromedial arteries* which enter the tuber cinereum, mammillary bod-

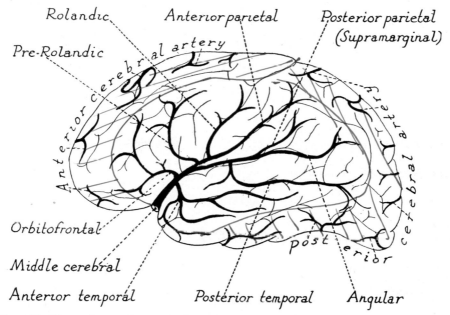

FIG. 326. The main arteries on the lateral surface of the hemisphere. Semischematic

mose with the marginal branches of the anterior and middle cerebral arteries. This extensive anastomosis probably explains the fact that occlusion of the posterior cerebral rarely produces a complete softening of the deprived area. The most striking symptom is a contralateral homonymous hemianopia in which macular vision is often spared, due to the overlapping of the middle and posterior cerebral territories at the occipital pole.

The central or ganglionic branches. The ganglionic arteries which supply the diencephalon, corpus striatum and internal

ies and interpeduncular fossa are derived from the most proximal portion of the posterior cerebral and from the whole extent of the posterior communicating arteries. Some twigs come directly from the carotid just before its bifurcation (Fig. 328). A rostral and caudal group may be distinguished. The rostral group supplies the hypophysis, infundibulum and tuberal regions of the hypothalamus. A number of vessels, known as the *thalamoperforating arteries*, penetrate more deeply and are distributed to the anterior and medial portions of the thalamus. The caudal group supplies the mammillary region of the hypothalamus, the subthalamic structures, and likewise sends fibers to the medial wall and nuclei of the thalamus including the massa intermedia. Other vessels from the caudal group are distributed to the midbrain, supplying the raphéal region of the tegmentum, the nucleus ruber and medial portions of the pes pedunculi.

The *posterolateral* or *thalamogeniculate* arteries arise more laterally from the posterior cerebral arteries (Figs. 327, 329). They penetrate the lateral geniculate body and

putamen and the recurving portion of the caudate tail (Fig. 329). These branches also feed the lateral part of the globus pallidus and the dorsal portion of the posterior limb of the internal capsule (Fig. 329). In some cases all the striate arteries may be derived from the middle cerebral (Alexander). One of the striate arteries has been described as the vessel most prone to rupture under pathological conditions and has hence been called the "artery of cerebral hemorrhage" (Charcot). Anatomically such an artery cannot be usually distinguished. It

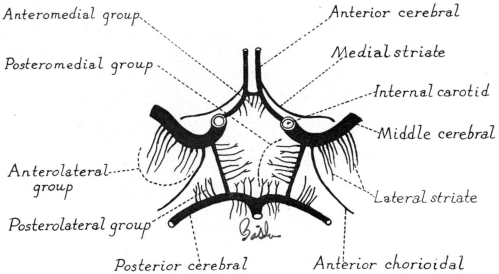

FIG. 327. Diagram showing arterial circle of Willis and origin of the ganglionic arteries

supply the larger caudal half of the thalamus including the geniculate bodies, pulvinar and most of the lateral nuclear mass.

The *anterolateral* or *striate arteries* which pierce the anterior perforated substance arise mainly from the basal portion of the middle cerebral artery and to a lesser extent from the anterior cerebral (Figs. 328, 329). As a rule, those from the anterior cerebral supply the anteroventral portion of the head of the caudate nucleus and adjacent portions of the putamen and internal capsule. The rest of the putamen, caudate nucleus and anterior limb of the internal capsule are supplied by branches from the middle cerebral, excepting only the most caudal tip of the

is very doubtful that the striate arteries aid in the vascular supply of the thalamus, though such vessels (lenticulo-optic) have been described by some investigators.

The anterior and posterior chorioidal arteries may also be regarded as central branches. The *anterior chorioidal* arises from the middle cerebral, close to the origin of the posterior communicating artery (Figs. 328, 329). It passes backward along the optic tract, some of its branches actually perforating the latter, and enters the chorioidal fissure in the lower part of the inferior horn. The artery supplies the chorioid plexus of the lateral ventricle, the hippocampus, the medial and intermediate portions of the globus pallidus and the larger ventral part of the posterior limb of the internal capsule, including the entire retro-lenticular portion of the capsule (Fig. 330). It also sends branches to the amygdaloid nucleus, the recurving ventral portion of the caudate tail and the posterior tip of the putamen (Fig. 329). Some of the twigs are believed to go the pulvinar and superior surface of the thalamus. According to Alexander the anterior chorioidal artery is the vessel most susceptible to thrombosis

small twigs to the superomedial surface of the thalamus (Fig. 329).

The arterial supply of the diencephalon, basal ganglia and internal capsule may be briefly summarized. The *striatum* (caudate nucleus and putamen) is supplied by the striate arteries derived mainly from the middle cerebral and to a lesser extent from the anterior cerebral. Only the recurving portion of the caudate tail and the posterior tip of the putamen are supplied by the anterior chorioidal artery (Fig. 329). The medial

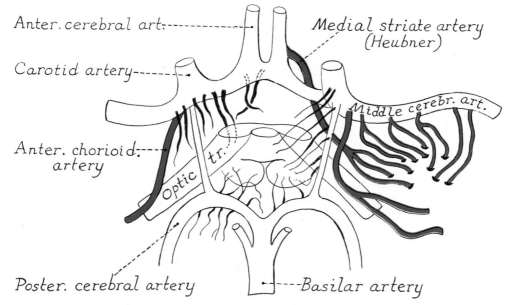

FIG. 328. The circle of Willis and the ganglionic arteries. (Based on data from Alexander and from Foley, Kinney and Alexander.) On the left side the carotid artery has been turned to expose its dorsal surface. Anterior chorioidal and striate arteries in red; hypothalamic arteries in black.

on account of its long free subarachnoid course and its relatively small caliber. It is significant that the globus pallidus and hippocampus, the two most vulnerable parts of the brain, are supplied by this artery (Alexander).

The *posterior chorioidal arteries* of which there are usually two, are branches of the posterior cerebral. They encircle the cerebral peduncles and after giving off branches to the midbrain roof, are distributed to the tela chorioidea and chorioid plexus of the third ventricle, furnishing also a number of

and intermediate segments of the *pallidum* are fed by the anterior chorioidal artery. The lateral segment of the pallidum has a variable supply. It may be fed by the striate vessels or by the anterior chorioidal. More commonly it receives branches from both.

The *thalamus* is irrigated mainly by the posterolateral (thalamogeniculate) and posteromedial (thalamoperforating) arteries, the former supplying the caudal and lateral regions, the latter the anterior and medial ones. Smaller contributions, especially for the superior surface are made by the posterior and perhaps the anterior chorioidal arteries. The anterior *hypothalamus* and preoptic region receive their blood supply from the anteromedian ganglionic arteries, the rest of the hypothalamus from the posteromedian group which also irrigates the *subthalamic structures.*

The anterior limb of the *internal capsule* and the dorsal part of the posterior limb are irrigated by the striate arteries (Fig. 330).

vertebral artery while passing over the ventral surface of the medulla gives off three branches which enter the brain substance: the larger *posterior inferior cerebellar artery,* and the smaller *anterior and posterior spinal arteries* (Fig. 324). The vertebrals then fuse into the unpaired *basilar artery* which extends to the superior border of the pons and there bifurcates into the posterior cerebral arteries. During its course the basilar gives off the following branches: the *anterior inferior cerebellar arteries,* the *internal audi-*

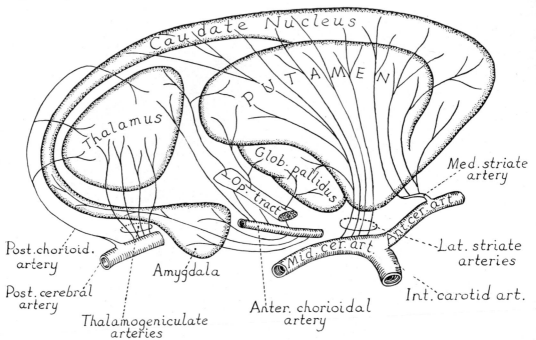

FIG. 329. Diagram of arterial supply to the corpus striatum. (Modified from Aitken)

The ventral part of the posterior limb and the retrolenticular portion are fed by the anterior chorioidal artery. The genu as a rule receives one or two direct twigs from the internal carotid (Alexander).

Arteries of the midbrain and hindbrain. With the exception of the most anterior portion of the cerebral peduncles, which gets a variable contribution from the anterior chorioidal arteries, the blood supply to the midbrain and hindbrain is furnished by branches of the vertebral system. Each

tory arteries which do not supply the brain but pass laterally through the internal auditory meatus, a number of paramedian and circumferential *pontile branches,* and the *superior cerebellar arteries* (Fig. 259). From the proximal portion of each posterior cerebral artery arise a number of branches which furnish the main blood supply of the midbrain. The further course and distribution of these arterial trunks to the medulla, pons, cerebellum and midbrain have been fully discussed in their respective chapters.

THE CEREBRAL VEINS AND VENOUS SINUSES

The veins of the brain do not run together with the arteries. Emerging as fine branches from the substance of the brain, they form a pial plexus from which arise the larger venous channels or cerebral veins proper. These likewise run in the pia for a variable distance, then pass through the subarachnoid space and empty into a system of intercommunicating endothelium-lined channels, the *sinuses of the dura mater* placed between the meningeal and periosteal

The *superior sagittal sinus* extends from the foramen cecum to the internal occipital protuberance, lying along the attached border of the falx cerebri, constantly increasing in caliber as it proceeds caudally. In its middle portion it gives off a number of lateral diverticula, the *venous lacunae*, into which protrude the arachnoid villi or Pacchionian granulations (p. 83). The narrower and shorter *inferior sagittal sinus* extends caudally along the free border of the falx. On reaching the anterior border of the tentorium it is joined by the *great*

Retrolenticular portion of internal capsule

Optic radiation

a

genu

Pons

b

Globus pallidus

Putamen

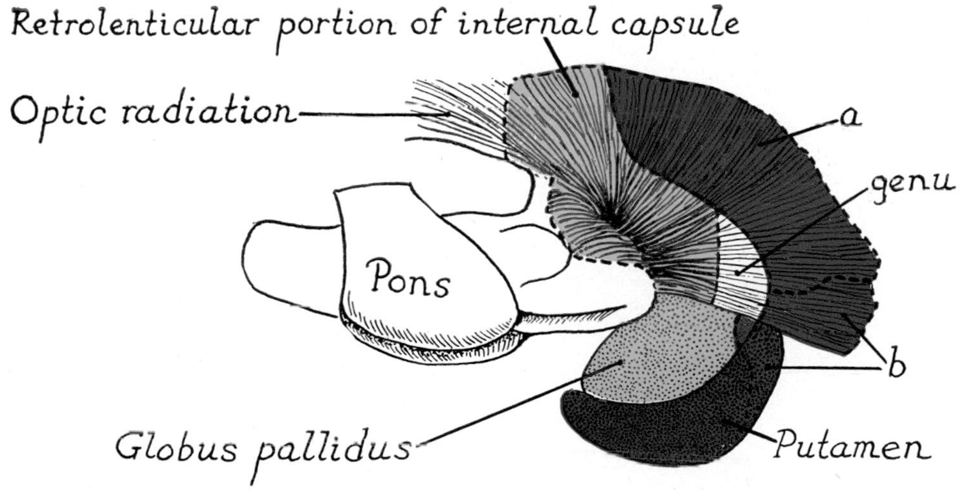

FIG. 330. Lateral view of internal capsule. The lenticular nucleus has been detached from capsule and depressed ventrolaterally. Supply of anterior chorioidal artery shown in yellow; that of striate arteries in red. a, branches of middle cerebral artery; b, branches of anterior cerebral artery. The genu is supplied by one or two direct branches from the carotid arteries. (Alexander)

layers of the dura. The walls of these sinuses, unlike those of other veins, are composed of the tough fibrous tissue of the dura, hence they exhibit a greater tautness and do not collapse when sectioned. The various sinuses converge at the internal occipital protuberance into two transversely running sinuses, one for each side, which enter the jugular foramen to form the internal jugular vein. Besides draining the blood from the brain, the sinuses communicate with the superficial veins of the head by a number of small vessels which perforate the cranial bones as *emissary veins* (Fig. 331).

cerebral vein of Galen which drains the deeper structures of the brain, and the two together are continued as the *sinus rectus* which runs backwards and downwards along the line of attachment of falx and tentorium and joins the superior sagittal sinus near the internal occipital protuberance (Fig. 331). From this place arise the two *transverse sinuses*, each of which passes laterally and forward in the transverse groove of the occipital bone. On reaching the occipito-petrosal junction it curves sharply caudally and as the *sigmoid sinus* leaves the skull through the jugular foramen. The place of union of the superior sagittal, straight and transverse sinuses is known as the *con-fluens sinuum* (torcular Herophilii) which also receives the small unpaired *occipital sinus* coming from the region of the foramen magnum and ascending in the falx cerebelli. The *confluens* is of asymmetrical form and shows many individual variations. In relatively few cases is there an actual union of the four sinuses. Most often the superior sagittal and the straight sinus divide near the blood from the superficial cerebral veins which empty into the superior sagittal sinus, while the left transverse, through the vein of Galen and straight sinus, drains the deep-lying structures of the brain.

The important *cavernous sinus* is a large irregular space located on the sides of the sphenoid bone, lateral to the sella turcica. It is really a mass of intercommunicating cavernous channels enclosing the carotid

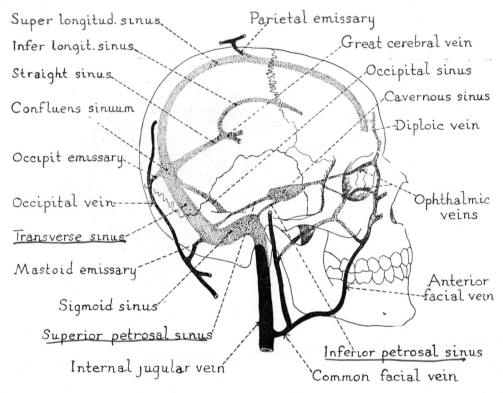

FIG. 331. The dural sinuses (stippled) and their principal connections with the extracranial veins. (After Blumberg from Tandler-Ranzi.)

the internal protuberance into two branches which then participate in the formation of the transverse sinuses. Usually the right branch of the sagittal and the left branch of the straight sinus are the larger ones. In other cases there may be no real confluens at all, the superior sagittal communicating with the right, the sinus rectus with the left transverse sinus, though occasionally the reverse may occur. In a general way therefore, the right transverse sinus receives

artery, the oculomotor, trochlear and abducens nerves, and the ophthalmic branch of the trigeminal. It is connected with the opposite sinus by channels which pass anterior and posterior to the hypophysis, and by the *basilar venous plexus* which extends along the basilar portion of the occipital bone to the foramen magnum and there communicates with the venous plexuses of the vertebral canal (Fig. 332). The venous ring surrounding the hypophysis and composed of the two cavernous sinuses and their connecting channels, is often known as the circular sinus. Each cavernous sinus may likewise be regarded as a confluens sinuum. In front it receives the two ophthalmic veins through the orbital fissure and the small *sphenoparietal sinus* which runs along the under surface of the lesser wing of the sphenoid (Figs. 331, 332). Posteriorly it empties into the superior and inferior pe-

also connected with the transverse sinus by the larger *mastoid emissary*. Smaller emissaries from the sigmoid sinus pass through the condyloid and hypoglossal foramina and communicate with the vertebral and deep cervical veins. The cavernous sinus, besides receiving the ophthalmic veins, is connected with the internal jugular vein and with the pterygoid and pharyngeal plexuses by fine venous nets or *rete* which pass through the

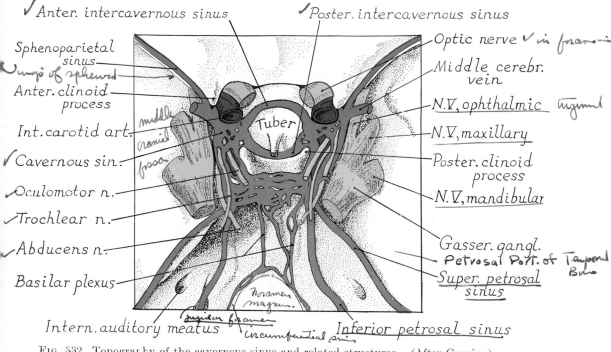

FIG. 332. Topography of the cavernous sinus and related structures. (After Corning)

trosal sinuses through which it is connected respectively with the transverse sinus and the bulb of the internal jugular vein.

As already stated the dural sinuses communicate with extracranial veins by a number of emissaries (Fig. 331). Thus the superior sagittal sinus is connected with the frontal and nasal veins through the frontal diploic veins and the emissaries of the foramen cecum, and also sends a *parietal emissary* to the superficial temporal vein. The confluens sinuum usually gives off an *occipital emissary* to the occipital vein which is

oval, spinous, lacerated, carotid and jugular foramina.

The cerebral veins. The cerebral veins which like the dural sinuses are devoid of valves, are usually divided into an external or superficial and an internal or ventricular group. The former drain the blood from the cortex and subcortical medullary substance and empty into the superior sagittal sinus or into the several basal sinuses, cavernous, petrosal and transverse. The internal veins drain the chorioid plexuses of the forebrain, the deep medullary substance, the basal ganglia and dorsal portions of the diencephalon, and are collected into the *great vein of Galen (vena magna cerebri)* which enters the straight sinus at the junction of the latter with the inferior sagittal sinus (Fig. 331). The two groups are not however anatomically distinct, but on the contrary are widely interconnected by numerous anastomotic channels, both intracerebral and extracerebral, so that large surface areas

sure occur suddenly, will there be marked hyperaemia and more or less extensive hemorrhages, as in birth injuries and occasionally in cases of adult thrombosis (Schlesinger; Schwartz and Fink).

The external cerebral veins arise from the cortex and subcortical medullary substance, anastomose freely in the pia and form a number of larger vessels which empty into the various sinuses. They include the super-

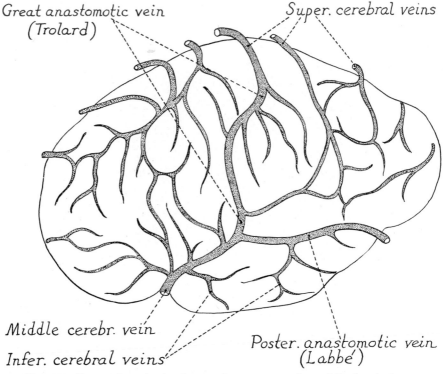

FIG. 333. External cerebral veins on the convex surface of the hemisphere

can be drained through the vein of Galen, and conversely territories supplied by internal veins may be handled when necessity arises by surface vessels. This anastomotic venous arrangement facilitates the drainage of capillary beds by shifting the blood from one area to another and readily equalizes regional increases in pressure due to occlusion or other factors. As a result, the occlusion of even a large vein, if not too rapid, will produce but slight and transitory effects. Only when the occlusion or increase in pres-

ior and inferior cerebral veins and the superficial middle cerebral vein (superficial Sylvian vein). The *superior cerebral veins,* about 10 to 15 in number, collect the blood from the convex and medial surfaces of the brain and open into the superior sagittal sinus or its venous lacunae (Fig. 333). Many of them, especially the larger posterior ones, run obliquely forward through the subarachnoid space and enter the sinus in a direction opposed to that of the blood flow, often after a short intradural course parallel to the sinus. Some of the veins from the medial surface drain into the inferior sagittal sinus. The *inferior cerebral veins* drain the basal surface of the hemisphere and the lower portion of its lateral surface. Those on the lateral surface usually empty into the *superficial middle cerebral vein (superficial Sylvian vein)* which runs along the Sylvian fissure and terminates in the cavernous or

ferior veins arising from extensive pial plexuses drain in part at least into the basal sinuses. Those from the tentorial surface of the brain empty into the transverse and superior petrosal sinuses. Those from the anterior temporal lobe and from the inter-peduncular regions drain partly into the cavernous and sphenoparietal sinuses, while

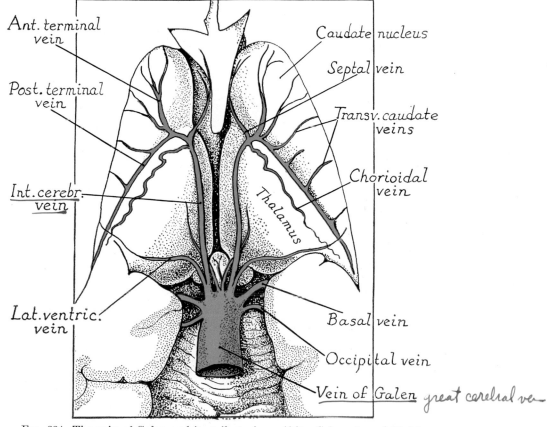

FIG. 334. The vein of Galen and its tributaries. (After Schwartz and Fink)

sphenoparietal sinus (Figs. 332, 333). The middle vein receives many anastomotic branches from the superior cerebral veins and in many cases two of these channels become quite prominent. These are the *great anastomotic vein of Trolard* and the *posterior anastomotic vein of Labbé* which connect the middle cerebral vein respectively with the superior sagittal and the transverse sinus. On the basal surface the small in-

some veins from the orbital region join the superior or the inferior sagittal sinus.

In addition, large cortical areas, especially on the basal and medial surfaces, are drained by a number of vessels which empty into the great vein of Galen before the latter bifurcates into the two internal cerebral veins (Figs. 334, 335). These vessels may be regarded as extracerebral anastomotic veins which connect the superficial and deep

Trolard middle ÷ sup.
Labbé inf ÷ middle

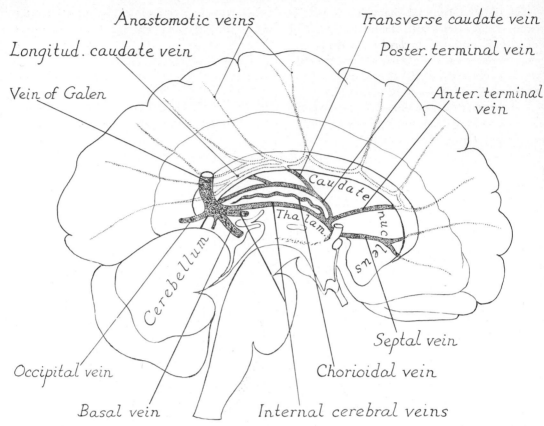

Anastomotic veins

Longitud. caudate vein

Vein of Galen

Transverse caudate vein

Poster. terminal vein

Anter. terminal vein

Caudate nucleus

Thalam.

Cerebellum

Septal vein

Occipital vein

Chorioidal vein

Basal vein

Internal cerebral veins

FIG. 335. Diagram showing the tributaries of the internal cerebral veins. (After Schlesinger)

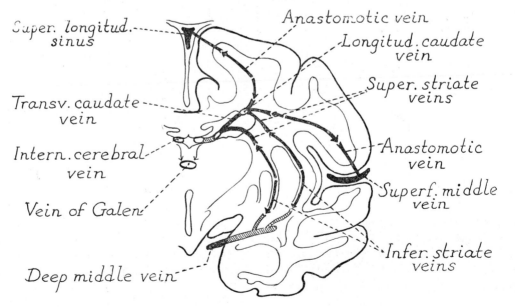

Super. longitud. sinus

Anastomotic vein

Longitud. caudate vein

Super. striate veins

Transv. caudate vein

Intern. cerebral vein

Anastomotic vein

Superf. middle vein

Vein of Galen

Infer. striate veins

Deep middle vein

FIG. 336. Diagrammatic cross-section through the brain of a Rhesus monkey, showing the connections between the deep and the surface veins. (Schlesinger)

systems. The more important ones include the occipital vein, the basal vein (vein of Rosenthal) and the posterior callosal vein. Some of the veins draining the cerebellum likewise terminate in the great cerebral vein or in one of its larger tributaries.

The *occipital vein* drains the inferior and medial surfaces of the occipital lobe and possibly also the adjacent parietal regions. The *basal vein* is formed by the union of (a) the *anterior cerebral vein* which accompanies the artery of the same name and drains the orbital surface of the frontal lobe and the anterior portions of the corpus callosum and gyrus cinguli; (b) the *deep middle cerebral vein* (*deep Sylvian vein*) which lies deeply in the lower portion of the lateral fissure and which aids in the drainage of the insular and adjacent opercular cortex; and (c) a number of vessels, the *inferior striate veins*, which come from the ventral portions of the corpus striatum, and emerge through the anterior perforated space, many of them emptying into the deep middle vein. At the anterior perforated space all these unite to form the basal vein which winds backward around the cerebral peduncles to reach the vein of Galen, receiving additional tributaries from the interpeduncular region, the midbrain and the inferior horn of the lateral ventricle. It seems certain that the hypothalamus and ventral portion of the thalamus are drained to a considerable extent by the basal veins. The *posterior callosal vein* collects blood from the posterior portion of the corpus callosum and adjacent medial surface of the brain.

The following account of the internal veins is based mainly on the work of Schlesinger (1939) and Schwartz and Fink (1926). The *great vein of Galen* (*vena magna cerebri*) empties into the anterior end of the straight sinus (Fig. 331). It is a short trunk whose thin delicate walls are easily torn even in the adult. Peripherally, the vein curves ventrally beneath the splenium of the corpus callosum and after receiving the tributaries mentioned above, bifurcates into the two *internal cerebral veins* (*small veins of Galen*)

which together with their branches comprise the ventricular or internal group of veins (Figs. 334, 335). At or near the bifurcation each internal cerebral vein gives off two branches, the *epithalamic* and the *lateral ventricular vein*. The former drains the dorsal portion of the diencephalon. Blood from the ventral portion of the thalamus and from the hypothalamus is collected by vessels which empty basally into the pial venous plexus of the interpeduncular fossa whence it is conveyed in part to the cavernous or sphenoparietal sinuses, in part to the basal vein of Rosenthal. The *lateral ventricular vein* runs laterally on the superior surface of the thalamus and tail of caudate nucleus and is lost in the medullary substance at the angle of the lateral ventricle. One small branch of the vein usually goes to the chorioid plexus, another enters the white substance of the hippocampal gyrus. Occasionally, the lateral ventricular vein terminates directly in the vena magna (Schwartz and Fink).

The two internal cerebral veins then pass forward in the tela chorioidea of the third ventricle (velum interpositum), and in the region of the interventricular foramen each vein breaks up into its four terminal tributaries: the chorioidal, the septal and the anterior and posterior terminal veins (Figs. 334, 335). The tortuous *chorioidal vein* runs along the lateral border of the chorioid plexus into the inferior horn. It drains the plexus and adjacent hippocampal regions. Additional drainage of the plexus is through the chorioidal branch of the basal vein, and to a smaller extent through the small branch of the lateral ventricular vein.

The *posterior terminal vein* runs backward in the terminal sulcus between thalamus and caudate nucleus. The *anterior terminal vein* runs forward and branches in the head of the caudate nucleus. Both vessels receive a number of tributaries, the *transverse caudate veins*, which cross the caudate nucleus, reach the lateral angle of the ventricle and enter the adjacent white substance of the brain. Here they change their direction abruptly to form the *longitudinal caudate veins*. The latter divide at acute angles into a number of branches which fan out radially in the medullary substance, following as a rule the fibers of the corpus callosum (Fig. 335). Some of the branches are short and drain the deep capillary plexuses of the white matter. Others extend almost to the cortex and may be regarded as intracerebral anastomotic channels connecting the ventricular and surface veins. In addition, the transverse and longitudinal caudate veins give rise to another group of branches, the *superior striate veins*. These dip vertically into the brain substance, passing through and on both sides of the caudate nucleus, perforate the internal capsule and break up into a number of smaller vessels which drain the dense capillary plexus of the lenticular nucleus (Fig. 336). Basally this capillary plexus is drained by the *inferior striate veins* which converge ventrally toward the anterior perforated space and enter the deep middle vein.

The *septal vein* (*vein of the septum pellucidum*) supplies the septum pellucidum and rostral portion of the corpus callosum. Then its distal branches dip beneath the head of the caudate nucleus and enter the medullary substance to be carried by the callosal fibers to the base of the frontal lobe (Figs. 334, 335).

It is evident from the above that the internal veins are primarily concerned with the drainage of the ventricular surface, the chorioid plexuses, the deep medullary substance, the caudate nucleus, and the dorsal portions of the lenticular nucleus and thalamus. All these structures can however be also drained by surface vessels through the numerous intracerebral and extracerebral anastomotic veins.

The veins of the hindbrain and midbrain have been discussed in their respective chapters.

BIBLIOGRAPHY

COMPREHENSIVE TEXTS AND ATLASES

BUMKE, O., AND FOERSTER, O. *Handbuch der Neurologie.* Vol. 1, Julius Springer, Berlin, 1935.

DÉJÉRINE, J. *Anatomie des centres nerveux.* 2 vols., Rueff et Cie., Paris, I, 1895; II, 1901.

JELGERSMA, G. *Atlas anatomicum cerebri humani.* Scheltema & Holkema, Amsterdam, 1931.

KAPPERS, C. U. A., HUBER, G. C., AND CROSBY, E. C. *The comparative anatomy of the nervous system of vertebrates, including man.* 2. vols., The Macmillan Co., New York, 1936.

RAMÓN Y CAJAL, S. *Histologie du système nerveux de l'homme et des vertébrés.* 2 vols., A. Maloine, Paris, I, 1909; II, 1911.

RILEY, H. A. *An atlas of the basal ganglia, brain stem and spinal cord, based on myelin-stained material.* The Williams & Wilkins Co., Baltimore, 1943.

WINKLER, C. *Opera omnia.* Vols. 1–10. E. F. Bohn, Haarlem, 1918–1933.

ZIEHEN, T. *Anatomie des Zentralnervensystems.* Vol. 4 in K. von Bardeleben's *Handbuch der Anatomie des Menschen.* G. Fischer, Jena, 1896–1934.

GENERAL AND SPECIAL REFERENCES INCLUDING THOSE QUOTED IN TEXT

ABD-EL-MALEK, S. On the presence of sensory fibers in the ocular nerves. J. Anat., 1938, 72: 524–530.

ADRIAN, E. D. Mechanism of sense organs. Physiol. Rev., 1930, 10: 336–347.

ALEXANDER, L. The vascular supply of the striopallidum. Assoc. Res. Nerv. & Ment. Dis., 1942, 21: 77–132.

ALLEN, W. F. Application of the Marchi method to the study of the radix mesencephalica trigemini in the guinea pig. J. Comp. Neurol., 1919, 30: 169–216.

ALLEN, W. F. Distribution of the fibers originating from the different basal cerebellar nuclei. J. Comp. Neurol., 1924, 36: 399–439.

ALLEN, W. F. Experimental-anatomical studies on the visceral bulbospinal pathway in the cat and guinea pig. J. Comp. Neurol., 1927, 42: 393–456.

ANDRÉ-THOMAS, M., AND DURUPT, A. *Localisations cerebelleuses.* Doin et fils, Paris, 1914.

ANDRÉ-THOMAS, M. Le faisceau rubro-spinal existe-t-il chez l'homme? Rev. neurol., 1936, 65: 252–265.

ARONSON, L. The conduction of labyrinthine impulses to the cortex. J. Nerv. & Ment. Dis., 1933, 78: 250–259.

BALADO, M., AND FRANKE, E. Das Corpus geniculatum externum. Monogr. u. Gesammtgebiete der Neur. u. Psychiat., 1937, 62: 1–116.

BARD, P. A diencephalic mechanism for the expression of rage with special reference to the sympathetic nervous system. Am. J. Physiol., 1928, 84: 490–515.

BARD, P. Central nervous mechanisms for emotional behavior patterns in animals. Assoc. Res. Nerv. & Ment. Dis., 1939, 19: 190–218.

BARNARD, J. W. A phylogenetic study of the visceral afferent areas associated with the facial, glossopharyngeal, and vagus nerves, and their fiber connections. The efferent facial nucleus. J. Comp. Neurol., 1936, 65: 503–603.

BARNARD, J. W. The hypoglossal complex of vertebrates. J. Comp. Neurol., 1940, 72: 489–524.

BARNES, S. Degenerations in hemiplegia: with special reference to a ventrolateral pyramidal tract, the accessory fillet and Pick's bundle. Brain, 1901, 24: 463–501.

BARTELMEZ, G. W., AND HOERR, N. L. The vestibular club endings in Ameiurus. Further evidence on the morphology of the synapse. J. Comp. Neurol., 1933, 57: 401–428.

BEAMS, H. W., AND KING, R. L. The effect of ultracentrifuging the spinal ganglia cells of the rat, with special reference to Nissl bodies. J. Comp. Neurol., 1935, 61: 175–184.

BEATTIE, J., BROW, G. R., AND LONG, C. N. H. The hypothalamus and the sympathetic nervous system. II. The higher connections of the sympathetic nervous system as studied by experimental lesions of the hypothalamus. Assoc. Res. Nerv. & Ment. Dis., 1930, 9: 295–316.

BECK, E. Die myeloarchitektonische Felderung des in der Sylvischen Furche gelegenen Teiles des menschlichen Schläfenlappens. J. f. Psychol. u. Neurol., 1929, 36: 1–21.

BENJAMIN, J. W. Nucleus of the oculomotor nerve, with special reference to innervation of pupil and fibers from pretectal region. J. Nerv. & Ment. Dis., 1939, 89: 294–310.

BENSLEY, R. R., AND GERSH, I. Studies on cell structure by the freezing-drying method. III. The distribution in cells of the basophil substances in particular the Nissl substance of the nerve cell. Anat. Rec., 1933, **57**: 369–385.

BERNHEIMER, S. Über Ursprung und Verlauf des Nervus oculomotorius im Mittelhirn. Monatschr. f. Psych. u. Neurol., 1904, **15**: 151–153.

BIELSCHOWSKY, M. Morphologie er Ganglienzelle. In von Möllendorff's *Handb. d. mikr. Anat. d. Menschen*. Berlin, 1928, **4**: 8–96.

BODIAN, D. The structure of the vertebrate synapse. A study of the axon endings on Mauthner's cell and neighboring centers in the goldfish. J. Comp. Neurol., 1937, **68**: 117–159.

BODIAN, D. Further notes on the vertebrate synapse. J. Comp. Neurol., 1940, **73**: 323–335.

BOEKE, J. Nerve endings, motor and sensory. In Penfield's *Cytology & Cellular Pathology of the Nervous System*. New York, 1932, **1**: 243–315.

BOK, S. T. Das Rückenmark. In von Möllendorff's *Handb. d. mikr. Anat. d. Menschen*. Berlin, 1928, **4**: 478–578.

BOLK, L. *Das Cerebellum der Säugethiere*. Bohn, Haarlem, 1906.

VON BONIN, G. Architecture of the precentral motor cortex and some adjacent areas. In Bucy's *The precentral motor cortex*, 1944, pp. 7–82.

BOON, A. A. Comparative anatomy and physiopathology of the autonomic hypothalamic centers. Doctorale Dissertation, Univ. Amsterdam, 1938, 1–129.

BÖRNSTEIN, W. S. Localization of cortical taste area in man and method of measuring impairment of taste in man. Yale J. Biol. & Med., 1940, **13**: 133–156.

BOWDEN, R. E. M., AND GUTMANN, E. Denervation and re-innervation of human voluntary muscle. Brain, 1944, **67**: 273–313.

BOZLER, E. Über die Struktur der Ganglienzellen. Zeitschr. vergl. Physiol., 1927, 6.

BRAIN, W. R. *Diseases of the nervous system*. Oxford Med. Publications, London, 1947.

BRICKNER, R. M. *The intellectual function of the frontal lobes*. The Macmillan Co., New York, 1936.

BROCK, S. *The basis of clinical neurology*. Wm. Wood & Co., Baltimore, 1945.

BRODMANN, K. Die Kortexgliederung des Menschen. J. f. Psychol. u. Neurol., 1907–1908, **10**: 231.

BRODMANN, K. *Vergleichende Lokalisationslehre der Grosshirnrinde in ihren Prinzipien dargestellt auf Grund des Zellenbaues*. J. A. Barth, Leipzig, 1909.

BROUWER, B. Klinisch-anatomische Untersuchung über den Oculomotoriuskern. Ztschr. f. d. ges. Neurol. & Psychiat., Berlin, 1918, **40**: 152–193.

BROUWER, B. Über die Projektion der Makula auf die Area striata des Menschen. J. f Psychol. u. Neurol., 1930, **40**: 147–159.

BROUWER, B. Projection of the retina on the cortex in man. Assoc. Res. Nerv. & Ment. Dis. 1934, **13**: 529–534.

BROUWER, B., AND ZEEMAN, W. P. C. The projection of the retina in the primary optic neuron in monkeys. Brain, 1926, **49**: 1–35.

BRUN, R. Das Kleinhirn. Anatomie, Physiologie und Entwicklungsgeschichte. Schweiz. Arch. f. Neurol. u. Psychiat., 1925, **16**: 183–197. II. Die Bahnen und Verbindungen des Kleinhirns. Ibid., **17**: 89–108.

BUCHANAN, A. R. The course of the secondary vestibular fibers in the cat. J. Comp. Neurol., 1937, **67**: 183–204.

BUCY, P. C. *The precentral motor cortex*. Univ. Ill. Press, 1944, 605.

CAMPBELL, A. W. *Histological studies on the localisation of cerebral function*. Cambridge Univ. Press, 1905.

VAN CAMPENHOUT, E. Contribution to the problem of the development of the sympathetic nervous system. J. Exp. Zoöl., 1930, **56**: 295–320.

CANNON, W. B. *Bodily changes in pain, hunger, fear and rage. An account of recent researches into the function of emotional excitement*. D. Appleton & Co., New York, 1929.

CANNON, W. B., AND ROSENBLUETH, A. *Autonomic neuro-effector systems*. The Macmillan Co., New York, 1937.

CASTALDI, L. Studi sulla struttura e sullo sviluppo del mesencefalo. Arch. Ital. Anat., 1923, **20**: 23–225; 1924, **21**: 172–263; 1926, **23**: 481–609; 1928, **25**: 157–306.

DE CASTRO, F. Sensory ganglia of the cranial and spinal nerves, normal and pathological. In Penfield's *Cytology & cellular pathology of the nervous system*. New York, 1932, **1**: 93–143.

DE CASTRO, F. Sympathetic ganglia, normal and pathological. In Penfield's *Cytology & cellular pathology of the nervous system*. New York, 1932, **1**: 319–379.

CLARK, D. A. Muscle counts of motor units: a study in innervation ratios. Am. J. Physiol., 1931, **96**: 296–304.

CLARK, D. A., HUGHES, J., AND GASSER, H. S. Afferent functions in the group of nerve fibers of slowest conduction velocity. Am. J. Physiol., 1935, **114**: 69–76.

CLARK, W. E. L. The structure and connections of the thalamus. Brain, 1932, **55**: 406–470.

CLARK, W. E. L. The thalamic connections of the temporal lobe of the brain of the monkey. J. Anat., 1936, **70:** 447–465.

CLARK, W. E. L. Functional localization in the thalamus and hypothalamus. J. Ment. Sci., 1936, **82:** 99–118.

CLARK, W. E. L., BEATTIE, J., RIDDOCH, G., AND DOTT, N. M. *The hypothalamus.* Oliver & Boyd, Edinburgh, 1938.

CLARKE, R. H., AND HORSLEY, V. On the intrinsic fibres of the cerebellum, its nuclei and its efferent tracts. Brain, 1905, **28:** 13–29.

COGHILL, G. E. Correlated anatomical and physiological studies of the growth of the nervous system of amphibia. I. J. Comp. Neurol., 1914, **24:** 161–223.

COGHILL, G. E. *Anatomy and the problem of behavior.* Oxford University Press, London, 1929.

COLLIER, J., AND BUZZARD, F. The degenerations resulting from lesions of posterior nerve roots and from transverse lesions of the spinal cord in man. A study of twenty cases. Brain, 1903, **26:** 559–591.

COOPER, E. R. A. The development of the substantia nigra. Brain, 1946, **69:** 22–33.

COOPER, E. R. A. The development of the human red nucleus and corpus striatum. Brain, 1946, **69:** 34–44.

CORBIN, K. B. Observations on the peripheral distribution of fibers arising in the mesencephalic nucleus of the fifth cranial nerve. J. Comp. Neurol., 1940, **73:** 153–177.

CORBIN, K. B., AND HARRISON, F. Function of the mesencephalic root of the fifth cranial nerve. J. Neurophysiol., 1940, **3:** 423–435.

COWDRY, E. V. The Neurone. General character. In Penfield's *Cytology & cellular pathology of the nervous system.* New York, 1932, **1:** 1–41.

CRITCHLEY, M. The anterior cerebral artery and its syndromes. Brain, 1930, **53:** 120–165.

CROSBY, E. C., AND WOODBURNE, R. T. The comparative anatomy of the preoptic area and the hypothalamus. Ass. Res. Nerv. & Ment. Dis., 1940, **20:** 52–169.

CROSBY, E. C., AND HUMPHREY, T. Studies of the vertebrate telencephalon. II. The nuclear pattern of the anterior olfactory nucleus, tuberculum olfactorum and the amygdaloid complex in adult man. J. Comp. Neurol., 1941, **74:** 309–352.

CROUCH, R. L. The efferent fibers of the Edinger-Westphal nucleus. J. Comp. Neurol., 1936, **64:** 365–373.

DAVIS, L. E. An anatomical study of the inferior longitudinal fasciculus. Arch. Neurol. & Psychiat., 1921, **5:** 370–381.

DAVISON, C., AND DEMUTH, D. L. Disturbance in sleep mechanism. Arch. Neurol. & Psychiatr., 1945, **54:** 241–255; 1946, **55:** 111–133, 364–381.

DEL RIO-HORTEGA, P. Microglia. In Penfield's *Cytology & cellular pathology of the nervous system.* New York, 1932, **2:** 483–534.

DETWILER, S. R. *Neuroembryology: an experimental study.* The Macmillan Co., New York, 1936.

DETWILER, S. R. Observations upon the migration of neural crest cells, and upon the development of the spinal ganglia and vertebral arches in Amblystoma. Am. J. Anat., 1937, **61:** 63–94.

DETWILER, S. R., AND KEHOE, K. Further observations on the origin of the sheath cells of Schwann. J. Exper. Zool., 1939, **81:** 415–435.

DOGIEL, A. S. *Der Bau der Spinalganglien des Menschen und der Säugetiere.* G. Fischer, Jena, 1908.

DOW, R. S. Efferent connections of the flocculonodular lobe in Macaca mulatta. J. Comp. Neurol., 1938, **68:** 297–305.

DUSSER DE BARENNE, J. G. Experimental researches on sensory localization in the cerebral cortex of the monkey. Proc. Roy. Soc., 1924, **96B:** 272–291.

DUSSER DE BARENNE, J. G. Some aspects of the problem of "corticalization" of function and of functional localization in the cerebral cortex. Assoc. Res. Nerv. & Ment. Dis., 1934, **13:** 85–106.

DUSSER DE BARENNE, J. G., AND SAGER, O. Sensory functions of the optic thalamus of the monkey (Macacus rhesus): symptomatology and functional localization investigated with the method of local strychninization. Arch. Neurol. & Psychiat., 1937, **38:** 913–926.

*ECCLES, J. C. An electrical hypothesis of synaptic and neuro-muscular transmission. Ann. N. Y. Acad. Sci., 1946, **47:** 429–455.

VON ECONOMO, C. F. *The cytoarchitectonics of the human cerebral cortex.* Oxford Med. Publications, London, 1929.

VON ECONOMO, C. F. Der Zellaufbau der Grosshirnrinde und die progressive Cerebration. Ergebn. d. Physiol., 1929, **29:** 83–128.

ECTORS, L. The function of the cerebellum. In Confinia neurologica. 1942, **4:** 181–212.

EDINGER, L. *Vorlesungen über den Bau der nervösen Zentralorgane des Menschen und der Tiere.* F. C. W. Vogel, Leipzig, 1911.

ELWYN, A. The structure and development of the proprioceptors. Assoc. Res. Nerv. & Ment. Dis., 1929, **6:** 244–280.

ELZE, C. Zentrales Nervensystem. Vol. 3 in Braus' *Anatomie des Menschen.* Julius Springer, Berlin, 1932.

ERLANGER, J., AND GASSER, H. S. *Electrical signs of nervous activity.* Univ. of Penn. Press. Philadelphia, 1937.

ESSICK, C. R. The corpus ponto-bulbare: a hitherto undescribed nuclear mass in the human hind brain. Am. J. Anat., 1907–1908, **7:** 119–135.

FERRARO, A., AND BARRERA, S. E. Posterior column fibers and their termination in Macacus rhesus. J. Comp. Neurol., 1935, **62:** 507–530.

FERRARO, A., AND BARRERA, S. E. Differential features of cerebellar and vestibular phenomena in Macacus rhesus. Arch. Neurol. & Psychiat., 1938, **39:** 902–918.

FITZGERALD, J. E., AND WINDLE, W. F. Some observations on early human fetal movements. J. Comp. Neur., 1942, **76:** 156–167.

FOERSTER, O. *Die Leitungsbahnen des Schmerzgefühls und die chirurgische Behandlung der Schmerzzustände.* Urban & Schwarzenberg, Berlin, 1927.

FOERSTER, O. Über die Vasodilatoren in den peripheren Nerven und hintern Rückenmarkswurzeln beim Menschen. Dtsch. Z. Nervenheilk., 1928, **107:** 41–56.

FOERSTER, O. Spezielle Anatomie und Physiologie der peripheren Nerven. In Lewandowsky's *Handbuch der Neurologie,* 1929, Suppl. Pt. **2:** 815–974.

FOERSTER, O. The dermatomes in man. Brain, 1933, **56:** 1–39.

FOERSTER, O. Motor cortex in man in the light of Hughlings Jackson's doctrines. Brain, 1936, **59:** 135–159.

FOERSTER, O. Symptomatologie der Erkrankungen des Rückenmarks und seiner Wurzeln. In Bumke and Foerster's *Handbuch der Neurologie,* 1936, **5:** 1–400.

FOERSTER, O. Symptomatologie der Erkrankungen des Grosshirns. Motorische Felder und Bahnen. In Bumke and Foerster's *Handbuch der Neurologie,* 1936, **6:** 1–357.

FOERSTER, O. Spezielle Physiologie und spezielle funktionelle Pathologie der quergestreiften Muskeln. In Bumke und Foerster's *Handbuch der Neurologie,* 1937, **3:** 1–639.

FOERSTER, O., AND GAGEL, O. Die Vorderseitenstrangdurchschneidung beim Menschen. Eine klinischpathophysiologisch-anatomische Studie. Ztschr. f. d. ges. Neurol. u. Psychiat., 1932, **138:** 1–92.

FOERSTER, O., AND GAGEL, O. Über afferente Nervenfasern in den vorderen Wurzeln. Ztschr. f. d. ges. Neurol. u. Psychiat., 1933, **144:** 313–324.

FOERSTER, O., GAGEL, O., AND SHEEHAN, D. Veränderungen an den Endösen im Rückenmark des Affen nach Hinterwurzeldurchschneidung. Ztschr. Anat. Entwgesch., 1933, **101:** 553–565.

FOIX, C., ET HILLEMAND, P. Les artères de l'axe encéphalique jusqu'au diencéphale inclusivement. Rev. neurol., 1925, **32:** 705–739.

FOLEY, J. M., KINNEY, T. D., AND ALEXANDER, L. The vascular supply of the hypothalamus in man. J. Neuropath. & Exp. Neurol., 1942, **1:** 265–296.

FREEMAN, W., AND WATTS, J. W. An interpretation of the functions of the frontal lobe: based upon observations in 48 cases of prefrontal lobotomy. Yale J. Biol. & Med., 1939, **11:** 527–539.

FREEMAN, W., AND WATTS, J. W. Psychosurgery, intelligence, emotion and social behavior following frontal lobectomy. Springfield, 1942.

FRORIEP, A. Über ein Ganglion des Hypoglossus und Wirbelanlagen in der Occipitalregion. Arch. f. Anat. u. Physiol., 1882, 279–302.

FULTON, J. F. Note on the definition of "motor" and "premotor" areas. Brain, 1935, **58:** 311–316.

FULTON, J. F. *Physiology of the nervous system.* Oxford Med. Publications, New York, 1943.

FULTON, J. F. Levels of autonomic function with particular reference to the cortex. Assoc. Res. Nerv. & Ment. Dis., 1939, **19:** 219–236.

FULTON, J. F., AND INGRAHAM, F. D. Emotional disturbances following experimental lesions of the base of the brain (pre-chiasmal). J. Physiol., 1929, **67:** 27–28.

FULTON, J. F., AND KENNARD, M. A. A study of flaccid and spastic paralysis produced by lesions of the cerebral cortex in primates. Assoc. Res. Nerv. & Ment. Dis., 1934, **13:** 158–210.

GAGEL, O. Zur Histologie und Topographie der vegetativen Zentren im Rückenmark. Ztschr. Anat. Entwgesch., 1928, **85:** 213–250.

GASKELL, W. H. *The involuntary nervous system.* Longmans, Green & Co., London, 1916.

GASSER, H. S. Conduction in nerves in relation to fiber types. Assoc. Res. Nerv. & Ment. Dis., 1935, **15:** 35–59.

GASSER, H. S., AND ERLANGER, J. The rôle of fiber size in the establishment of a nerve block by pressure or cocaine. Am. J. Physiol., 1929, **88:** 581–591.

GERARD, M. W. Afferent impulses of the trigeminal nerve: The intramedullary course of the painful, thermal and tactile impulses. Arch. Neurol. & Psychiat., 1923, **9:** 306–338.

GEREBTZOFF, M. A. Les voies centrales de la sensibilité et du goût et leurs terminaisons thalamiques. Cellule, 1939, **48:** 91–146.

GEREBTZOFF, M. A. Recherches sur la projection corticale du labyrinthe; des effets de la stimulation labyrinthique sur l'activité électrique de l'écorce cérébrale. Arch. internat. de physiol., 1940, **50:** 59–99.

GHISELLI, E. E. The superior colliculus in vision. J. Comp. Neurol., 1937, **67:** 451–467.

GIBSON, W. C. Degeneration of the boutons terminaux in the spinal cord: an experimental study. Arch. Neurol. & Psychiat., 1937, **38:** 1145–1157.

GREVING, R. Makroskopische Anatomie und Histologie des vegetativen Nervensystems. In Bumke and Foerster's *Handb. d. Neurologie.* 1935, **1:** 811–886.

GRINKER, R. R. *Neurology.* C. C. Thomas, Springfield, 1943.

GUTMANN, E., GUTTMANN, L., MEDAWAR, P. B., AND YOUNG, J. Z. Rate of regeneration of nerve. J. Exp. Biol., 1942, **19:** 14–44.

GUTMANN, E., AND YOUNG, J. Z. The re-innervation of muscle after various periods of atrophy. J. Anat., 1944, **78:** 15–43.

HÄGGQUIST, G. Analysis of fibers of the pyramidal tract. Acta Psychiat. et Neurol., 1937, **12:** 457–466.

HARRISON, R. G. The outgrowth of the nerve fiber as a mode of protoplasmic movement. Jour. Exp. Zool., 1910, **9:** 787–847.

HARRISON, R. G. On the origin and development of the nervous system studied by the methods of experimental embryology. (Croonian Lecture.) Proc. Roy. Soc., 1935, **118B:** 155–196.

HAYMAKER, W., AND WOODHALL, B. *Peripheral nerve injuries.* W. B. Saunders Co., Philadelphia, 1945.

HEAD, H. *Studies in neurology.* 2 vols. Oxford Univ. Press, London, 1920.

HEAD, H. Speech and cerebral localization. Brain, 1923, **46:** 355–528.

HEAD, H. *Aphasia and kindred disorders of speech.* Cambridge Univ. Press, 1926.

HERREN, R. Y., AND ALEXANDER, L. Sulcal and intrinsic blood vessels of human spinal cord. Arch. Neurol. & Psychiat., 1939, **41:** 678–687.

HERRICK, C. J. The doctrine of nerve components and some of its applications. J. Comp. Neurol., 1904, **13:** 301–312.

HERRICK, C. J. *Introduction to neurology.* W. B. Saunders Co., Philadelphia, 1931.

HERRICK, C. J. *The brains of rats and men.* Univ. of Chicago Press, Chicago, 1926.

HERRICK, C. J. Morphogenesis of the brain. J. Morphol., 1933, **54:** 233–258.

HERRICK, C. J., AND COGHILL, G. E. The development of reflex mechanisms in Amblystoma. J. Comp. Neurol., 1915, **25:** 65–85.

HINES, M. On cerebral localization. Physiol. Rev., 1929, **9:** 462–574.

HINES, M. The motor cortex. Bull. Johns Hopkins Hosp., 1937, **60:** 313–336.

HINSEY, J. C. The innervation of skeletal muscle. Physiol. Rev., 1934, **14:** 514–585.

HINSEY, J. C. Are there efferent fibers in the dorsal roots? J. Comp. Neurol., 1934, **59:** 117–137.

HINSEY, J. C. The hypothalamus and somatic responses. Assoc. Res. Nerv. & Ment. Dis., 1940, **20:** 657–685.

HIRASAWA, K., AND KATO, K. Fasern, insbesondere die corticalen extrapyramidalen aus den Areae 8 (α, β, τ, δ.) and 9(c, d,) der Grosshirnrinde beim Affen. Folia anat. japon., 1935, **13:** 189–217.

HIRT, A. Über den Aufbau des Spinalganglions und seine Beziehungen zum Sympathicus. Ztschr. f. d. ges. Anat., 1928, **87:** 275–318.

HOCHSTETTER, F. *Beiträge zur Entwicklungsgeschichte des Gehirns.* Franz Deuticke, Wien, I, 1919; II, 1929.

HOFF, E. C. Central nerve terminals in the mammalian spinal cord and their examination by experimental degeneration. Proc. Roy. Soc., 1932, **111B:** 175–188.

HOFF, E. C. The distribution of the spinal terminals (boutons) of the pyramidal tract, determined by experimental degeneration. Proc. Roy. Soc., 1932, **111B:** 226–237.

HOFF, E. C., AND HOFF, H. E. Spinal terminations of the projection fibers from the motor cortex of primates. Brain, 1934, **57:** 454–474.

HOLMES, G. The cerebellum of man. Brain, 1939, **62:** 1–30.

HOLMES, G., AND MAY, W. P. On the exact origin of the pyramidal tracts in man and other mammals. Brain, 1909, **32:** 1–43.

HOLMES, G., AND STEWART, T. G. On the connections of the inferior olive with the cerebellum in man. Brain, 1908, **31:** 125–137.

HOLMES, W., AND YOUNG, J. Z. Nerve regeneration after immediate and delayed suture. J. Anat., 1942, **77:** 63–96.

HOOKER, D. Fetal Behavior. Assoc. Res. Nerv. & Ment. Dis., 1939, **19:** 237–243.

HOOKER, D. *The origin of overt behavior.* Univ. Michigan, Ann Arbor, 1944.

HORSLEY, V., AND CLARKE, R. H. The structure and functions of the cerebellum examined by a new method. Brain, 1908, **31:** 45–124.

HUBER, G. C., AND CROSBY, E. C. Somatic and visceral connections of the diencephalon. Assoc. Res. Nerv. & Ment. Dis., 1930, **9:** 199–248.

HUNT, J. R. The sensory field of the facial nerve. Brain, 1915, **38:** 418–446.

HUNT, J. R. Progressive atrophy of the globus pallidus (primary atrophy of the pallidal system). A system disease of the paralysis agitans type, characterized by atrophy of the motor cells of the corpus striatum. A contribution of the functions of the corpus striatum. Brain, 1917, **40:** 58–148.

HURSH, J. B. Conduction velocity and diameter of nerve fibers. Am. J. Physiol., 1939, **127:** 131–139.

HYNDMAN, O. R. Physiology of the spinal cord. II. The influence of chordotomy on existing motor disturbances. J. Nerv. & Ment. Dis., 1943, **98:** 343–358.

INGRAM, W. R. The hypothalamus: A review of the experimental data. Psychosomat. Med., 1939, **1:** 48–91.

INGRAM, W. R., AND RANSON, S. W. The nucleus of Darkschewitsch and nucleus interstitialis in the brain of man. J. Nerv. & Ment. Dis., 1935, **81:** 125–237.

INGVAR, S. Zur Phylo- und Ontogenese des Kleinhirns. Folia neuro-biol., 1918, **11:** 205–495.

JACOBSEN, C. F. The effect of extirpations on higher brain processes. Physiol. Rev., 1939, **19:** 303–322.

JACOBSOHN, L. Über die Kerne des menschlichen Rückenmarks. Aus dem Anhang zu den Abhandlungen der koenigl. preuss. Akademie der Wissenschaften vom Jahre 1908.

JACOBSOHN, L. Über die Kerne des menschlichen Hirnstamms. Aus dem Anhang zu den Abhandlungen der koenigl. preuss. Akademie der Wissenschaften vom Jahre 1909.

JAKOB, A. The anatomy, clinical syndromes and physiology of the extrapyramidal system. Arch. Neurol. & Psychiat., 1925, **13:** 596–620.

JAKOB, A. Das Kleinhirn. In von Möllendorf's *Handb. d. mikr. Anat. d. Menschen.* Berlin, 1928, **4:** 674–916.

JERMULOWITZ, W. Untersuchungen über die Kerne am Boden der Rautengrube. Arb. a. d. Neur. Inst. d. Wiener Univ., 1934, **36:** 290–302.

JOHNSTON, J. B. *Nervous system of vertebrates.* Blakiston, Philadelphia, 1906.

JOHNSTON, J. B. The radix mesencephalica trigemini. J. Comp. Neurol., 1909, **19:** 593–644.

KAHR, S., AND SHEEHAN, D. The presence of efferent fibers in posterior spinal roots. Brain, 1933, **56:** 265–281.

KAPPERS, C. U. A. The development of the cortex and the functions of its different layers. Acta Psychiat. Neurol., 1928, **3:** 115–132.

KAPPERS, C. U. A. Principles of development of the nervous system. (Neurobiotaxis.) In Penfield's *Cytology & cellular pathology of the nervous system.* New York, 1932, **1:** 45–89.

KARPLUS, J. P. Die Physiologie der vegetativen Zentren. In Bumke and Foerster's *Handb. d. Neurologie*, 1937, **2:** 402–475.

KEENE, M. F. L. Connections of the posterior commissure. J. Anat., 1938, **72:** 488–501.

KENNARD, M. A. Corticospinal fibers arising in the premotor area of the monkey as demonstrated by the Marchi method. Arch. Neurol. & Psychiat., 1935, **33:** 698–711.

KENNARD, M. A., VIETS, H. R., AND FULTON, J. F. The syndrome of the premotor cortex in man: Impairment of skilled movement, forced grasping, spasticity and vasomotor disturbances. Brain, 1934, **57:** 69–84.

KINGSBURY, B. F. The fundamental plan of the vertebrate brain. J. Comp. Neurol., 1922, **34:** 461–491.

DE KLEIJN, A., AND VERSTEEGH, C. Some remarks upon the present position of the physiology of the labyrinth. J. Laryng. Otol., 1927, **42:** 649–655.

KODAMA, S. Beiträge zur normalen Anatomie des Corpus Luysi beim Menschen. Arb. a. d. Inst. Sendai, 1928, Heft 13.

KOELLIKER, A. Nervensystem des Menschen und der Tiere. Vol. 2 of *Handb. der Gewebelehre des Menschen.* Engelmann, Leipzig, 1896.

KOHNSTAMM, O. Der Nucleus salivatorius chordae tympani (nervi intermedii). Anat. Anz., 1902, **21:** 362–363.

KOHNSTAMM, O. Der Nucleus salivatorius inferior und das cranio-viscerale System. Neurol. Centralbl., 1903, **22:** 699.

KUBIK, C., AND ADAMS, R. D. Occlusion of the basilar artery. A clinical and pathological study. Brain, 1946, **69:** 73–121.

KUNTZ, A. The development of the sympathetic nervous system in mammals. J. Comp. Neurol., 1910, **20:** 211.

KUNTZ, A. *The autonomic nervous system.* Lea & Febiger, Philadelphia, 1934.

KUNTZ, A., AND RICHINS, C. A. Reflex pupillodilator mechanisms. J. Neurophysiol., 1946, **9:** 1–7.

LANDACRE, F. L. The origin of the sensory components of the cranial ganglia. Anat. Rec., 1910, **4:** 71–79.

LANGLEY, J. N. *The autonomic nervous system.* Vol. I. W. Heffer & Sons, Cambridge, 1921.

LANGWORTHY, O. R. A study of the innervation of the tongue musculature with particular reference to the proprioceptive mechanism. J. Comp. Neurol., 1924, **36:** 273–293.

LANGWORTHY, O. R., AND TAUBER, E. S. The control of the pupillary reaction by the central nervous system: a review. J. Nerv. & Ment. Dis., 1937, **86:** 462–475.

LARSELL, O. Studies on the nervus terminalis: mammals. J. Comp. Neurol., 1919, **30**: 3–68.

LARSELL, O. The cerebellum: A review and interpretation. Arch. Neurol. & Psychiat., 1937, **38**: 580–607.

LARSELL, O., AND DOW, R. S. Innervation of the human lung. Am. J. Anat., 1933, **52**: 125–146.

LARUELLE, L. Les centres végétatifs du diencéphale médian: partie anatomique. Rev. neurol., 1934, **1**: 809–844.

LASHLEY, K. S. *Brain mechanisms and intelligence*. Univ. of Chicago Press, Chicago, 1929.

LASSEK, A. M. The human pyramidal tract. II. A numerical investigation of the Betz cells of the motor area. Arch. Neurol. & Psychiat., 1940, **44**: 718–724.

LASSEK, A. M. The human pyramidal tract. VII. A critical review of its origin. J. Nerv. & Ment. Dis., 1944, **9**: 22–28.

LASSEK, A. M., DOWD, L. W., AND WEIL, A. The quantitative distribution of the pyramidal tract in the dog. J. Comp. Neurol., 1930, **51**: 153–163.

LASSEK, A. M., AND EVANS, J. P. The human pyramidal tract. XII. The effect of hemispherectomies on the fiber components of the pyramids. J. Comp. Neurol., 1945, **83**: 113–119.

LASSEK, A. M., AND RASMUSSEN, G. L. The human pyramidal tract. A fiber and numerical analysis. Arch. Neurol. & Psychiat., 1939, **42**: 872–876.

LAVRENTIEV, B. J. The innervation of the heart. Amer. Rev. Soviet Medicine, 1946, **3**: 229–235.

LEIDLER, R. The localization of vertigo in the brain stem. Confinia neurologica, 1938, **1**: 367–406.

LEVIN, P. M. The efferent fibers of the frontal lobe of the monkey, Macaca mulatta. J. Comp. Neurol., 1936, **63**: 369–419.

LOEWI, O. Chemical transmission of nerve impulses. Science in Progress, 1945, **4**: 98–119.

LORENTE DE NÓ, R. Etudes sur le cerveau posterieur. Trav. du Lab. de recherches biol. de l'Univ. de Madrid, 1924, **22**: 51–65.

LORENTE DE NÓ. The structure of the cerebral cortex. In Fulton's *Physiology of the nervous system*. 1938, 291–325.

MACNALTY, A. S., AND HORSLEY, V. On the cervical spino-bulbar and spinocerebellar tracts and on the question of topographical representation in the cerebellum. Brain, 1909, **32**: 237–255.

MAGNUS, R. *Körperstellung*. Julius Springer, Berlin, 1924.

MAGNUS, R. AND DE KLEIJN, A. Die Abhängigkeit des Tonus der Extremitätenmuskeln von der Kopfstellung. Pflüg. Arch., 1912, **145**: 455–548.

MAGOUN, H. W. Descending connections from the hypothalamus. Assoc. Res. Nerv. & Ment. Dis., 1940, **20**: 270–285.

MAGOUN, H. W., ATLAS, D., HARE, W. K., AND RANSON, S. W. The afferent path of the pupillary light reflex in the monkey. Brain, 1936, **59**: 234–249.

MAGOUN, H. W., AND RHINES, R. An inhibitory mechanism in the bulbar reticular formation. J. Neurophysiol., 1946, **9**: 165–171.

MALONE, E. F. Über die Kerne des menschlichen Diencephalon. Aus dem Anhang zu den Abhandlungen der koenigl. preuss. Akademie der Wissenschaften vom Jahre 1910.

MALONE, E. F. Recognition of members of the somatic motor chain of nerve cells by means of a fundamental type of cell structure. Anat. Rec., 1913, **7**: 67–82.

MALONE, E. F. Nucleus cardiacus nervi vagi and the three distinct types of nerve cells which innervate the three types of muscles. Am. J. Anat., 1913, **15**: 121–129.

MARBURG, O. *Mikroskopisch-topographischer Atlas des menschlichen Zentralnervensystems*. Franz Deuticke, Leipzig, 1927.

MARBURG, O. Das dorsale Längsbündel von Schütz. Arb. a. d. Neur. Inst. d. Wiener Univ., 1931, **33**: 135–164.

MARBURG, O. Modern views regarding anatomy and physiology of the vestibular tracts. Laryngoscope, 1939, **49**: 631–652.

MARBURG, O. Primary endings of the optic nerve in man and in animals. Arch. of Ophthalm., 1942, **28**: 61–78.

MARQUIS, D. G. Phylogenetic interpretation of functions of the visual cortex. Arch. Neurol. & Psychiat., 1935, **33**: 807–815.

MARQUIS, D. G., AND HILGARD, E. R. Conditioned responses to light in monkeys after removal of occipital lobes. Brain, 1937, **60**: 1–13.

MARSHALL, C. The functions of the pyramidal tracts. Quart. Rev. Biol., 1936, **11**: 35–56.

MASSAZZA, A. La citoarchitettonica del midollo spinale umano. Riv. di Patol. nerv. e. ment., 1922, **28**: 22.

MERRITT, H. H., AND FREMONT-SMITH, F. *The cerebrospinal fluid*. W. B. Saunders Co., Philadelphia, 1938.

METTLER, F. A. Corticifugal fiber connections of the cortex of Macaca mulatta. J. Comp. Neurol., 1935, **61**: 221–256; 509–542; **62**: 263–291; **63**: 23–47.

METTLER, F. A. Relation between pyramidal and extrapyramidal function. Assoc. Res. Nerv. & Ment. Dis., 1942, **21**: 150–227.

METTLER, F. A.   Fiber connections of the corpus striatum of the monkey and the baboon. J. Comp. Neurol., 1945, **82**: 169–204.

METTLER, F. A., AND LUBIN, A. J.   Termination of the brachium pontis. J. Comp. Neurol., 1942, **77**: 391–397.

MINGAZZINI, G.   Medulla oblongata und Brücke. In von Möllendorff's *Handb. d. mikr. Anat. d. Menschen*, Berlin, 1928, **4**: 579–643.

MINGAZZINI, G.   Mittelhirn. In von Möllendorff's *Handb. d. mik. Anat. d. Menschen.* Berlin, 1928, **4**: 644–673.

MINCKLER, J., KLEMME, R. M., AND MINCKLER, D.   The course of efferent fibers from the human premotor cortex. J. Comp. Neurol., 1944, **81**: 259–277.

MINKOWSKI, M.   Experimentelle Untersuchungen über die Beziehungen der Grosshirnrinde und der Netzhaut zu den primären optischen Zentren, besonders zum Corpus geniculatum externum.   Arb. a. d. Hirnanat. Inst. Zürich, 1913 **7**: 255–362.

VON MONAKOW, C.   Der rote Kern, die Haube und die Regio hypothalamica bei einigen Säugetieren und beim Menschen. Arb. a. d. Hirnanat. Inst. Zurich, 1910, **5**: 103–225.

MORGAN, L. O.   The corpus striatum. Arch. Neurol. & Psychiat., 1927, **18**: 495–549.

MORUZI, AL., AND LECHINTSKI.   Quelques observations au sujet des voies de transmission des sensations gustatives chez l'homme. Rev. Neurol., 1938, **70**: 478–483.

MÜLLER, E., AND INGVAR, S.   Über den Ursprung des Sympathicus beim Hühnchen. Arch. f. mikr. Anat., 1923, **99**: 650.

MÜLLER, L. R.   *Lebensnerven und Lebenstriebe.* Julius Springer, Berlin, 1931.

MUSKENS, L. J. J.   *Das supra-vestibuläre System.* N. v. Noord-Hollandsche, Amsterdam, 1934.

MUSSEN, A. T.   The cerebellum. Arch. Neurol. & Psychiat., 1931, **25**: 702–722.

NACHMANSOHN, D.   Chemical mechanism of nerve activity. Ann. N. Y. Acad. Sci., 1946, **47**: 395–428.

NIELSEN, J. M.   Agnosia, apraxia, aphasia. P. B. Hoeber, New York, 1946.

OBERSTEINER, H.   *Anleitung beim Studium des Baues der Nervösen Zentralorgane im gesunden und kranken Zustande.* Franz Deuticke, Leipzig, 1912.

ORTON, S. T.   *Reading, writing and speech problems in children.* W. W. Norton, New York, 1937.

PAPEZ, J. W.   Reticulospinal tracts in the cat. J. Comp. Neurol., 1926, **41**: 345–399.

PAPEZ, J. W.   Subdivisions of facial nucleus. J. Comp. Neurol., 1927, **43**: 159–191.

PAPEZ, J. W.   *Comparative neurology.* T. Y. Crowell Co., New York, 1929.

PAPEZ, J. W.   A proposed mechanism of emotion. Arch. Neurol. & Psychiat., 1937, **38**: 725–743.

PAPEZ, J. W.   Reciprocal connections of the striatum and pallium in the brain of Pithecus (Macacus) rhesus. J. Comp. Neurol., 1938, **69**: 329–349.

PAPEZ, J. W.   A summary of fiber connections of the basal ganglia with each other and with other portions of the brain. Assoc. Res. Nerv. & Ment. Dis., 1940, **21**: 21–68.

PAPEZ, J. W., AND STOTLER, W. A.   Connections of the red nucleus. Arch. Neurol. & Psychiat., 1940, **44**: 776–791.

PARKER, G. H.   *The elementary nervous system.* J. B. Lippincott Co., Philadelphia, 1919.

PATTON, H. D., RUCH, T. C., AND WALKER, A. E.   Experimental hypogeusia from Horsley-Clarke lesions of the thalamus in Macaca mulatta. J. Neurophysiol., 1944, **7**: 171–184.

PAVLOV, I. P.   *Conditioned reflexes. An investigation of the physiological activity of the cerebral cortex.* Oxford Univ. Press, London, 1927.

PEARSON, A. A.   The spinal accessory nerve in human embryos. J. Comp. Neurol., 1938, **68**: 243–266.

PEARSON, A. A.   The hypoglossal nerve in human embryos. J. Comp. Neurol., 1939, **71**: 21–39.

PEARSON, A. A.   The development of the nervous terminalis in man. J. Comp. Neurol., 1941, **75**: 39–64.

PEARSON, A. A.   Further observations on the intramedullary sensory type neurons along the hypoglossal nerve. J. Comp. Neurol., 1945, **82**: 93–100.

PENFIELD, W. G.   Alterations of the Golgi apparatus in nerve cells. Brain, 1920, **43**: 290–305.

PENFIELD, W. G.   *Cytology and cellular pathology of the nervous system.* Paul B. Hoeber, Inc., New York, 1932.

PENFIELD, W. G.   Neuroglia, normal and pathological. In Penfield's *Cytology & cellular pathology of the nervous system.* New York, 1932, **2**: 423–479.

PENFIELD, W. G., AND BOLDREY, E.   Somatic motor and sensory representation in the cerebral cortex of man as studied by electrical stimulation. Brain, 1937, **60**: 389–443.

PENFIELD, W. G., AND EVANS, J.   Functional defects produced by cerebral lobectomies. Assoc. Res. Nerv. & Ment. Dis., 1932, **13**: 352–377.

PENFIELD, W. G., AND EVANS, J.   The frontal lobe in man: a clinical study of maximum removals. Brain, 1935, **58**: 115–133.

PENFIELD, W. G., AND MCNAUGHTON, F.   Dural

headache and innervation of the dura mater. Arch Neurol. & Psychiat., 1940, **44**: 43–75.

PINES, I. L. Über die Innervation der Hypophysis cerebri. II. Mitteilung: Über die Innervation des Mittel- und Hinterlappens der Hypophyse. Ztschr. f. d. ges. Neurol. u. Psychiat., 1925, **100**: 123.

PITTS, R. F. Organization of the respiratory center. Physiol. Rev., 1946, **26**: 609–630.

POLIAK, S. *The main afferent fiber systems of the cerebral cortex in primates.* Univ. Calif. Publ. in Anat., 1932.

POPPI, U. Über die Fasersysteme der Substantia nigra. Arb. a. d. Neurol. Inst. Wien, 1927, **29**: 8–49.

POTTS, T. K. The main peripheral connections of the human sympathetic nervous system. J. Anat., 1924–5, **59**: 129–135.

PUTNAM, T. J. Studies on the central visual system. III. The general relationships between the external geniculate body, optic radiation and visual cortex in man: report of two cases. Arch. Neurol. & Psychiat., 1926, **16**: 566–596.

PUTNAM, T. J. Studies on the central visual system. IV. The details of the organization of the geniculostriate system of man. Arch. Neurol. & Psychiat., 1926, **16**: 683–707.

PUTNAM, T. J. The cerebral circulation. J. Neurol. & Psychopath., 1937, **17**: 193–212.

RADEMAKER, G. G. J. *Die Bedeutung der roten Kerne und des übrigen Mittelhirns für Muskeltonus, Körperstellung, und Labyrinth-reflexe.* Julius Springer, Berlin, 1926.

RAMÓN Y CAJAL, S. *Studien über die Hirnrinde des Menschen.* 5 Hefte, J. A. Barth, Leipzig, 1900–1906.

RAMÓN Y CAJAL, S. *Degeneration and regeneration of the nervous system.* Oxford Univ. Press, London, 1928.

RAMÓN Y CAJAL, S. Die Neuronenlehre. In Bumke and Foerster's *Handb. d. Neurologie.* Berlin, 1935, **1**: 887–994.

RANSON, S. W. The structure of the spinal ganglia and of the spinal nerves. J. Comp. Neurol., 1912, **22**: 159–175.

RANSON, S. W. The course within the spinal cord of the non-medullated fibers of the dorsal roots: a study of Lissauer's tract in the cat. J. Comp. Neurol., 1913, **23**: 259–281.

RANSON, S. W. Cutaneous sensory fibers and sensory conduction. Arch. Neurol. & Psychiat., 1931, **26**: 1122–1144.

RANSON, S. W. Some functions of the hypothalamus. In *The Harvey Lectures*, Baltimore, 1936–1937, Series 32, 92–121.

RANSON, S. W., AND BILLINGSLEY, P. R. The conduction of painful afferent impulses in the spinal nerves. Am. J. Physiol., 1916, **40**: 571–584.

RANSON, S. W., AND BILLINGSLEY, P. R. The superior cervical ganglion and the cervical portion of the sympathetic trunk. J. Comp. Neurol., 1918, **29**: 313–358.

RANSON, S. W., AND DAVENPORT, H. K. Sensory unmyelinated fibers in the spinal nerves. Am. J. Anat., 1931, **48**: 331–353.

RANSON, S. W., DROEGMUELLER, W. H., DAVENPORT, H. K., AND FISHER, C. Number, size and myelination of the sensory fibers in the cerebrospinal nerves. Assoc. Res. Nerv. & Ment. Dis., 1935, **15**: 3–34.

RANSON, S. W., AND MAGOUN, H. W. The central path of the pupillo-constrictor reflex in response to light. Arch. Neurol. & Psychiat., 1933, **30**: 1193–1204.

RANSON, S. W., RANSON, S. W., JR., AND RANSON, M. Fiber connections of corpus striatum as seen in Marchi preparations. Arch. Neurol. & Psychiat., 1941, **46**: 230–249.

RASMUSSEN, A. T. Secondary vestibular tracts in the cat. J. Comp. Neurol., 1932, **54**: 43–159.

RASMUSSEN, A. T. *The principal nervous pathways.* The Macmillan Co., New York, 1941.

DE RÉNYI, G. S. The structure of cells in tissues as revealed by microdissection. J. Comp. Neurol., 1929, **48**: 441–457.

RIDDOCH, G. The reflex functions of the completely divided spinal cord in man, compared with those associated with less severe lesions. Brain, 1917, **40**: 264–402.

VAN RIJNBERK, G. Das Kleinhirn. Ergebn. d. Physiol., 1931, **31**: 592–843.

RILEY, H. A. The mammalian cerebellum. A comparative study of the arbor vitae and folial pattern. Assoc. Res. Nerv. & Ment. Dis., 1929, **6**: 37–192.

RILEY, H. A. The central nervous system control of the ocular movements and the disturbances of this mechanism. Arch. of Ophth., 1930, **4**: 640–661, 885–910.

RIOCH, D. McK. Studies on the diencephalon of carnivora. I. The nuclear configuration of the thalamus, epithalamus and hypothalamus of the dog and cat. J. Comp. Neurol., 1929, **49**: 1–119.

ROGERS, F. T. Studies of the brain stem. VI. An experimental study of the corpus striatum of the pigeon as related to various instinctive types of behavior. J. Comp. Neurol., 1922, **35**: 21–59.

ROSE, M. Cytoarchitektonik und Myeloarchitektonik der Grosshirnrinde. In Bumke and Foerster's *Handb. d. Neurologie.* 1935, **1**: 588–778.

RUNDLES, R. W., AND PAPEZ, J. W. Connections between the striatum and the substantia nigra in a human brain. Arch. Neurol. & Psychiat., 1937, **38**: 550–563.

ROUSSY, G., AND MOSINGER, M. Rapports anatomiques et physiologiques de l'hypothalamus et de l'hypophyse. Ann. de méd., 1933, **33**: 301–324.

RYLANDER, G. *Personality changes after operation on the frontal lobes: a clinical study of 32 cases.* London, 1939.

SACHS, E. On the structure and functional relations of the optic thalamus. Brain, 1909, **32**: 95–186.

SAITO, M. Experimentelle Untersuchungen über die inneren Verbindungen der Kleinhirnrinde und deren Beziehungen zu Pons und Medulla oblongata. Arb. a. d. Neurol. Inst. Wien, 1922, **23**: 74–106; 1923, **24**: 77–84.

SAND, R. Beitrag zur Kenntnis der corticobulbären und corticopontinen Pyramidenfasern beim Menschen. Arb. a. d. Neurol. Inst. Wien., 1903, **10**: 185–222.

SCARFF, J. E. Primary cortical centers for movements of upper and lower limbs in man. Arch. Neurol. & Psychiat., 1940, **44**: 243–299.

SCHARRER, E. Arteries and veins in the mammalian brain. Anat. Rec., 1940, **78**: 173–196.

SCHARRER, E., AND SCHARRER, B. Neurosecretion. Physiol. Rev., 1945, **25**: 171–181.

SCHLESINGER, B. Venous drainage of the brain, with special reference to Galenic system. Brain, 1939, **62**: 274–291.

SCHULTE, H. VON W., AND TILNEY, F. Development of the neuraxis in the domestic cat to the stage of twenty-one somites. Ann. New York Acad. Sc., 1915, **24**: 319–346.

SCHWARTZ, H. G. Reflex activity within the sympathetic nervous system. Am. J. Physiol., 1934, **109**: 593–604.

SCHWARTZ, H. G., AND O'LEARY, J. L. Section of spinothalamic tract in medulla . . . Surgery, 1941, **9**: 183–193.

SCHWARTZ, H. G., AND WEDDELL, G. Observations on the pathways transmitting the sensation of taste. Brain, 1938, **61**: 99–115.

SCHWARTZ, PH., UND FINK, L. Morphologie und Entstehung der geburtstraumatischen Blutungen im Gehirn und Schädel des Neugeborenen. Zeitschr. f. Kinderheilkunde, 1926, **40**: 427–474.

SEDDON, H. J. Three types of nerve injury. Brain, 1943, **66**: 237–288.

SHEEHAN, D. Vergleichend-anatomische Untersuchungen über die Kerne am Aquaeductus Sylvii. Arb. Neurol. Inst. Wien, 1933, **35**: 1.

SHELLSHEAR, J. L. A contribution to our knowledge of the arterial supply of cerebral cortex in man. Brain, 1927, **50**: 236–253.

SHEPS, J. G. The nuclear configuration and cortical connections of the human thalamus. J. Comp. Neurol., 1945, **83**: 1–56.

SHERRINGTON, C. S. Experiments in examination of the peripheral distribution of the fibers of the posterior roots of some spinal nerves. Philos. Trans., 1893, **184B**: 641–763.

SHERRINGTON, C. S. *The integrative action of the nervous system.* Yale Univ. Press, New Haven, 1920.

SHERRINGTON, C. S. *The brain and its mechanisms.* Cambridge Univ. Press. Cambridge, 1933.

SHMIDT, E. V. The pyramidal syndrome. Amer. Rev. Soviet Medicine, 1946, **4**: 30–36.

SJÖQVIST, O. Studies on pain conduction in the trigeminal nerve: contribution to surgical treatment of facial pain. Acta Psychiat. et Neurol., Suppl., 1938, **17**: 1–139.

SMYTH, G. E. The systemization and central connections of the spinal tract and nucleus of the trigeminal nerve. Brain, 1939, **62**: 41–87.

SMYTH, G. E. The significance of lesions in the dentate nuclei apparently consecutive to disease of the frontal lobes. Brain, 1941, **64**: 63–72.

SPATZ, H. Anatomie des Mittelhirns. In Bumke and Foerster's *Handb. der Neurologie.* 1935, **1**: 474–540.

SPIEGEL, E. A. *Die Zentren des autonomen Nervensystems.* Julius Springer, Berlin, 1928.

SPIEGEL, E. A. Labyrinth and cortex. The electroencephalogram of the cortex in the stimulation of the labyrinth. Arch. Neurol. & Psychiat., 1934, **31**: 469–482.

SPIEGEL, E. A., AND HUNSICKER, W. C., JR. The conduction of cortical impulses to the autonomic system. J. Nerv. & Ment. Dis., 1936, **83**: 252–274.

STENGEL, E. Über den Ursprung der Nervenfasern der Neurohypophyse im Zwischenhirn. Arb. a. d. Neurol. Inst. Wien., 1926, **28**: 25–37.

STERN, K. Note on the nucleus ruber magnocellularis and its efferent pathway in man. Brain, 1936, **61**: 284–289.

STERN, K. Der Zellaufbau des menschlichen Mittelhirns. Ztschr. f. d. ges. Neurol. u. Psychiat., 1936, **154**: 521–598.

STERN, K. Thalamo-frontal projection in man. J. Anat., 1942, **76**: 302–307.

STOFFELS, J. La projection des noyaux antérieurs du thalamus sur l'écorce inter-hémisphérique étude anatomo-expérimentale. Mém. Acad. roy. de méd. de Belgique, 1939, **1**: 1–59.

STÖHR, P., JR. Das peripherische Nervensystem.

In von Möllendorff's *Handb. d. mik. Anat. d. Menschen.* Berlin, 1928, **4:** 202–447.

STOPFORD, J. S. B. The arteries of the pons and medulla oblongata. J. Anat. & Phys., 1915, **50:** 131–164, 1916, **50:** 255–280.

STOOKEY, B. *Surgical and mechanical treatment of peripheral nerves.* Philadelphia, 1922.

STOOKEY, B., AND SCARFF, J. Injuries of peripheral nerves. In *Neurosurgery and thoracic surgery.* W. B. Saunders Co., Philadelphia, 1943, pp. 81–184.

STOPFORD, J. S. B. *Sensation and the sensory pathway.* Longmans, Green & Co., London, 1930.

STRAUS, W. L., JR., AND HOWELL, A. B. The spinal accessory nerve and its musculature. Quart. Rev. Biol., 1936, **11:** 387–405.

STRONG, O. S. The cranial nerves of amphibia: a contribution to the morphology of the vertebrate nervous system. J. Morph., 1895, **10:** 101–230.

STRONG, O. S. A case of unilateral cerebellar agenesia. J. Comp. Neurol., 1915, **25:** 361–391.

STRONG, O. S. Some observations on the course of the fibers from Clarke's column in the normal human spinal cord. Bull. Neurol. Inst. New York, 1936, **5:** 378–386.

SUH, T. H., AND ALEXANDER, L. Vascular system of the human spinal cord. Arch. Neurol. & Psychiat., 1939, **41:** 659–677.

SUNDERLAND, S. Course and rate of regeneration of motor fibers following lesions of the radial nerve. Arch. Neur. & Psychiat., 1946, **56:** 133–157.

SZANTROCH, Z. L'histogénèse des ganglions nerveux du coeur. Extr. Bull. de l'Acad. Polonaise, 1929.

TAIT, J. Is all hearing cochlear? Ann. Otol. Rhinol. Laryngol., 1932, **41:** 681–704.

THELANDER, H. E. The course and distribution of the radix mesencephalica trigemini in the cat. J. Comp. Neurol., 1924, **37:** 207–220.

TILNEY, F. The hippocampus and its relation to the corpus callosum. J. Nerv. & Ment. Dis., 1939, **89:** 433–513.

TILNEY, F., AND RILEY, H. A. *The form and function of the central nervous system.* Paul B. Hoeber, Inc., New York, 1938.

TOENNIES, J. F. Reflex discharges over dorsal roots. J. Neurophysiol., 1938, **1:** 378–390.

TOWER, S. S. The pyramidal tract. In Bucy's *The precentral motor cortex.* Univ. Ill. Press, 1944, pp. 149–172.

TOZER, F. M., AND SHERRINGTON, C. S. Receptors and afferents of the third, fourth and sixth cranial nerves. Proc. Roy. Soc., London, 1910, Ser. B, **82:** 450–457.

VAN BUSKIRK, C. The seventh nerve complex. J. Comp. Neurol., 1945, **82:** 303–333.

VERHAART, W. J. C., AND KENNARD, M. A. Corticofugal degeneration following thermocoagulation of areas 4, 6, and 4-s in Macaca mulatta. J. Anat., 1940, **74:** 239–254.

VILLAVERDE, J. M. Sur la terminaison des fibres calleuses dans l'écorce cérébrale. Trav. Lab. Inv. Biol. Univ. Madrid, 1932, **27:** 275–297.

VOGT, C., AND VOGT, O. Ergebnisse unserer Hirnforschung. J. f. Psychol. u. Neurol., 1919, **25:** 273–462.

VOGT, C., AND VOGT, O. Zur Lehre der Erkrankungen der striären Systeme. J. f. Psychol. u. Neurol., 1919–1920, **25:** 627–846.

VONDERAHE, A. R. The anatomic basis of emotion. Ohio State Med. J., 1943, **39:** 325–330.

WALKER, A. E. The thalamus of the chimpanzee. IV. Thalamic projections to the cerebral cortex. J. Anat., 1938, **73:** 37–93.

WALKER, A. E. *The primate thalamus.* Univ. of Chicago Press, Chicago, 1938.

WALLENBERG, A. Das sensible System. Ztschr. f. Nervenheilkunde, 1928, **101:** 111–155.

WALSHE, F. M. R. The mode of representation of movement in the motor cortex. Brain, 1943, **66:** 104–139.

WALSHE, F. M. R. On the "syndrome of the premotor cortex." . . . Brain, 1935, **58:** 49–80.

WALSHE, F. M. R. The anatomy and physiology of cutaneous sensibility: a critical review. Brain, 1942, **65:** 48–112.

WANG, S. C. Localization of the salivatory center in the medulla of the cat. J. Neurophysiol., 1943, **6:** 195–202.

WARD, A. A., AND REED, H. L. Mechanism of pupillary dilatation elicited by cortical stimulation. J. Neurophysiol., 1946, **9:** 329–335.

WARRINGTON, W. B., AND GRIFFITH, F. On the cells of the spinal ganglia and on the relationship of their histological structure to axonal distribution. Brain, 1904, **27:** 297–326.

WATERSTON, D. Observations on sensation. The sensory functions of the skin for touch and pain. J. Physiol., 1933, **77:** 251–257.

WEED, L. H. A reconstruction of the nuclear masses in the lower portion of the human brain stem. Publ. Carnegie Inst., Washington, 1914.

WEED, L. H. The cerebrospinal fluid. Physiol. Rev., 1922, **2:** 171–203.

WEED, L. H. The meninges, with special reference to the cell coverings of the leptomeninges. In Penfield's *Cytology & cellular pathology of the nervous system.* New York, 1932, **2:** 613–634.

WEIL, A., AND LASSEK, A. The quantitative distribution of the pyramidal tract in man. Arch. Neurol. & Psychiat., 1929, **22**: 495–510.

WEISENBURG, T. H. A study of aphasia. Arch. Neurol. & Psychiat., 1934, **31**: 1–33.

WEISS, P., AND WANG, H. Neurofibrils in living ganglion cells of the chick, cultivated in vitro. Anat. Rec., 1936, **67**: 105–117.

WESTBROOK, W. H. L., AND TOWER, S. S. An analysis of the problem of emergent fibers in posterior spinal roots, dealing with the rate of growth and extraneous fibers into the roots after ganglionectomy. J. Comp. Neurol., 1940, **72**: 383–398.

WHITE, J. C., AND SMITHWICK, R. H. *The autonomic nervous system.* The Macmillan Co., New York, 1941.

WILSON, S. A. K. *Modern problems in neurology.* Edward Arnold & Co., London, 1928.

WILSON, E. E., WINDLE, W. F., AND FITZGERALD, J. E. Development of the tractus solitarius. J. Comp. Neurol., 1941, **74**: 287–307.

WILSON, W. C., AND MAGOUN, H. W. The functional significance of the inferior olive in the cat. J. Comp. Neurol., 1945, **83**: 69–77.

WINDLE, W. F. Non-bifurcating nerve fibers of the trigeminal nerve. J. Comp. Neurol., 1926, **40**: 229–240.

WINDLE, W. F. Correlation between the development of local reflexes and reflex arcs in the spinal cord of cat embryos. J. Comp. Neurol., 1934, **59**: 487–505.

WINDLE, W. F. *Physiology of the fetus.* Saunders Co., Philadelphia, 1940.

WINDLE, W. F., AND FITZGERALD, J. E. Development of the human mesencephalic trigeminal root and related neurons. J. Comp. Neurol., 1942, **77**: 597–608.

WOOLLARD, H. H. Observations on the terminations of cutaneous nerves. Brain, 1935, **58**: 352–367.

WORLEY, L. G. The Golgi apparatus. An interpretation of its structure and significance. Ann. N. Y. Acad. Sci., 1946, **47**: 1–56.

YAGITA, K. Weitere Untersuchungen über das Speichelzentrum. Anat. Anz., 1909, **35**: 70–75.

YOUNG, J. Z., AND ZUCKERMAN, S. The course of fibers in the dorsal nerve roots of Macaca mulatta, the rhesus monkey. J. Anat., 1937, **71**: 447–457.

INDEX

Lower facial is supplied by opposite VII only
pterygoid part of VII faces crossed only.
chewing muscles receive bilateral